To. Ginny
From - Dave, Lynn and Jeannine

THE
METHODIST HYMNAL

Order of Worship I

Let the Services of Worship begin at the time appointed, and let the People kneel or bow in silent prayer upon entering the Sanctuary.

THE PRELUDE. The People in devout meditation.

THE CALL TO WORSHIP. Which may be said or sung.

A HYMN. If a Processional, the Hymn shall precede the Call to Worship, and the People shall then rise at the second stanza and join in singing.

THE PRAYER OF CONFESSION. To be said by all, the People seated and bowed, or kneeling. The following, or other Prayer of Confession, may be said:

Our Heavenly Father, who by Thy love hast made us, and through Thy love hast kept us, and in Thy love wouldst make us perfect, we humbly confess that we have not loved Thee with all our heart and soul and mind and strength, and that we have not loved one another as Christ hath loved us. Thy life is within our souls, but our selfishness hath hindered Thee. We have resisted Thy Spirit. We have neglected Thine inspirations.

Forgive what we have been; help us to amend what we are; and in Thy Spirit direct what we shall be; that Thou mayest come into the full glory of Thy creation, in us and in all men, through Jesus Christ our Lord. Amen.

THE SILENT MEDITATION. The People seated and bowed, or kneeling.

THE WORDS OF ASSURANCE. By the Minister.

THE LORD'S PRAYER. Which may be said or sung.

THE ANTHEM OR CHANT. Which may be the *Venite* or the *Te Deum*.

THE RESPONSIVE READING. The People to stand and remain standing until after the Affirmation of Faith.

THE GLORIA PATRI.

THE AFFIRMATION OF FAITH. To be said by the Minister and People.

THE LESSON FROM THE HOLY SCRIPTURES. The Old and New Testament.

THE PASTORAL PRAYER. The People seated and bowed, or kneeling.

THE OFFERTORY. The Dedication of Offerings. With Prayer or Offertory Sentences.

A HYMN. The People standing

THE SERMON.

THE PRAYER. The People seated and bowed, or kneeling.

THE INVITATION TO CHRISTIAN DISCIPLESHIP.

A HYMN OR DOXOLOGY. The People standing. The closing Hymn may be a Recessional Hymn.

THE BENEDICTION. The People seated and bowed, or kneeling.

THE SILENT PRAYER.

THE POSTLUDE.

Order of Worship II[1]

Let the Services of Worship begin at the time appointed, and let the People kneel or bow in silent prayer upon entering the Sanctuary.

THE PRELUDE.

THE CALL TO WORSHIP.

THE INVOCATION.

A HYMN.

THE AFFIRMATION OF FAITH.

I believe in God, the Father Almighty, Maker of heaven and earth; and in Jesus Christ, His only Son our Lord; who was conceived by the Holy Spirit, born of the Virgin Mary, suffered under Pontius Pilate, was crucified, dead, and buried; the third day He rose from the dead; He ascended into heaven, and sitteth at the right hand of God the Father Almighty; from thence He shall come to judge the quick and the dead. I believe in the Holy Spirit; the holy catholic Church; the communion of saints; the forgiveness of sins; the resurrection of the body, and the life everlasting. Amen.

THE ANTHEM.

THE RESPONSIVE READING.

THE GLORIA PATRI.

THE LESSON FROM THE HOLY SCRIPTURES.

THE SILENT MEDITATION.

THE PASTORAL PRAYER.

THE LORD'S PRAYER.

THE OFFERTORY. The Dedication of Offerings with Prayer or Offertory Sentences.

A HYMN.

THE SERMON.

A PRAYER.

THE INVITATION TO CHRISTIAN DISCIPLESHIP.

A HYMN.

THE BENEDICTION.

THE POSTLUDE.

[1] Orders of Worship I, III, and IV will be found on pages 504-506.

The Methodist Hymnal

OFFICIAL HYMNAL OF
THE METHODIST CHURCH

THE METHODIST PUBLISHING HOUSE

NASHVILLE	CINCINNATI	CHICAGO	NEW YORK
DALLAS	RICHMOND	BALTIMORE	KANSAS CITY
BOSTON	DETROIT	PITTSBURGH	PORTLAND
	SAN FRANCISCO		

Printed in the United States of America

PREFACE

For each worshiping generation "the people called Methodists" have provided a revised edition of the HYMNAL. In every revision, however urgent the need for different devotional expression, the constraining motive has accorded with the counsel of the apostle: "Let the word of Christ dwell in you richly in all wisdom; teaching and admonishing one another in psalms and hymns and spiritual songs, singing with grace in your hearts to the Lord."

The General Conference of the Methodist Episcopal Church of 1928 appointed a Commission on the Revision of the HYMNAL and PSALTER, consisting of five Bishops, five ministers, and five laymen. The Bishops were: William F. Anderson, Edwin Holt Hughes, Frederick D. Leete, H. Lester Smith, and Titus Lowe; the ministers: Henry Hitt Crane, Joseph M. M. Gray, Earl Enyeart Harper, John W. Langdale, and Oscar Thomas Olson; the laymen: Karl P. Harrington, James R. Houghton, Howard Wilder Lyman, Robert G. McCutchan, and Albert Riemenschneider.

The General Conference of the Methodist Episcopal Church, South, of 1930, appointed a similar Commission. The Bishops were: Warren A. Candler, John M. Moore, Urban V. W. Darlington, Sam R. Hay, and A. Frank Smith; the ministers: Nolan B. Harmon, Ivan Lee Holt, D. N. Hotchkiss, Fitzgerald S. Parker, and Wilbur Fisk Tillett; the laymen: Walter Kirkland Greene, J. Abner Sage, Guy E. Snavely, Henry N. Snyder, and Charles C. Washburn.

The Methodist Protestant Church accepted an invitation to participate in the preparation of the HYMNAL, extended at the time of the organization of the Joint Commission and appointed these ministers as its representatives: President John C. Broomfield, Hugh Latimer Elderdice, Harlan Luther Feeman, Charles Edward Forlines, J. W. Hawley, and Eugene C. Makosky.

Robert G. McCutchan was elected Editor of the HYMNAL.

The Joint Commission constantly held in mind the perpetuation of the Wesley tradition, the varied desires of the Church, the different ages of Church members, the continued value of evangelism, and the emphasis upon the application of the gospel to everyday life. Painstaking attention has been given to the selection and arrangement of the most helpful scriptural responsive readings. Numerous indexes have been provided for the widest and most convenient use of the HYMNAL.

Diligent search has been made for new hymns and tunes. Desirable hymns out of contemporary life have been found. Some hymns from former editions

PREFACE

have been restored. The hymns of the ages have been re-examined and many of surpassing merit, which hitherto have not appeared in Methodist hymn and tune books, have been introduced.

Certain features of the book deserve special mention. Hymns for children rather than about children have been selected. There is a section of hymns for use in the home by the family. Material has been supplied for the ennoblement of services of worship, and provision of hymns and special readings has been made for the worthy observance and celebration of church festival occasions such as Christmas and Easter.

In the selection of the music those tunes emphasizing the melodic content were given preference. Care was taken to continue the associations of words and music that have grown familiar by long usage.

Grateful acknowledgment is made to all who have granted permission for the use of their hymns and tunes. Every endeavor has been made to properly accredit these in the body of the book. To Van Denman Thompson, for his advice and assistance in editing the music, and to Philip S. Watters, for his literary criticism, gratitude is also due.

Methodism was born in song and has made a vitalizing contribution to evangelical hymnody. It is the devout hope of those who have had a part in its preparation that the use of this, THE METHODIST HYMNAL, will unite our people in corporate praise and devotion and enhance the musical ministry of Methodism. "Let us offer the sacrifice of praise to God continually, that is, the fruit of our lips giving thanks to His name."

CONTENTS

HYMNS

I. WORSHIP

II. GOD

III. JESUS CHRIST

IV. THE HOLY SPIRIT 172–183

V. THE GOSPEL

VI. THE CHRISTIAN LIFE

VII. THE LIVING CHURCH

VIII. THE CHRISTIAN HOME AND FAMILY 426–433

IX. HYMNS FOR CHILDREN 434–453

CONTENTS

X. THE KINGDOM OF GOD

XI. THE ETERNAL LIFE

XII. SPECIAL SEASONS AND SERVICES

RITUAL MUSIC FOR THE HOLY COMMUNION

RESPONSES AND SENTENCES

ANCIENT HYMNS AND CANTICLES

RITUAL AND RESPONSIVE READINGS

INDEXES

HYMNS

WORSHIP
Adoration and Praise

1

NICÆA. 11. 12. 12. 10.

REGINALD HEBER, 1783–1826   JOHN B. DYKES, 1823–1876

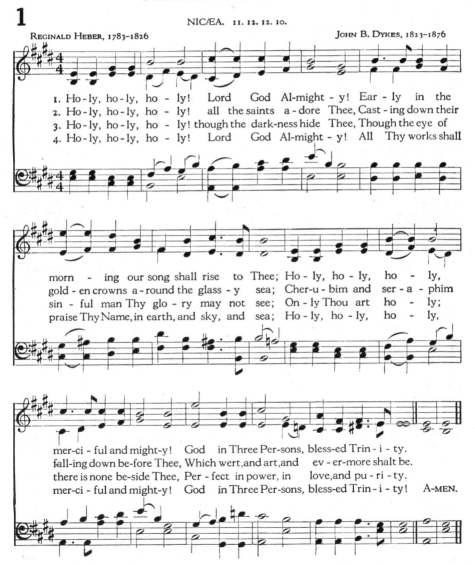

1. Ho-ly, ho-ly, ho - ly! Lord God Al-might - y! Ear - ly in the
morn - ing our song shall rise to Thee; Ho - ly, ho - ly, ho - ly,
mer-ci - ful and might-y! God in Three Per-sons, bless-ed Trin - i - ty.

2. Ho-ly, ho-ly, ho - ly! all the saints a - dore Thee, Cast - ing down their
gold - en crowns a - round the glass - y sea; Cher-u - bim and ser - a - phim
fall-ing down be-fore Thee, Which wert, and art, and ev - er-more shalt be.

3. Ho-ly, ho-ly, ho - ly! though the dark-ness hide Thee, Though the eye of
sin - ful man Thy glo - ry may not see; On - ly Thou art ho - ly;
there is none be-side Thee, Per - fect in power, in love, and pu - ri - ty.

4. Ho-ly, ho-ly, ho - ly! Lord God Al-might - y! All Thy works shall
praise Thy Name, in earth, and sky, and sea; Ho - ly, ho - ly, ho - ly,
mer-ci - ful and might-y! God in Three Per-sons, bless-ed Trin - i - ty! A-MEN.

Worship

2

ITALIAN HYMN (TRINITY). 6. 6. 4. 6. 6. 6. 4.

Anonymous

FELICE DE GIARDINI, 1716–1796

1. Come, Thou al - might - y King, Help us Thy Name to sing,
2. Come, Thou In - car - nate Word, Gird on Thy might - y sword,
3. Come, Ho - ly Com - fort - er, Thy sa - cred wit - ness bear,
4. To Thee, great One in Three, E - ter - nal prais - es be

Help us to praise! Fa - ther all - glo - ri - ous, O'er all vic -
Our pray'r at - tend; Come, and Thy peo - ple bless, And give Thy
In this glad hour: Thou who al - might - y art, Now rule in
Hence, ev - er - more: Thy sov - 'reign maj - es - ty May we in

to - ri - ous, Come, and reign o - ver us, An - cient of Days!
word suc - cess; Spir - it of ho - li - ness, On us de - scend!
ev - ery heart, And ne'er from us de - part, Spir - it of power!
glo - ry see, And to e - ter - ni - ty Love and a - dore! A-MEN.

3

OLD 100th. L. M.

From PSALM C
ISAAC WATTS, 1674–1748, alt.

Melody from GENEVAN PSALTER, 1551

1. Be - fore Je - ho - vah's awe - full throne, Ye na - tions, bow with sa - cred joy;
2. His sov - 'reign pow'r, with - out our aid, Made us of clay, and form'd us men;
3. We'll crowd His gates with thankful songs, High as the heav'ns our voic - es raise;
4. Wide as the world is His com - mand; Vast as e - ter - ni - ty His love;

Adoration and Praise

Know that the Lord is God a-lone, He can cre-ate, and He de-stroy.
And, when like wand'ring sheep we stray'd, He brought us to His fold a-gain.
And earth, with her ten thousand tongues, Shall fill His courts with sounding praise.
Firm as a rock His truth shall stand, When rolling years shall cease to move. A-MEN.

Another form of this tune will be found at No. 13
Alternative tune, Duke Street, No. 17

4

LYONS. 10. 10. 11. 11.

ROBERT GRANT, 1785–1838

Adapted from JOHANN M. HAYDN, 1737–1806

1. O wor-ship the King, all - glo-rious a-bove, O grate-ful-ly sing His
2. The earth, with its store of won-ders un-told, Al-might-y, Thy power hath
3. Thy boun-ti-ful care what tongue can re-cite? It breathes in the air, it
4. Frail chil-dren of dust, and fee-ble as frail, In Thee do we trust, nor

power and His love; Our Shield and De - fend - er, the An-cient of Days,
found-ed of old, Hath stab-lished it fast by a change-less de-cree,
shines in the light, It streams from the hills, it de-scends to the plain,
find Thee to fail; Thy mer-cies how ten-der, how firm to the end,

Pa - vil - ioned in splen-dor, and gird - ed with praise.
And round it hath cast, like a man - tle, the sea.
And sweet-ly dis-tills in the dew and the rain.
Our Mak-er, De-fend-er, Re-deem-er, and Friend. A-MEN.

5

LEONI (YIGDAL). 6. 6. 8. 4. D.

Daniel Ben Judah, 14th century
Revised version of The Yigdal

Arr. from a Hebrew melody

1. The God of Abra-ham praise, All prais-ed be His Name,
2. His spir-it flow-eth free, High surg-ing where it will:
3. He hath e-ter-nal life Im-plant-ed in the soul;

Who was, and is, and is to be, And still the same!
In proph-et's word He spoke of old— He speak-eth still.
His love shall be our strength and stay, While a-ges roll.

The one e-ter-nal God, Ere aught that now ap-pears;
Es-tab-lished is His law, And change-less it shall stand,
Praise to the liv-ing God! All prais-ed be His Name

The First, the Last: be-yond all thought His time-less years!
Deep writ up-on the hu-man heart, On sea, or land.
Who was, and is, and is to be, And still the same! A-men.

Adoration and Praise

LASST UNS ERFREUEN. 8. 8. 4. 4. 8. 8. with Alleluias

ATHELSTAN RILEY, 1858–

Melody from
GEISTLICHE KIRCHENGESÄNG, 1623

In unison

1. Ye watch-ers and ye ho - ly ones, Bright ser-aphs, cher - u - bim and thrones,
2. O high - er than the cher - u - bim, More glo-rious than the ser - a - phim,
3. O friends, in glad-ness let us sing, Su - per-nal an-thems ech - o - ing,

Harmony ... *Unison*

Raise the glad strain, Al - le - lu - ia! Cry out, do-min-ions, prince-doms, powers,
Lead their prais-es, Al - le - lu - ia! Thou bear-er of th' e - ter - nal Word,
Al - le - lu - ia, Al - le - lu - ia! To God the Fa-ther, God the Son,

Harmony

Vir - tues, arch - an - gels, an - gels' choirs, Al - le - lu - ia, Al - le -
Most gra-cious, mag - ni - fy the Lord, Al - le - lu - ia, Al - le -
And God the Spir - it, Three in One. Al - le - lu - ia, Al - le -

Unison

lu - ia, Al - le - lu - ia, Al - le - lu - ia, Al - le - lu - ia!
lu - ia, Al - le - lu - ia, Al - le - lu - ia, Al - le - lu - ia!
lu - ia, Al - le - lu - ia, Al - le - lu - ia, Al - le - lu - ia! A-MEN.

Worship

NUN DANKET. 6. 7. 6. 7. 6. 6. 6. 6.

MARTIN RINKART, 1586–1649
Tr. by CATHERINE WINKWORTH, 1829–1878

JOHANN CRÜGER, 1598–1662
Harmonized by
FELIX MENDELSSOHN-BARTHOLDY, 1809–1847

1. Now thank we all our God With heart and hands and voic - es,
2. O may this boun - teous God, Through all our life be near us,
3. All praise and thanks to God The Fa - ther now be giv - en,

Who won - drous things hath done, In whom His world re - joic - es;
With ev - er joy - ful hearts And bless - ed peace to cheer us;
The Son, and Him who reigns With them in high - est heav - en,

Who, from our moth - ers' arms, Hath blessed us on our way
And keep us in His grace, And guide us when per - plexed,
The one e - ter - nal God, Whom earth and heaven a - dore;

With count-less gifts of love, And still is ours to - day.
And free us from all ills In this world and the next.
For thus it was, is now, And shall be ev - er - more. A-MEN.

Adoration and Praise

ALL THE WORLD. 10. 4. 6. 6. 6. 6. 10. 4.

GEORGE HERBERT, 1593–1632

JOHN PORTER, 1877–

1. Let all the world in ev-ery cor-ner sing: My God and
all the world in ev-ery cor-ner sing: My God and

King! The heavens are not too high, His praise may thith-er fly; The
King! The Church with psalms must shout, No door can keep them out: But,

earth is not too low, His prais-es there may grow. Let all the world in
more than all, the heart Must bear the lon-gest part. Let all the world in

ev-ery cor-ner sing: My God and King! 2. Let God and King!

Music copyright, 1934, by Robert G. McCutchan. Used by permission

Worship

9

WENTWORTH. 8. 4. 8. 4. 8. 4.
(First Tune)

ADELAIDE A. PROCTER, 1825–1864

FREDERICK C. MAKER, 1844–1927

1. My God, I thank Thee, who hast made The earth so bright,
2. I thank Thee, too, that Thou hast made Joy to a-bound,
3. I thank Thee, Lord, that Thou hast kept The best in store;

So full of splen-dor and of joy, Beau-ty and light;
So man-y gen-tle thoughts and deeds Cir-cling us 'round,
We have e-nough, yet not too much, To long for more;

So man-y glo-rious things are here, No-ble and right.
That in the dark-est spot of earth Some love is found.
A yearn-ing for a deep-er peace Not known be-fore. A-MEN.

9

FOWLER. 8. 4. 8. 4. 8. 4.
(Second Tune)

ADELAIDE A. PROCTER, 1824–1864

ROBERT G. McCUTCHAN, 1877–

1. My God, I thank Thee, who hast made The earth so bright,
2. I thank Thee, too, that Thou hast made Joy to a-bound,
3. I thank Thee, Lord, that Thou hast kept The best in store;

Adoration and Praise

So full of splen-dor and of joy, Beau-ty and light;
So man-y gen-tle thoughts and deeds Cir-cling us 'round,
We have e-nough, yet not too much, To long for more;

So man-y glo-rious things are here, No-ble and right.
That in the dark-est spot of earth Some love is found.
A yearn-ing for a deep-er peace Not known be-fore. A-MEN.

10

WORSHIP. L. M.

RICHARD W. GILDER, 1844–1909

KARL P. HARRINGTON, 1861–

In unison

1. To Thee, E-ter-nal Soul, be praise! Who, from of old to our own days,
2. We thank Thee for each might-y one Through whom Thy liv-ing light hath shone;
3. We thank Thee for the love di-vine Made real in ev-ery saint of Thine;
4. We thank Thee for the word of might Thy Spir-it spake in dark-est night.
5. E-ter-nal Soul, our souls keep pure, That like Thy saints we may en-dure;

Through souls of saints and proph-ets, Lord, Hast sent Thy light, Thy love, Thy word.
And for each hum-ble soul and sweet That lights to heaven our wandering feet.
That bound-less love it-self that gives In serv-ice to each soul that lives.
Spake through the trum-pet voic-es loud Of proph-ets at Thy throne who bowed.
For-ev-er through Thy serv-ants, Lord, Send Thou Thy light, Thy love, Thy word. A-MEN.

Worship

11

HYFRYDOL. 8.7.8.7.D.

From the FOUNDLING HOSPITAL COLLECTION, 1796

Melody by
ROWLAND H. PRICHARD, 1811–1887

1. Praise the Lord! ye heavens, a - dore Him; Praise Him, an - gels, in the height;
2. Praise the Lord! for He is glo - rious; Nev - er shall His prom-ise fail;

Sun and moon, re - joice be - fore Him; Praise Him, all ye stars of light.
God hath made His saints vic - to - rious; Sin and death shall not pre - vail.

Praise the Lord! for He hath spo - ken; Worlds His might - y voice o - beyed;
Praise the God of our sal - va - tion! Hosts on high, His power pro-claim;

Laws which nev - er shall be bro - ken For their guid-ance hath He made.
Heaven, and earth, and all cre - a - tion, Laud and mag - ni - fy His Name. A-MEN.

Alternative tune, Austrian Hymn, No. 382

Adoration and Praise

12

HYMN TO JOY. 8. 7. 8. 7. D.

HENRY VAN DYKE, 1852–1933

Arr. from LUDWIG VAN BEETHOVEN, 1770–1827

1. Joy - ful, joy - ful, we a - dore Thee, God of glo - ry, Lord of love;
2. All Thy works with joy sur-round Thee, Earth and heav'n re - flect Thy rays,
3. Thou art giv - ing and for - giv - ing, Ev - er bless - ing, ev - er blest,
4. Mor - tals join the might - y cho - rus, Which the morn - ing stars be - gan;

Hearts un - fold like flow'rs be - fore Thee, Open - ing to the sun a - bove.
Stars and an - gels sing a - round Thee, Cen - ter of un - bro - ken praise;
Well-spring of the joy of liv - ing, O - cean-depth of hap - py rest!
Fa - ther - love is reign - ing o'er us, Broth-er - love binds man to man.

Melt the clouds of sin and sad - ness; Drive the dark of doubt a - way;
Field and for - est, vale and moun-tain, Flow - ery mead-ow, flash - ing sea,
Thou our Fa - ther, Christ our Broth - er—All who live in love are Thine;
Ev - er sing - ing, march we on - ward, Vic - tors in the midst of strife;

Giv - er of im - mor - tal glad-ness, Fill us with the light of day!
Chant-ing bird and flow - ing foun-tain, Call us to re - joice in Thee.
Teach us how to love each oth - er, Lift us to the Joy Di-vine.
Joy - ful mu - sic leads us sun-ward In the tri-umph song of life. A - MEN.

Worship

13

OLD 100TH. L. M.

From Psalm C
Ascribed to WILLIAM KETHE, d., c. 1593

Melody from GENEVAN PSALTER, 1551

1. All peo - ple that on earth do dwell, Sing to the Lord with cheerful voice.
2. Know that the Lord is God in - deed; With - out our aid He did us make;
3. O en - ter then His gates with praise, Ap - proach with joy His courts un - to;
4. For why the Lord our God is good; His mer - cy is for ev - er sure;

Him serve with mirth, His praise forth tell; Come ye be-fore Him and re-joice.
We are His folk, He doth us feed, And for His sheep He doth us take.
Praise, laud, and bless His Name al - ways, For it is seem - ly so to do.
His truth at all times firm - ly stood, And shall from age to age en-dure. A - MEN.

Another form of this tune will be found at No. 3

14

IRISH. C. M.

From Psalm XXXIV. NEW VERSION
TATE AND BRADY, 1698

Melody from
A COLLECTION OF HYMNS AND SACRED POEMS, 1749

1. Through all the chang-ing scenes of life, In trou - ble and in joy,
2. O mag - ni - fy the Lord with me, With me ex - alt His Name;
3. O make but tri - al of His love; Ex - pe - rience will de - cide
4. Fear Him, ye saints, and you will then Have noth - ing else to fear;
5. For God pre - serves the souls of those Who on His truth de-pend;

The prais - es of my God shall still My heart and tongue em-ploy.
When in dis - tress to Him I called, He to my res - cue came.
How blest are they, and on - ly they, Who in His truth con-fide.
Make you His serv - ice your de-light; Your wants shall be His care.
To them and their pos-ter - i - ty His bless-ing shall de-scend. A - MEN.

Adoration and Praise

ANGEL VOICES. 8. 5. 8. 5. 8. 4. 3.

FRANCIS POTT, 1832–1909

ARTHUR S. SULLIVAN, 1842–1900

1. An - gel voic - es, ev - er sing - ing Round Thy throne of light,
2. Thou who art be - yond the far - thest Mor - tal eye can scan,
3. Yea, we know that Thou re - joic - est O'er each work of Thine;

An - gel harps for ev - er ring - ing, Rest not day nor night;
Can it be that Thou re - gard - est Songs of sin - ful man?
Thou didst ears and hands and voic - es For Thy praise de - sign;

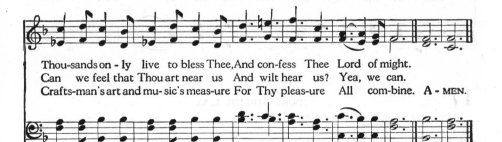

Thou-sands on - ly live to bless Thee, And con-fess Thee Lord of might.
Can we feel that Thou art near us And wilt hear us? Yea, we can.
Crafts-man's art and mu-sic's meas-ure For Thy pleas-ure All com-bine. A - MEN.

4 Here, great God, to-day we offer
   Of Thine own to Thee;
And for Thine acceptance proffer,
   All unworthily,
Hearts and minds, and hands and voices,
   In our choicest
      Melody.

5 Honor, glory, might, and merit
   Thine shall ever be,
Father, Son, and Holy Spirit,
   Blessèd Trinity:
Of the best that Thou hast given,
   Earth and heaven
      Render Thee.

Worship

16

CŒLITES PLAUDANT. 11. 11. 11. 5

Anonymous

Rouen church melody

1. Hon - or and glo - ry, power and sal - va - tion Be in the
2. Bow down be - fore Him, peo - ple and na - tions, See ye His

high - est un - to Him who reign - eth. Change-less in heav - en,
glo - ry, clear - ly now ap - pear - ing. Come ye and worship Him,

o - ver earth-ly chang - es, God, the e - ter - nal.
God in the high - est, Rul - er for ev - er. A-MEN.

17

DUKE STREET. L. M.

Stanzas 1, 4, ISAAC WATTS, 1674-1748
Stanzas 2, 3, Anonymous

JOHN HATTON, d. 1793

1. From all that dwell be - low the skies, Let the Cre - a - tor's praise a - rise;
2. In ev-ery land be - gin the song; To ev-ery land the strains be-long:
3. Your loft-y themes, ye mor - tals, bring; In songs of praise di - vine-ly sing;
4. E - ter-nal are Thy mer - cies, Lord; E - ter-nal truth at - tends Thy word:

Adoration and Praise

Let the Re-deem-er's Name be sung, Through every land, by ev - ery tongue.
In cheer-ful sounds all voic - es raise, And fill the world with loud-est praise.
The great sal - va - tion loud pro-claim, And shout for joy the Sav-iour's Name.
Thy praise shall sound from shore to shore, Till suns shall rise and set no more. A-MEN.

18

DIX. 7. 7. 7. 7. 7. 7.

FOLLIOTT S. PIERPOINT, 1835–1917

Abridged from a chorale by
CONRAD KOCHER, 1786–1872

1. For the beau - ty of the earth, For the glo - ry of the skies,
2. For the beau - ty of each hour Of the day and of the night,
3. For the joy of ear and eye; For the heart and mind's de - light;
4. For the joy of hu - man love, Broth-er, sis - ter, par - ent, child,

For the love which from our birth O - ver and a - round us lies:
Hill and vale, and tree and flower, Sun and moon, and stars of light:
For the mys - tic har - mo - ny Link-ing sense to sound and sight:
Friends on earth, and friends a - bove; For all gen - tle thoughts and mild:

Lord of all, to Thee we raise This our hymn of grate - ful praise. A-MEN.

5 For Thy church, that evermore
   Lifteth holy hands above,
   Offering up on every shore
   Her pure sacrifice of love:
Lord of all, to Thee we raise
This our hymn of grateful praise.

6 For Thyself, best Gift Divine!
   To our race so freely given;
   For that great, great love of Thine,
   Peace on earth, and joy in heaven!
Lord of all, to Thee we raise
This our hymn of grateful praise.

Worship

ARIEL. 8. 8. 6. D.

Isaac Watts, 1674–1748

Arr. by Lowell Mason, 1792–1872

1. Let all on earth their voic - es raise,
2. He framed the globe; He built the sky;
3. Come the great day, the glo - rious hour,

To sing the great Je - ho-vah's praise, And bless His ho - ly Name:
He made the shin - ing worlds on high, And reigns in glo - ry there:
When earth shall feel His sav - ing power, All na - tions fear His Name;

His glo - ry let the peo - ple know, His won-ders to the na-tions show,
His beams are maj - es - ty and light; His beau-ties, how di - vine - ly bright!
Then shall the race of men con-fess The beau-ty of His ho - li - ness,

His sav - ing grace pro-claim, His sav - ing grace pro - claim.
His dwell - ing place, how fair! His dwell-ing place, how fair!
His sav - ing grace pro-claim, His sav - ing grace pro - claim. A - men.

Opening of Worship

KREMSER. Irregular

Anonymous
Tr. by THEODORE BAKER

Netherland Folk Song, 1625
Arr. by EDWARD KREMSER, 1838-1914

1. We gath - er to - geth - er to ask the Lord's bless - ing;
2. Be - side us to guide us, our God with us join - ing,
3. We all do ex - tol Thee, Thou Lead - er tri - um - phant,

He chas - tens and has - tens His will to make known;
Or - dain - ing, main - tain - ing His king - dom di - vine;
And pray that Thou still our De - fend - er wilt be.

The wick - ed op - press - ing now cease from dis - tress - ing,
So from the be - gin - ning the fight we were win - ning:
Let Thy con - gre - ga - tion es - cape trib - u - la - tion:

Sing prais - es to His Name: He for - gets not His own.
Thou, Lord, wast at our side, all glo - ry be Thine!
Thy Name be ev - er praised! O Lord, make us free! A - MEN.

Stanzas one and two in unison; stanza three in harmony

Worship

21

DUKE STREET. L. M.

ROBERT A. WEST, 1809–1865

JOHN HATTON, d. 1793

1. Come, let us tune our loft - iest song And raise to Christ our joy - ful strain;
2. His sov-'reign pow'r our bod - ies made; Our souls are His im - mor - tal breath;
3. Burn ev-ery breast with Je - sus' love; Bound ev-ery heart with rap-turous joy;
4. Ex - tol the Lamb with loft - iest song; As-cend for Him our cheer-ful strain;

Wor-ship and thanks to Him be - long, Who reigns, and shall for-ev - er reign.
And when His crea-tures sinn'd, He bled, To save us from e - ter-nal death.
And saints on earth, with saints a - bove, Your voic-es in His praise em-ploy.
Wor-ship and thanks to Him be - long, Who reigns and shall for-ev - er reign. A-MEN.

22

SILVER STREET. S. M.

ISAAC WATTS, 1674–1748

ISAAC SMITH, 1735–1800

1. Come, sound His praise a - broad And hymns of glo - ry sing: Je -
2. He formed the deeps un - known; He gave the seas their bound; The
3. Come, wor - ship at His throne, Come, bow be - fore the Lord: We
4. To - day at - tend His voice, Nor dare pro - voke His rod; Come,

ho - vah is the sov - ereign God, The u - ni - ver - sal King.
wa-tery worlds are all His own, And all the sol - id ground.
are His works and not our own; He formed us by His word.
like the peo-ple of His choice, And own your gra - cious God. A-MEN.

Opening of Worship

NETTLETON. 8. 7. 8. 7. D.

ROBERT ROBINSON, 1735–1790

JOHN WYETH (?), 1770–1858

23

1. Come, Thou Fount of ev - ery bless - ing, Tune my heart to sing Thy grace;
2. Here I raise mine Eb - en - e - zer; Hith - er by Thy help I'm come;
3. O to grace how great a debt - or Dai - ly I'm con-strained to be!

Streams of mer - cy, nev - er ceas - ing, Call for songs of loud - est praise.
And I hope, by Thy good pleas - ure, Safe - ly to ar - rive at home.
Let Thy good - ness, like a fet - ter, Bind my wan - dering heart to Thee:

Teach me some me - lo - dious son - net Sung by flam - ing tongues a - bove;
Je - sus sought me when a stran - ger, Wan-d'ring from the fold of God;
Prone to wan - der, Lord, I feel it, Prone to leave the God I love;

Praise the mount! I'm fixed up-on it, Mount of Thy re - deem-ing love.
He, to res - cue me from dan-ger, In - ter-posed His pre-cious blood.
Here's my heart, O take and seal it, Seal it for Thy courts a - bove. A - MEN.

Worship

24

MALVERN. L. M.

WILLIAM COWPER, 1731-1800

LOWELL MASON, 1792-1872

1. Je - sus, wher-e'er Thy peo - ple meet, There they be - hold Thy mer - cy - seat;
2. For Thou, with-in no walls con-fined, Dost dwell with those of hum-ble mind;
3. Great Shepherd of Thy cho - sen few, Thy for - mer mer - cies here re - new;
4. Here may we prove the power of prayer To strengthen faith and sweeten care;

Wher-e'er they seek Thee Thou art found, And ev - ery place is hallowed ground.
Such ev - er bring Thee where they come, And, going, take Thee to their home.
Here, to our wait - ing hearts, proclaim The sweetness of Thy sav - ing Name.
To teach our faint de - sires to rise, And bring all heav'n be - fore our eyes. A-MEN.

25

MORNINGTON. S. M.

Arr. from a chant by
GARRET WELLESLEY, 1735-1781

CHARLES WESLEY, 1707-1788

1. Je - sus, we look to Thee, Thy prom - ised pres - ence claim;
2. Thy Name sal - va - tion is, Which here we come to prove;
3. We meet, the grace to take Which Thou hast free - ly given;
4. Pres - ent we know Thou art; But, O, Thy - self re - veal!

Thou in the midst of us shalt be, As-sem - bled in Thy Name:
Thy Name is life, and health, and peace, And ev - er - last - ing love.
We meet on earth for Thy dear sake That we may meet in heaven.
Now, Lord, let ev - 'ry wait - ing heart The might-y com - fort feel. A-MEN.

Closing of Worship

26

SICILIAN MARINERS' HYMN. 8. 7. 8. 7. 8. 7.

JOHN FAWCETT, 1740–1817, alt.

Arr. from a Sicilian melody

1. Lord, dis - miss us with Thy bless - ing; Fill our hearts with
2. Thanks we give and ad - o - ra - tion For Thy gos - pel's

joy and peace; Let us each, Thy love pos - sess - ing,
joy - ful sound. May the fruits of Thy sal - va - tion

Tri - umph in re - deem - ing grace: Oh, re - fresh us,
In our hearts and lives a - bound; Ev - er faith - ful,

oh, re - fresh us, Trav - 'ling thro' this wil - der - ness.
ev - er faith - ful To the truth may we be found. A - MEN.

Alternative tune, Greenville, No. 187

Worship

27

SARDIS. 8. 7. 8. 7.

JOHN NEWTON, 1725–1807

Arr. from LUDWIG VAN BEETHOVEN, 1770–1827

1. May the grace of Christ our Sav-iour And the Fa-ther's bound-less love,
2. Thus may we a-bide in un-ion With each oth-er and the Lord,

With the Ho-ly Spir-it's fa-vor, Rest up-on us from a-bove.
And pos-sess, in sweet com-mun-ion, Joys which earth can-not af-ford. A-MEN.

28

BELMONT. C. M.

JOHN ELLERTON, 1826–1893, alt.

Adapted from SACRED MELODIES,
WILLIAM GARDINER, 1770–1853

1. The Lord be with us as each day His bless-ings we re-ceive;
2. The Lord be with us as we walk A-long our home-ward road;
3. The Lord be with us till the night En-fold our day of rest;
4. The Lord be with us thro' the hours Of slum-ber calm and deep,

His gift of peace on all we pray, Be-fore His courts we leave.
In si-lent thought or friend-ly talk, Our hearts be near to God.
Be He of ev-ery heart the light, Of ev-ery home the guest.
Pro-tect our homes, re-new our pow'rs And guard His peo-ple's sleep. A-MEN.

Closing of Worship

29

ELLERS. 10. 10. 10. 10.

JOHN ELLERTON, 1826–1893

EDWARD J. HOPKINS, 1818–1901

1. Sav - iour, a - gain to Thy dear Name we raise
2. Grant us Thy peace up - on our home - ward way;
3. Grant us Thy peace, Lord, through the com - ing night,
4. Grant us Thy peace through - out our earth - ly life,

With one ac - cord our part - ing hymn of praise;
With Thee be - gan, with Thee shall end the day:
Turn Thou for us its dark - ness in - to light;
Our balm in sor - row, and our stay in strife;

We stand to bless Thee ere our wor - ship cease,
Guard Thou the lips from sin, the hearts from shame,
From harm and dan - ger keep Thy chil - dren free,
Then, when Thy voice shall bid our con - flict cease,

And still our hearts to wait Thy word of peace.
That in this house have called up - on Thy Name.
For dark and light are both a - like to Thee.
Call us, O Lord, to Thine e - ter - nal peace. A - MEN.

Worship

30

HAYDN. 8. 4. 7. 8. 4. 7.

FRIEDRICH R. L. VON CANITZ, 1654-1699
Tr. by HENRY J. BUCKOLL, 1803-1871

Arr. from FRANCIS J. HAYDN, 1732-1809

1. Come, my soul, thou must be wak - ing; Now is break - ing O'er the earth an - oth - er day: Come to Him who made this splen - dor; See thou ren - der All thy fee - ble strength can pay.

2. Glad - ly hail the sun re - turn - ing; Read - y burn - ing Be the in - cense of thy powers; For the night is safe - ly end - ed; God hath tend - ed With His care thy help - less hours.

3. Pray that He may pros - per ev - er Each en - deav - or, When thine aim is good and true; But that He may ev - er thwart thee, And con - vert thee, When thou e - vil wouldst pur - sue.

4. Our God's boun - teous gifts a - buse not, Light re - fuse not, But His Spir - it's voice o - bey; Thou with Him shalt dwell, be - hold - ing Light en - fold - ing All things in un - cloud - ed day. A - MEN.

Morning Hymns

LAUDES DOMINI. 6. 6. 6. 6. 6. 6.

From the German, c. 1800
Tr. by EDWARD CASWALL, 1814–1878

JOSEPH BARNBY, 1838–1896

1. When morn-ing gilds the skies, My heart a-wak-ing cries,
2. When-e'er the sweet church bell Peals o-ver hill and dell,
3. The night be-comes as day, When from the heart we say,
4. Ye na-tions of man-kind, In this your con-cord find,

May Je-sus Christ be praised! A-like at work and prayer,
May Je-sus Christ be praised! O hark to what it sings,
May Je-sus Christ be praised! The powers of dark-ness fear,
May Je-sus Christ be praised! Let all the earth a-round

To Je-sus I re-pair; May Je-sus Christ be praised!
As joy-ous-ly it rings, May Je-sus Christ be praised!
When this sweet chant they hear, May Je-sus Christ be praised!
Ring joy-ous with the sound, May Je-sus Christ be praised! A-MEN.

5 In heaven's eternal bliss
The loveliest strain is this,
  May Jesus Christ be praised!
Let earth, and sea, and sky
From depth to height reply,
  May Jesus Christ be praised!

6 Be this, while life is mine,
My canticle divine,
  May Jesus Christ be praised!
Be this th' eternal song
Through all the ages long,
  May Jesus Christ be praised!

Worship

32

CHARLES WESLEY, 1707–1788

Old German melody
Arr. in J. G. WERNER'S CHORALBUCH, 1815

1. Christ, whose glo - ry fills the skies, Christ, the true, the on - ly Light,
2. Dark and cheer - less is the morn Un - ac - com - pa - nied by Thee;
3. Vis - it, then, this soul of mine; Pierce the gloom of sin and grief;

Sun of right - eous - ness, a - rise, Tri - umph o'er the shades of night;
Joy - less is the day's re - turn Till Thy mer - cy's beams I see;
Fill me, Ra - dian - cy Di - vine; Scat - ter all my un - be - lief;

Day-Spring from on high, be near; Day - Star, in my heart ap - pear.
Till they in - ward light im - part, Cheer my eyes and warm my heart.
More and more Thy - self dis - play, Shin - ing to the per - fect day. A - MEN.

33

TRUST. 8. 7. 8. 7.

MILTON S. LITTLEFIELD, 1864–1934

FELIX MENDELSSOHN–BARTHOLDY, 1809–1847

1. Come, O Lord, like morn - ing sun - light, Mak - ing all life new and free;
2. Come, O Lord, like o - cean flood-tides, Flow-ing in - land from the sea;
3. Come, O Lord, like moun - tain breez-es, Fresh-'ning life in vale and lea;
4. Come, O Lord, like eve - ning twi-light, Bring-ing peace on land and sea;

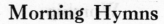

Morning Hymns

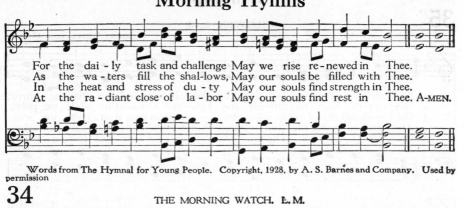

For the dai - ly task and challenge May we rise re-newed in Thee.
As the wa - ters fill the shal-lows, May our souls be filled with Thee.
In the heat and stress of du - ty May our souls find strength in Thee.
At the ra - diant close of la - bor May our souls find rest in Thee. A-MEN.

34   THE MORNING WATCH. L.M.

THOMAS KEN, 1637-1711   CARL F. PRICE, 1881-

1. A - wake, my soul, and with the sun Thy dai - ly
2. Shine on me, Lord, new life im - part! Fresh ar - dors
3. Lord, I my vows to Thee re - new; Dis - perse my
4. Di - rect, con - trol, sug - gest this day All I de -
5. Praise God, from whom all bless - ings flow; Praise Him, all

stage of du - ty run; Shake off dull sloth, and
kin - dle in my heart; One ray of Thine all -
sins as morn - ing dew, Guard my first springs of
sign, or do, or say, That all my powers, with'
crea - tures here be - low; Praise Him a - bove, ye

joy - ful rise To pay thy morn - ing sac - ri - fice!
quick - 'ning light Dis - pels the clouds and dark of night.
thought and will And with Thy - self my spir - it fill.
all their might, In Thy sole glo - ry may u - nite.
heav'n - ly host: Praise Fa - ther, Son, and Ho - ly Ghost. A - MEN.

Worship

35

MELCOMBE. L. M.

John Keble, 1792–1866

Samuel Webbe, 1740–1816

1. New ev-ery morn-ing is the love Our wak-'ning and up-ris-ing prove;
2. New mer-cies, each re-turn-ing day, Hov-er a-round us while we pray;
3. Old friends, old scenes, will love-lier be, As more of heav'n in each we see;
4. The triv-ial round, the com-mon task, Will fur-nish all we ought to ask:
5. On-ly, O Lord, in Thy dear love Fit us for per-fect rest a-bove;

Thro' sleep and dark-ness safe-ly brought, Re-stored to life and pow'r and thought.
New per-ils past, new sins for-given, New tho'ts of God, new hopes of heav'n.
Some soft-'ning gleam of love and pray'r Shall dawn on ev-ery cross and care.
Room to de-ny our-selves, a road To bring us dai-ly near-er God.
And help us this and ev-ery day, To live more near-ly as we pray. A-men.

Alternative tune, Canonbury, No. 116

36

MORNINGTON. S. M.

John Wesley, 1703–1791

Arr. from a chant by
Garret Wellesley, 1735–1781

1. We lift our hearts to Thee, O Day-Star from on high!
2. O let Thine o-rient beams The night of sin dis-perse,
3. How beau-teous na-ture now: How dark and sad be-fore!
4. May we this life im-prove, To mourn for er-rors past,
5. To God—the Fa-ther, Son, And Spir-it— One in Three,

The sun it-self is but Thy shade, Yet cheers both earth and sky.
The mists of er-ror and of vice Which shade the u-ni-verse!
With joy we view the pleas-ing change, And na-ture's God a-dore!
And live this short, re-volv-ing day As if it were our last.
Be glo-ry; as it was, is now, And shall for-ev-er be. A-men.

Morning Hymns

ST. ASAPH. 8. 7. 8. 7. D.

JAMES D. BURNS, 1823–1864   WILLIAM S. BAMBRIDGE, 1842–1923

1. At Thy feet, our God and Fa - ther, Who hast blessed us all our days,
2. Je - sus, for Thy love most ten - der On the cross for sin - ners shown,
3. Ev - ery day will be the bright - er When Thy gra - cious face we see;

We with grate - ful hearts would gath - er To be - gin the day with praise;
We would praise Thee and sur - ren - der All our hearts to be Thine own.
Ev - 'ry bur - den will be light - er When we know it comes from Thee.

Praise for light so bright - ly shin - ing On our steps from heaven a - bove;
With so blest a Friend pro - vid - ed, We up - on our way would go,
Spread Thy love's broad ban - ner o'er us; Give us strength to serve and wait,

Praise for mer - cies dai - ly twin - ing Round us gold - en cords of love.
Sure of be - ing safe - ly guid - ed, Guard - ed well from ev - 'ry foe.
Till Thy glo - ry breaks be - fore us Thro' the cit - y's o - pen gate. A - MEN.

Worship

WAREHAM. L. M.

AMBROSE OF MILAN, 340-397
Tr. by JOHN CHANDLER, 1806-1876
and LOUIS F. BENSON, 1855-1930

WILLIAM KNAPP, 1698-1768

1. O splen-dor of God's glo - ry bright, From light e - ter - nal bring-ing light;
2. Con-firm our will to do the right, And keep our hearts from en- vy's blight;
3. O joy-ful be the pass-ing day With tho'ts as clear as morn-ing's ray,
4. Dawn's glo-ry gilds the earth and skies; Do Thou, our per - fect Morn, a-rise;

Thou Light of life, light's liv-ing Spring, True Day, all days il - lu - min-ing:
Let faith her ea - ger fires re-new, And hate the false and love the true.
With faith like noon-tide shin-ing bright, Our souls un - shad-owed by the night.
The Fa-ther's help His chil-dren claim, And sing the Fa - ther's glo-rious Name. A-MEN.

39

OLD 134TH (ST. MICHAEL). S. M.

JAMES MONTGOMERY, 1771-1854

Adapted from GENEVAN PSALTER, 1551

1. Stand up, and bless the Lord, Ye peo - ple of His choice;
2. Though high a - bove all praise, A - bove all bless - ing high,
3. O for the liv - ing flame From His own al - tar brought,
4. God is our strength and song, And His sal - va - tion ours;
5. Stand up, and bless the Lord; The Lord your God a - dore;

Stand up, and bless the Lord your God With heart and soul and voice.
Who would not fear His ho - ly Name, And laud and mag - ni - fy?
To touch our lips, our minds in - spire, And wing to heav'n our thought!
Then be His love in Christ pro-claimed With all our ran-somed pow'rs.
Stand up, and bless His glo - rious Name, Hence-forth for ev - er-more. A - MEN.

Alternative tune, St. Thomas, No. 227

Morning Hymns

CONSOLATION. 11. 10. 11. 10.

HARRIET B. STOWE, 1812–1896

Arr. from FELIX MENDELSSOHN-BARTHOLDY, 1809–1847

1. Still, still with Thee, when pur - ple morn - ing break - eth,
2. A - lone with Thee, a - mid the mys - tic shad - ows,
3. Still, still with Thee! As to each new - born morn - ing
4. When sinks the soul, sub - dued by toil, to slum - ber,
5. So shall it be at last, in that bright morn - ing,

When the bird wak - eth, and the shad - ows flee;
The sol - emn hush of na - ture new - ly born;
A fresh and sol - emn splen - dor still is given,
Its clos - ing eyes look up to Thee in prayer;
When the soul wak - eth, and life's shad - ows flee;

Fair - er than morn - ing, love - li - er than day - light,
A - lone with Thee in breath - less ad - o - ra - tion,
So does this bless - ed con - scious - ness, a - wak - ing,
Sweet the re - pose be - neath Thy wings o'er - shad - ing,
O in that hour, fair - er than day - light dawn - ing,

Dawns the sweet con - scious - ness, I am with Thee.
In the calm dew and fresh - ness of the morn.
Breathe each day near - ness un - to Thee and heaven.
But sweet - er still, to wake and find Thee there.
Shall rise the glo - rious thought, I am with Thee. A - MEN.

Worship

41

OLDBRIDGE. 8. 8. 8. 4.

GODFREY THRING, 1823–1903

ROBERT N. QUAILE, 1867–

1. The ra-diant morn hath passed a - way, And spent too soon her gold - en store;
2. Our life is but an au-tumn sun, Its glo-rious noon how quick - ly past!
3. O by Thy soul - in - spir - ing grace Up - lift our hearts to realms on high;
4. Where saints are clothed in spot-less white, And eve-ning shad-ows nev - er fall;

The shad-ows of de - part - ing day Creep on once more.
Lead us, O Christ, our life - work done, Safe home at last.
Help us to look to that bright place Be - yond the sky,
Where Thou, e - ter - nal Light of light, Art Lord of all. A - MEN.

42

ABENDS. L. M.

SAMUEL LONGFELLOW, 1819–1892

HERBERT S. OAKELEY, 1830–1903

1. A - gain, as eve-ning's shad-ow falls, We gath-er in these hal-lowed walls;
2. May strug-gling hearts that seek re - lease Here find the rest of God's own peace;
3. O God, our light! to Thee we bow; With-in all shad-ows stand-est Thou;
4. Life's tu-mult we must meet a - gain, We can-not at the shrine re-main;

And ves-per hymn and ves-per pray'r Rise ming-ling on the ho - ly air.
And, strengthen'd here by hymn and pray'r, Lay down the bur-den and the care.
Give deep-er calm than night can bring; Give sweet-er songs than lips can sing.
But in the spir-it's se - cret cell May hymn and pray'r for ev-er dwell. A-MEN.

Evening Hymns

43

AR HYD Y NOS. 8. 4. 8. 4. 8. 8. 8. 4.

REGINALD HEBER, 1783–1826
FREDERICK L. HOSMER, 1840–1929

Welsh traditional melody
Harmonized by L. O. EMERSON, 1820–1915

1. God, that mad-est earth and heav-en, Dark-ness and light;
2. When the con-stant sun re-turn-ing Un-seals our eyes,

Who the day for toil hast giv-en, For rest the night;
May we, born a-new like morn-ing, To la-bor rise;

May Thine an-gel guards de-fend us, Slum-ber sweet Thy mer-cy send us;
Gird us for the task that calls us, Let not ease and self en-thrall us,

Ho-ly dreams and hopes at-tend us, This live-long night.
Strong thro' Thee what-e'er be-fall us, O God most wise!   A - MEN.

Worship

44

CHAUTAUQUA (EVENING PRAISE). 7. 7. 7. 7. 4.

Mary A. Lathbury, 1841–1913

William F. Sherwin, 1826–1888

1. Day is dy-ing in the west; Heaven is touch-ing earth with rest:
2. Lord of life, be-neath the dome Of the u-ni-verse, Thy home,

Wait and wor-ship while the night Sets her eve-ning lamps a-light Thro' all the
Gath-er us who seek Thy face To the fold of Thy em-brace, For Thou art

sky. Ho-ly, ho-ly, ho-ly Lord God of Hosts! Heav'n and earth are
nigh. Ho-ly, ho-ly, ho-ly Lord God of Hosts! Heav'n and earth are

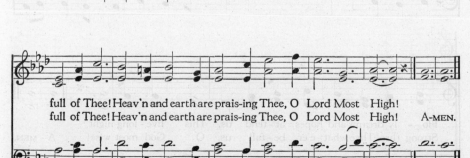

full of Thee! Heav'n and earth are prais-ing Thee, O Lord Most High!
full of Thee! Heav'n and earth are prais-ing Thee, O Lord Most High! A-men.

Evening Hymns

45

VESPER HYMN (Bortniansky). 8. 7. 8. 7. 8. 6. 8. 7.

SAMUEL LONGFELLOW, 1819–1892, alt.

DIMITRI S. BORTNIANSKY, 1752–1825

1. Now, on land and sea de-scend-ing, Brings the night its peace pro-found;
2. Soon as dies the sun-set glo-ry, Stars of heaven shine out a-bove,
3. Now, our wants and bur-dens leav-ing To His care who cares for all,
4. As the dark-ness deep-ens o'er us, Lo! e-ter-nal stars a-rise;

Let our ves-per hymn be blend-ing With the ho-ly calm a-round.
Tell-ing still the an-cient sto-ry—Their Cre-a-tor's change-less love.
Cease we fear-ing, cease we griev-ing: At His touch our bur-dens fall.
Hope and faith and love rise glo-rious, Shin-ing in the spir-it's skies.

Ju-bi-la-te! Ju-bi-la-te! Ju-bi-la-te! A-men!

Let our ves-per hymn be blend-ing With the ho-ly calm a-round.
Tell-ing still the an-cient sto-ry—Their Cre-a-tor's changeless love.
Cease we fear-ing, cease we griev-ing: At His touch our bur-dens fall.
Hope and faith and love rise glo-rious, Shin-ing in the spir-it's skies. A-MEN.

Worship

ST. LEONARD. C. M. D.

ADELAIDE A. PROCTER, 1825–1864

HENRY HILES, 1826–1904

1. The shad-ows of the eve-ning hours Fall from the dark-ening sky;
2. Slow-ly the rays of day-light fade: So fade with-in our heart
3. Let peace, O Lord, Thy peace, O God, Up-on our souls de-scend;

Up-on the fra-grance of the flowers The dews of eve-ning lie:
The hopes in earth-ly love and joy, That one by one de-part.
From mid-night fears and per-ils, Thou Our trem-bling hearts de-fend.

Be-fore Thy throne, O Lord of heaven, We kneel at close of day;
Slow-ly the bright stars, one by one, With-in the heav-ens shine:
Give us a res-pite from our toil, Calm and sub-due our woes;

Look on Thy chil-dren from on high, And hear us while we pray.
Give us, O Lord, fresh hopes in heav'n, And trust in things di-vine.
Through the long day we la-bor, Lord, O give us now re-pose. A-MEN.

Evening Hymns

47

MERCY. 7. 7. 7. 7.

GEORGE W. DOANE, 1799–1859

LOUIS M. GOTTSCHALK, 1829–1869
Arr. by EDWIN P. PARKER, 1836–1925

1. Soft - ly now the light of day Fades up - on our sight a - way;
2. Thou, whose all - per - vad - ing eye Naught es - capes, with - out, with - in,
3. Soon from us the light of day Shall for - ev - er pass a - way;

Free from care, from la - bor free, Lord, we would com - mune with Thee.
Par - don each in - firm - i - ty, O - pen fault, and se - cret sin.
Then, from sin and sor - row free, Take us, Lord, to dwell with Thee. A-MEN.

Alternative tune, Seymour, No. 200

48

ABENDS. L. M.

HENRY TWELLS, 1823–1900

HERBERT S. OAKELEY, 1830–1903

1. At e - ven, ere the sun was set, The sick, O Lord, a - round Thee lay;
2. Once more 'tis e - ven - tide, and we, Op - pressed with va - rious ills, draw near:
3. O Sav - iour Christ, our woes dis - pel; For some are sick, and some are sad,
4. And none, O Lord, have per - fect rest, For none are whol - ly free from sin;

O in what di - vers pains they met! O with what joy they went a - way!
What if Thy form we can - not see? We know and feel that Thou art here.
And some have nev - er loved Thee well, And some have lost the love they had.
And they who fain would serve Thee best, Are con-scious most of wrong with - in. A-MEN.

5 O Saviour Christ, Thou too art man;
    Thou hast been troubled, tempted, tried;
  Thy kind but searching glance can scan
    The very wounds that shame would hide.

6 Thy touch has still its ancient power,
    No word from Thee can fruitless fall:
  Hear, in this solemn evening hour,
    And in Thy mercy heal us all.

Worship

49

NIGHTFALL. 11. 11. 11. 5.

Petrus Herbert, ?–1571
Tr. by Catherine Winkworth, 1829–1878

Joseph Barnby, 1838–1896

1. Now God be with us, for the night is clos - ing; The light and
2. Let e - vil thoughts and spir - its flee be - fore us; Till morn - ing
3. Let ho - ly thoughts be ours when sleep o'er-takes us; Our ear - liest
4. We have no ref - uge, none on earth to aid us But Thee, O
5. Praise be to Thee through Je - sus our sal - va - tion: God, Three in

dark-ness are of His dis - pos - ing, And 'neath His shad - ow
com - eth, watch, O Mas - ter, o'er us; In soul and bod - y
thoughts be Thine when morn-ing wakes us. All sick and mourn - ers
Fa - ther, who Thine own hast made us. Keep us in life; for -
One, the Ru - ler of cre - a - tion, High throned, o'er all Thine

here to rest we yield us, For He will shield us.
Thou from harm de - fend us, Thine an - gels send us.
we to Thee com-mend them, Do Thou be - friend them.
give our sins; de - liv - er Us now and ev - er.
eye of mer - cy cast - ing, Lord Ev - er - last - ing. A - men.

Alternative tune, Flemming, No. 327

50

EVENING PRAYER. 8. 7. 8. 7.

James Edmeston, 1791–1867

George C. Stebbins, 1846–

1. Sav - iour, breathe an eve-ning bless - ing, Ere re - pose our spir - its seal;
2. Though de - struc - tion walk a - round us, Though the ar - rows past us fly,
3. Though the night be dark and drear - y, Dark-ness can - not hide from Thee;
4. Should swift death this night o'er-take us, And our couch be - come our tomb,

Evening Hymns

Sin and want we come con-fess-ing: Thou canst save, and Thou canst heal.
An-gel guards from Thee sur-round us: We are safe, if Thou art nigh.
Thou art He who, nev-er wea-ry, Watch-est where Thy peo-ple be.
May the morn in heav'n a-wake us, Clad in light and death-less bloom. A-MEN.

Copyright, 1920. Renewal. Hope Publishing Company, owner

51   TALLIS' CANON (EVENING HYMN). L. M.

THOMAS KEN, 1637–1711   THOMAS TALLIS, c. 1520–1585

1. All praise to Thee, my God, this night, For all the bless-ings of the light!
2. For-give me, Lord, for Thy dear Son, The ill that I this day have done,
3. Teach me to live, that I may dread The grave as lit-tle as my bed,
4. O may my soul on Thee re-pose; And with sweet sleep mine eye-lids close,
5. Praise God, from whom all bless-ings flow; Praise Him, all crea-tures here be-low;

ORGAN

Keep me, O keep me, King of kings, Be-neath Thine own al-might-y wings!
That with the world, my-self, and Thee, I, ere I sleep, at peace may be.
Teach me to die, that so I may Rise glo-rious at the Judg-ment Day.
Sleep, that may me more vig-orous make To serve my God when I a-wake.
Praise Him a-bove, ye heav-enly host: Praise Fa-ther, Son, and Ho-ly Ghost. A-MEN.

Another arrangement of this tune will be found at No. 74

Worship

52

DU FRIEDENSFÜRST, HERR JESU CHRIST. 7. 6. 7. 6. 8. 8.

Anonymous; 6th century
Tr. by JOHN M. NEALE, 1818–1866

BARTHOLOMÄUS GESIUS, 1555–1613 or 1614
Harmonized by J. S. BACH, 1685–1750

1. The day is past and o - ver; All thanks, O Lord, to Thee;
2. The joys of day are o - ver; We lift our hearts to Thee,
3. The toils of day are o - ver; We raise our hymn to Thee,
4. Be Thou our souls' pre - serv - er, O God, for Thou dost know

We pray Thee that of - fense - less The hours of dark may be: O
And call on Thee that sin - less The hours of dark may be: O
And ask that free from per - il The hours of dark may be: O
How man - y are the per - ils Thro' which we have to go: Lov -

Je - sus, keep us in Thy sight, And guard us through the com - ing night!
Je - sus, make their dark - ness light, And guard us through the com - ing night!
Je - sus, keep us in Thy sight, And guard us through the com - ing night!
er of men, O hear our call, And guard and save us from them all! A-MEN.

53

MERRIAL. 6. 5. 6. 5.

SABINE BARING-GOULD, 1834–1924

JOSEPH BARNBY, 1838–1896

1. Now the day is o - ver, Night is draw - ing nigh,
2. Je - sus, give the wea - ry Calm and sweet re - pose;
3. Grant to lit - tle chil - dren Vi - sions bright of Thee;
4. Com - fort ev - ery suf - ferer Watch - ing late in pain;

Evening Hymns

Shad - ows of the eve - ning Steal a - cross the sky;
With Thy ten-derest bless - ing May our eye - lids close.
Guard the sail - ors toss - ing On the deep, blue sea.
Those who plan some e - vil, From their sins re - strain. A-MEN.

5 Through the long night watches
  May Thine angels spread
  Their white wings above me,
  Watching round my bed.

6 When the morning wakens,
  Then may I arise
  Pure, and fresh, and sinless
  In Thy holy eyes.

54

ST. CLEMENT. 9. 8. 9. 8.

JOHN ELLERTON, 1826–1893

CLEMENT C. SCHOLEFIELD, 1839–1904

1. The day Thou gav - est, Lord, is end - ed, The dark - ness
2. We thank Thee that Thy Church un - sleep - ing, While earth rolls
3. As o'er each con - ti - nent and is - land The dawn leads
4. So be it, Lord; Thy throne shall nev - er, Like earth's proud

falls at Thy be - hest; To Thee our morn - ing hymns as -
on - ward in - to light, Through all the world her watch is
on an - oth - er day, The voice of prayer is nev - er
em - pires, pass a - way; Thy king - dom stands, and grows for -

cend - ed, Thy praise shall hal - low now our rest.
keep - ing, And rests not now by day or night.
si - lent, Nor die the strains of praise a - way.
ev - er, Till all Thy crea - tures own Thy sway. A - MEN.

Worship

55

WOODSTOCK. C. M.

PHOEBE H. BROWN, 1783–1861

DEODATUS DUTTON, Jr., 1808–1832

1. I love to steal a-while a-way From ev-ery cum-bering care,
2. I love to think on mer-cies past, And fu-ture good im-plore,
3. I love by faith to take a view Of bright-er scenes in heaven;
4. Thus, when life's toil-some day is o'er, May its de-part-ing ray

And spend the hours of clos-ing day In hum-ble, grate-ful prayer.
And all my cares and sor-rows cast On God, whom I a-dore.
The pros-pect doth my strength re-new, While here by tem-pests driven.
Be calm at this im-pres-sive hour, And lead to end-less day. A-MEN.

56

HURSLEY. L. M.

JOHN KEBLE, 1792–1866

Adapted from KATHOLISCHES GESANGBUCH, c. 1774

1. Sun of my soul, Thou Sav-iour dear, It is not night if Thou be near:
2. When the soft dews of kind-ly sleep My wea-ried eye-lids gen-tly steep,
3. A-bide with me from morn till eve, For with-out Thee I can-not live;
4. If some poor wandering child of Thine Have spurn'd, to-day, the voice di-vine,

O may no earthborn cloud a-rise To hide Thee from Thy ser-vant's eyes.
Be my last tho't, how sweet to rest For ev-er on my Sav-iour's breast.
A-bide with me when night is nigh, For with-out Thee I dare not die.
Now, Lord, the gra-cious work be-gin; Let him no more lie down in sin. A-MEN.

5 Watch by the sick; enrich the poor
  With blessings from Thy boundless store;
  Be every mourner's sleep to-night,
  Like infant's slumbers, pure and light.

6 Come near and bless us when we wake,
  Ere through the world our way we take;
  Till, in the ocean of Thy love,
  We lose ourselves in heaven above.

Alternative tune. Abends, No. 42

Evening Hymns

57

VESPER HYMN (Rendle). 7. 7. 7. 7. 6. 4.

MAY ROWLAND, 1870–

LILY RENDLE, 1875–

1. The day is slow - ly wend - ing To - ward its si - lent end - ing,
2. Be - neath Thy might - y car - ing The birds and beasts are shar - ing
3. Though long our day of test - ing, Now comes the hour of rest - ing.
4. The Sav - iour's cross is win - ning For - give - ness for the sin - ning,
5. All e - vil thoughts ex - pell - ing, Now make in us Thy dwell - ing.

But 'mid the light de - clin - ing The eve - ning star is shin - ing:
The Love that sends the show - ers, The Hand that gives the flow - ers:
May wea - ri - ness and sad - ness Be lulled to peace and glad - ness
And while we kneel con - fess - ing, We hum - bly wait Thy bless - ing:
O Spir - it, pure and ho - ly, Pos - sess these hearts so low - ly:

O Fa - ther, while we sleep, Thy chil - dren keep! A - MEN.

58

JAM LUCIS. L. M.

From the YATTENDON HYMNAL, 1899
Founded on NICOLAUS SELNECKER, 1532–1592

Plainsong melody

A-MEN.

1 Now cheer our hearts this | eventide,
Lord Jesus | Christ, and with us bide;
Thou that canst never | set in night,
Our heavenly | Sun, our glorious Light.

2 May we and all who | bear Thy Name
By gentle | love Thy Cross proclaim,
Thy gift of peace on | earth secure,
And for Thy | truth the world endure.

God

59

ANCIENT OF DAYS. 11. 10. 11. 10.

WILLIAM C. DOANE, 1832-1913

J. ALBERT JEFFERY, 1854-1929

In unison

1. An - cient of Days, who sit - test throned in glo - ry,
2. O Ho - ly Fa - ther, who hast led Thy chil - dren
3. O Ho - ly Je - sus, Prince of Peace and Sav - iour,
4. O Ho - ly Ghost, the Lord and the Life - giv - er,
5. O Tri - une God, with heart and voice a - dor - ing,

To Thee all knees are bent, all voic - es pray;
In all the a - ges, with the fire and cloud,
To Thee we owe the peace that still pre - vails,
Thine is the quick - 'ning power that gives in - crease;
Praise we the good - ness that doth crown our days;

Thy love has blessed the wide world's won - drous sto - ry
Through seas dry - shod, through wea - ry wastes be - wil - dering;
Still - ing, the rude wills of men's wild be - hav - ior,
From Thee have flowed, as from a pleas - ant riv - er,
Pray we that Thou wilt hear us, still im - plor - ing

With light and life since E - den's dawn - ing day.
To Thee, in rev - erent love, our hearts are bowed.
And calm - ing pas - sion's fierce and storm - y gales.
Our plen - ty, wealth, pros - per - i - ty, and peace.
Thy love and fa - vor kept to us al - ways. A - MEN.

Majesty and Power

LOBE DEN HERRN. 14. 14. 4. 7. 8.

Joachim Neander, 1650–1680
Tr. by Catherine Winkworth, 1829–1878

From Praxis Pietatis Melica, 1668

60

1. Praise to the Lord, the Al-might-y, the King of cre-a-tion!
2. Praise to the Lord, who o'er all things so won-drous-ly reign-eth,
3. Praise to the Lord, who doth pros-per thy work and de-fend thee;

O my soul, praise Him, for He is thy health and sal-va-tion!
Shield-eth thee un-der His wings, yea, so gen-tly sus-tain-eth!
Sure-ly His good-ness and mer-cy here dai-ly at-tend thee.

All ye who hear, Now to His tem-ple draw near;
Hast thou not seen How thy de-sires e'er have been
Pon-der a-new What the Al-might-y can do,

Join me in glad ad-o-ra-tion!
Grant-ed in what He or-dain-eth?
If with His love He be-friend thee. A-MEN.

God

61

TAPPAN. C. M.

H. KIRKE WHITE, 1785–1806

GEORGE KINGSLEY, 1811–1884

1. The Lord our God is clothed with might, The winds o-
2. Re - bel, ye waves, and o'er the land With threat-ening
3. Ye winds of night, your force com - bine; With - out His
4. His voice sub - lime is heard a - far; In dis - tant
5. Ye na - tions, bend, in rev - erence bend; Ye mon - archs,

bey His will; He speaks, and in His heaven-ly height, He speaks, and
as - pect roar; The Lord up - lifts His awe - full hand, The Lord up -
high be - hest, Ye shall not, in the moun-tain pine, Ye shall not,
peals it dies; He yokes the whirl-wind to His car, He yokes the
wait His nod; And bid the cho - ral song as - cend, And bid the

in His heaven - ly height The roll - ing sun stands still.
lifts His awe - full hand And chains you to the shore.
in the moun-tain pine, Dis - turb the spar - row's nest.
whirl-wind to His car And sweeps the howl - ing skies.
cho - ral song as - cend To cel - e - brate our God. A - MEN.

Alternative tune, Tallis' Ordinal, No. 478

62

KEBLE. L. M.

OLIVER W. HOLMES, 1809–1894

JOHN B. DYKES, 1823–1876

1. Lord of all be - ing, throned a - far, Thy glo - ry flames from sun and star;
2. Sun of our life, Thy quickening ray Sheds on our path the glow of day;
3. Our midnight is Thy smile withdrawn; Our noon-tide is Thy gra - cious dawn;
4. Lord of all life, be - low, a - bove, Whose light is truth, whose warmth is love,
5. Grant us Thy truth to make us free, And kind - ling hearts that burn for Thee,

Majesty and Power

Cen - ter and soul of ev - ery sphere, Yet to each lov - ing heart how near!
Star of our hope, Thy soft-ened light Cheers the long watch-es of the night.
Our rain-bow arch Thy mer-cy's sign; All, save the clouds of sin, are Thine!
Be - fore Thy ev - er - blaz - ing throne We ask no lus - ter of our own.
Till all Thy liv - ing al - tars claim One ho - ly light, one heaven-ly flame. A - MEN.

Alternative tune, Louvan, No. 307

63
MILLENNIUM. 6. 6. 6. 6. 8. 8.

Isaac Watts, 1674–1748

Composer unknown
Early American (?)

1. The Lord Je - ho - vah reigns, His throne is built on high;
2. The thun - ders of His hand Keep the wide world in awe;
3. Through all His might - y works A - maz - ing wis - dom shines;
4. And will this sov - ereign King Of glo - ry con - de - scend,

The gar-ments He as-sumes Are light and maj - es - ty; His glo - ries
His wrath and jus-tice stand To guard His ho - ly law; And where His
Sub - dues the pow'rs of hell, Con-founds their dark de - signs; Strong is His
And will He write His name, My Fa - ther and my Friend? I love His

shine with beams so bright, No mor - tal eye can bear the sight.
love re - solves to bless, His truth con - firms and seals the grace.
arm, and shall ful - fill His great de - crees and sov - ereign will.
name, I love His word; Join all my powers to praise the Lord! A - MEN.

Alternative tune, Darwall, No. 171

God

JOANNA. 11. 11. 11. 11.

WALTER C. SMITH, 1824–1908

Welsh melody
Arr. by VAN DENMAN THOMPSON, 1890–

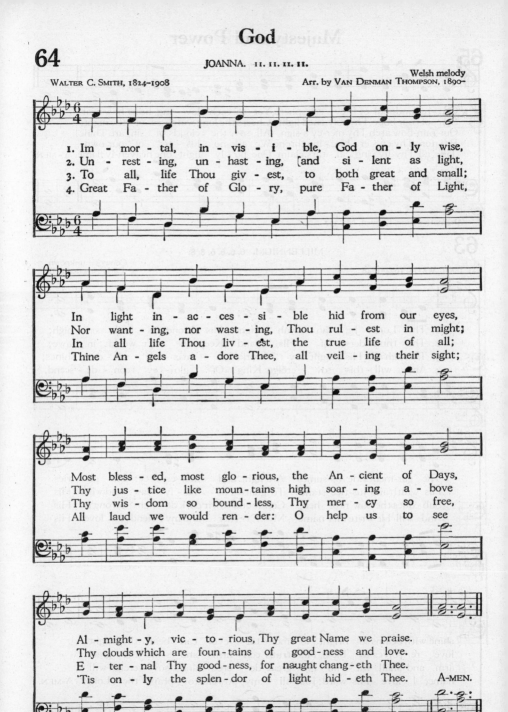

1. Im - mor - tal, in - vis - i - ble, God on - ly wise,
2. Un - rest - ing, un - hast - ing, [and si - lent as light,
3. To all, life Thou giv - est, to both great and small;
4. Great Fa - ther of Glo - ry, pure Fa - ther of Light,

In light in - ac - ces - si - ble hid from our eyes,
Nor want - ing, nor wast - ing, Thou rul - est in might;
In all life Thou liv - est, the true life of all;
Thine An - gels a - dore Thee, all veil - ing their sight;

Most bless - ed, most glo - rious, the An - cient of Days,
Thy jus - tice like moun - tains high soar - ing a - bove
Thy wis - dom so bound - less, Thy mer - cy so free,
All laud we would ren - der: O help us to see

Al - might - y, vic - to - rious, Thy great Name we praise.
Thy clouds which are foun - tains of good - ness and love.
E - ter - nal Thy good - ness, for naught chang - eth Thee.
'Tis on - ly the splen - dor of light hid - eth Thee. A-MEN.

Majesty and Power

65

LASST UNS ERFREUEN. 8. 8. 4. 4. 8. 8. with Alleluias

St. Francis of Assisi, 1182–1226
Tr. by William H. Draper, 1855–1933

Melody from Geistliche Kirchengesäng, 1623

In unison

1. All crea-tures of our God and King, Lift up your voice and with us
2. Thou rush-ing wind that art so strong, Ye clouds that sail in heaven a -
3. Thou flow-ing wa - ter, pure and clear, Make mu - sic for thy Lord to
4. Dear moth-er earth, who day by day. Un - fold-est bless-ings on our

sing Al - le - lu - ia! Al - le - lu - ia! Thou burn-ing sun with gold - en
long, O praise Him! Al - le - lu - ia! Thou ris - ing morn, in praise re -
hear, Al - le - lu - ia! Al - le - lu - ia! Thou fire so mas - ter - ful and
way, O praise Him! Al - le - lu - ia! The flowers and fruits that in thee

beam, Thou sil - ver moon with soft - er gleam! O praise Him, O
joice, Ye lights of eve-ning, find a voice! O praise Him, O
bright, Thou giv - est man both warmth and light! O praise Him, O
grow, Let them His glo - ry al - so show! O praise Him, O

praise Him! Al-le - lu - ia! Al - le - lu - ia! Al - le - lu - ia! A-men.

5 And all ye men of tender heart,
Forgiving others, take your part,
O sing ye!
Alleluia!
Ye who long pain and sorrow bear,
Praise God and on Him cast your care!
O praise Him! Alleluia!

6 Let all things their Creator bless,
And worship Him in humbleness,
O praise Him!
Alleluia!
Praise, praise the Father, praise the Son,
And praise the Spirit, Three in One!
O praise Him! Alleluia!

God

CREATION. L. M. D.

JOSEPH ADDISON, 1672-1719

From The Creation
FRANCIS J. HAYDN, 1732-1809

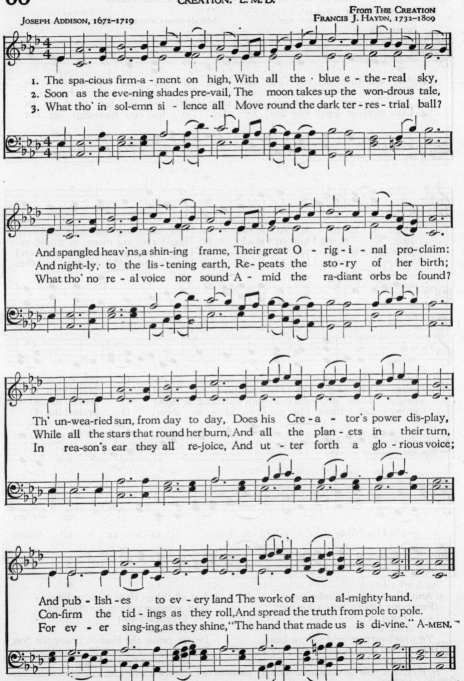

1. The spa-cious firm-a-ment on high, With all the blue e-the-real sky,
2. Soon as the eve-ning shades pre-vail, The moon takes up the won-drous tale,
3. What tho' in sol-emn si-lence all Move round the dark ter-res-trial ball?

And spangled heav'ns, a shin-ing frame, Their great O-rig-i-nal pro-claim:
And night-ly, to the lis-tening earth, Re-peats the sto-ry of her birth;
What tho' no re-al voice nor sound A-mid the ra-diant orbs be found?

Th' un-wea-ried sun, from day to day, Does his Cre-a-tor's power dis-play,
While all the stars that round her burn, And all the plan-ets in their turn,
In rea-son's ear they all re-joice, And ut-ter forth a glo-rious voice;

And pub-lish-es to ev-ery land The work of an al-mighty hand.
Con-firm the tid-ings as they roll, And spread the truth from pole to pole.
For ev-er sing-ing, as they shine, "The hand that made us is di-vine." A-MEN.

Majesty and Power

67

EIN' FESTE BURG. 8. 7. 8. 7. 6. 6. 6. 6. 7.

MARTIN LUTHER, 1483–1546
Tr. by FREDERICK H. HEDGE, 1805–1890

MARTIN LUTHER, 1483–1546

1. A might-y for-tress is our God, A bul-wark nev-er fail - ing;
2. Did we in our own strength con-fide, Our striv-ing would be los - ing;
3. And though this world, with dev-ils filled, Should threat-en to un - do us,
4. That word a - bove all earth - ly powers, No thanks to them, a - bid - eth;

Our help-er He, a - mid the flood Of mor-tal ills pre - vail - ing:
Were not the right Man on our side, The Man of God's own choos - ing:
We will not fear, for God hath willed His truth to tri-umph through us:
The Spir-it and the gifts are ours Through Him who with us sid - eth:

For still our an - cient foe Doth seek to work us woe; His craft and power are great,
Dost ask who that may be? Christ Je-sus, it is He; Lord Sa - ba-oth, His name,
The Prince of Dark-ness grim—We trem-ble not for him; His rage we can en - dure,
Let goods and kin-dred go, This mor-tal life al - so; The bod - y they may kill:

And, armed with cru - el hate, On earth is not his e - qual.
From age to age the same, And He must win the bat - tle.
For lo, his doom is sure, One lit - tle word shall fell him.
God's truth a - bid - eth still, His king-dom is for - ev - er. A - MEN.

God

68

DUNDEE (FRENCH). C. M.

WILLIAM COWPER, 1731-1800

From the SCOTTISH PSALTER, 1615

1. God moves in a mys - te - rious way His won - ders to per - form;
2. Ye fear - ful saints, fresh cour - age take; The clouds ye so much dread
3. Judge not the Lord by fee - ble sense, But trust Him for His grace;
4. His pur - pos - es will ri - pen fast, Un - fold - ing ev - ery hour:
5. Blind un - be - lief is sure to err, And scan His work in vain:

He plants His foot-steps in the sea, And rides up - on the storm.
Are big with mer - cy, and shall break In bless-ings on your head.
Be - hind a frown-ing prov - i - dence He hides a smil - ing face.
The bud may have a bit - ter taste, But sweet will be the flower.
God is His own in - ter - pre - ter, And He will make it plain. A-MEN.

Alternative tune, Manoah, No. 378

69

DENNIS. S. M.

Arr. from HANS G. NÄGELI, 1773-1836
by LOWELL MASON, 1792-1872

PHILIP DODDRIDGE, 1702-1751

1. How gen - tle God's com-mands! How kind His pre - cepts are!
2. Be - neath His watch-ful eye His saints se - cure - ly dwell;
3. Why should this anx - ious load Press down your wea - ry mind?
4. His good - ness stands ap - proved, Un - changed from day to day:

Come, cast your bur - dens on the Lord, And trust His con - stant care.
That hand which bears all na - ture up Shall guard His chil - dren well.
Haste to your heavenly Fa - ther's throne, And sweet re - fresh-ment find.
I'll drop my bur - den at His feet, And bear a song a - way. A-MEN.

Providence

70

MARTYRDOM (AVON). C. M.

PSALM XXIII
SCOTTISH PSALTER, 1650

HUGH WILSON, 1764-1824

1. The Lord's my Shep-herd, I'll not want; He makes me down to lie
2. My soul He doth re - store a - gain; And me to walk doth make
3. Yea, though I walk in death's dark vale, Yet will I fear no ill;
4. My ta - ble Thou hast fur - nish-ed In pres - ence of my foes;
5. Good-ness and mer - cy all my life Shall sure-ly fol - low me;

In pas-tures green; He lead-eth me The qui - et wa-ters by.
With - in the paths of right-eous-ness, Ev'n for His own name's sake.
For Thou art with me, and Thy rod And staff me com-fort still.
My head Thou dost with oil a-noint, And my cup o - ver - flows.
And in God's house for ev-er-more My dwell-ing place shall be.   A-MEN.

Alternative tune, Stracathro, No. 340

71

PRAETORIUS. C. M.

JOSEPH ADDISON, 1672-1719

HARMONIAE HYMNORUM SCHOLAE GORLICENSIS, 1599

1. How are Thy ser - vants blest, O Lord! How sure is their de - fense!
2. From all our griefs and fears, O Lord, Thy mer - cy sets us free;
3. In midst of dan - gers, fears, and death, Thy good-ness we a - dore;
4. Our life, while Thou pre - serv - est life, A sac - ri - fice shall be;

E - ter - nal wis - dom is their guide, Their help Om - nip - o - tence.
While in the con - fi - dence of prayer Our hearts take hold on Thee.
We praise Thee for Thy mer - cies past, And hum - bly hope for more.
And death, when death shall be our lot, Shall join our souls to Thee.   A-MEN.

Alternative tune, Martyrdom (Avon), No. 70

God

TERRA BEATA. S. M. D.

MALTBIE D. BABCOCK, 1858–1901

FRANKLIN L. SHEPPARD

1. This is my Fa-ther's world, And to my list-ening ears, All na-ture sings, and round me rings The mu-sic of the spheres. This is my Fa-ther's world: I rest me in the thought Of rocks and trees, of skies and seas; His hand the won-ders wrought.

2. This is my Fa-ther's world, The birds their car-ols raise, The morn-ing light, the lil-y white, De-clare their Mak-er's praise. This is my Fa-ther's world: He shines in all that's fair; In the rust-ling grass I hear Him pass, He speaks to me ev-ery-where.

3. This is my Fa-ther's world, O let me ne'er for-get That though the wrong seems oft so strong, God is the Rul-er yet. This is my Fa-ther's world: Why should my heart be sad? The Lord is King: let the heav-ens ring! God reigns: let the earth be glad! A-MEN.

Music arranged from a traditional English melody by Franklin L. Sheppard in 1915. Used by permission.
Words used by permission of Charles Scribner's Sons.

Providence

73

FINLANDIA. 10. 10. 10. 10. 10. 10.

Katharina von Schlegel, 1697-?
Tr. by Jane L. Borthwick, 1813-1897

Jean Sibelius, 1865–
Arr. for The Hymnal, 1933

1. Be still, my soul: the Lord is on thy side; Bear pa-tient-ly the
2. Be still, my soul: thy God doth un-der-take To guide the fu-ture
3. Be still, my soul: the hour is has-tening on When we shall be for

cross of grief or pain; Leave to thy God to or-der and pro-vide;
as He has the past. Thy hope, thy con-fi-dence let noth-ing shake;
ev-er with the Lord, When dis-ap-point-ment, grief, and fear are gone,

In ev-ery change He faith-ful will re-main. Be still, my soul: thy
All now mys-te-rious shall be bright at last. Be still, my soul: the
Sor-row for-got, love's pur-est joys re-stored. Be still, my soul: when

best, thy heavenly Friend Thro' thorn-y ways leads to a joy-ful end.
waves and winds still know His voice who ruled them while He dwelt be-low.
change and tears are past, All safe and bless-ed we shall meet at last. A-MEN.

God

TALLIS' CANON (EVENING HYMN). L. M.

PSALM XCI
UNITED PRESBYTERIAN BOOK OF PSALMS, 1871

THOMAS TALLIS, c. 1520–1585

1. The man who once has found a - bode With -
2. I of the Lord my God will say, "He
3. He shall with all - pro - tect - ing care Pre -
4. His out - spread pin - ions shall thee hide; Be -

in the se - cret place of God, Shall with Al - might - y
is my ref - uge and my stay; To Him for safe - ty
serve thee from the fowl - er's snare; When fear - ful plagues a -
neath His wings shalt thou con - fide; His faith - ful - ness shall

God a - bide, And in His shad - ow safe - ly hide.
I will flee; My God, in Him my trust shall be."
round pre - vail, No fa - tal stroke shall thee as - sail.
ev - er be A shield and buck - ler un - to thee. A - MEN.

5 No nightly terrors shall alarm;
   No deadly shaft by day shall harm,
   Nor pestilence that walks by night,
   Nor plagues that waste in noonday light.

6 Because thy trust is God alone,
   Thy dwelling-place the Highest One,
   No evil shall upon thee come,
   Nor plague approach thy guarded home.

Another arrangement of this tune will be found at No. 51

Love and Mercy

75

STUTTGART. 8. 7. 8. 7.

JOHN BOWRING, 1792–1872

Adapted from a melody in
PSALMODIA SACRA, GOTHA, 1715

1. God is love; His mer - cy bright-ens All the path in which we rove;
2. Chance and change are bus - y ev - er; Man de - cays and a - ges move;
3. E'en the hour that dark - est seem- eth Will His change-less good - ness prove;
4. He with earth - ly cares en - twin - eth Hope and com - fort from a - bove;

Bliss He wakes and woe He light - ens: God is wis-dom, God is love.
But His mer - cy wan - eth nev - er: God is wis-dom, God is love.
Thro' the gloom His bright-ness streameth: God is wis-dom, God is love.
Ev - ery-where His glo - ry shin - eth: God is wis-dom, God is love. A-MEN.

76

WELLESLEY. 8. 7. 8. 7.

FREDERICK W. FABER, 1814–1863

LIZZIE S. TOURJÉE, 1858–1913

1. There's a wide-ness in God's mer - cy, Like the wide - ness of the sea;
2. There is wel-come for the sin - ner, And more grac - es for the good;
3. For the love of God is broad - er Than the meas - ure of man's mind,
4. If our love were but more sim - ple We should take Him at His word;

There's a kind - ness in His jus-tice, Which is more than lib - er - ty.
There is mer - cy with the Sav-iour; There is heal - ing in His blood.
And the heart of the E - ter - nal Is most won - der - ful - ly kind.
And our lives would be all sun-shine In the sweet-ness of our Lord. A-MEN.

God

REGENT SQUARE. 8. 7. 8. 7. 8. 7.

From PSALM CIII
HENRY F. LYTE, 1793–1847

HENRY SMART, 1813–1879

1. Praise, my soul, the King of heav-en, To His feet thy trib-ute bring;
2. Praise Him for His grace and fa-vor To our fa-thers in dis-tress;
3. Fa - ther - like, He tends and spares us; Well our fee-ble frame He knows;
4. An - gels in the height, a-dore Him; Ye be-hold Him face to face;

Ran-somed, healed, re - stored, for - giv-en, Ev - er -more His prais-es sing;
Praise Him, still the same as ev - er, Slow to chide, and swift to bless;
In His hands He gen - tly bears us, Res - cues us from all our foes;
Saints tri - um - phant, bow be-fore Him; Gath-ered in from ev - er-y race;

Al - le - lu - ia! Al - le - lu - ia! Praise the Ev - er - last - ing King.
Al - le - lu - ia! Al - le - lu - ia! Glo - rious in His faith - ful - ness.
Al - le - lu - ia! Al - le - lu - ia! Wide - ly yet His mer - cy flows.
Al - le - lu - ia! Al - le - lu - ia! Praise with us the God of grace. A-MEN.

This tune in a higher key will be found at No. 87

ST. MAGNUS. C. M.

GEORGE A. GORDON, 1853–1929

JEREMIAH CLARK, 1670–1707

1. O Will of God be-neath our life, The sea be-neath the wave:
2. O Truth of God be-neath our faith, The rock on which we rest:
3. O Love of God be-neath our loves, The foun-tain to the stream:
4. O Life of God be-neath our death, The sun be-hind our gloom:

Love and Mercy

From Thee we rise in mys - tic strife, In Thee we find our grave.
Thy Mind is near, Thy Spir - it saith Our home is in Thy breast.
The riv - er of Thy peace it moves, Its tide our sur - est dream.
Thy Christ pro-claims in ev - ery breath, The world of fade-less bloom. A-MEN.

79

ORIEL. 8. 7. 8. 7. 8. 7.

PERCY DEARMER, 1867-1936

C. ETT, CANTICA SACRA, 1840

1. To the Name that is sal - va - tion, Praise and hom-age let us pay;
2. Fair-est Name be - yond all speak-ing, Full - est end of all de - sire;
3. 'Tis the Name of mer - cy, speed-ing Just and un - just with His ray;
4. Name of awe and Name of pleas-ure, Glow di - vine of grace un-told;
5. Hail, O Fa - ther, all cre - a - ting, Now, as when the world be - gan;

Life of ev - ery gen - er - a - tion, Law that all the stars o - bey;
Close, yet far be - yond all seek - ing, Good - ness, beau - ty, truth, en - tire;
Power that rules by pa - tient lead - ing, Not by force, the eas - ier way:
Sum of val - ues, whose full treas-ure Striv - ing art can ne'er un-fold;
Mas - ter Mind, a - mazed we hail Thee, As the light-year depths we scan;

Love and light by whose cre - a - tion All that is stands fast to - day.
Wis-dom, nev - er ven-geance wreak-ing, Ra-diance nev - er vexed with ire.
So that man, in free-dom heed-ing, May the law of love o - bey.
Sea of vir - tue pass-ing meas-ure, Life that doth all life up - hold.
Spir - it of tran-scend-ent un - ion, True and just Thy ways to man! A-MEN.

80

STUTTGART. 8. 7. 8. 7.

From Psalm ciii
United Presbyterian Book of Psalms, 1871

Adapted from a melody in
Psalmodia Sacra, 1715

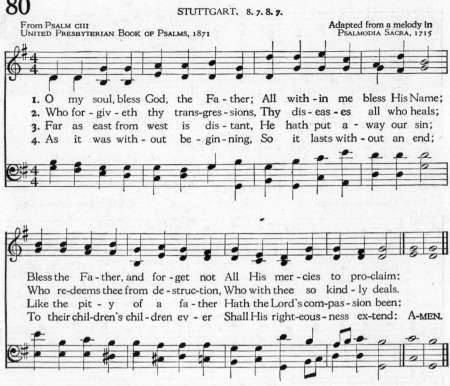

1. O my soul, bless God, the Fa-ther; All with-in me bless His Name;
2. Who for-giv-eth thy trans-gres-sions, Thy dis-eas-es all who heals;
3. Far as east from west is dis-tant, He hath put a-way our sin;
4. As it was with-out be-gin-ning, So it lasts with-out an end;

Bless the Fa-ther, and for-get not All His mer-cies to pro-claim:
Who re-deems thee from de-struc-tion, Who with thee so kind-ly deals.
Like the pit-y of a fa-ther Hath the Lord's com-pas-sion been:
To their chil-dren's chil-dren ev-er Shall His right-eous-ness ex-tend: A-men.

5 Unto such as keep His covenant
   And are steadfast in His way;
   Unto those who still remember
   His commandments, and obey.

6 Bless the Father, all His creatures,
   Ever under His control;
   All throughout His vast dominion
   Bless the Father, O my soul.

81

INNOCENTS. 7. 7. 7. 7.

John Milton, 1608-1674

From The Parish Choir, 1850

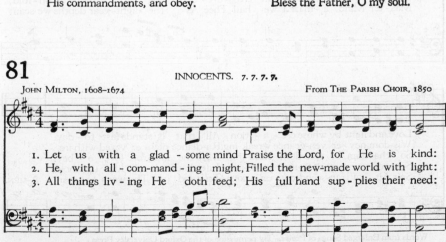

1. Let us with a glad-some mind Praise the Lord, for He is kind:
2. He, with all-com-mand-ing might, Filled the new-made world with light:
3. All things liv-ing He doth feed; His full hand sup-plies their need:

Love and Mercy

For His mer-cies shall en-dure, Ev - er faith-ful, ev - er sure. A-MEN.

Another arrangement of this tune will be found at No. 449

82

DE PAUW. L. M.

ISAAC WATTS, 1674–1748

ROBERT G. McCUTCHAN, 1877–

1. High   in   the heav'ns, E - ter - nal   God, Thy   good - ness
2. For   ev - er   firm   Thy   jus - tice   stands, As   moun - tains
3. My   God,   how ex - cel - lent   Thy   grace, Whence all   our
4. Life,   like   a   foun - tain rich and   free,   Springs from the

in   full   glo - ry   shines; Thy   truth shall   break   through
their   foun - da - tions   keep; Wise   are   the   won - ders
hope   and   com - fort   spring! The   sons   of   men   in
pres - ence   of   my   Lord; And   in   Thy   light   our

ev - ery   cloud   That veils and   dark - ens   Thy   de - signs.
of   Thy   hands; Thy judg-ments   are   a   might - y   deep.
their dis - tress   Fly   to   the   shad - ow   of   Thy   wing.
souls shall   see   The glo - ries   prom - ised   in   Thy   word. A-MEN.

Jesus Christ

VENI IMMANUEL. 8. 8. 8. 8. 8. 8.

From the Latin, 12th century
Stanza 1 Tr. by JOHN M. NEALE, 1818–1866
Stanzas 2, 3 Tr. by HENRY S. COFFIN, 1877–

Ancient plain song, 13th century

In unison

1. O come, O come, Im - man - u - el, And ran - som cap - tive
2. O come, Thou Wis - dom from on high, And or - der all things,
3. O come, De - sire of na - tions, bind All peo - ples in one

Is - ra - el, That mourns in lone - ly ex - ile here
far and nigh; To us the path of know - ledge show,
heart and mind; Bid en - vy, strife, and quar - rels cease;

Harmony

Un - til the Son of God ap - pear. Re - joice! Re - joice! Im -
And cause us in her ways to go. Re - joice! Re - joice! Im -
Fill the whole world with heav - en's peace. Re - joice! Re - joice! Im -

man - u - el Shall come to thee, O Is - ra - el!
man - u - el Shall come to thee, O Is - ra - el!
man - u - el Shall come to thee, O Is - ra - el! A - MEN.

Advent and Nativity

HYFRYDOL. 8. 7. 8. 7. D.

CHARLES WESLEY, 1707–1788

ROWLAND H. PRICHARD, 1811–1887

1. Come, Thou long - ex - pect - ed Je - sus, Born to set Thy
2. Born Thy peo - ple to de - liv - er, Born a child and

peo - ple free; From our fears and sins re - lease us; Let us
yet a King. Born to reign in us for ev - er, Now Thy

find our rest in Thee. Is - rael's Strength and Con - so - la - tion,
gra - cious King-dom bring. By Thine own e - ter - nal Spir - it

Hope of all the earth Thou art; Dear De - sire of
Rule in all our hearts a - lone; By Thine all - suf -

ev - ery na - tion, Joy of ev - ery long - ing heart.
fi - cient mer - it, Raise us to Thy glo - rious throne. A-MEN.

85

ELLACOMBE. 7. 6. 7. 6. D.

JAMES MONTGOMERY, 1771–1854

GESANGBUCH DER HERZOGL, 1784

1. Hail, to the Lord's A - noint - ed, Great Da-vid's great - er Son!
2. He comes with suc - cor speed - y To those who suf - fer wrong;
3. He shall come down like show - ers Up - on the fruit - ful earth,
4. To Him shall prayer un - ceas - ing And dai - ly vows as - cend;

Hail, in the time ap - point - ed, His reign on earth be - gun!
To help the poor and need - y, And bid the weak be strong;]
Love, joy, and hope, like flow - ers, Spring in His path to birth:]
His king - dom still in - creas - ing, A king - dom with - out end:

He comes to break op - pres - sion, To set the cap - tive free;
To give them songs for sigh - ing, Their dark-ness turn to light,
Be - fore Him, on the moun - tains, Shall peace, the her - ald, go,
The tide of time shall nev - er His cov - e - nant re - move;

To take a - way trans-gres - sion, And rule in eq - ui - ty.
Whose souls, con-demned and dy - ing, Are pre - cious in His sight.
And right - eous-ness, in foun - tains, From hill to val - ley flow.
His Name shall stand for ev - er; That Name to us is Love. A-MEN.

Advent and Nativity

MENDELSSOHN. 7. 7. 7. 7. D. with Refrain

CHARLES WESLEY, 1707–1788
Alt. by GEORGE WHITEFIELD, 1714–1770

FELIX MENDELSSOHN-BARTHOLDY, 1809–1847
Adapted by WILLIAM H. CUMMINGS, 1831–1915

1. Hark! the her-ald an-gels sing, "Glo-ry to the new-born King;
2. Christ, by high-est heaven a-dored, Christ, the ev-er-last-ing Lord:
3. Hail the heav'n-born Prince of Peace! Hail the Sun of right-eous-ness!

Peace on earth, and mer-cy mild; God and sin-ners rec-on-ciled."
Long de-sired, be-hold Him come, Find-ing here His hum-ble home.
Light and life to all He brings, Risen with heal-ing in His wings.

Joy-ful, all ye na-tions, rise, Join the tri-umph of the skies;
Veiled in flesh the God-head see, Hail th' in-car-nate De-i-ty!
Mild He lays His glo-ry by, Born that man no more may die,

With an-gel-ic hosts pro-claim, "Christ is born in Beth-le-hem!"
Pleased as man with men to dwell, Je-sus our Im-man-u-el.
Born to raise the sons of earth, Born to give them sec-ond birth.

Hark! the her-ald an-gels sing, "Glo-ry to the new-born King." A-MEN.

Jesus Christ

REGENT SQUARE. 8. 7. 8. 7. 8. 7.

JAMES MONTGOMERY, 1771–1854

HENRY SMART, 1813–1879

1. An - gels, from the realms of glo - ry, Wing your flight o'er
2. Shep - herds, in the field a - bid - ing, Watch - ing o'er your
3. Sa - ges, leave your con - tem - pla - tions, Bright - er vi - sions
4. Saints, be - fore the al - tar bend - ing, Watch - ing long in

all the earth; Ye who sang cre - a - tion's sto - ry,
flocks by night, God with man is now re - sid - ing;
beam a - far; Seek the great De - sire of na - tions;
hope and fear, Sud - den - ly the Lord, de - scend - ing,

Now pro - claim Mes - si - ah's birth: Come and wor - ship,
Yon - der shines the in - fant Light: Come and wor - ship,
Ye have seen His na - tal star: Come and wor - ship,
In His tem - ple shall ap - pear: Come and wor - ship,

Come and wor - ship, Wor - ship Christ, the new - born King.
Come and wor - ship, Wor - ship Christ, the new - born King.
Come and wor - ship, Wor - ship Christ, the new - born King.
Come and wor - ship, Wor - ship Christ, the new - born King. A - MEN.

This tune in a lower key will be found at No. 77

Advent and Nativity

CHRISTMAS. C. M.

NAHUM TATE, 1652–1715

Arr. from GEORGE F. HANDEL, 1685–1759

1. While shep - herds watched their flocks by night, All seat - ed on the ground, The an - gel of the Lord came down, And glo - ry shone a - round, And glo - ry shone a - round.

2. "Fear not!" said he— for might - y dread Had seized their trou - bled mind— "Glad tid - ings of great joy I bring, To you and all man - kind, To you and all man - kind.

3. "To you, in Da - vid's town this day, Is born of Da - vid's line, The Sav - iour, who is Christ the Lord; And this shall be the sign, And this shall be the sign:

4. "The heaven - ly Babe you there shall find To hu - man view dis - played, All mean - ly wrapped in swath - ing bands, And in a man - ger laid, And in a man - ger laid." A-MEN.

5 Thus spake the seraph; and forthwith
 Appeared a shining throng
Of angels praising God on high,
 Who thus addressed their song:

6 "All glory be to God on high,
 And to the earth be peace:
Good will henceforth from heaven to men,
 Begin and never cease!"

Jesus Christ

ANTIOCH. C. M.

From PSALM XCVIII
ISAAC WATTS, 1674-1748

Arr. from GEORGE F. HANDEL, 1685-1759

1. Joy to the world! the Lord is come: Let earth re-
2. Joy to the world! the Sav-iour reigns: Let men their
3. No more let sins and sor-rows grow, Nor thorns in-
4. He rules the world with truth and grace, And makes the

ceive her King; Let ev-er-y heart pre-pare Him room,
songs em-ploy; While fields and floods, rocks, hills and plains,
fest the ground; He comes to make His bless-ings flow
na-tions prove The glo-ries of His right-eous-ness,

And heaven and na-ture sing, And heaven and na-ture
Re-peat the sound-ing joy, Re-peat the sound-ing
Far as the curse is found, Far as the curse is
And won-ders of His love, And won-ders of His

And heaven and na-ture sing,
Re-peat the sound-ing joy,
Far as the curse is found,
And won-ders of His love,

And
Re-
Far
And

sing, And heaven, and heaven and na-ture sing.
joy, Re-peat, re-peat the sound-ing joy.
found, Far as, far as the curse is found.
love, And won-ders, won-ders of His love. A-MEN.

heaven and na-ture sing,
peat the sound-ing joy,
as the curse is found,
won-ders of His love,

Advent and Nativity

90

DIX. 7. 7. 7. 7. 7. 7.

WILLIAM C. DIX, 1837–1898

Abridged from a chorale by
CONRAD KOCHER, 1786–1872

1. As with glad - ness men of old Did the guid - ing
2. As with joy - ous steps they sped To that low - ly
3. As they of - fered gifts most rare At that man - ger
4. Ho - ly Je - sus, ev - ery day Keep us in the

star be - hold; As with joy they hailed its light,
man - ger bed, There to bend the knee be - fore
rude and bare, So may we with ho - ly joy,
nar - row way; And, when earth - ly things are past,

Lead - ing on - ward, beam - ing bright; So, most gra - cious
Him whom heaven and earth a - dore; So may we with
Pure, and free from sin's al - loy, All our cost - liest
Bring our ran - somed souls at last Where they need no

Lord, may we Ev - er - more be led to Thee.
will - ing feet Ev - er seek Thy mer - cy seat.
treas - ures bring, Christ, to Thee, our heaven - ly King.
star to guide, Where no clouds Thy glo - ry hide. A - MEN.

Jesus Christ

91

STELLA (Parker). 8. 3. 3. 6. D.

PAUL GERHARDT, 1607–1676
Tr. by CATHERINE WINKWORTH, 1829–1878

HORATIO W. PARKER, 1863–1919

1. All my heart this night re-joic-es, As I hear,
   Far and near, Sweet-est an-gel voic-es;
   "Christ is born," their choirs are sing-ing, Till the air,
   Ev-ery-where, Now with joy is ring-ing,

2. Hark! a voice from yon-der man-ger, Soft and sweet,
   Doth en-treat: "Flee from woe and dan-ger;
   Breth-ren, come; from all that grieves you, You are freed;
   All you need I will sure-ly give you."

3. Come, then, let us has-ten yon-der; Here let all,
   Great and small, Kneel in awe and won-der;
   Love Him who with love is yearn-ing; Hail the Star,
   That from far Bright with hope is burn-ing! A-MEN.

Advent and Nativity

CAROL. C. M. D.

Edmund H. Sears, 1810-1876

Richard S. Willis, 1819-1900

1. It came up-on the mid-night clear, That glo-rious song of old,
2. Still thro' the clo-ven skies they come, With peace-ful wings un-furled,
3. And ye, be-neath life's crush-ing load, Whose forms are bend-ing low,
4. For lo! the days are has-tening on, By pro-phet-bards fore-told,

From an-gels bend-ing near the earth, To touch their harps of gold:
And still their heaven-ly mu-sic floats O'er all the wea-ry world:
Who toil a-long the climb-ing way With pain-ful steps and slow,
When with the ev-er-cir-cling years Comes round the age of gold;

"Peace on the earth, good will to men, From heaven's all-gra-cious King."
A-bove its sad and low-ly plains They bend on hov-ering wing,
Look now! for glad and gold-en hours Come swift-ly on the wing:
When peace shall o-ver all the earth Its an-cient splen-dors fling,

The world in sol-emn still-ness lay, To hear the an-gels sing.
And ev-er o'er its Ba-bel sounds The bless-ed an-gels sing.
O rest be-side the wea-ry road, And hear the an-gels sing!
And the whole world send back the song Which now the an-gels sing.

A-men.

Jesus Christ

93

YORKSHIRE. 10. 10. 10. 10. 10. 10.

JOHN BYROM, 1692–1763

JOHN WAINWRIGHT, 1723 (?)–1768

1. Chris - tians, a - wake! sa - lute the hap - py morn
2. Then to the watch - ful shep - herds it was told,
3. He spake; and straight - way the ce - les - tial choir
4. Then may we hope, th'an - gel - ic hosts a - mong,

Where - on the Sav - iour of the world was born;
Who heard th'an - gel - ic her - ald's voice, "Be - hold,
In hymns of joy, un - known be - fore, con - spire;
To sing, re - deemed, a glad tri - um - phal song;

Rise to a - dore the mys - ter - y of love,
I bring good ti - dings of a Sav - iour's birth
The prais - es of re - deem - ing love they sang,
He that was born up - on this joy - ful day

Which hosts of an - gels chant - ed from a - bove;
To you and all the na - tions up - on earth;
And heaven's whole orb with al - le - lu - ias rang;
A - round us all His glo - ry shall dis - play;

Advent and Nativity

With them the joy - ful ti - dings first be - gun
This day hath God ful - filled His prom - ised word;
God's high - est glo - ry was their an - them still,
Saved by His love, for ev - er we shall sing

Of God In - car - nate and the Vir - gin's Son.
This day is born a Sav - iour, Christ the Lord."
Peace up - on earth, and un - to men good will.
E - ter - nal praise to heaven's Al - might - y King. A-MEN.

94

GARTON. 6. 7. 6. 7.

CHRISTINA G. ROSSETTI, 1830–1894

Traditional Irish melody

1. Love came down at Christ-mas, Love all love - ly, Love Di - vine;
2. Wor - ship we the God - head, Love In - car - nate, Love Di - vine;
3. Love shall be our to - ken, Love be yours and love be mine,

Love was born at Christ-mas, Star and an - gels gave the sign.
Wor-ship we our Je - sus: But where-with for sa - cred sign?
Love to God and all men, Love for plea and gift and sign. A - MEN.

Words used by permission of the Society for Promoting Christian Knowledge

Jesus Christ

95

MARGARET (ELLIOTT). Irregular

Emily E. S. Elliott, 1836–1897

Timothy R. Matthews, 1826–1910

1. Thou didst leave Thy throne and Thy king - ly crown, When Thou cam - est to earth for me; But in Beth - le - hem's home there was found no room For Thy ho - ly Na - tiv - i - ty. O come to my heart, Lord Je - sus, There is room in my heart for Thee.

2. Heav - en's arch - es rang when the an - gels sang, Pro - claim - ing Thy roy - al de - gree; But in low - ly birth didst Thou come to earth, And in great hu - mil - i - ty. O come to my heart, Lord Je - sus, There is room in my heart for Thee.

3. The fox - es found rest, and the birds their nest In the shade of the for - est tree; But Thy couch was the sod, O Thou Son of God, In the des - erts of Gal - i - lee. O come to my heart, Lord Je - sus, There is room in my heart for Thee.

4. Thou cam'st, O Lord, with the liv - ing word That should set Thy peo - ple free; But with mock - ing scorn, and with crown of thorn, They bore Thee to Cal - va - ry. O come to my heart, Lord Je - sus, There is room in my heart for Thee.

5. When heaven's arch - es shall ring and her choir shall sing At Thy com - ing to vic - to - ry, Let Thy voice call me home, say - ing, "Yet there is room, There is room at my side for thee!" And my heart shall re - joice, Lord Je - sus, When Thou com-est and callest for me. A-MEN.

Advent and Nativity

96

ADESTE FIDELES (PORTUGUESE HYMN). Irregular, with Refrain

Anonymous. Latin, 18th century
Tr. by FREDERICK OAKELEY, 1802–1880, and others

Source unknown, 18th century melody

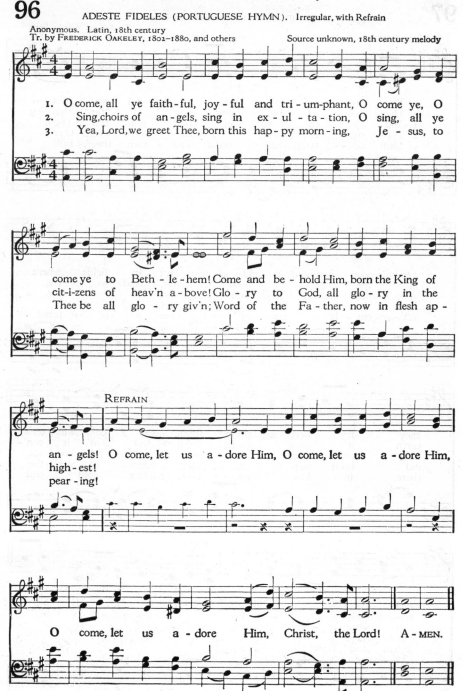

1. O come, all ye faith-ful, joy-ful and tri-um-phant, O come ye, O
2. Sing, choirs of an-gels, sing in ex-ul-ta-tion, O sing, all ye
3. Yea, Lord, we greet Thee, born this hap-py morn-ing, Je-sus, to

come ye to Beth-le-hem! Come and be-hold Him, born the King of
cit-i-zens of heav'n a-bove! Glo-ry to God, all glo-ry in the
Thee be all glo-ry giv'n; Word of the Fa-ther, now in flesh ap-

REFRAIN

an-gels! O come, let us a-dore Him, O come, let us a-dore Him,
high-est!
pear-ing!

O come, let us a-dore Him, Christ, the Lord! A-MEN.

Jesus Christ

THE FIRST NOEL. Irregular with Refrain

Old English carol

Traditional melody, from
W. Sandys' Christmas Carols, 1833

1. The first No - el, the an - gel did say, Was to
2. They look - ed up and saw a star Shin - ing
3. And by the light of that same star Three
4. This star drew nigh to the north - west, O'er
5. Then en - tered in those wise - men three, Full

cer - tain poor shep-herds in fields as they lay; In fields where
in the east, be - yond them far, And to the
wise - men came from coun - try far; To seek for a
Beth - le - hem it took its rest, And there it
rev - er - ent - ly up - on the knee, And of - fered

they lay keep - ing their sheep, On a cold win - ter's
earth it gave great light, And so it con -
king was their in - 'tent, And to fol - low the
did both stop and stay, Right o - ver the
there, in His pres - ence, Their gold and

REFRAIN

night that was so deep. No - el, No - el, No -
tin-ued both day and night.
star wher - ev - er it went.
place where Je - sus lay.
myrrh and frank - in - cense.

Advent and Nativity

el, No - el, Born is the King of Is - ra - el.

98

CHRISTMAS SONG. 6. 6. 6. 6. 12. 12.

Josiah G. Holland, 1819–1881

Karl P. Harrington, 1861–

1. There's a song in the air! There's a star in the sky! There's a moth-er's deep prayer And a ba-by's low cry! And the star rains its fire while the beau-ti-ful sing, For the man-ger of Beth-le-hem cra-dles a King!

2. There's a tu-mult of joy O'er the won-der-ful birth, For the Vir-gin's sweet boy Is the Lord of the earth. Ay! the star rains its fire while the beau-ti-ful sing, For the man-ger of Beth-le-hem cra-dles a King!

3. In the light of that star Lie the a - ges impearled; And that song from a - far Has swept o - ver the world. Ev - ery hearth is a - flame, and the beau-ti-ful sing In the homes of the na-tions that Je-sus is King!

4. We re-joice in the light, And we ech - o the song That comes down thro' the night From the heav - en - ly throng. Ay! we shout to the love - ly e - van - gel they bring, And we greet in His cra-dle our Sav-iour and King! A-men.

Jesus Christ

99

WEIHNACHT. 8. 6. 8. 6. D.

Leigh R. Brewer, 1839-1916

Karl P. Harrington, 1861–

1. Long years a - go o'er Beth-lehem's hills Was seen a won-drous thing; As
2. That song is sung by rich and poor, Wher-e'er the Christ is known; 'Tis

shep-herds watched their sleep-ing flocks They heard the an-gels sing. The an-them rolled a-
sung in words, and sung in deeds, Which bind all hearts in one. An-gels are still the

mong the clouds When earth was hushed and still; Its notes pro-claimed sweet peace on earth,
cho - ris-ters, But we the shep-herds are, To bear the mes- sage which they bring,

In unison

To all man-kind good will: "Glo - ry to God in the high-est," The
To those both near and far: "Glo - ry to God in the high-est," The

an-gels' song re-sounds, "Glo-ry to God in the high - est!"
an-gels' song re-sounds, "Glo-ry to God in the high - est!" A-MEN.

Music copyright by Karl P. Harrington. Renewal, 1933

Advent and Nativity

ST. LOUIS. 8. 6. 8. 6. 7. 6. 8. 6.

PHILLIPS BROOKS, 1835–1893   LEWIS H. REDNER, 1831–1908

1. O lit - tle town of Beth - le - hem, How still we see thee lie!
2. For Christ is born of Ma - ry, And gath - ered all a - bove,
3. How si - lent - ly, how si - lent - ly The won - drous gift is given!
4. O ho - ly Child of Beth - le - hem! De - scend to us, we pray;

A - bove thy deep and dream - less sleep The si - lent stars go by;
While mor - tals sleep, the an - gels keep Their watch of won - dering love.
So God im - parts to hu - man hearts The bless - ings of His heaven.
Cast out our sin, and en - ter in, Be born in us to - day.

Yet in thy dark streets shin - eth The ev - er - last - ing Light;
O morn - ing stars, to - geth - er Pro - claim the ho - ly birth,
No ear may hear His com - ing, But in this world of sin,
We hear the Christ - mas an - gels The great glad tid - ings tell;

The hopes and fears of all the years Are met in thee to - night.
And prais - es sing to God the King, And peace to men on earth!
Where meek souls will re - ceive Him still, The dear Christ en - ters in.
O come to us, a - bide with us, Our Lord Im - man - u - el! A - MEN.

Jesus Christ

WALLACE. Irregular

KATHARINE LEE BATES, 1859–1929

CLARENCE G. HAMILTON, 1865–1935

1. The Kings of the East are rid-ing To-night to Beth-le-hem;
2. To a strange sweet song of Zi-on The star-ry host troops forth:
3. There beams a-bove a man-ger The child face of a star;

The sun-set glows di-vid-ing, The Kings of the East are rid-ing,
The gold-en glaived O-ri-on To a strange sweet song of Zi-on,
A-mid the stars a stran-ger, It beams a-bove a man-ger.

A star their jour-ney guid-ing, Gleam-ing with gold and gem.
The Arch-er and the Li-on, The watch-ers of the North:
What means this e-ther rang-er To pause where poor folk are?

The Kings of the East are rid-ing To-night to Beth-le-hem.
To a strange sweet song of Zi-on The star-ry host troops forth.
There beams a-bove a man-ger The child face of a star. A-MEN.

Words used by permission of Houghton Mifflin Company
Music used by permission of Clarence G. Hamilton

Advent and Nativity

102

KINGS OF ORIENT. 8. 8. 8. 6. with Refrain

JOHN H. HOPKINS, 1820–1891   JOHN H. HOPKINS, 1820–1891

1. We three kings of O - ri - ent are; Bear-ing gifts we trav-erse a - far
2. Born a King on Beth - le-hem's plain, Gold I bring to crown Him a - gain,
3. Frank-in - cense to of - fer have I; In - cense owns a De - i - ty nigh;
4. Myrrh is mine: its bit - ter per - fume Breathes a life of gath-er-ing gloom:
5. Glo-rious now be - hold Him a - rise, King and God and Sac - ri - fice;

Field and foun - tain, moor and moun-tain, Fol - low - ing yon - der star.
King for ev - er, ceas - ing nev - er O - ver us all to reign.
Prayer and prais - ing all men rais - ing, Wor - ship Him, God on high.
Sor - rowing, sigh - ing, bleed - ing, dy - ing, Sealed in the stone-cold tomb.
Al - le - lu - ia, Al - le - lu - ia! Sounds thro' the earth and skies.

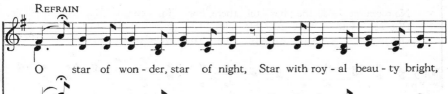

REFRAIN

O   star of won - der, star of night, Star with roy - al beau - ty bright,

West-ward lead - ing, still pro - ceed - ing, Guide us to Thy per - fect light. A - MEN.

Jesus Christ

103

WAITS' CAROL. 8. 8. 8. 8. 8. with Alleluias

GRACE M. STUTSMAN

GRACE M. STUTSMAN
Arranged for this book

1. In Beth-le - hem 'neath star-lit skies, Al - le - lu - ia, Al - le - lu - ia!
2. The hos - tel rang with song and shout, Al - le - lu - ia, Al - le - lu - ia!
3. And so, good friends, we wish you well; Al - le - lu - ia, Al - le - lu - ia!

A Babe with-in a man - ger lies, Al - le - lu - ia, Al - le - lu - ia!
Yet none there were who looked with-out, Al - le - lu - ia, Al - le - lu - ia!
To you we sing, this glad No - el; Al - le - lu - ia, Al - le - lu - ia!

No room in - side the hos - tel there, For Jos - eph or Ma - don - na fair;
But ah! With-in that sta - ble old The beasts a won-drous sight be - hold:
Our sweet-est car - ols gay - ly ring To wel-come Christ, the In - fant King;

No one to light - en their de-spair, Al - le - lu - ia, Al - le - lu - ia!
Three wise men bear-ing gifts of gold! Al - le - lu - ia, Al - le - lu - ia!
To you the joy - ous news we bring, Al - le - lu - ia, Al - le - lu - ia! A-MEN.

Copyright, 1935, by Grace M. Stutsman. Used by permission

Advent and Nativity

104

CRANHAM. Irregular

CHRISTINA G. ROSSETTI, 1830–1894

GUSTAV HOLST, 1874–1934

1. In the bleak mid - win - ter, Frost - y wind made moan,
2. Our God, heaven can - not hold Him, Nor earth sus - tain;
3. An - gels and arch - an - gels May have gath - ered there,
4. What can I give Him, Poor as I am?

Earth stood hard as i - ron, Wa - ter like a stone;
Heaven and earth shall flee a - way When He comes to reign;
Cher - u - bim and ser - a - phim Throng - ed the air;
If I were a shep - herd, I would bring a lamb;

Snow had fall - en, snow on snow, Snow on snow,
In the bleak mid - win - ter A sta - ble - place suf - ficed The
But His moth - er on - ly, In her maid - en bliss,
If I were a wise man, I would do my part; Yet

In the bleak mid - win - ter, Long a - go.
Lord God Al - might - y, Je - sus Christ.
Wor-shiped the Be - lov - ed With a kiss.
what I can I give Him— Give my heart. A - MEN.

Jesus Christ

105

W ZLOBIE LEZY (POLISH CAROL). 4. 4. 7. 4. 4. 7. 4. 4. 4. 4. 7.

From the Polish
English words by E. M. G. Reed, 1885-1933

Arr. by E. M. G. Reed, 1885-1933

In unison

1. In - fant ho - ly, In - fant low - ly, For His bed a cat - tle stall;
2. Flocks were sleep-ing; Shep-herds keep-ing Vig - il till the morn-ing new

Ox - en low-ing, Lit - tle know-ing Christ the Babe is Lord of all.
Saw the glo - ry, Heard the sto - ry, Tid - ings of a gos - pel true.

Swift are wing - ing An - gels sing - ing, No - els ring - ing,
Thus re - joic - ing, Free from sor - row, Prais - es voic - ing

Advent and Nativity

Tid-ings bring-ing: Christ the Babe is Lord of all.
Greet the morrow: Christ the Babe was born for you.

A-MEN.

106

STILLE NACHT. Irregular

JOSEPH MOHR, 1792–1848
Tr. compiled from various sources

FRANZ GRÜBER, 1787–1863

1. Si - lent night, ho - ly night, All is calm, all is bright;
2. Si - lent night, ho - ly night, Dark - ness flies, all is light;
3. Si - lent night, ho - ly night, Son of God, love's pure light;
4. Si - lent night, ho - ly night, Won - drous Star, lend thy light;

Round yon Vir - gin Moth - er and Child! Ho - ly In-fant, so ten-der and mild,
Shep - herds hear the an - gels sing, "Al - le - lu - ia! hail the King!
Ra - diant beams from Thy ho - ly face, With the dawn of re - deem-ing grace,
With the an - gels let us sing, Al - le - lu - ia to our King;

Sleep in heav - en - ly peace, Sleep in heav - en - ly peace.
Christ the Sav - iour is born, Christ the Sav - iour is born."
Je - sus, Lord, at Thy birth, Je - sus, Lord, at Thy birth.
Christ the Sav - iour is born, Christ the Sav - iour is born.

A - MEN.

Jesus Christ

107

TEMPUS ADEST FLORIDUM. 7. 6. 7. 6. D.

A Spring Carol, c. 14th century
Arr. by ERNEST MACMILLAN, 1893–

JOSEPH S. COOK, 1859–1933

In unison

1. Gen - tle Ma - ry laid her Child Low - ly in a man - ger;
2. An - gels sang a - bout His birth; Wise men sought and found Him;
3. Gen - tle Ma - ry laid her Child Low - ly in a man - ger;

There He lay, the un - de - filed, To the world a Stran - ger.
Heav - en's star shone bright - ly forth— Glo - ry all a - round Him.
He is still the un - de - filed, But no more a Stran - ger.

Such a Babe in such a place, Can He be the Sav - iour?
Shep-herds saw the won-drous sight, Heard the an - gels sing - ing;
Son of God, of hum - ble birth, Beau - ti - ful the sto - ry;

Ask the saved of all the race Who have found His fa - vor.
All the plains were lit that night, All the hills were ring - ing.
Praise His Name in all the earth, Hail the King of glo - ry! A-MEN.

Advent and Nativity

GLORIA. 8. 7. 8. 7. with Refrain

Anonymous

Old French carol

1. Heark-en, all! what ho - ly sing-ing Now is sound-ing from the sky!
2. On the plain, the sim - ple shep-herds Watch'd their flocks the long night thro';
3. See, with-in the man-ger low-ly, Wide the Christ child spreads His arms.

'Tis a hymn with gran-deur ring-ing, Sung by voic-es clear and high.
From on high they heard the voic-es, Sound-ing thro' the heav'n-ly blue.
Raise to Him your joy-ful voic-es, Sing we all No - el, No - el.

REFRAIN

Glo - - - - - - - ri - a in ex-cel-sis De - o, Glo -

- - - - - - - ri - a in ex-cel-sis De - o!

From the mystery play, The Nativity. Copyright, 1922, by Oliver Ditson Company. Used by permission

Jesus Christ

109

GREENSLEEVES. 8. 7. 8. 7. with Refrain

WILLIAM C. DIX, 1837–1898

Old English melody

In unison

1. What Child is this, who, laid to rest, On Ma-ry's lap is sleep-ing?
2. Why lies He in such mean es-tate Where ox and ass are feed-ing?
3. So bring Him in-cense, gold and myrrh, Come, peas-ant, King to own Him;

Whom an-gels greet with an-thems sweet, While shep-herds watch are keep-ing?
Good Chris-tian, fear: for sin-ners here The si-lent Word is plead-ing.
The King of kings sal-va-tion brings, Let lov-ing hearts en-throne Him.

REFRAIN. *Unison or Harmony*

This, this is Christ the King, Whom shep-herds guard and an-gels sing:

Haste, haste to bring Him laud, The Babe, the Son of Ma-ry. A-MEN.

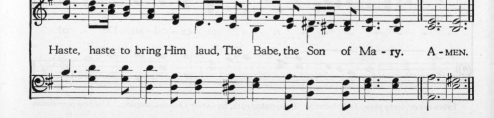

Advent and Nativity

110

IN DULCI JUBILO. 6. 6. 7. 7. 7. 8. 5. 5.

From the Latin
Tr. by JOHN M. NEALE, 1818–1866

14th century German melody
Harmonized by WINFRED DOUGLAS, 1867–

1. Good Chris-tian men, re - joice, With heart and soul and voice;
2. Good Chris-tian men, re - joice, With heart and soul and voice;
3. Good Chris-tian men, re - joice, With heart and soul and voice;

Give ye heed to what we say: Je - sus Christ is born to - day;
Now ye hear of end - less bliss; Je - sus Christ was born for this!
Now ye need not fear the grave; Je - sus Christ was born to save!

Ox and ass be - fore Him bow, And He is in the man - ger now.
He hath oped the heav'n - ly door, And man is bless - ed ev - er - more.
Calls you one and calls you all, To gain His ev - er - last - ing hall.

Christ is born to - day! Christ is born to - day!
Christ was born for this! Christ was born for this!
Christ was born to save! Christ was born to save! A - MEN.

Jesus Christ

111

CRUSADER'S HYMN. 5. 6. 8. 5. 5. 8.

From the German, 17th century

From SCHLESISCHEN VOLKSLIEDER, 1842
Arr. by RICHARD S. WILLIS, 1819-1900

1. Fair-est Lord Je-sus, Rul-er of all na-ture, O Thou of God and man the Son,
2. Fair are the mead-ows, Fair-er still the woodlands, Robed in the bloom-ing garb of spring:
3. Fair is the sun-shine, Fair-er still the moon-light, And all the twink-ling star-ry host:

Thee will I cher-ish, Thee will I hon-or, Thee, my soul's Glo-ry, Joy, and Crown.
Je-sus is fair-er, Je-sus is pur-er, Who makes the woe-ful heart to sing.
Je-sus shines bright-er, Je-sus shines pur-er Than all the an-gels heaven can boast. A-MEN.

112

SHIRLEYN. C. M.

HARRY WEBB FARRINGTON, 1880-1931

EARL E. HARPER, 1895-

1. I know not how that Beth-le-hem's Babe Could in the God-head be;
2. I know not how that Cal-va-ry's cross A world from sin could free;
3. I know not how that Jo-seph's tomb Could solve death's mys-ter-y;

I on-ly know the man-ger Child Has brought God's life to me.
I on-ly know its match-less love Has brought God's love to me.
I on-ly know a liv-ing Christ, Our im-mor-tal-i-ty. A-MEN.

Life

113

CUSHMAN. 11. 10. 11. 10.

J. Edgar Park, 1879–   Herbert B. Turner, 1852–1927

1. We would see Jesus; lo! His star is shining
2. We would see Jesus, Mary's Son most holy,
3. We would see Jesus, on the mountain teaching,
4. We would see Jesus, in His work of healing,
5. We would see Jesus; in the early morning

A-bove the sta-ble while the an-gels sing;
Light of the vil-lage life from day to day;
With all the lis-tening peo-ple gath-ered round;
At ev-en-tide be-fore the sun was set;
Still as of old He call-eth, "Fol-low me";

There in a man-ger on the hay re-clin-ing;
Shin-ing re-vealed through ev-ery task most low-ly,
While birds and flowers and sky a-bove are preach-ing,
Di-vine and hu-man, in His deep re-veal-ing,
Let us a-rise, all mean-er serv-ice scorn-ing:

Haste, let us lay our gifts be-fore the King.
The Christ of God, the Life, the Truth, the Way.
The bless-ed-ness which sim-ple trust has found.
Of God and man in lov-ing serv-ice met.
Lord, we are Thine, we give our-selves to Thee.   A-men.

Jesus Christ

SALVE DOMINE. 7. 6. 7. 6. D.

John S. B. Monsell, 1811-1875

Lawrence W. Watson, 1860-1925

1. Light of the world, we hail Thee, Flush-ing the east-ern skies;
2. Light of the world, Thy beau - ty Steals in - to ev - ery. heart,
3. Light of the world, il - lu - mine This dark-ened earth of Thine,

Nev - er shall dark - ness veil Thee A - gain from hu - man eyes;
And glo - ri - fies with du - ty Life's poor - est, hum - blest part;
Till ev - ery-thing that's hu - man Be filled with the di - vine;

Too long, a - las, with - hold - en, Now spread from shore to shore;
Thou rob - est in Thy splen - dor The sim - plest ways of men,
Till ev - ery tongue and na - tion, From sin's do - min - ion free,

Thy light, so glad and gold - en, Shall set on earth no more.
And help - est them to ren - der Light back to Thee a - gain.
Rise in the new cre - a - tion Which springs from love and Thee. A-MEN.

Life

115

THIS ENDRIS NYGHT. C. M.

EDWARD DENNY, 1796–1889

Old English carol, 15th century

1. What grace, O Lord, and beau-ty shone A-round Thy steps be-low;
2. For, ev-er on Thy bur-dened heart A weight of sor-row hung;
3. Thy foes might hate, de-spise, re-vile, Thy friends un-faith-ful prove;
4. O give us hearts to love like Thee! Like Thee, O Lord, to grieve
5. One with Thy-self, may ev-ery eye In us, Thy breth-ren, see

What pa-tient love was seen in all Thy life and death of woe!
Yet no un-gen-tle, murmuring word Es-caped Thy si-lent tongue.
Un-wea-ried in for-give-ness still, Thy heart could on-ly love.
Far more for oth-ers' sins than all The wrongs that we re-ceive.
The gen-tle-ness and grace that spring From un-ion, Lord, with Thee. A-MEN.

116

CANONBURY. L. M.

A. CLEVELAND COXE, 1818–1896

ROBERT SCHUMANN, 1810–1856

1. How beau-teous were the marks di-vine, That in Thy meek-ness used to shine,
2. O who like Thee, so mild, so bright, Thou Son of man, Thou Light of light?
3. O who like Thee so hum-bly bore The scorn, the scoffs of men, be-fore?
4. O won-drous Lord, my soul would be Still more and more con-formed to Thee,

That lit Thy lone-ly path-way, trod In won-drous love, O Son of God!
O who like Thee did ev-er go, So pa-tient, thro' a world of woe?
So meek, so low-ly, yet so high, So glo-rious in hu-mil-i-ty.
And learn of Thee, the low-ly One, And like Thee, all my jour-ney run. A-MEN.

Jesus Christ

117

INCARNATION. 7. 6. 7. 6. D.

WILBUR FISK TILLETT, 1854–1936

ALFRED WOOLER, 1867–

1. O Son of God in-car-nate, O Son of man di-vine!
2. O Mind of God in-car-nate, O Thought in flesh en-shrined!
3. O Heart of God in-car-nate, Love-bear-er to man-kind!
4. O Will of God in-car-nate, So hu-man, so di-vine!

In whom God's glo-ry dwell-eth, In whom man's vir-tues shine;
In hu-man form Thou speak-est To men the Fa-ther's mind:
From Thee we learn what love is, In Thee love's ways we find:
Free wills to us Thou giv-est, That we may make them Thine:

God's light to earth Thou bring-est To drive sin's night a-way,
God's thought to earth Thou bring-est That men in Thee may see
God's love to earth Thou bring-est In liv-ing deeds that prove
God's will to earth Thou bring-est That all who would o-bey,

And through Thy life so ra-diant, Earth's dark-ness turns to day.
What God is like, and see-ing, Think God's tho'ts aft-er Thee.
How sweet to serve all oth-ers, When we all oth-ers love.
May learn from Thee their du-ty, The truth, the life, the way. A-MEN.

Life

118

ST. MICHEL'S. C. M. D.

JAY T. STOCKING, 1870–1936

From W. GAWLER'S HYMNS AND PSALMS, 1789

1. O Mas - ter Work-man of the race, Thou Man of Gal - i - lee,
2. O Car - pen - ter of Naz - a - reth, Build-er of life di - vine,
3. O Thou who dost the vi - sion send And giv - est each his task,

Who with the eyes of ear - ly youth E - ter - nal things did see:
Who shap - est man to God's own law, Thy - self the fair de - sign:
And with the task suf - fi - cient strength: Show us Thy will, we ask;

We thank Thee for Thy boy - hood faith That shone Thy whole life through;
Build us a tower of Christ-like height, That we the land may view,
Give us a con-science bold and good; Give us a pur - pose true,

"Did ye not know it is my work My Fa - ther's work to do?"
And see, like Thee, our no-blest work Our Fa - ther's work to do.
That it may be our high-est joy, Our Fa - ther's work to do. A-MEN.

Jesus Christ

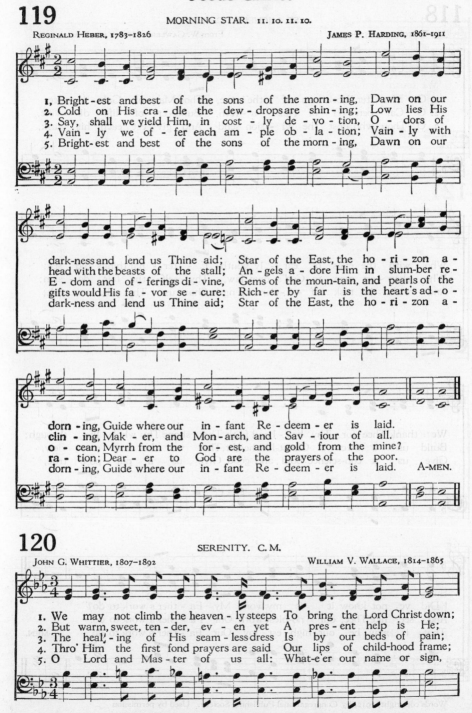

119

MORNING STAR. 11. 10. 11. 10.

REGINALD HEBER, 1783–1826

JAMES P. HARDING, 1861–1911

1. Bright-est and best of the sons of the morn-ing, Dawn on our
2. Cold on His cra-dle the dew-drops are shin-ing; Low lies His
3. Say, shall we yield Him, in cost-ly de-vo-tion, O-dors of
4. Vain-ly we of-fer each am-ple ob-la-tion; Vain-ly with
5. Bright-est and best of the sons of the morn-ing, Dawn on our

dark-ness and lend us Thine aid; Star of the East, the ho-ri-zon a-
head with the beasts of the stall; An-gels a-dore Him in slum-ber re-
E-dom and of-ferings di-vine, Gems of the moun-tain, and pearls of the
gifts would His fa-vor se-cure: Rich-er by far is the heart's ad-o-
dark-ness and lend us Thine aid; Star of the East, the ho-ri-zon a-

dorn-ing, Guide where our in-fant Re-deem-er is laid.
clin-ing, Mak-er, and Mon-arch, and Sav-iour of all.
o-cean, Myrrh from the for-est, and gold from the mine?
ra-tion; Dear-er to God are the prayers of the poor.
dorn-ing, Guide where our in-fant Re-deem-er is laid. A-MEN.

120

SERENITY. C. M.

JOHN G. WHITTIER, 1807–1892

WILLIAM V. WALLACE, 1814–1865

1. We may not climb the heaven-ly steeps To bring the Lord Christ down;
2. But warm, sweet, ten-der, ev-en yet A pres-ent help is He;
3. The heal-ing of His seam-less dress Is by our beds of pain;
4. Thro' Him the first fond prayers are said Our lips of child-hood frame;
5. O Lord and Mas-ter of us all: What-e'er our name or sign,

Life

In vain we search the low-est deeps, For Him no depths can drown.
And faith has still its Ol - i - vet, And love its Gal - i - lee.
We touch Him in life's throng and press, And we are whole a - gain.
The last low whis-pers of our dead Are bur-dened with His name.
We own Thy sway, we hear Thy call, We test our lives by Thine! A - MEN.

121

BROOKFIELD. L. M.

MILTON S. LITTLEFIELD, 1864-1934

THOMAS B. SOUTHGATE, 1814-1868

1. O Son of Man, Thou mad - est known, Through qui - et
2. O Work - man true, may we ful - fill In dai - ly
3. Thou Mas - ter Work - man, grant us grace The chal - lenge
4. And thus we pray in deed and word, Thy king - dom

work in shop and home, The sa - cred - ness of com - mon
life Thy Fa - ther's will; In du - ty's call, Thy call we
of our tasks to face; By loy - al scorn of sec - ond
come on earth, O Lord; In work that gives ef - fect to

things, The chance of life that each day brings.
hear To full - er life, through work sin - cere.
best, By ef - fort true, to meet each test.
prayer, Thy pur - pose for Thy world we share. A - MEN.

Words from The School Hymnal. Copyright, 1920, by A. S. Barnes and Company. Used by permission

Jesus Christ

122

YORKSHIRE. 10. 10. 10. 10. 10. 10.

Samuel Greg, 1804-1876

John Wainwright, 1723(?)-1768

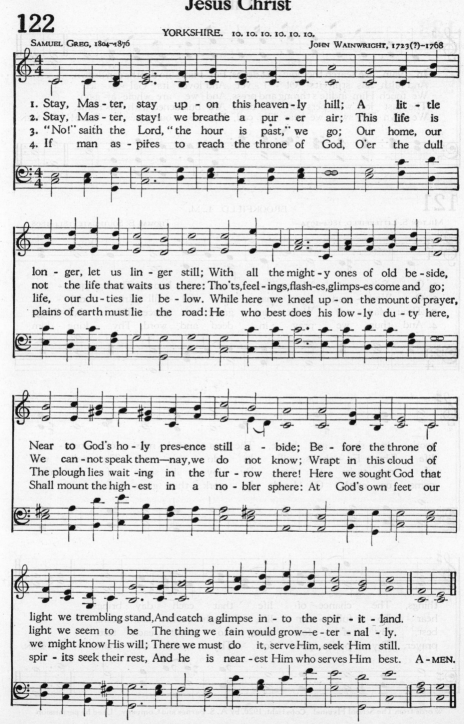

1. Stay, Mas-ter, stay up-on this heaven-ly hill; A lit-tle
2. Stay, Mas-ter, stay! we breathe a pur-er air; This life is
3. "No!" saith the Lord, "the hour is past," we go; Our home, our
4. If man as-pires to reach the throne of God, O'er the dull

lon-ger, let us lin-ger still; With all the might-y ones of old be-side,
not the life that waits us there: Tho'ts, feel-ings, flash-es, glimps-es come and go;
life, our du-ties lie be-low. While here we kneel up-on the mount of prayer,
plains of earth must lie the road: He who best does his low-ly du-ty here,

Near to God's ho-ly pres-ence still a-bide; Be-fore the throne of
We can-not speak them—nay, we do not know; Wrapt in this cloud of
The plough lies wait-ing in the fur-row there! Here we sought God that
Shall mount the high-est in a no-bler sphere: At God's own feet our

light we trembling stand, And catch a glimpse in-to the spir-it-land.
light we seem to be The thing we fain would grow—e-ter-nal-ly.
we might know His will; There we must do it, serve Him, seek Him still.
spir-its seek their rest, And he is near-est Him who serves Him best. A-MEN.

Life

123

MT. HOLYOKE. 8. 7. 8. 7. D.

HENRY BURTON, 1840–1930

MAURICE L. WOSTENHOLM, 1887–

1. There's a light up-on the moun-tains, And the day is at the spring,
2. In the fad-ing of the star-light We may see the com-ing morn;
3. There's a hush of ex-pec-ta-tion And a qui-et in the air,
4. He is break-ing down the bar-riers, He is cast-ing up the way;
5. Hark! we hear a dis-tant mu-sic, And it comes with full-er swell;

When our eyes shall see the beau-ty And the glo-ry of the King:
And the lights of men are pal-ing In the splen-dors of the dawn;
And the breath of God is mov-ing In the fer-vent breath of prayer;
He is call-ing for His an-gels To build up the gates of day:
'Tis the tri-umph-song of Je-sus, Of our King, Im-man-u-el!

Wea-ry was our heart with wait-ing, And the night-watch seemed so long,
For the east-ern skies are glow-ing As with light of hid-den fire,
For the suf-fer-ing, dy-ing Je-sus Is the Christ up-on the throne,
But His an-gels here are hu-man, Not the shin-ing hosts a-bove,
Go ye forth with joy to meet Him! And, my soul, be swift to bring

But His tri-umph-day is break-ing, And we hail it with a song.
And the hearts of men are stir-ring With the throbs of deep de-sire.
And the tra-vail of our spir-it Is the tra-vail of His own.
For the drum-beats of His ar-my Are the heart-beats of our love.
All thy sweet-est and thy dear-est For the tri-umph of our King! A-MEN.

Jesus Christ

124

STELLA (English). 8. 8. 8. 8. 8. 8.

Eustace R. Conder, 1820-1892

Founded on an old English melody

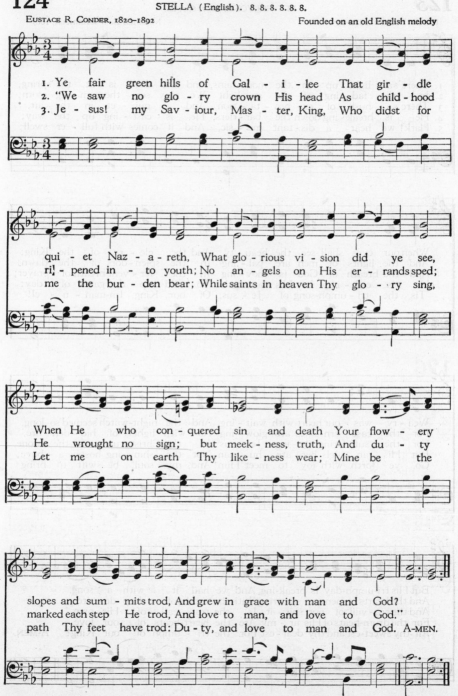

1. Ye fair green hills of Gal - i - lee That gir - dle
2. "We saw no glo - ry crown His head As child - hood
3. Je - sus! my Sav - iour, Mas - ter, King, Who didst for

qui - et Naz - a - reth, What glo - rious vi - sion did ye see,
rip - ened in - to youth; No an - gels on His er - rands sped;
me the bur - den bear; While saints in heaven Thy glo - ry sing,

When He who con - quered sin and death Your flow - er - y
He wrought no sign; but meek - ness, truth, And du - ty
Let me on earth Thy like - ness wear; Mine be the

slopes and sum - mits trod, And grew in grace with man and God?
marked each step He trod, And love to man, and love to God."
path Thy feet have trod: Du - ty, and love to man and God. A-MEN.

Passion

125

ST. DROSTANE. L. M.

Henry H. Milman, 1791–1868

John B. Dykes, 1823–1876

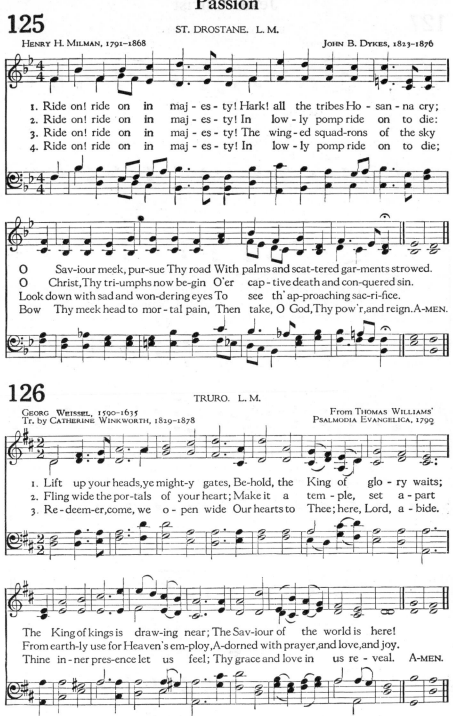

1. Ride on! ride on in maj - es - ty! Hark! all the tribes Ho - san - na cry;
2. Ride on! ride on in maj - es - ty! In low - ly pomp ride on to die:
3. Ride on! ride on in maj - es - ty! The wing - ed squad-rons of the sky
4. Ride on! ride on in maj - es - ty! In low - ly pomp ride on to die;

O Sav-iour meek, pur-sue Thy road With palms and scat-tered gar-ments strowed.
O Christ, Thy tri-umphs now be-gin O'er cap - tive death and con-quered sin.
Look down with sad and won-dering eyes To see th' ap-proaching sac-ri-fice.
Bow Thy meek head to mor - tal pain, Then take, O God, Thy pow'r, and reign. A-men.

126

TRURO. L. M.

Georg Weissel, 1590–1635
Tr. by Catherine Winkworth, 1829–1878

From Thomas Williams'
Psalmodia Evangelica, 1799

1. Lift up your heads, ye might-y gates, Be-hold, the King of glo - ry waits;
2. Fling wide the por-tals of your heart; Make it a tem - ple, set a - part
3. Re - deem-er, come, we o - pen wide Our hearts to Thee; here, Lord, a - bide.

The King of kings is draw-ing near; The Sav-iour of the world is here!
From earth-ly use for Heav-en's em-ploy, A-dorned with prayer, and love, and joy.
Thine in - ner pres-ence let us feel; Thy grace and love in us re - veal. A-men.

Jesus Christ

127

ELLACOMBE. 7. 6. 7. 6. D.

Jeannette Threlfall, 1821–1880

Gesangbuch der Herzogl, 1784

1. Ho - san - na, loud ho - san - na The lit - tle chil-dren sang;
2. From Ol - i - vet they fol - lowed 'Mid an ex - ult - ant crowd,
3. "Ho - san - na in the high - est!" That an - cient song we sing,

Through pil - lared court and tem - ple The love - ly an - them rang;
The vic - tor palm-branch wav - ing, And chant - ing clear and loud;
For Christ is our Re - deem - er, The Lord of heaven our King.

To Je - sus, who had blessed them Close fold - ed to His breast,
The Lord of men and an - gels Rode on in low - ly state,
O may we ev - er praise Him With heart and life and voice,

The chil - dren sang their prais - es, The sim - plest and the best.
Nor scorned that lit - tle chil - dren Should on His bid - ding wait.
And in His bliss-ful pres - ence E - ter - nal - ly re - joice! A - men.

Passion

ST. THEODULPH. 7. 6. 7. 6. D.

Theodulph of Orleans, ?-821
Tr. by John M. Neale, 1818-1866

Melchior Teschner, 16th or 17th century

1. All glo - ry, laud, and hon - or, To Thee, Re - deem - er, King,
2. The com - pa - ny of an - gels Are prais - ing Thee on high,
3. To Thee, be - fore Thy pas - sion They sang their hymns of praise;

To whom the lips of chil - dren Made sweet ho - san - nas ring.
And mor - tal men and all things Cre - a - ted make re - ply.
To Thee, now high ex - alt - ed, Our mel - o - dy we raise.

Thou art the King of Is - ra - el, Thou Da - vid's roy - al Son,
The peo - ple of the He - brews With palms be - fore Thee went;
Thou didst ac - cept their prais - es; Ac - cept the praise we bring,

Who in the Lord's Name com - est, The King and Bless - ed One.
Our praise and prayer and an - thems Be - fore Thee we pre - sent.
Who in all good de - light - est, Thou good and gra - cious King. A-MEN.

Jesus Christ

129

TOURS. 7. 6. 7. 6. D.

JOHN KING, 1789–1858

BERTHOLD TOURS, 1838–1897

1. When, His sal - va - tion bring - ing, To Zi - on Je - sus came,
2. And since the Lord re - tain - eth His love for chil - dren still,
3. For should we fail pro - claim - ing Our great Re - deem - er's praise,

The chil - dren all stood sing - ing, Ho - san - na to His name;
Though now as King He reign - eth On Zi - on's heaven - ly hill,
The stones, our si - lence sham - ing, Would their ho - san - nas raise.

Nor did their zeal of - fend Him, But, as He rode a - long,
We'll flock a - round His ban - ner Who sits up - on the throne,
But shall we on - ly ren - der The trib - ute of our words?

He bade them still at - tend Him, And smiled to hear their song.
And cry a - loud, "Ho - san - na To Da - vid's roy - al Son."
No! while our hearts are ten - der, They, too, shall be the Lord's. A - MEN.

Passion

PERCIVAL–SMITH. C. M. D.

CALVIN W. LAUFER, 1874–1938

CALVIN W. LAUFER, 1874–1938

In unison

1. O Thou E-ter-nal Christ of God, Ride on! Ride on! Ride on!
2. O Ho-ly Sav-iour of man-kind, Ride on! Ride on! Ride on!
3. O Thou whose dreams en-thrall the heart, Ride on! Ride on! Ride on!
4. O Thou who art the Life and Light, Ex-alt-ed Lord and King,

Es-tab-lish Thou for ev-er-more The tri-umph now be-gun.
We bear with Thee the scourge and cross If so Thy will is done.
Ride on till tyr-an-ny and greed Are ev-er-more un-done.
We hail Thine au-gust maj-es-ty And loud ho-san-na sing,

A might-y host, by Thee re-deemed, Is march-ing in Thy train:
And be the road up-hill or down, Un-bro-ken or well trod,
In mart and court and par-lia-ment The com-mon good in-crease,
Un-til in ev-ery land and clime Thine ends of love are won:

Thine is the King-dom and the power, And Thou in love shalt reign.
We go with Thee to claim and build A cit-y un-to God.
Till men at last shall ring the bells Of broth-er-hood and peace.
O Christ, Re-deem-er, Broth-er, Friend, Ride on! Ride on! Ride on!

A-MEN.

Jesus Christ

131

SUOMI. L. M. D.

Finnish Cavalry March
Thirty Years' War

ERNEST F. McGREGOR, 1879–

1. Lift high the tri-umph song to-day! From Ol - i - vet to Cal - va - ry
2. We climb a - gain the wood-ed slopes Of Ol - i - vet and Cal - va - ry;
3. We join the throng to wel-come Him: From Ol - i - vet and Cal - va - ry—
4. We o-pen wide the gates of love! By Ol - i - vet, by Cal - va - ry,

We tread a - gain that an - cient way Our Sav-iour rode in maj - es - ty.
We share with Him those ra - diant hopes, Which led at last to vic - to - ry.
De - scend the heights to shad-ows dim, Thro' death with Him to lib - er - ty.
Ac - claim Him Christ, from God a - bove, Our King, thro' all e - ter - ni - ty.

Let now the loud ho - san - nas ring! The Prince of Peace is pass-ing by;
Let now the loud ho - san - nas ring! The Prince of Peace is pass-ing by;
Let now the loud ho - san - nas ring! The Prince of Peace is pass-ing by;
Let now the loud ho - san - nas ring! The Prince of Peace is pass-ing by;

The Lord of Life, our Sav-iour, King, Goes bravely forth, to reign and die.
The Lord of Life, our Sav-iour, King, Goes glad-ly forth, to live—and die.
The Lord of Life, our Sav-iour, King, Goes humbly forth, to serve—and die.
The Lord of Life, our Sav-iour, King, Goes no-bly forth, no more to die. A-MEN.

Passion

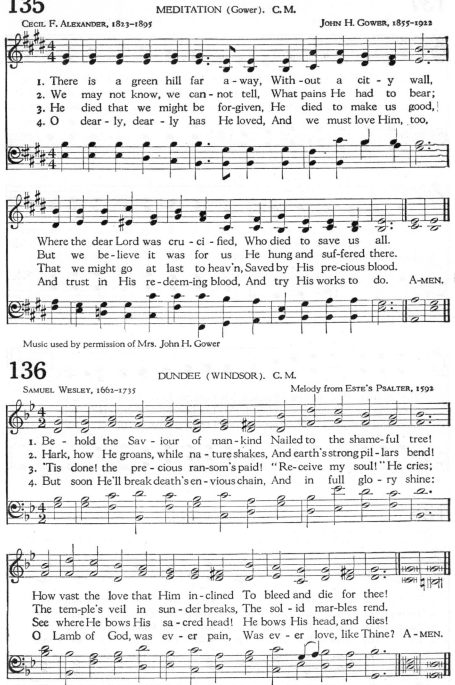

135

MEDITATION (Gower). C.M.

CECIL F. ALEXANDER, 1823–1895

JOHN H. GOWER, 1855–1922

1. There is a green hill far a-way, With-out a cit-y wall,
2. We may not know, we can-not tell, What pains He had to bear;
3. He died that we might be for-given, He died to make us good,
4. O dear-ly, dear-ly has He loved, And we must love Him, too,

Where the dear Lord was cru-ci-fied, Who died to save us all.
But we be-lieve it was for us He hung and suf-fered there.
That we might go at last to heav'n, Saved by His pre-cious blood.
And trust in His re-deem-ing blood, And try His works to do. A-MEN.

Music used by permission of Mrs. John H. Gower

136

DUNDEE (WINDSOR). C.M.

SAMUEL WESLEY, 1662–1735

Melody from ESTE'S PSALTER, 1592

1. Be - hold the Sav - iour of man - kind Nailed to the shame-ful tree!
2. Hark, how He groans, while na - ture shakes, And earth's strong pil - lars bend!
3. 'Tis done! the pre - cious ran-som's paid! "Re-ceive my soul!" He cries;
4. But soon He'll break death's en - vious chain, And in full glo - ry shine:

How vast the love that Him in-clined To bleed and die for thee!
The tem-ple's veil in sun - der breaks, The sol - id mar-bles rend.
See where He bows His sa - cred head! He bows His head, and dies!
O Lamb of God, was ev - er pain, Was ev - er love, like Thine? A - MEN.

Alternative tune, Martyrdom (Avon), No. 70

Jesus Christ

137

SELENA. 8. 8. 8. 8. 8. 8.

CHARLES WESLEY, 1707–1788

ISAAC B. WOODBURY, 1819–1858

1. O Love di-vine, what hast Thou done! Th' in-carnate God hath died for me!
2. Is cru-ci-fied for me and you, To bring us reb-els back to God:
3. Be-hold Him, all ye that pass by, The bleeding Prince of life and peace!

The Fa-ther's co-e-ter-nal Son Bore all my sins up-on the tree!
Be-lieve, be-lieve the rec-ord true, Ye all are bought with Je-sus' blood:
Come, sin-ners, see your Sav-iour die, And say, was ev-er grief like His?

The Son of God for me hath died: My Lord, my Love, is cru-ci-fied:
Par-don for all flows from His side: My Lord, my Love, is cru-ci-fied.
Come, feel with me His blood applied: My Lord, my Love, is cru-ci-fied. A-MEN.

138

STABAT MATER. 8. 8. 7.

From the Latin, 13th century
Tr. compiled by LOUIS F. BENSON, 1855–1930

French Church melody

1. Near the cross her vig-il keep-ing, Stood the moth-er,
2. Through her soul, in an-guish groan-ing, Bowed in sor-row,
3. Near Thy cross, O Christ, a-bid-ing, Grief and love my
4. By Thy guar-dian cross up-hold me, In Thy dy-ing,

Passion

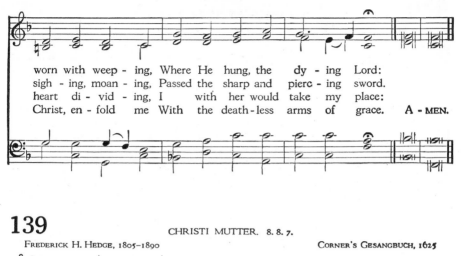

worn with weep - ing, Where He hung, the dy - ing Lord:
sigh - ing, moan - ing, Passed the sharp and pierc - ing sword.
heart di - vid - ing, I with her would take my place:
Christ, en - fold me With the death - less arms of grace. A - MEN.

139

CHRISTI MUTTER. 8. 8. 7.

FREDERICK H. HEDGE, 1805–1890

CORNER'S GESANGBUCH, 1625

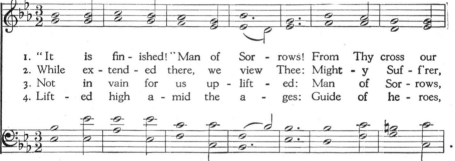

1. "It is fin - ished!" Man of Sor - rows! From Thy cross our
2. While ex - tend - ed there, we view Thee: Might - y Suf - f'rer,
3. Not in vain for us up - lift - ed: Man of Sor - rows,
4. Lift - ed high a - mid the a - ges: Guide of he - roes,

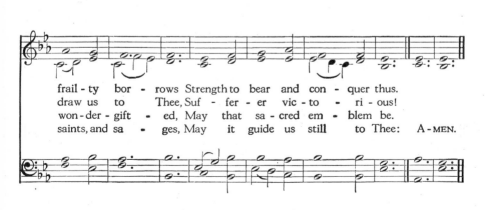

frail - ty bor - rows Strength to bear and con - quer thus.
draw us to Thee, Suf - fer - er vic - to - ri - ous!
won - der - gift - ed, May that sa - cred em - blem be.
saints, and sa - ges, May it guide us still to Thee: A - MEN.

5 Still to Thee, whose love unbounded
  Sorrow's depths for us has sounded,
  Perfected by conflicts sore.

6 Honored be Thy cross forever:
  Star, that points our high endeavor,
  Whither Thou hast gone before!

Jesus Christ

CLEANSING FOUNTAIN. C. M. D.

WILLIAM COWPER, 1731–1800

Early American melody
Arr. from LOWELL MASON, 1792–1872

1. There is a foun-tain filled with blood Drawn from Im-man-uel's veins;
2. The dy-ing thief re-joiced to see That foun-tain in his day;
3. Dear dy-ing Lamb, Thy pre-cious blood Shall nev-er lose its power,
4. E'er since, by faith, I saw the stream Thy flow-ing wounds sup-ply,
5. Then in a no-bler, sweet-er song, I'll sing Thy power to save,

And sin-ners, plunged be-neath that flood, Lose all their guilt-y stains,
And there may I, though vile as he, Wash all my sins a-way,
Till all the ran-somed Church of God Be saved, to sin no more,
Re-deem-ing love has been my theme, And shall be till I die,
When this poor lisp-ing, stam-mering tongue Lies si-lent in the grave,

Lose all their guilt-y stains, Lose all their guilt-y stains; And
Wash all my sins a-way, Wash all my sins a-way; And
Be saved, to sin no more, Be saved, to sin no more; Till
And shall be till I die, And shall be till I die; Re-
Lies si-lent in the grave, Lies si-lent in the grave; When

sin-ners, plunged be-neath that flood, Lose all their guilt-y stains.
there may I, though vile as he, Wash all my sins a-way.
all the ran-somed Church of God Be saved, to sin no more.
deem-ing love has been my theme, And shall be till I die.
this poor lisp-ing, stam-mering tongue Lies si-lent in the grave. A-MEN.

Passion

141

PASSION CHORALE. 7. 6. 7. 6. D.

Authorship uncertain
Tr. by PAUL GERHARDT, 1607–1676
Tr. by JAMES W. ALEXANDER, 1804–1859

HANS L. HASSLER, 1564–1612
Harmonized by J. S. BACH, 1685–1750

1. O sa-cred Head, now wound-ed, With grief and shame weighed down,
2. What Thou, my Lord, hast suf-fered Was all for sin-ners' gain:
3. What lan-guage shall I bor-row To thank Thee, dear-est Friend,

Now scorn-ful-ly sur-round-ed With thorns, Thine on-ly crown;
Mine, mine was the trans-gres-sion, But Thine the dead-ly pain.
For this Thy dy-ing sor-row, Thy pit-y with-out end?

How pale Thou art with an-guish, With sore a-buse and scorn!
Lo, here I fall, my Sav-iour! 'Tis I de-serve Thy place;
O make me Thine for ev-er; And should I faint-ing be,

How does that vis-age lan-guish Which once was bright as morn!
Look on me with Thy fa-vor, Vouch-safe to me Thy grace.
Lord, let me nev-er, nev-er Out-live my love to Thee. A-MEN.

Alternative tune, Munich, No. 386

Jesus Christ

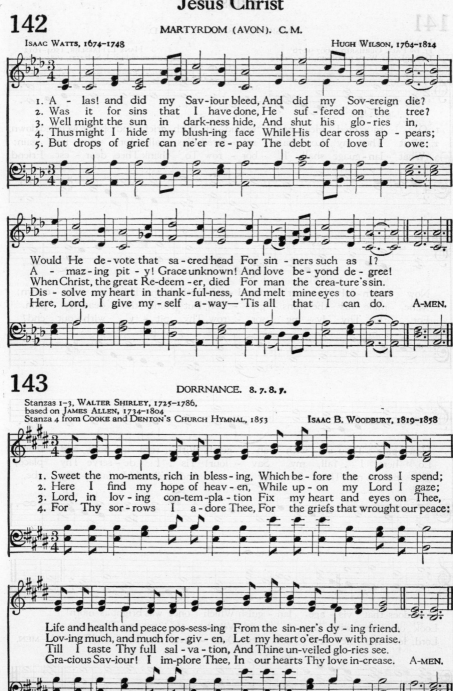

142

MARTYRDOM (AVON). C. M.

ISAAC WATTS, 1674-1748

HUGH WILSON, 1764-1824

1. A - las! and did my Sav-iour bleed, And did my Sov-ereign die?
2. Was it for sins that I have done, He suf-fered on the tree?
3. Well might the sun in dark-ness hide, And shut his glo-ries in,
4. Thus might I hide my blush-ing face While His dear cross ap - pears;
5. But drops of grief can ne'er re-pay The debt of love I owe:

Would He de-vote that sa-cred head For sin-ners such as I?
A - maz-ing pit - y! Grace unknown! And love be-yond de-gree!
When Christ, the great Re-deem-er, died For man the crea-ture's sin.
Dis-solve my heart in thank-ful-ness, And melt mine eyes to tears
Here, Lord, I give my-self a-way— 'Tis all that I can do. A-MEN.

143

DORRNANCE. 8. 7. 8. 7.

Stanzas 1-3, WALTER SHIRLEY, 1725-1786,
based on JAMES ALLEN, 1734-1804
Stanza 4 from COOKE and DENTON'S CHURCH HYMNAL, 1853

ISAAC B. WOODBURY, 1819-1858

1. Sweet the mo-ments, rich in bless-ing, Which be-fore the cross I spend;
2. Here I find my hope of heav-en, While up-on my Lord I gaze;
3. Lord, in lov-ing con-tem-pla-tion Fix my heart and eyes on Thee,
4. For Thy sor-rows I a-dore Thee, For the griefs that wrought our peace:

Life and health and peace pos-sess-ing From the sin-ner's dy-ing friend.
Lov-ing much, and much for-giv-en, Let my heart o'er-flow with praise.
Till I taste Thy full sal-va-tion, And Thine un-veiled glo-ries see.
Gra-cious Sav-iour! I im-plore Thee, In our hearts Thy love in-crease. A-MEN.

Passion

144

ST. CHRISTOPHER. 7. 6. 8. 6. 8. 6. 8. 6.

ELIZABETH C. CLEPHANE, 1830-1869

FREDERICK C. MAKER, 1844-1927

1. Be - neath the cross of Je - sus I fain would take my stand,
2. Up - on that cross of Je - sus Mine eye at times can see
3. I take, O cross, thy shad - ow For my a - bid - ing place;

The shad - ow of a might - y rock With - in a wea - ry land;
The ver - y dy - ing form of One Who suf - fered there for me; .
I ask no oth - er sun-shine than The sun-shine of His face;

A home with - in the wil - der - ness, A rest up - on the way,
And from my strick - en heart with tears Two won - ders I con - fess:
Con - tent to let the world go by, To know no gain nor loss,

From the burn-ing of the noon-tide heat, And the bur - den of the day.
The won-ders of re-deem-ing love And my un-wor-thi-ness.
My sin - ful self my on - ly shame, My glo - ry all the cross. A - MEN.

Jesus Christ

145

LONDONDERRY. 11. 10. 11. 10. D.

Thomas Tiplady, 1882–

Irish traditional melody

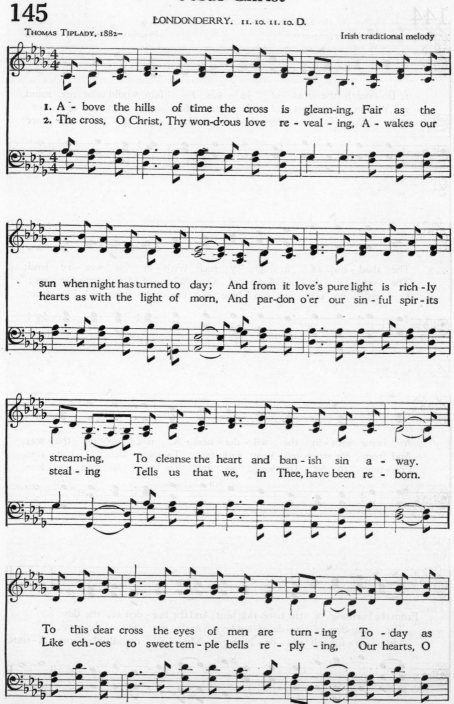

1. A-bove the hills of time the cross is gleam-ing, Fair as the
2. The cross, O Christ, Thy won-drous love re-veal-ing, A-wakes our

sun when night has turned to day; And from it love's pure light is rich-ly
hearts as with the light of morn, And par-don o'er our sin-ful spir-its

stream-ing, To cleanse the heart and ban-ish sin a-way.
steal-ing Tells us that we, in Thee, have been re-born.

To this dear cross the eyes of men are turn-ing To-day as
Like ech-oes to sweet tem-ple bells re-ply-ing, Our hearts, O

Passion

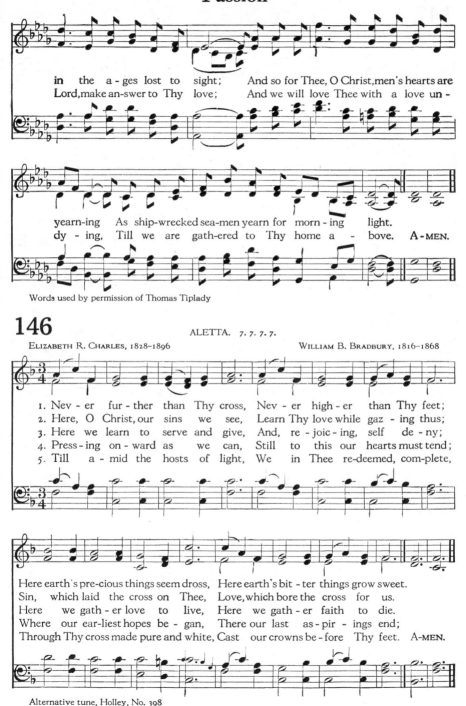

in the a - ges lost to sight; And so for Thee, O Christ, men's hearts are
Lord, make an - swer to Thy love; And we will love Thee with a love un -

yearn - ing As ship-wrecked sea-men yearn for morn - ing light.
dy - ing, Till we are gath-ered to Thy home a - bove. A-MEN.

Words used by permission of Thomas Tiplady

146

ALETTA. 7. 7. 7. 7.

ELIZABETH R. CHARLES, 1828–1896

WILLIAM B. BRADBURY, 1816–1868

1. Nev - er fur - ther than Thy cross, Nev - er high - er than Thy feet;
2. Here, O Christ, our sins we see, Learn Thy love while gaz - ing thus;
3. Here we learn to serve and give, And, re - joic - ing, self de - ny;
4. Press - ing on - ward as we can, Still to this our hearts must tend;
5. Till a - mid the hosts of light, We in Thee re-deemed, com-plete,

Here earth's pre-cious things seem dross, Here earth's bit - ter things grow sweet.
Sin, which laid the cross on Thee, Love, which bore the cross for us.
Here we gath - er love to live, Here we gath - er faith to die.
Where our ear - liest hopes be - gan, There our last as - pir - ings end;
Through Thy cross made pure and white, Cast our crowns be - fore Thy feet. A-MEN.

Alternative tune, Holley, No. 398

Jesus Christ

147

HENDON. 7. 7. 7. 7. 7.

Johann C. Schwedler, 1672–1730
Tr. by Benjamin H. Kennedy, 1804–1889

H. A. César Malan, 1787–1864

1. Ask ye what great thing I know
2. Who de-feats my fier-cest foes?
3. Who is life in life to me?
4. This is that great thing I know;

That de-lights and stirs me so? What the high re-
Who con-soles my sad-dest woes? Who re-vives my
Who the death of death will be? Who will place me
This de-lights and stirs me so: Faith in Him who

ward I win? Whose the name I glo-ry in?
faint-ing heart, Heal-ing all its hid-den smart?
on His right, With the count-less hosts of light?
died to save, Him who tri-umphed o'er the grave,

Je-sus Christ, the Cru-ci-fied.
Je-sus Christ, the Cru-ci-fied.
Je-sus Christ, the Cru-ci-fied.
Je-sus Christ, the Cru-ci-fied. A-men.

148

EUCHARIST. L. M.

ISAAC WATTS, 1674–1748

ISAAC B. WOODBURY, 1819–1858

1. When I sur-vey the won-drous cross On which the Prince of Glo-ry died,
2. For - bid it, Lord, that I should boast, Save in the death of Christ, my God:
3. See, from His head, His hands, His feet, Sor-row and love flow min-gled down:
4. Were the whole realm of na - ture mine, That were an of - fering far too small;

My rich-est gain I count but loss, And pour con-tempt on all my pride.
All the vain things that charm me most, I sac - ri - fice them to His blood.
Did e'er such love and sor - row meet, Or thorns compose so rich a crown?
Love so a-maz-ing, so di - vine, De-mands my soul, my life, my all. A-MEN.

Alternative tune, Hamburg, No. 334

149

RATHBUN. 8. 7. 8. 7.

JOHN BOWRING, 1792–1872

ITHAMAR CONKEY, 1815–1867

1. In the cross of Christ I glo-ry, Tow-ering o'er the wrecks of time;
2. When the woes of life o'er-take me, Hopes de-ceive, and fears an-noy,
3. When the sun of bliss is beam-ing Light and love up - on my way,
4. Bane and bless-ing, pain and pleas-ure, By the cross are sanc - ti - fied;
5. In the cross of Christ I glo-ry, Tow-ering o'er the wrecks of time;

All the light of sa - cred sto - ry Gath-ers round its head sub-lime.
Nev-er shall the cross for-sake me: Lo! it glows with peace and joy.
From the cross the ra - diance streaming Adds more lus-ter to the day.
Peace is there, that knows no meas-ure, Joys that thro' all time a-bide.
All the light of sa - cred sto - ry Gath-ers round its head sub-lime. A-MEN.

Jesus Christ

150

HYMN TO JOY. 8. 7. 8. 7. D.

WILLIAM J. IRONS, 1812–1883

Arr. from LUDWIG VAN BEETHOVEN, 1770–1827

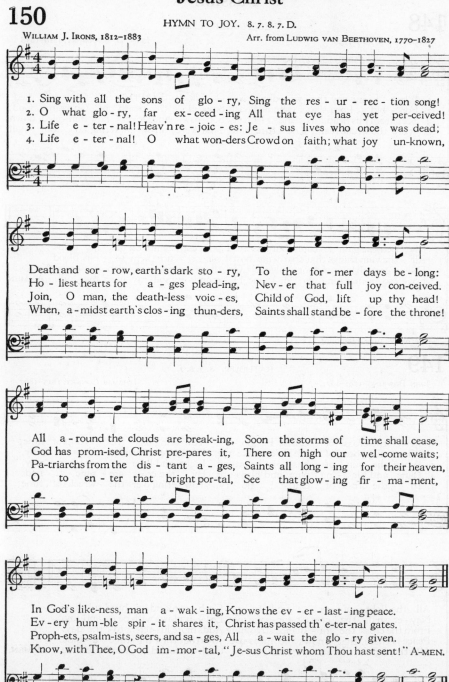

1. Sing with all the sons of glo - ry, Sing the res - ur - rec - tion song!
2. O what glo - ry, far ex - ceed - ing All that eye has yet per-ceived!
3. Life e - ter - nal! Heav'n re - joic - es: Je - sus lives who once was dead;
4. Life e - ter - nal! O what won-ders Crowd on faith; what joy un-known,

Death and sor - row, earth's dark sto - ry, To the for - mer days be - long:
Ho - liest hearts for a - ges plead-ing, Nev - er that full joy con-ceived.
Join, O man, the death-less voic - es, Child of God, lift up thy head!
When, a - midst earth's clos - ing thun-ders, Saints shall stand be - fore the throne!

All a - round the clouds are break-ing, Soon the storms of time shall cease,
God has prom-ised, Christ pre-pares it, There on high our wel-come waits;
Pa-triarchs from the dis - tant a - ges, Saints all long - ing for their heaven,
O to en - ter that bright por-tal, See that glow - ing fir - ma-ment,

In God's like-ness, man a - wak - ing, Knows the ev - er - last-ing peace.
Ev - ery hum - ble spir - it shares it, Christ has passed th' e-ter-nal gates.
Proph-ets, psalm-ists, seers, and sa - ges, All a - wait the glo - ry given.
Know, with Thee, O God im - mor - tal, "Je-sus Christ whom Thou hast sent!" A - MEN.

Resurrection

151

ST. KEVIN. 7. 6. 7. 6. D.

JOHN OF DAMASCUS, 8th century
Tr. by JOHN M. NEALE, 1818-1866

ARTHUR S. SULLIVAN, 1842-1900

1. Come, ye faith-ful, raise the strain Of tri-umph-ant glad-ness:
2. 'Tis the spring of souls to-day: Christ hath burst His pris-on,
3. "Al - le - lu - ia!" now we cry To our King Im-mor-tal,

God hath brought His peo-ple forth In - to joy from sad-ness.
From the frost and gloom of death Light and life have ris-en.
Who, tri - um-phant, burst the bars Of the tomb's dark por-tal;

Now re - joice, Je - ru - sa-lem, And with true af-fec-tion
All the win-ter of our sins, Long and dark, is fly-ing
"Al - le - lu - ia!" with the Son, God the Fa-ther prais-ing;

Wel - come in un - wea-ried strains Je - sus' res-ur-rec-tion.
From His light, to whom we give Thanks and praise un - dy-ing.
"Al - le - lu - ia!" yet a - gain To the Spir-it rais-ing. A - MEN.

Jesus Christ

152

MASEFIELD. 6. 6. 6. 5. D.

JOHN MASEFIELD, 1875–

JOHN PORTER, 1877–

1. Sing, men and an - gels, sing, For God our Life and King
2. Sing, crea - tures, sing; the dust That lives by lure and lust
3. Aft - er the win - ter snows A wind of heal - ing blows,

Has given us light and spring And morn - ing break - ing.
Is kin - dled by the thrust Of life un - dy - ing:
And thorns put forth a rose And li - lies cheer us:

Now may man's soul a - rise As kins - man to the skies,
This hope our Mas - ter bare Has made all for - tunes fair;
Life's ev - er - last - ing spring Hath robbed death of his sting;

And God un - seals his eyes To an a - wak - ing.
And man can on and dare, His death de - fy - ing.
Hence-forth a cry can bring Our Mas - ter near us. A - MEN.

Resurrection

153

LONGDEN. 8. 7. 8. 7. D.

CHRISTOPHER WORDSWORTH, 1807–1885, and others

VAN DENMAN THOMPSON, 1890–

1. Al - le - lu - ia! Al - le - lu - ia! Hearts to heaven and voic - es raise;
2. Now the i - ron bars are bro - ken, Christ from death to life is born,
3. Al - le - lu - ia! Al - le - lu - ia! Glo - ry be to God on high;

Sing to God a hymn of glad - ness, Sing to God a hymn of praise:
Glo - rious life, and life im - mor - tal, On this ho - ly Eas - ter morn:
Al - le - lu - ia to the Sav - iour Who has won the vic - to - ry;

He who on the cross as Sav - iour For the world's sal - va - tion bled,
Christ has tri - umphed, and we con - quer By His might - y en - ter - prise;
Al - le - lu - ia to the Spir - it, Fount of love and sanc - ti - ty;

Je - sus Christ, the King of Glo - ry, Now is ris - en from the dead.
We with Him to life e - ter - nal By His res - ur - rec - tion rise.
Al - le - lu - ia! Al - le - lu - ia! To the Tri - une Maj - es - ty. A - MEN.

Music copyright, 1935, by Van Denman Thompson. Used by permission

Jesus Christ

154

EASTER HYMN. 7. 7. 7. 7. with Alleluias

CHARLES WESLEY, 1707–1788, and others

From LYRA DAVIDICA, 1708

1. Christ the Lord is risen to - day, Al - - - le - lu - ia!
2. Lives a - gain our glo - rious King, Al - - - le - lu - ia!
3. Love's re - deem - ing work is done, Al - - - le - lu - ia!
4. Soar we now where Christ has led, Al - - - le - lu - ia!

Sons of men and an - gels say, Al - - - le - lu - ia!
Where, O death, is now thy sting? Al - - - le - lu - ia!
Fought the fight, the bat - tle won, Al - - - le - lu - ia!
Fol - lowing our ex - alt - ed Head, Al - - - le - lu - ia!

Raise your joys and tri - umphs high, Al - - - le - lu - ia!
Once He died, our souls to save, Al - - - le - lu - ia!
Death in vain for - bids Him rise, Al - - - le - lu - ia!
Made like Him, like Him we rise, Al - - - le - lu - ia!

Sing, ye heavens, and earth re - ply, Al - - le - lu - ia!
Where's thy vic-tory, boast-ing grave? Al - - le - lu - ia!
Christ hath o - pened Par - a - dise, Al - - le - lu - ia!
Ours the cross, the grave, the skies, Al - - le - lu - ia! A-MEN.

Resurrection

155

LLANFAIR. 7. 7. 7. 7. with Alleluias

From the Latin, 14th century
Stanza 3, CHARLES WESLEY, 1707–1788

ROBERT WILLIAMS, c. 1781–1821

1. Je - sus Christ is risen to - day, Al - - le - lu - ia!
2. Hymns of praise then let us sing, Al - - le - lu - ia!
3. Sing we to our God a - bove, Al - - le - lu - ia!

Our tri - um - phant ho - ly day, Al - - le - lu - ia!
Un - to Christ, our heaven - ly King, Al - - le - lu - ia!
Praise e - ter - nal as His love; Al - - le - lu - ia!

Who did once, up - on the cross, Al - - le - lu - ia!
Who en - dured the cross and grave, Al - - le - lu - ia!
Praise Him, all ye heaven - ly host, Al - - le - lu - ia!

In unison

Suf - fer to re - deem our loss. Al - le - lu - ia!
Sin - ners to re - deem and save. Al - le - lu - ia!
Fa - ther, Son, and Ho - ly Ghost. Al - le - lu - ia! A-MEN.

Music from the Revised Church Hymnary (Har. D. E.). By permission of the Oxford University Press

Jesus Christ

156

VICTORY. 8. 8. 8. 4. with Alleluias

Authorship uncertain
Tr. by FRANCIS POTT, 1832–1909

GIOVANNI P. DA PALESTRINA, 1525–1594

Al - le - lu - ia! Al - le - lu - ia! Al - le - lu - ia!

1. The strife is
2. The pow'rs of
3. The three sad
4. Lord, by the

o'er, the bat - tle done; The vic - to - ry of life is won;
death have done their worst, But Christ their le - gions hath dis - persed;
days have quick - ly sped; He ris - es glo - rious from the dead:
stripes which wound - ed Thee, From death's dread sting Thy ser - vants free,

The song of tri - umph has be - gun. Al - le - lu - ia!
Let shouts of ho - ly joy out - burst. Al - le - lu - ia!
All glo - ry to our ris - en Head! Al - le - lu - ia!
That we may live and sing to Thee. Al - le - lu - ia! A - MEN.

157

SPLENDOUR (PUER NOBIS NASCITUR). L. M.

Authorship uncertain
Tr. by JOHN M. NEALE, 1818–1866, alt.

MICHAEL PRAETORIUS, 1571–1621

1. Joy dawned a - gain on Eas - ter - Day, The sun shone out with fair - er ray,
2. O Je - sus, King of gen - tle - ness, Do Thou our in - most hearts possess;
3. Je - sus who art the Lord of all, In this our Eas - ter fes - ti - val,
4. All praise, O ris - en Lord, we give To Thee, who, dead, a - gain dost live;

Resurrection

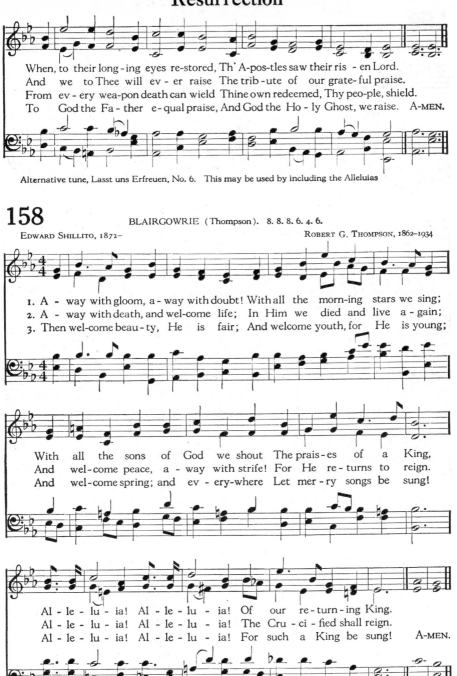

When, to their long-ing eyes re-stored, Th' A-pos-tles saw their ris-en Lord.
And we to Thee will ev-er raise The trib-ute of our grate-ful praise.
From ev-ery wea-pon death can wield Thine own redeemed, Thy peo-ple, shield.
To God the Fa-ther e-qual praise, And God the Ho-ly Ghost, we raise. A-MEN.

Alternative tune, Lasst uns Erfreuen, No. 6. This may be used by including the Alleluias

158

BLAIRGOWRIE (Thompson). 8. 8. 8. 6. 4. 6.

EDWARD SHILLITO, 1872–   ROBERT G. THOMPSON, 1862–1934

1. A-way with gloom, a-way with doubt! With all the morn-ing stars we sing;
2. A-way with death, and wel-come life; In Him we died and live a-gain;
3. Then wel-come beau-ty, He is fair; And welcome youth, for He is young;

With all the sons of God we shout The prais-es of a King,
And wel-come peace, a-way with strife! For He re-turns to reign.
And wel-come spring; and ev-ery-where Let mer-ry songs be sung!

Al-le-lu-ia! Al-le-lu-ia! Of our re-turn-ing King.
Al-le-lu-ia! Al-le-lu-ia! The Cru-ci-fied shall reign.
Al-le-lu-ia! Al-le-lu-ia! For such a King be sung! A-MEN.

Words used by permission of Edward Shillito

Jesus Christ

ROTTERDAM. 7. 6. 7. 6. D.

JOHN of DAMASCUS, c. 750
Tr. by JOHN M. NEALE, 1818-1866

Berthold Tours, 1838-1897

1. The day of res - ur - rec - tion, Earth, tell it out a - broad,
2. Our hearts be pure from e - vil, That we may see a - right
3. Now let the heavens be joy - ful! Let earth her song be - gin!

The pass - o - ver of glad - ness, The pass - o - ver of God.
The Lord in rays e - ter - nal Of res - ur - rec - tion light;
Let the round world keep tri - umph, And all that is there - in!

From death to life e - ter - nal, From earth un - to the sky,
And, lis - tening to His ac - cents, May hear, so calm and plain,
Let all things seen and un - seen Their notes in glad - ness blend,

Our Christ hath brought us o - ver With hymns of vic - to - ry.
His own "All hail!" and, hear - ing, May raise the vic - tor-strain.
For Christ the Lord hath ris - en, Our joy that hath no end. A - MEN.

Alternative tune, Lancashire, No. 278

Resurrection

160

TREFAENAN. 8. 7. 8. 7. 8. 8. 8. 7.

PERCY DEARMER, 1867–1936

From a Welsh traditional melody

1. Life is good, for God con-trives it, Deep on deep its won-der lies;
2. Fail-ure cuts the way to tri-umph, Win-ter shapes the leaves of spring:
3. Lord, in Thee shines man's per-fec-tion—Kind and self-less, strong, and brave;

Death is good, for man sur-vives it, Lives a-gain in bet-ter guise:
Eas-ter came be-cause the Mas-ter Loved the light of truth to bring.
And Thy life and res-ur-rec-tion Tells of joy be-yond the grave.

This they knew the night they hailed Him, When He came thro' that which veiled Him,
Vain-ly priests in ha-tred slew Him: He came back, His loved ones knew Him,
All man-kind is no-bled thro' Thee; All are broth-ers com-ing to Thee,

Al-le-lu-ia, Al-le-lu-ia! Smil-ing, won-der-ful, and wise.
Al-le-lu-ia, Al-le-lu-ia! Where, O death, is now thy sting?
Al-le-lu-ia, Al-le-lu-ia! Thine the power to guide and save. A-MEN.

Words from Enlarged Songs of Praise. By permission of Oxford University Press
Arrangement of music copyright, 1935, by Whitmore & Smith, Nashville. Tenn.

Jesus Christ

161

HERMAS. 6. 5. 6. 5. D. with Refrain

VENANTIUS FORTUNATUS, c. 530–609
Tr. by JOHN ELLERTON, 1826–1893

FRANCES R. HAVERGAL, 1836–1879

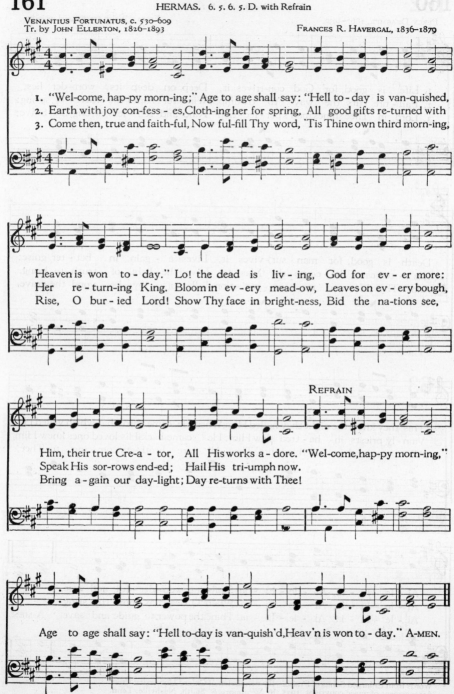

1. "Wel-come, hap-py morn-ing;" Age to age shall say: "Hell to-day is van-quished,
2. Earth with joy con-fess - es, Cloth-ing her for spring, All good gifts re-turned with
3. Come then, true and faith-ful, Now ful-fill Thy word, 'Tis Thine own third morn-ing,

Heaven is won to - day." Lo! the dead is liv - ing, God for ev - er more:
Her re - turn-ing King. Bloom in ev -ery mead-ow, Leaves on ev - ery bough,
Rise, O bur - ied Lord! Show Thy face in bright-ness, Bid the na-tions see,

REFRAIN

Him, their true Cre-a - tor, All His works a - dore. "Wel-come, hap-py morn-ing,"
Speak His sor-rows end-ed; Hail His tri-umph now.
Bring a - gain our day-light; Day re-turns with Thee!

Age to age shall say: "Hell to-day is van-quish'd, Heav'n is won to - day." A-MEN.

The Everliving Christ

AZMON. C. M.

CHARLES WESLEY, 1707–1788

CARL G. GLÄSER, 1784–1829
Arr. by LOWELL MASON, 1792–1872

1. O for a thou-sand tongues to sing My great Re-deem-er's praise,
2. My gra-cious Mas-ter and my God, As-sist me to pro-claim,
3. Je-sus! the Name that charms our fears, That bids our sor-rows cease,
4. He breaks the power of can-celed sin, He sets the pris-oner free;

The glo-ries of my God and King, The tri-umphs of His grace!
To spread thro' all the earth a-broad The hon-ors of Thy Name.
'Tis mu-sic in the sin-ner's ears, 'Tis life, and health, and peace.
His blood can make the foul-est clean; His blood a-vailed for me. A-MEN.

5 He speaks, and, listening to His voice,
New life the dead receive;
The mournful, broken hearts rejoice;
The humble poor believe.

6 Hear Him, ye deaf; His praise, ye dumb,
Your loosened tongues employ;
Ye blind, behold your Saviour come;
And leap, ye lame, for joy.

ST. MAGNUS. C. M.

THOMAS KELLY, 1769–1854

JEREMIAH CLARK, 1670–1707

1. The Head that once was crown'd with thorns Is crown'd with glo-ry now;
2. The high-est place that heaven af-fords Be-longs to Him by right,
3. The Joy of all who dwell a-bove, The Joy of all be-low,
4. The Cross He bore is life and health, Tho' shame and death to Him,

A roy-al di-a-dem a-dorns The might-y Vic-tor's brow.
The King of kings, and Lord of lords, And heaven's e-ter-nal Light:
To whom He man-i-fests His love And grants His Name to know.
His peo-ple's hope, His peo-ple's wealth, Their ev-er-last-ing theme. A-MEN.

Jesus Christ

CORONATION. C. M.

(*First Tune*)

EDWARD PERRONET, 1726–1792
Alt. by JOHN RIPPON, 1751–1836

OLIVER HOLDEN, 1765–1844

1. All hail the power of Je - sus' Name! Let an - gels pros-trate fall;
2. Ye cho - sen seed of Is - rael's race, Ye ran-somed from the fall,
3. Sin - ners, whose love can ne'er for - get The worm-wood and the gall,

Bring forth the roy - al di - a - dem, And crown Him Lord of all;
Hail Him who saves you by His grace, And crown Him Lord of all;
Go, spread your tro-phies at His feet, And crown Him Lord of all;

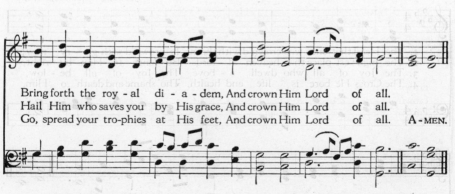

Bring forth the roy - al di - a - dem, And crown Him Lord of all.
Hail Him who saves you by His grace, And crown Him Lord of all.
Go, spread your tro-phies at His feet, And crown Him Lord of all. A - MEN.

4 Let every kindred, every tribe,
On this terrestrial ball,
To Him all majesty ascribe,
And crown Him Lord of all.

5 O that with yonder sacred throng
We at His feet may fall!
We'll join the everlasting song,
And crown Him Lord of all.

The Everliving Christ

164

MILES' LANE. C. M.

(*Second Tune*)

EDWARD PERRONET, 1726-1792
Alt. by JOHN RIPPON, 1751-1836

WILLIAM SHRUBSOLE, 1760-1806

1. All hail the power of Je - sus' Name! Let an - gels pros - trate fall;
2. Ye cho - sen seed of Is - rael's race, Ye ran - somed from the fall,
3. Sin - ners, whose love can ne'er for - get The worm - wood and the gall,

Bring forth the roy - al di - a - dem, And crown Him,
Hail Him who saves you by His grace, And crown Him,
Go, spread your tro - phies at His feet, And crown Him,

crown Him, crown Him, Crown Him Lord of all.
crown Him, crown Him, Crown Him Lord of all.
crown Him, crown Him, Crown Him Lord of all. A - MEN.

4 Let every kindred, every tribe,
On this terrestrial ball,
To Him all majesty ascribe,
And crown Him Lord of all.

5 O that with yonder sacred throng
We at His feet may fall!
We'll join the everlasting song,
And crown Him Lord of all.

Jesus Christ

DIADEM. C. M.
(*Third Tune*)

Edward Perronet, 1726–1792
Alt. by John Rippon, 1751–1836

James Ellor, 1819–1899

1. All hail the power of Je - sus' Name! Let an - gels pros-trate
2. Ye cho - sen seed of Is - rael's race, Ye ran-somed from the
3. Sin - ners, whose love can ne'er for - get The worm-wood and the
4. Let ev - ery kin - dred, ev - ery tribe, On this ter - res-trial
5. O that with yon - der sa - cred throng We at His feet may

fall, Let an - gels pros - trate fall; Bring forth the roy - al
fall, Ye ran - somed from the fall; Hail Him who saves you
gall, The worm - wood and the gall, Go, spread your tro - phies
ball, On this ter - res-trial ball, To Him all maj - es -
fall, We at His feet may fall! We'll join the ev - er -

di - a - dem, And crown . . . . Him,
by His grace, And crown . . . . Him,
at His feet, And crown . . . . Him,
ty as - cribe, And crown . . . . Him,
last - ing song, And crown . . . . Him,

crown Him, crown Him, crown Him, crown Him,

crown . . . .

crown Him, crown Him, crown Him, And crown Him Lord of all. A - men.

. . . . Him,

The Everliving Christ

165

CWM RHONDDA. 8. 7. 8. 7. 8. 7.

Welsh hymn melody
JOHN HUGHES, 1873–1932

THOMAS KELLY, 1769–1854

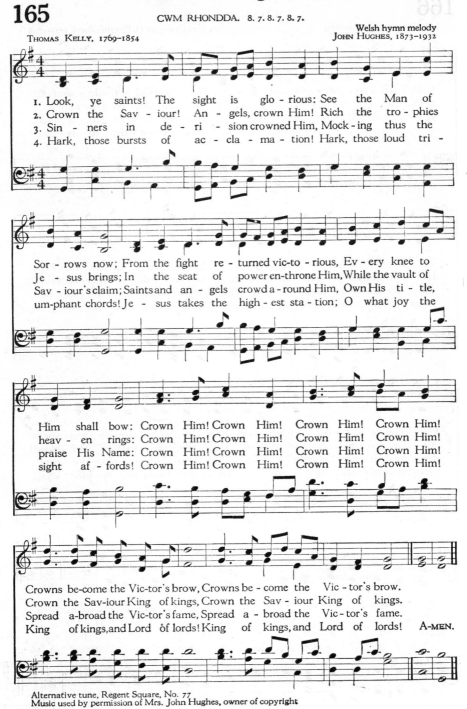

1. Look, ye saints! The sight is glorious: See the Man of Sorrows now; From the fight returned victorious, Every knee to Him shall bow: Crown Him! Crown Him! Crown Him! Crown Him! Crowns become the Victor's brow, Crowns become the Victor's brow.

2. Crown the Saviour! Angels, crown Him! Rich the trophies Jesus brings; In the seat of power enthrone Him, While the vault of heaven rings: Crown Him! Crown Him! Crown Him! Crown Him! Crown the Saviour King of kings, Crown the Saviour King of kings.

3. Sinners in derision crowned Him, Mocking thus the Saviour's claim; Saints and angels crowd around Him, Own His title, praise His Name: Crown Him! Crown Him! Crown Him! Crown Him! Spread abroad the Victor's fame, Spread abroad the Victor's fame.

4. Hark, those bursts of acclamation! Hark, those loud triumphant chords! Jesus takes the highest station; O what joy the sight affords! Crown Him! Crown Him! Crown Him! Crown Him! King of kings, and Lord of lords! King of kings, and Lord of lords! A-MEN.

Alternative tune, Regent Square, No. 77
Music used by permission of Mrs. John Hughes, owner of copyright

Jesus Christ

166

AUTUMN. 8. 7. 8. 7. D.

John Bakewell, 1721–1819

Arr. from François H. Barthélémon, 1741–1808

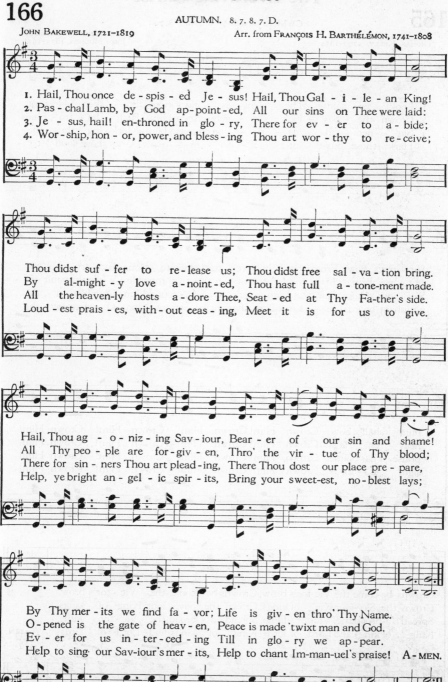

1. Hail, Thou once de-spis-ed Je-sus! Hail, Thou Gal-i-le-an King!
2. Pas-chal Lamb, by God ap-point-ed, All our sins on Thee were laid:
3. Je-sus, hail! en-throned in glo-ry, There for ev-er to a-bide;
4. Wor-ship, hon-or, power, and bless-ing Thou art wor-thy to re-ceive;

Thou didst suf-fer to re-lease us; Thou didst free sal-va-tion bring.
By al-might-y love a-noint-ed, Thou hast full a-tone-ment made.
All the heaven-ly hosts a-dore Thee, Seat-ed at Thy Fa-ther's side.
Loud-est prais-es, with-out ceas-ing, Meet it is for us to give.

Hail, Thou ag-o-niz-ing Sav-iour, Bear-er of our sin and shame!
All Thy peo-ple are for-giv-en, Thro' the vir-tue of Thy blood;
There for sin-ners Thou art plead-ing, There Thou dost our place pre-pare,
Help, ye bright an-gel-ic spir-its, Bring your sweet-est, no-blest lays;

By Thy mer-its we find fa-vor; Life is giv-en thro' Thy Name.
O-pened is the gate of heav-en, Peace is made 'twixt man and God.
Ev-er for us in-ter-ced-ing Till in glo-ry we ap-pear.
Help to sing our Sav-iour's mer-its, Help to chant Im-man-uel's praise! A-MEN.

The Everliving Christ

HARWELL. 8. 7. 8. 7. 7. 7. with Alleluias

THOMAS KELLY, 1769-1854

LOWELL MASON, 1792-1872

1. Hark! ten thou - sand harps and voic - es Sound the note of praise a - bove;
2. King of glo - ry, reign for ev - er, Thine an ev - er - last - ing crown;
3. Sav - iour, has - ten Thine ap - pear - ing; Bring, O bring the glo - rious day

Je - sus reigns and heav'n re - joic - es, Je - sus reigns, the God of love:
Noth - ing from Thy love shall sev - er Those whom Thou hast made Thine own:
When, the aw - ful sum-mons hear - ing, Heav'n and earth shall pass a - way:

See, He sits on yon - der throne; Je - sus rules the world a -
Hap - py ob - jects of Thy grace, Des - tined to be - hold Thy
Then, with gold - en harps we'll sing, "Glo - ry, glo - ry to our

See, He sits on yon - der throne; Je - sus rules the world a -
Hap - py ob - - - jects of Thy grace, Des - tined to be - hold Thy
Then, with gold - - - en harps we'll sing, "Glo - ry, glo - - ry to our

lone. Al - le - lu - ia! Al - le - lu - ia! Al - le - lu - ia! A - men.
face. Al - le - lu - ia! Al - le - lu - ia! Al - le - lu - ia! A - men.
King!" Al - le - lu - ia! Al - le - lu - ia! Al - le - lu - ia! A - men.

Jesus Christ

168

ARIEL. 8. 8. 6. D.

Samuel Medley, 1738-1799

Arr. by Lowell Mason, 1792-1872

1. O could I speak the match-less worth,
O could I sound the glo-ries forth Which in my Sav-iour shine,
I'd sing His glo-rious right-eous-ness, And mag-ni-fy the won-drous grace
Which made sal-va-tion mine, Which made sal-va-tion mine.

2. I'd sing the char-ac-ters He bears,
And all the forms of love He wears, Ex-alt-ed on His throne:
In loft-iest songs of sweet-est praise, I would to ev-er-last-ing days
Make all His glo-ries known, Make all His glo-ries known.

3. Well, the de-light-ful day will come
When my dear Lord will bring me home, And I shall see His face;
Then with my Sav-iour, Broth-er, Friend, A blest e-ter-ni-ty I'll spend,
Tri-um-phant in His grace, Tri-um-phant in His grace. A-men.

The Everliving Christ

169

HANOVER. 10. 10. 11. 11.

CHARLES WESLEY, 1707–1788

WILLIAM CROFT, 1678–1727

1. Ye ser-vants of God, your Mas-ter pro-claim,
2. God rul-eth on high, al-might-y to save;
3. "Sal-va-tion to God, who sits on the throne!"
4. Then let us a-dore, and give Him His right,

And pub-lish a-broad His won-der-ful Name;
And still He is nigh, His pres-ence we have:
Let all cry a-loud, and hon-or the Son:
All glo-ry and power, all wis-dom and might,

The Name all-vic-to-rious of Je-sus ex-tol;
The great con-gre-ga-tion His tri-umph shall sing,
The prais-es of Je-sus the an-gels pro-claim,
All hon-or and bless-ing, with an-gels a-bove,

His king-dom is glo-rious, and rules o-ver all.
As-crib-ing sal-va-tion to Je-sus, our King.
Fall down on their fa-ces, and wor-ship the Lamb.
And thanks nev-er ceas-ing for in-fi-nite love.   A-MEN.

Jesus Christ

170

DIADEMATA. S. M. D.

MATTHEW BRIDGES, 1800-1894 and
GODFREY THRING, 1823-1903

GEORGE J. ELVEY, 1816-1893

1. Crown Him with man-y crowns, The Lamb up-on His throne;
2. Crown Him the Lord of life, Who tri-umphed o'er the grave,
3. Crown Him the Lord of peace, Whose power a scep-ter sways
4. Crown Him the Lord of love; Be-hold His hands and side,

Hark! how the heaven-ly an-them drowns All mu-sic but its own.
And rose vic-to-rious in the strife For those He came to save;
From pole to pole, that wars may cease, And all be prayer and praise:
Those wounds, yet vis-i-ble a-bove, In beau-ty glo-ri-fied:

A-wake, my soul, and sing Of Him who died for thee,
His glo-ries now we sing Who died, and rose on high,
His reign shall know no end, And round His pierc-ed feet
All hail, Re-deem-er, hail! For Thou hast died for me:

And hail Him as thy match-less King Through all e-ter-ni-ty.
Who died—e-ter-nal life to bring, And lives, that death may die.
Fair flowers of par-a-dise ex-tend Their fra-grance ev-er sweet.
Thy praise and glo-ry shall not fail Through-out e-ter-ni-ty. A-MEN.

The Everliving Christ

171

DARWALL. 6. 6. 6. 6. 8. 8.

CHARLES WESLEY, 1707–1788

JOHN DARWALL, 1731–1789

1. Re - joice, the Lord is King: Your Lord and King a - dore!
2. Je - sus, the Sav - iour, reigns, The God of truth and love;
3. His King - dom can - not fail, He rules o'er earth and heaven;

Re - joice, give thanks, and sing, And tri - umph
When He had purged our stains, He took His
The keys of death and hell Are to our

ev - er - more: Lift up your heart, lift up your voice!
seat a - bove: Lift up your heart, lift up your voice!
Je - sus given: Lift up your heart, lift up your voice!

Re - joice, a - gain I say, re - joice!
Re - joice, a - gain I say, re - joice!
Re - joice, a - gain I say, re - joice! A - MEN.

Alternative tune, Lenox, No. 189

The Holy Spirit

172

ST. MARTIN'S. C. M.

ISAAC WATTS, 1674-1748

WILLIAM TANS'UR, 1700-1783

1. Come, Ho - ly Spir - it, heaven-ly Dove, With all Thy quick'ning pow'rs;
2. Look how we grov - el here be - low, Fond of these earth - ly toys;
3. In vain we tune our for - mal songs, In vain we strive to rise;
4. And shall we then for ev - er live At this poor dy - ing rate?
5. Come, Ho - ly Spir - it, heaven-ly Dove, With all Thy quick'ning pow'rs;

Kin - dle a flame of sa - cred love In these cold hearts of ours.
Our souls, how heav - i - ly they go, To reach e - ter - nal joys.
Ho - san-nas lan - guish on our tongues, And our de - vo - tion dies.
Our love so faint, so cold to Thee, And Thine to us so great!
Come, shed a - broad a Sav - iour's love, And that shall kin - dle ours. A-MEN.

Alternative tune, Azmon, No. 162

173

MERCY. 7. 7. 7. 7.

SAMUEL LONGFELLOW, 1819-1892

Arr. from LOUIS M. GOTTSCHALK, 1829-1869

1. Ho - ly Spir - it, Truth di - vine, Dawn up - on this soul of mine;
2. Ho - ly Spir - it, Love di - vine, Glow with - in this heart of mine;
3. Ho - ly Spir - it, Power di - vine, Fill and nerve this will of mine;
4. Ho - ly Spir - it, Right di - vine, King with - in my con-science reign;

Word of God, and in - ward Light, Wake my spir - it, clear my sight.
Kin - dle ev - ery high de - sire; Per - ish self in Thy pure fire.
By Thee may I strong-ly live, Brave-ly bear, and no - bly strive.
Be my Lord, and I shall be Firm - ly bound, for ev - er free. A - MEN.

The Holy Spirit

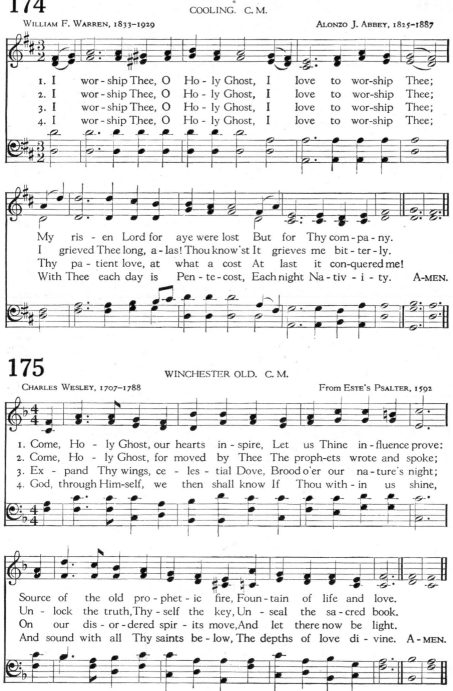

174

COOLING. C. M.

WILLIAM F. WARREN, 1833–1929

ALONZO J. ABBEY, 1825–1887

1. I wor-ship Thee, O Ho-ly Ghost, I love to wor-ship Thee;
2. I wor-ship Thee, O Ho-ly Ghost, I love to wor-ship Thee;
3. I wor-ship Thee, O Ho-ly Ghost, I love to wor-ship Thee;
4. I wor-ship Thee, O Ho-ly Ghost, I love to wor-ship Thee;

My ris-en Lord for aye were lost But for Thy com-pa-ny.
I grieved Thee long, a-las! Thou know'st It grieves me bit-ter-ly.
Thy pa-tient love, at what a cost At last it con-quered me!
With Thee each day is Pen-te-cost, Each night Na-tiv-i-ty. A-MEN.

175

WINCHESTER OLD. C. M.

CHARLES WESLEY, 1707–1788

From ESTE'S PSALTER, 1592

1. Come, Ho-ly Ghost, our hearts in-spire, Let us Thine in-fluence prove:
2. Come, Ho-ly Ghost, for moved by Thee The proph-ets wrote and spoke;
3. Ex-pand Thy wings, ce-les-tial Dove, Brood o'er our na-ture's night;
4. God, through Him-self, we then shall know If Thou with-in us shine,

Source of the old pro-phet-ic fire, Foun-tain of life and love.
Un-lock the truth, Thy-self the key, Un-seal the sa-cred book.
On our dis-or-dered spir-its move, And let there now be light.
And sound with all Thy saints be-low, The depths of love di-vine. A-MEN.

The Holy Spirit

176

OLIVET. 6. 6. 4. 6. 6. 4.

Founded on VENI SANCTE SPIRITUS, 12th or 13th century
RAY PALMER, 1808–1887

LOWELL MASON, 1792–1872

1. Come, Ho - ly Ghost, in love, Shed on us from a - bove
2. Come, ten - derest Friend, and best, Our most de - light - ful Guest,
3. Come, Light se - rene, and still Our in - most bo - soms fill,
4. Come, all the faith - ful bless; Let all who Christ con - fess

Thine own bright ray! Di - vine - ly good Thou art; Thy sa - cred
With sooth - ing power: Rest, which the wea - ry know; Shade, 'mid the
Dwell in each breast; We know no dawn but Thine, Send forth Thy
His praise em - ploy; Give vir - tue's rich re - ward, Vic - to - rious

gifts im - part To glad - den each sad heart: O come to - day!
noon - tide glow; Peace, when deep griefs o'er - flow: Cheer us, this hour!
beams di - vine, On our dark souls to shine, And make us blest!
death ac - cord, And, with our glo - rious Lord, E - ter - nal joy! A - MEN.

177

ST. CUTHBERT. 8. 6. 8. 4.

HARRIET AUBER, 1773–1862

JOHN B. DYKES, 1823–1876

1. Our blest Re - deem - er, ere He breathed His ten - der last fare - well,
2. He came in tongues of liv - ing flame, To teach, con - vince, sub - due;
3. He comes sweet in - fluence to im - part, A gra - cious, will - ing Guest,
4. And His that gen - tle voice we hear, Soft as the breath of even,

The Holy Spirit

A Guide, a Com-fort-er, be-queathed With us to dwell.
All-power-ful as the wind He came, As view-less, too.
While He can find one hum-ble heart Where-in to rest.
That checks each fault, that calms each fear, And speaks of heaven. A-MEN.

5 And every virtue we possess,
    And every victory won,
  And every thought of holiness
    Are His alone.

6 Spirit of purity and grace,
    Our weakness, pitying, see:
  O make our hearts Thy dwelling place,
    And worthier Thee!

178

MARYTON. L. M.

EARL MARLATT, 1892–   H. PERCY SMITH, 1825-1898

1. Spir - it of Life, in this new dawn, Give us the
2. Spir - it Cre - a - tive, give us light, Lift - ing the
3. Spir - it Re - deem - ing, give us grace When cru - ci -
4. Spir - it Con - sol - ing, let us find Thy hand when
5. Spir - it of Love, at eve - ning time, When wea - ry

faith that fol - lows on, Let - ting Thine all - per -
rav - eled mists of night; Touch Thou our dust with
fied to seek Thy face; To read for - give - ness
sor - rows leave us blind; In the gray val - ley
feet re - fuse to climb, Give us Thy vi - sion,

vad - ing power Ful - fill the dream of this high hour.
spir - it - hand And make us souls that un - der - stand.
in Thine eyes To - day with Thee in Par - a - dise.
let us hear Thy si - lent voice: "Lo, I am near."
eyes that see, Be - yond the dark, the dawn and Thee. A - MEN.

Words used by permission of Earl Marlatt

The Holy Spirit

179

MORECAMBE. 10. 10. 10. 10.

GEORGE CROLY. 1780-1860   FREDERICK C. ATKINSON, 1841-1897

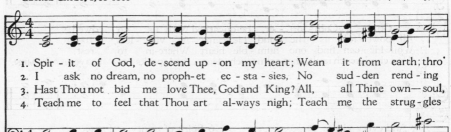

1. Spir - it of God, de - scend up - on my heart; Wean it from earth; thro'
2. I ask no dream, no proph-et ec - sta - sies, No sud - den rend - ing
3. Hast Thou not bid me love Thee, God and King? All, all Thine own—soul,
4. Teach me to feel that Thou art al-ways nigh; Teach me the strug - gles

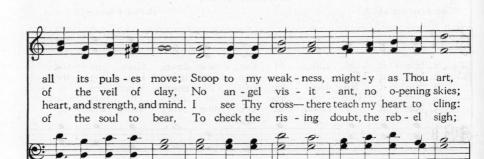

all its puls - es move; Stoop to my weak - ness, might -y as Thou art,
of the veil of clay, No an - gel vis - it - ant, no o-pening skies;
heart, and strength, and mind. I see Thy cross—there teach my heart to cling:
of the soul to bear, To check the ris - ing doubt, the reb - el sigh;

And make me love Thee as I ought to love.
But take the dim - ness of my soul a - way.
O let me seek Thee, and O let me find!
Teach me the pa - tience of un - an - swered prayer. A -MEN.

5 Teach me to love Thee as Thine angels love,
    One holy passion filling all my frame;
    The kindling of the heaven-descended Dove,
    My heart an altar, and Thy love the flame.

The Holy Spirit

180

TRENTHAM. S. M.

Edwin Hatch, 1835-1889

Robert Jackson, 1842-1914

1. Breathe on me, Breath of God, Fill me with life a-new, That I may
2. Breathe on me, Breath of God, Un-til my heart is pure, Un-til with
3. Breathe on me, Breath of God, Till I am whol-ly Thine, Till all this
4. Breathe on me, Breath of God, So shall I nev-er die, But live with

love what Thou dost love, And do what Thou wouldst do.
Thee I will one will, To do and to en-dure.
earth-ly part of me Glows with Thy fire di-vine.
Thee the per-fect life Of Thine e-ter-ni-ty. A-MEN.

Words used by permission of Miss B. Hatch and the Oxford University Press
Music used by permission of Mrs. Ethel Taylor

181

GARDEN CITY. S. M.

Edward R. Sill, 1841-1887

Horatio W. Parker, 1863-1919

1. Send down Thy truth, O God: Too long the shad-ows frown;
2. Send down Thy spir-it free, Till wil-der-ness and town
3. Send down Thy love, Thy life, Our less-er lives to crown,
4. Send down Thy peace, O Lord: Earth's bit-ter voic-es drown

Too long the dark-ened way we've trod: Thy truth, O Lord, send down.
One tem-ple for Thy wor-ship be: Thy spir-it, O send down.
And cleanse them of their hate and strife: Thy liv-ing love send down.
In one deep o-cean of ac-cord: Thy peace, O God, send down. A - MEN.

Music used by permission of Mrs. H. W. Parker
Alternative tune, St. Thomas, No. 227

The Holy Spirit

182

ST. LEONARD. C. M. D.

HENRY H. TWEEDY, 1868–

HENRY HILES, 1826–1904

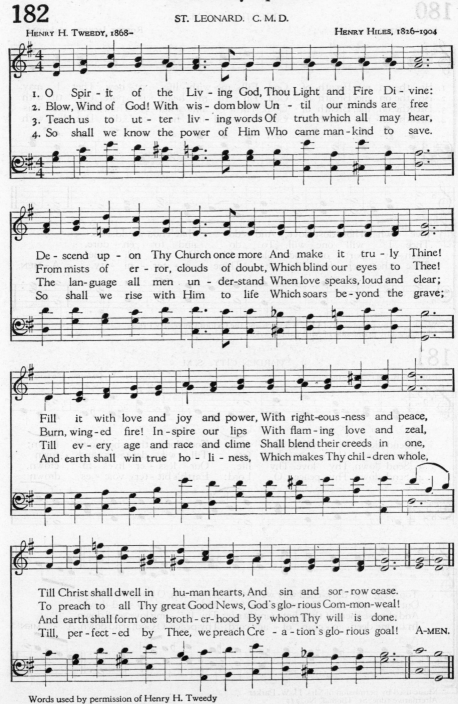

1. O Spir-it of the Liv-ing God, Thou Light and Fire Di-vine:
2. Blow, Wind of God! With wis-dom blow Un-til our minds are free
3. Teach us to ut-ter liv-ing words Of truth which all may hear,
4. So shall we know the power of Him Who came man-kind to save.

De-scend up-on Thy Church once more And make it tru-ly Thine!
From mists of er-ror, clouds of doubt, Which blind our eyes to Thee!
The lan-guage all men un-der-stand When love speaks, loud and clear;
So shall we rise with Him to life Which soars be-yond the grave;

Fill it with love and joy and power, With right-eous-ness and peace,
Burn, wing-ed fire! In-spire our lips With flam-ing love and zeal,
Till ev-ery age and race and clime Shall blend their creeds in one,
And earth shall win true ho-li-ness, Which makes Thy chil-dren whole,

Till Christ shall dwell in hu-man hearts, And sin and sor-row cease.
To preach to all Thy great Good News, God's glo-rious Com-mon-weal!
And earth shall form one broth-er-hood By whom Thy will is done.
Till, per-fect-ed by Thee, we preach Cre-a-tion's glo-rious goal! A-MEN.

The Holy Spirit

BEALOTH. S. M. D.

CHARLES WESLEY, 1707–1788

From MASON'S SACRED HARP, 1843

183

1. Spir - it of faith, come down, Re - veal the things of God;
2. No man can tru - ly say That Je - sus is the Lord,
3. O that the world might know The all - a - ton - ing Lamb!

And make to us the God - head known, And wit - ness with the blood.
Un - less Thou take the veil a - way, And breathe the Liv - ing Word.
Spir - it of faith, de - scend and show The vir - tue of His Name.

'Tis Thine the blood to ap - ply And give us eyes to see,
Then, on - ly then, we feel Our in - terest in His blood,
The grace which all may find, The sav - ing power, im - part;

Who did for ev - ery sin - ner die, Hath sure - ly died for me.
And cry, with joy un-speak - a - ble, "Thou art my Lord, my God!"
And tes - ti - fy to all man-kind, And speak in ev - ery heart. A-MEN.

The Gospel

STOCKTON. 8. 6. 8. 6. with Refrain

JOHN H. STOCKTON, 1813–1877

JOHN H. STOCKTON, 1813–1877

1. Come, ev - ery soul by sin op-pressed, There's mer - cy with the Lord,
2. For Je - sus shed His pre - cious blood Rich bless -ings to be - stow;
3. Yes, Je - sus is the Truth, the Way, That leads you in - to rest;
4. Come then, and join this ho - ly band, And on to glo - ry go,

And He will sure - ly give you rest, By trust - ing in His word.
Plunge now in - to the crim - son flood That wash - es white as snow.
Be - lieve in Him with - out de - lay, And you are ful - ly blest.
To dwell in that ce - les - tial land, Where joys im - mor - tal flow.

REFRAIN

On - ly trust Him, on - ly trust Him, On - ly trust Him now;

He will save you, He will save you, He will save you now. A-MEN.

The Call

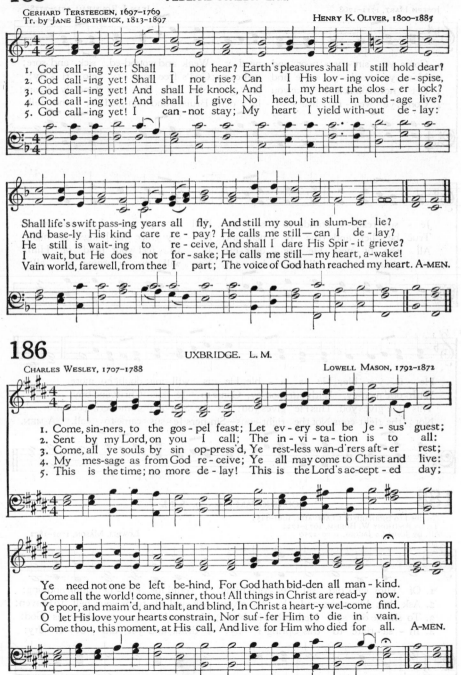

185

FEDERAL STREET. L. M.

GERHARD TERSTEEGEN, 1697–1769
Tr. by JANE BORTHWICK, 1813–1897

HENRY K. OLIVER, 1800–1885

1. God call-ing yet! Shall I not hear? Earth's pleasures shall I still hold dear?
2. God call-ing yet! Shall I not rise? Can I His lov-ing voice de-spise,
3. God call-ing yet! And shall He knock, And I my heart the clos-er lock?
4. God call-ing yet! And shall I give No heed, but still in bond-age live?
5. God call-ing yet! I can-not stay; My heart I yield with-out de-lay:

Shall life's swift pass-ing years all fly, And still my soul in slum-ber lie?
And base-ly His kind care re-pay? He calls me still—can I de-lay?
He still is wait-ing to re-ceive, And shall I dare His Spir-it grieve?
I wait, but He does not for-sake; He calls me still—my heart, a-wake!
Vain world, farewell, from thee I part; The voice of God hath reached my heart. A-MEN.

186

UXBRIDGE. L. M.

CHARLES WESLEY, 1707–1788

LOWELL MASON, 1792–1872

1. Come, sin-ners, to the gos-pel feast; Let ev-ery soul be Je-sus' guest;
2. Sent by my Lord, on you I call; The in-vi-ta-tion is to all;
3. Come, all ye souls by sin op-press'd, Ye rest-less wan-d'rers aft-er rest;
4. My mes-sage as from God re-ceive; Ye all may come to Christ and live:
5. This is the time; no more de-lay! This is the Lord's ac-cept-ed day;

Ye need not one be left be-hind, For God hath bid-den all man-kind.
Come all the world! come, sinner, thou! All things in Christ are read-y now.
Ye poor, and maim'd, and halt, and blind, In Christ a heart-y wel-come find.
O let His love your hearts constrain, Nor suf-fer Him to die in vain.
Come thou, this moment, at His call, And live for Him who died for all. A-MEN.

The Gospel

187

GREENVILLE. 8. 7. 8. 7. 8. 7.

JOSEPH HART, 1712–1768

JEAN J. ROUSSEAU, 1712–1778

1. Come, ye sin-ners, poor and need-y, Weak and wound-ed, sick and sore;
2. Now, ye need-y, come and wel-come; God's free boun-ty glo-ri-fy;
3. Let not con-science make you lin-ger, Nor of fit-ness fond-ly dream;
4. Come, ye wea-ry, hea-vy-la-den, Bruised and man-gled by the fall;

Je-sus read-y stands to save you, Full of pit-y, love and power:
True be-lief and true re-pent-ance, Ev-ery grace that brings you nigh,
All the fit-ness He re-quir-eth Is to feel your need of Him:
If you tar-ry till you're bet-ter, You will nev-er come at all;

He is a-ble, He is a-ble, He is will-ing: doubt no more.
With-out mon-ey, With-out mon-ey, Come to Je-sus Christ and buy.
This He gives you, This He gives you; 'Tis the Spir-it's glim-mering beam.
Not the right-eous, Not the right-eous—Sin-ners Je-sus came to call. A-MEN.

188

ROCKINGHAM (Mason). L. M.

Ascribed to BERNARD of CLAIRVAUX, 1091–1153
Tr. by ANTHONY W. BOEHM, 1673–1722
Alt. by JOHN C. JACOBI, 1670–1750

LOWELL MASON, 1792–1872

1. Of Him who did sal-va-tion bring, I could for ev-er think and sing:
2. Ask but His grace, and lo, 'tis given! Ask, and He turns your hell to heaven:
3. To shame our sins He blushed in blood; He closed His eyes to show us God:
4. In-sa-tiate to this Spring I fly; I drink, and yet am ev-er dry:

The Call

A - rise, ye need-y, He'll re-lieve; A-rise, ye guilt-y, He'll for-give.
Though sin and sor-row wound my soul, Je-sus, Thy balm will make it whole.
Let all the world fall down and know That none but God such love can show.
Ah! who a-gainst Thy charms is proof? Ah! who that loves, can love e-nough? A-MEN.

189

LENOX. 6. 6. 6. 6. 8. 8.

CHARLES WESLEY, 1707-1788

LEWIS EDSON, 1748-1820

1. Blow ye the trumpet, blow! The glad-ly sol-emn sound; Let all the na-tions know,
2. Je - sus, our great High Priest, Hath full atonement made; Ye wea-ry spir - its, rest;
3. The gos-pel trumpet hear, The news of heav'nly grace; And, saved from earth, appear

To earth's re - mot - est bound, The year of ju - bi - lee is come!
Ye mourn-ful souls, be glad: The year of ju - bi - lee is come!
Be - fore your Sav - iour's face: The year of ju - bi - lee is come!

The year of ju - bi - lee is come! Re - turn, ye ransomed sin - ners, home.
The year of ju - bi - lee is come! Re - turn, ye ransomed sin - ners, home.
The year of ju - bi - lee is come! Re - turn, ye ransomed sin - ners, home. A-MEN.

The Gospel

190

INVITATION. 6. 6. 6. 6. D.

John M. Wigner, 1844–

Frederick C. Maker, 1844-1927

1. Come to the Sav - iour now, He gen - tly call - eth thee;
2. Come to the Sav - iour now, Ye who have wan - dered far;
3. Come to the Sav - iour, all, What-e'er your bur - dens be;

In true re - pent - ance bow, Be - fore Him bend the knee;
Re - new your sol - emn vow, For His by right you are;
Hear now His lov - ing call, "Cast all your care on me."

He wait - eth to be - stow Sal - va - tion, peace, and love,
Come, like poor wan - dering sheep Re - turn - ing to His fold;
Come, and for ev - ery grief In Je - sus you will find

True joy on earth be - low, A home in heaven a - bove.
His arm will safe - ly keep, His love will ne'er grow cold.
A sure and safe re - lief, A lov - ing Friend and kind. A-MEN.

The Call

191

HOLLINGSIDE. 7. 7. 7. 7. D.

CHARLES WESLEY, 1707–1788

JOHN B. DYKES, 1823–1876

1. Sin - ners, turn: why will ye die? God, your Ma - ker, asks you why;
2. Sin - ners, turn: why will ye die? God, your Sav - iour, asks you why;
3. Sin - ners, turn: why will ye die? God, the Spir - it, asks you why;

God, who did your be - ing give, Made you with Him - self to live;
God, who did your souls re - trieve, Died Him - self, that ye might live.
He, who all your lives hath strove, Wooed you to em - brace His love;

He the fa - tal cause de - mands, Asks the work of His own hands:
Will ye let Him die in vain? Cru - ci - fy your Lord a - gain?
Will ye not His grace re - ceive? Will ye still re - fuse to live?

Why, ye thank-less crea-tures, why Will ye cross His love, and die?
Why, ye ran-somed sin - ners, why Will ye slight His grace, and die?
Why, ye long-sought sin - ners, why Will ye grieve your God, and die? A - MEN.

The Gospel

192

ST. BEES. 7. 7. 7. 7.

ANNA L. BARBAULD, 1743–1825

JOHN B. DYKES, 1823–1876

1. Come, said Jesus' sacred voice, Come, and make my path your choice;
2. Thou who, house-less, sole, for-lorn, Long hast borne the proud world's scorn,
3. Ye who, tossed on beds of pain, Seek for ease, but seek in vain;
4. Hith-er come, for here is found Balm that flows for ev-ery wound,

I will guide you to your home; Wea-ry pil-grim, hith-er come.
Long hast roamed the bar-ren waste, Wea-ry pil-grim, hith-er haste.
Ye, by fierc-er an-guish torn, In re-morse for guilt who mourn;
Peace that ev-er shall en-dure, Rest e-ter-nal, sa-cred, sure. A-MEN.

193

STEPHANOS. 8. 5. 8. 3.

From the Greek, 8th century
JOHN M. NEALE, 1818–1866

HENRY W. BAKER, 1821–1877

1. Art thou wea-ry, art thou trou-bled, Art thou sore dis-tressed?
2. Hath He marks to lead me to Him, If He be my guide?
3. Hath He di-a-dem, as mon-arch, That His brow a-dorns?
4. If I find Him, if I fol-low, What His guer-don here?
5. If I still hold close-ly to Him, What hath He at last?

"Come to me," saith One, "and, com-ing, Be at rest."
"In His feet and hands are wound-prints, And His side."
"Yea, a crown, in ver-y sure-ty, But of thorns."
"Many a sor-row, many a la-bor, Many a tear."
"Sor-row van-quished, la-bor end-ed, Jor-dan passed." A-MEN.

6 If I ask Him to receive me,
   Will He say me nay?
  " Not till earth and not till heaven
   Pass away."

7 Finding, following, keeping, struggling,
   Is He sure to bless?
  "Saints, apostles, prophets, martyrs,
   Answer, 'Yes.'"

Alternative tune, Bullinger, No. 223

The Call

194

MEIRIONYDD. 7. 6. 7. 6. D.

WILLIAM C. DIX, 1837–1898

Welsh hymn melody

1. "Come un-to me, ye wea-ry, And I will give you rest."
2. "Come un-to me, ye faint-ing, And I will give you life."
3. "And who-so-ev-er com-eth, I will not cast him out."

O bless-ed voice of Je-sus, Which comes to hearts op-pressed!
O cheer-ing voice of Je-sus, Which comes to aid our strife!
O wel-come voice of Je-sus, Which drives a-way our doubt!

It tells of ben-e-dic-tion, Of par-don, grace, and peace,
The foe is stern and ea-ger, The fight is fierce and long;
Which calls us, ver-y sin-ners, Un-wor-thy though we be

Of joy that hath no end-ing, Of love which can-not cease.
But Thou hast made us might-y, And strong-er than the strong.
Of love so free and bound-less, To come, dear Lord, to Thee! A-MEN.

The Gospel

195

WOODWORTH. L. M.

WILLIAM B. COLLYER, 1782–1854

WILLIAM B. BRADBURY, 1816–1868

1. Re - turn, O wan - der - er, re - turn, And seek an in-jured Fa-ther's face;
2. Re - turn, O wan - der - er, re - turn, And seek a Fa-ther's melt-ing heart;
3. Re - turn, O wan - der - er, re - turn; Thy Sav-iour bids thy spir - it live;
4. Re - turn, O wan - der - er, re - turn, And wipe a - way the fall - ing tear;

Those warm de-sires that in thee burn Were kindled by re-claim-ing grace.
His pit-ying eyes thy grief dis-cern, His hand shall heal thine in-ward smart.
Go to His bleed-ing feet, and learn How free-ly Je - sus can for - give.
'Tis God who says, "No longer mourn;" 'Tis mercy's voice invites thee near. A-MEN.

196

BERA. L. M.

JOSEPH GRIGG, c. 1720–1768

JOHN E. GOULD, 1822–1875

1. Be - hold! A Stran-ger at the door! He gen - tly knocks, has knocked be-fore;
2. O love - ly at - ti - tude! He stands With melt-ing heart and la - den hands;
3. But will He prove a Friend in - deed? He will: the ver - y Friend you need:
4. Rise, touched with grat-i - tude di - vine; Turn out His en - e - my and thine,

Has wait-ed long, is wait-ing still: You treat no oth - er friend so ill.
O match-less kind-ness! and He shows This match-less kind-ness to His foes.
The Friend of sin-ners — yes, 'tis He, With gar-ments dyed on Cal-va - ry.
That soul-de-stroy-ing mon-ster, sin, And let the heaven-ly Stran-ger in. A-MEN.

The Call

197

ST. HILDA. 7. 6. 7. 6. D.

William W. How, 1823–1897

Justin H. Knecht, 1752–1817
Edward Husband, 1843–1908

1. O Je - sus, Thou art stand - ing Out - side the fast-closed door,
2. O Je - sus, Thou art knock - ing: And lo, that hand is scarred,
3. O Je - sus, Thou art plead - ing In ac - cents meek and low,

In low - ly pa - tience wait - ing To pass the thresh - old o'er:
And thorns Thy brow en - cir - cle, And tears Thy face have marred.
"I died for you, my chil - dren, And will ye treat me so?"

Shame on us, Chris - tian breth - ren, His name and sign who bear;
O love that pass - eth know - ledge, So pa - tient - ly to wait!
O Lord, with shame and sor - row We o - pen now the door;

O shame, thrice shame up - on us, To keep Him stand - ing there!
O sin that hath no e - qual, So fast to bar the gate!
Dear Sav - iour, en - ter, en - ter, And leave us nev - er - more. A-MEN.

The Gospel

WOODWORTH. L.M.

198

Charlotte Elliott, 1789–1871

William B. Bradbury, 1816–1868

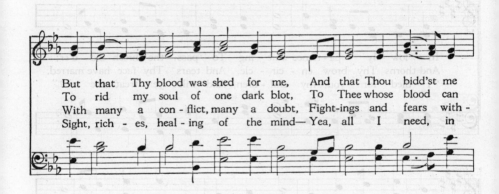

1. Just as I am, with - out one plea,
2. Just as I am, and wait - ing not
3. Just as I am, though tossed a - bout
4. Just as I am, poor, wretch - ed, blind;

But that Thy blood was shed for me, And that Thou bidd'st me
To rid my soul of one dark blot, To Thee whose blood can
With many a con - flict, many a doubt, Fight-ings and fears with -
Sight, rich - es, heal - ing of the mind— Yea, all I need, in

come to Thee, O Lamb of God, I come, I come!
cleanse each spot, O Lamb of God, I come, I come!
in, with - out, O Lamb of God, I come, I come!
Thee to find, O Lamb of God, I come, I come! A - men.

5 Just as I am! Thou wilt receive,
Wilt welcome, pardon, cleanse, relieve;
Because Thy promise I believe,
O Lamb of God, I come!

6 Just as I am! Thy love unknown,
Hath broken every barrier down;
Now, to be Thine, yea, Thine alone,
O Lamb of God, I come!

Repentance

DUANE STREET. L. M. D.

JOHN CENNICK, 1718-1755

GEORGE COLES, 1792-1858

1. Je - sus, my all, to heaven is gone, He whom I fix my hopes up - on;
2. This is the way I long have sought, And mourned be-cause I found it not;
3. Lo! glad I come; and Thou, blest Lamb, Shalt take me to Thee, as I am;

His track I see, and I'll pur - sue The nar - row way, till Him I view.
My grief a bur - den long has been, Be - cause I was not saved from sin.
Noth - ing but sin have I to give: Noth - ing but love shall I re - ceive.

The way the ho - ly proph-ets went, The road that leads from ban -ish - ment,
The more I strove a -gainst its power, I felt its weight and guilt the more;
Then will I tell to sin-ners 'round What a dear Sav - iour I have found;

The King's high-way of ho - li - ness, I'll go, for all His paths are peace.
Till late I heard my Sav-iour say, "Come hith-er, soul, I am the way."
I'll point to Thy re-deem-ing blood, And say, "Be-hold the way to God." A-MEN.

The Gospel

200

SEYMOUR. 7. 7. 7. 7.

CHARLES WESLEY, 1707–1788   CARL M. VON WEBER, 1786–1826

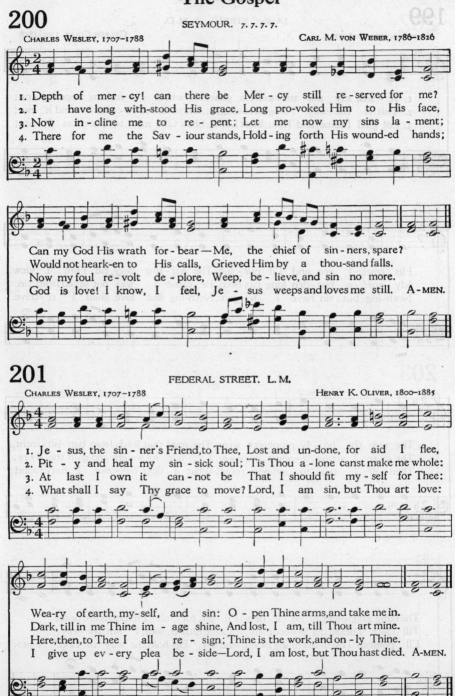

1. Depth of mer - cy! can there be Mer - cy still re - served for me?
2. I have long with-stood His grace, Long pro-voked Him to His face,
3. Now in - cline me to re - pent; Let me now my sins la - ment;
4. There for me the Sav - iour stands, Hold-ing forth His wound-ed hands;

Can my God His wrath for - bear — Me, the chief of sin - ners, spare?
Would not heark-en to His calls, Grieved Him by a thou-sand falls.
Now my foul re - volt de - plore, Weep, be - lieve, and sin no more.
God is love! I know, I feel, Je - sus weeps and loves me still. A-MEN.

201

FEDERAL STREET. L. M.

CHARLES WESLEY, 1707–1788   HENRY K. OLIVER, 1800–1885

1. Je - sus, the sin - ner's Friend, to Thee, Lost and un-done, for aid I flee,
2. Pit - y and heal my sin - sick soul; 'Tis Thou a - lone canst make me whole:
3. At last I own it can - not be That I should fit my - self for Thee;
4. What shall I say Thy grace to move? Lord, I am sin, but Thou art love:

Wea-ry of earth, my-self, and sin: O - pen Thine arms, and take me in.
Dark, till in me Thine im - age shine, And lost, I am, till Thou art mine.
Here, then, to Thee I all re - sign; Thine is the work, and on - ly Thine.
I give up ev - ery plea be - side—Lord, I am lost, but Thou hast died. A-MEN.

Faith

202

NAOMI. C. M.

CHARLES WESLEY, 1707–1788

HANS G. NÄGELI, 1773–1836

1. Fa - ther, I stretch my hands to Thee; No oth - er help I know:
2. What did Thine on - ly Son en - dure, Be - fore I drew my breath!
3. Sure - ly Thou canst not let me die; O speak, and I shall live;
4. Au - thor of faith! to Thee I lift My wea - ry, long - ing eyes:

If Thou with-draw Thy - self from me, Ah! whith - er shall I go?
What pain, what la - bor, to se - cure My soul from end - less death!
And here I will un - wea-ried lie, Till Thou Thy Spir - it give.
O let me now re - ceive that gift! My soul with - out it dies. A-MEN.

203

EVANSTON. C. M.

CHARLES WESLEY, 1707–1788

KARL P. HARRINGTON, 1861–

1. Fa - ther of Je - sus Christ, my Lord, My Sav - iour and my Head,
2. In hope, a - gainst all hu - man hope, Self - des - perate, I be - lieve;
3. To Thee the glo - ry of Thy power And faith - ful - ness I give;
4. Faith, might-y faith, the prom - ise sees, And looks to that a - lone;

I trust in Thee, whose powerful word Hath raised Him from the dead.
Thy quickening word shall raise me up, Thou shalt Thy Spir - it give.
I shall in Christ, at that glad hour, And Christ in me shall live.
Laughs at im - pos - si - bil - i - ties, And cries, "It shall be done!" A-MEN.

Music copyright by Karl P. Harrington. Renewal, 1933

The Gospel

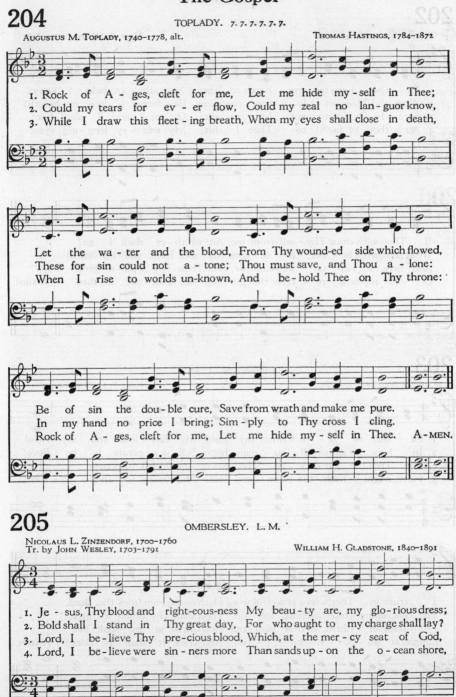

204

TOPLADY. 7. 7. 7. 7. 7. 7.

Augustus M. Toplady, 1740–1778, alt.

Thomas Hastings, 1784–1872

1. Rock of A - ges, cleft for me, Let me hide my-self in Thee;
2. Could my tears for ev - er flow, Could my zeal no lan-guor know,
3. While I draw this fleet-ing breath, When my eyes shall close in death,

Let the wa - ter and the blood, From Thy wound-ed side which flowed,
These for sin could not a - tone; Thou must save, and Thou a - lone:
When I rise to worlds un-known, And be-hold Thee on Thy throne:

Be of sin the dou - ble cure, Save from wrath and make me pure.
In my hand no price I bring; Sim - ply to Thy cross I cling.
Rock of A - ges, cleft for me, Let me hide my - self in Thee. A-men.

205

OMBERSLEY. L. M.

Nicolaus L. Zinzendorf, 1700–1760
Tr. by John Wesley, 1703–1791

William H. Gladstone, 1840–1891

1. Je - sus, Thy blood and right-eous-ness My beau - ty are, my glo-rious dress;
2. Bold shall I stand in Thy great day, For who aught to my charge shall lay?
3. Lord, I be-lieve Thy pre-cious blood, Which, at the mer - cy seat of God,
4. Lord, I be-lieve were sin - ners more Than sands up - on the o - cean shore,

Faith

'Midst flam-ing worlds, in these ar-rayed, With joy shall I lift up my head.
Ful - ly ab-solved thro' these I am, From sin and fear, from guilt and shame.
For ev - er doth for sin-ners plead, For me, e'en for my soul, was shed.
Thou hast for all a ran-som paid, For all a full a - tone-ment made. A-MEN.

Alternative tune, Malvern, No. 24

206

KEBLE. L. M.

ALFRED TENNYSON, 1809–1892

JOHN B. DYKES, 1823–1876

1. Strong Son of God, im - mor - tal Love, Whom we, that have not
2. Thou wilt not leave us in the dust: Thou mad - est man, he
3. Thou seem - est hu - man and di - vine, The high - est, ho - liest
4. Our lit - tle sys - tems have their day; They have their day and

seen Thy face, By faith, and faith a - lone, em - brace,
knows not why, He thinks he was not made to die;
man - hood, Thou: Our wills are ours, we know not how;
cease to be: They are but bro - ken lights of Thee,

Be - liev - ing where we can - not prove;
And Thou hast made him: Thou art just.
Our wills are ours, to make them Thine.
And Thou, O Lord, art more than they. A - MEN.

The Gospel

207

GETHSEMANE. 7. 7. 7. 7. 7. 7.

Robert Grant, 1785–1838
Alt. by Thomas Cotterill, 1779–1823, and others

Richard Redhead, 1820–1901

1. By Thy birth and by Thy tears, By Thy hu-man griefs and fears, By Thy con-flict in the hour Of the sub-tle tempt-er's power: Sav-iour, look with pity-ing eye; Sav-iour, help me, or I die.

2. By Thy lone-ly hour of prayer, By Thy fear-ful con-flict there, By Thy cross and dy-ing cries, By Thy one great sac-ri-fice: Sav-iour, look with pity-ing eye; Sav-iour, help me, or I die.

3. By Thy tri-umph o'er the grave, By Thy power the lost to save, By Thy high, ma-jes-tic throne, By the em-pire all Thine own, Sav-iour, look with pity-ing eye; Sav-iour, help me, or I die. A-men.

Forgiveness

208

OLD 134TH (ST. MICHAEL). S. M.

CHARLES WESLEY, 1707-1788

Adapted from the GENEVAN PSALTER, 1551

1. How can a sin-ner know His sins on earth for-given?
2. What we have felt and seen With con-fi-dence we tell;
3. We who in Christ be-lieve That He for us hath died,
4. We by His spir-it prove And know the things of God,

How can my gra-cious Sav-iour show My name in-scribed in heaven?
And pub-lish to the sons of men The signs in-fal-li-ble.
We all His un-known peace re-ceive, And feel His blood ap-plied.
The things which free-ly of His love He hath on us be-stowed. A-MEN.

209

AMAZING GRACE. C. M.

JOHN NEWTON, 1725-1807

Early American melody

1. A-maz-ing grace! how sweet the sound, That saved a wretch like me!
2. 'Twas grace that taught my heart to fear, And grace my fears re-lieved;
3. Thro' man-y dan-gers, toils, and snares, I have al-read-y come;
4. The Lord has prom-ised good to me, His word my hope se-cures;

I once was lost, but now am found, Was blind, but now I see.
How pre-cious did that grace ap-pear The hour I first be-lieved!
'Tis grace hath bro't me safe thus far, And grace will lead me home.
He will my shield and por-tion be As long as life en-dures. A-MEN.

Alternative tune, Spohr, No. 363

The Gospel

VOX DILECTI. C. M. D.

(*First Tune*)

HORATIUS BONAR, 1808–1889

JOHN B. DYKES, 1823–1876

1. I heard the voice of Je-sus say, "Come un-to me and rest;
2. I heard the voice of Je-sus say, "Be-hold, I free-ly give
3. I heard the voice of Je-sus say, "I am this dark world's light;

Lay down, thou wea-ry one, lay down Thy head up-on my breast."
The liv-ing wa-ter; thirst-y one, Stoop down, and drink, and live."
Look un-to me, thy morn shall rise, And all thy day be bright."

I came to Je-sus as I was, Wea-ry and worn and sad;
I came to Je-sus, and I drank Of that life-giv-ing stream;
I looked to Je-sus, and I found In Him my star, my sun;

I found in Him a rest-ing place, And He has made me glad.
My thirst was quenched, my soul re-vived, And now I live in Him.
And in that light of life I'll walk, Till trav-el-ing days are done. A-MEN.

Forgiveness

210

TRUMAN. C. M. D.

(Second Tune)

Horatius Bonar, 1808–1889

Joseph P. Holbrook, 1822–1888

1. I heard the voice of Je - sus say, "Come un - to me and rest;
2. I heard the voice of Je - sus say, "Be - hold, I free - ly give
3. I heard the voice of Je - sus say, "I am this dark world's light;

Lay down, thou wea - ry one, lay down Thy head up - on my breast."
The liv - ing wa - ter; thirst - y one, Stoop down, and drink, and live."
Look un - to me, thy morn shall rise, And all thy day be bright."

I came to Je - sus as I was, Wea - ry and worn and sad;
I came to Je - sus, and I drank Of that life - giv - ing stream;
I looked to Je - sus, and I found In Him my star, my sun;

I found in Him a rest - ing place, And He has made me glad.
My thirst was quenched, my soul re - vived, And now I live in Him.
And in that light of life I'll walk, Till trav - eling days are done. A - MEN.

The Gospel

211

LENOX. 6. 6. 6. 6. 8. 8.

CHARLES WESLEY, 1707-1788

LEWIS EDSON, 1748-1820

1. A - rise, my soul, a - rise; Shake off thy guilt - y fears:
The bleed - ing Sac - ri - fice In my be - half ap - pears:
Be - fore the throne my Sure - ty stands, Be - fore the throne my
Sure - ty stands, My name is writ - ten on His hands.

2. He ev - er lives a - bove, For me to in - ter - cede;
His all - re - deem - ing love, His pre - cious blood, to plead;
His blood a - toned for all our race, His blood a - toned for
all our race, And sprin - kles now the throne of grace.

3. Five bleed - ing wounds He bears, Re - ceived on Cal - va - ry;
They pour ef - fect - ual prayers, They strong - ly plead for me:
"For - give him, O for - give," they cry, "For - give him, O for -
give," they cry, "Nor let that ran - somed sin - ner die!" A-MEN.

4 The Father hears Him pray,
   His dear anointed One;
He cannot turn away
   The presence of His Son;
His Spirit answers to the blood,
And tells me I am born of God.

5 My God is reconciled;
   His pardoning voice I hear;
He owns me for His child,
   I can no longer fear:
With confidence I now draw nigh,
And, "Father, Abba, Father," cry.

Forgiveness

212

HAPPY DAY. L. M. with Refrain

PHILIP DODDRIDGE, 1702–1751

Adapted from EDWARD F. RIMBAULT, 1816–1876

1. O hap-py day, that fixed my choice On Thee, my Sav-iour and my God!
2. O hap-py bond, that seals my vows To Him who mer-its all my love!
3. 'Tis done: the great trans-ac-tion's done! I am my Lord's, and He is mine;
4. Now rest, my long-di-vid-ed heart; Fixed on this bliss-ful cen-ter, rest:
5. High heav'n, that heard the sol-emn vow, That vow re-newed shall dai-ly hear,

Well may this glow-ing heart re-joice, And tell its rap-tures all a-broad.
Let cheer-ful an-thems fill His house, While to that sa-cred shrine I move.
He drew me and I fol-lowed on, Charmed to con-fess the Voice di-vine.
Here have I found a no-bler part, Here heavenly pleas-ures fill my breast.
Till in life's lat-est hour I bow, And bless in death a bond so dear.

REFRAIN

Hap-py day, hap-py day, When Je-sus washed my sins a-way:

He taught me how to watch and pray, And live re-joic-ing ev-er-y day.

Hap-py day, hap-py day, When Je-sus washed my sins a-way. A-MEN.

The Gospel

213

OLIVET. 6. 6. 4. 6. 6. 6. 4.

RAY PALMER, 1808-1887

LOWELL MASON, 1792-1872

1. My faith looks up to Thee, Thou Lamb of Cal - va - ry,
2. May Thy rich grace im - part Strength to my faint - ing heart,
3. While life's dark maze I tread, And griefs a - round me spread,
4. When ends life's tran - sient dream, When death's cold, sul - len stream

Sav - iour di - vine! Now hear me while I pray, Take all my
My zeal in - spire; As Thou hast died for me, O may my
Be Thou my guide; Bid dark - ness turn to day, Wipe sor - row's
Shall o'er me roll; Blest Sav - iour, then, in love, Fear and dis -

guilt a - way, O let me from this day Be whol - ly Thine!
love to Thee Pure, warm, and change-less be, A liv - ing fire!
tears a - way, Nor let me ev - er stray From Thee a - side.
trust re-move; O bear me safe a - bove, A ran-somed soul! A - MEN.

214

MOLLESON. C. M.

Anonymous. From the Latin
Tr. by EDWARD CASWALL, 1814-1878

DOUGLAS FLETCHER, 1884-

1. My God, I love Thee, not be-cause I hope for heaven there-by,
2. Thou, O my Je - sus, Thou didst me Up - on the cross em - brace;
3. Then why, O bless - ed Je - sus Christ, Should I not love Thee well?
4. Not with the hope of gain - ing aught, Not seek - ing a re - ward;
5. So would I love Thee, dear - est Lord, And in Thy praise will sing;

Consecration

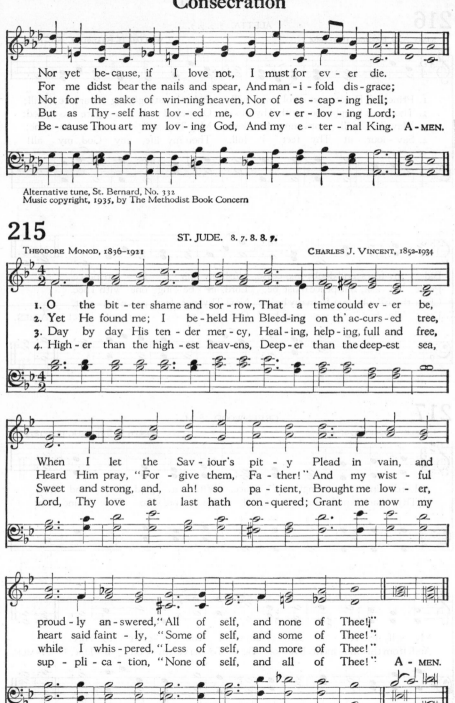

Nor yet be-cause, if I love not, I must for ev - er die.
For me didst bear the nails and spear, And man - i - fold dis-grace;
Not for the sake of win-ning heaven, Nor of es - cap - ing hell;
But as Thy-self hast lov - ed me, O ev - er - lov - ing Lord;
Be - cause Thou art my lov - ing God, And my e - ter - nal King. A - MEN.

Alternative tune, St. Bernard, No. 332
Music copyright, 1935, by The Methodist Book Concern

215

ST. JUDE. 8. 7. 8. 8. 7.

THEODORE MONOD, 1836-1921   CHARLES J. VINCENT, 1852-1934

1. O the bit - ter shame and sor - row, That a time could ev - er be,
2. Yet He found me; I be - held Him Bleed-ing on th' ac-curs - ed tree,
3. Day by day His ten - der mer - cy, Heal-ing, help - ing, full and free,
4. High - er than the high - est heav-ens, Deep - er than the deep-est sea,

When I let the Sav - iour's pit - y Plead in vain, and
Heard Him pray, "For - give them, Fa - ther!" And my wist - ful
Sweet and strong, and, ah! so pa - tient, Brought me low - er,
Lord, Thy love at last hath con - quered; Grant me now my

proud - ly an - swered, "All of self, and none of Thee!"
heart said faint - ly, "Some of self, and some of Thee!"
while I whis - pered, "Less of self, and more of Thee!"
sup - pli - ca - tion, "None of self, and all of Thee!" A - MEN.

The Gospel

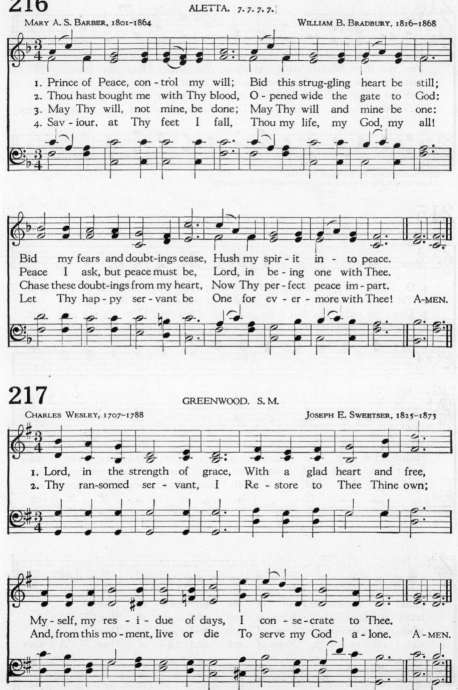

216

ALETTA. 7. 7. 7. 7.

Mary A. S. Barber, 1801–1864

William B. Bradbury, 1816–1868

1. Prince of Peace, con-trol my will; Bid this strug-gling heart be still;
2. Thou hast bought me with Thy blood, O-pened wide the gate to God:
3. May Thy will, not mine, be done; May Thy will and mine be one:
4. Sav-iour, at Thy feet I fall, Thou my life, my God, my all!

Bid my fears and doubt-ings cease, Hush my spir-it in-to peace.
Peace I ask, but peace must be, Lord, in be-ing one with Thee.
Chase these doubt-ings from my heart, Now Thy per-fect peace im-part.
Let Thy hap-py ser-vant be One for ev-er-more with Thee! A-MEN.

217

GREENWOOD. S. M.

Charles Wesley, 1707–1788

Joseph E. Sweetser, 1825–1873

1. Lord, in the strength of grace, With a glad heart and free,
2. Thy ran-somed ser-vant, I Re-store to Thee Thine own;

My-self, my res-i-due of days, I con-se-crate to Thee.
And, from this mo-ment, live or die To serve my God a-lone. A-MEN.

Consecration

218

ARIEL. 8. 8. 6. D.

CHARLES WESLEY, 1707–1788

Arr. by LOWELL MASON, 1792–1872

1. O Love divine, how sweet Thou art!
When shall I find my willing heart All taken up by Thee?
I thirst, I faint, I die to prove The greatness of redeeming love,
The love of Christ to me, The love of Christ to me.

2. Stronger His love than death or hell;
Its riches are unsearchable; The first-born sons of light
Desire in vain its depths to see; They cannot reach the mystery,
The length, the breadth, the height, The length, the breadth, the height.

3. God only knows the love of God;
O that it now were shed abroad In my poor stony heart!
For Thee I long, for love divine; This only portion, Lord, be mine;
Be mine this better part! Be mine this better part! A-MEN.

The Gospel

219

SOMETHING FOR JESUS. 6. 4. 6. 4. 6. 6. 6. 4.

SYLVANUS D. PHELPS, 1816-1895

ROBERT LOWRY, 1826-1899

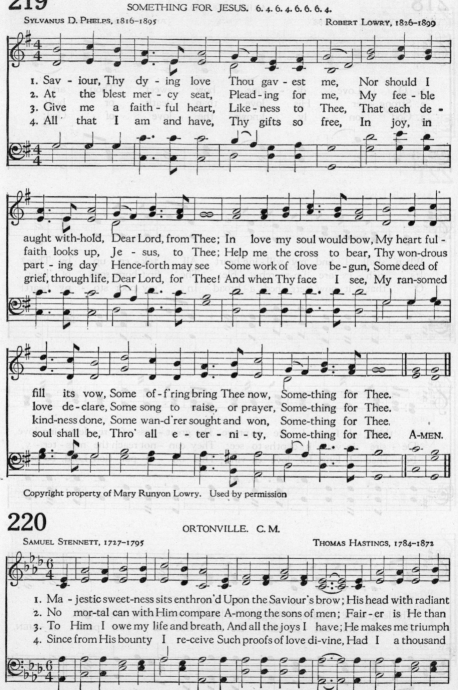

1. Sav - iour, Thy dy - ing love Thou gav - est me, Nor should I
2. At the blest mer - cy seat, Plead - ing for me, My fee - ble
3. Give me a faith - ful heart, Like - ness to Thee, That each de -
4. All that I am and have, Thy gifts so free, In joy, in

aught with-hold, Dear Lord, from Thee; In love my soul would bow, My heart ful -
faith looks up, Je - sus, to Thee; Help me the cross to bear, Thy won-drous
part - ing day Hence-forth may see Some work of love be - gun, Some deed of
grief, through life, Dear Lord, for Thee! And when Thy face I see, My ran-somed

fill its vow, Some of - f'ring bring Thee now, Some-thing for Thee.
love de - clare, Some song to raise, or prayer, Some-thing for Thee.
kind-ness done, Some wan-d'rer sought and won, Some-thing for Thee.
soul shall be, Thro' all e - ter - ni - ty, Some-thing for Thee. A-MEN.

Copyright property of Mary Runyon Lowry. Used by permission

220

ORTONVILLE. C. M.

SAMUEL STENNETT, 1727-1795

THOMAS HASTINGS, 1784-1872

1. Ma - jestic sweet-ness sits enthron'd Upon the Saviour's brow; His head with radiant
2. No mor-tal can with Him compare A-mong the sons of men; Fair - er is He than
3. To Him I owe my life and breath, And all the joys I have; He makes me triumph
4. Since from His bounty I re-ceive Such proofs of love di-vine, Had I a thousand

Consecration

glo-ries crown'd, His lips with grace o'er-flow, His lips with grace o'er-flow.
all the fair That fill the heav'n-ly train, That fill the heav'n-ly train.
o-ver death, He saves me from the grave, He saves me from the grave.
hearts to give, Lord, they should all be Thine, Lord, they should all be Thine. A-MEN.

Alternative tune, Abergele, No. 328

221

AMEN, JESUS HAN SKAL RAADE. 8. 7. 8. 7. 7. 7.

FRANCES R. HAVERGAL, 1836-1879   ANTON P. BERGGREEN, 1801-1880

1. Mas-ter, speak! Thy ser-vant hear-eth, Wait-ing for Thy gra-cious word,
2. Speak to me by name, O Mas-ter, Let me know it is to me;
3. Mas-ter, speak! Tho' least and low-est, Let me not un-heard de-part;
4. Mas-ter, speak! and make me read-y, When Thy voice is tru-ly heard,

Long-ing for Thy voice that cheer-eth; Mas-ter! let it now be heard.
Speak, that I may fol-low fast-er, With a step more firm and free,
Mas-ter, speak! For O, Thou know-est All the yearn-ing of my heart,
With o-be-dience glad and stead-y Still to fol-low ev-ery word.

I am lis-t'ning, Lord, for Thee: What hast Thou to say to me?
Where the Shep-herd leads the flock, In the sha-dow of the rock.
Know-est all its tru-est need: Speak! and make me blest in-deed.
I am lis-t'ning, Lord, for Thee: Mas-ter, speak! O, speak to me! A-MEN.

Alternative tune, Irby, No. 442

The Gospel

222

YOAKLEY. 8. 8. 8. 8. 8. 8.

Paul Gerhardt, 1607-1676
Tr. by John Wesley, 1703-1791, alt.

William Yoakley, 1820-?

1. Je - sus, Thy bound-less love to me No thought can reach, no tongue de - clare; O knit my thank - ful heart to Thee, And reign with - out a ri - val there! Thine whol - ly, Thine a - lone, I'd live, My - self to Thee en - tire - ly give.

2. O Love, how cheer - ing is Thy ray! All fear be - fore Thy pres - ence flies; Care, an - guish, sor - row, melt a - way, Wher - e'er Thy heal - ing beams a - rise: O Je - sus, noth - ing may I see, Noth - ing de - sire, or seek, but Thee!

3. In suf - fering be Thy love my peace; In weak - ness be Thy love my power; And when the storms of life shall cease, O Je - sus, in that sol - emn hour, In death as life be Thou my guide, And save me, who for me hast died. A - MEN.

Alternative tune, Old 113th (Lucerne), No. 513

Consecration

223

BULLINGER. 8. 5. 8. 3

Charles A. Dickinson, 1849–1906

Ethelbert W. Bullinger, 1837–1913

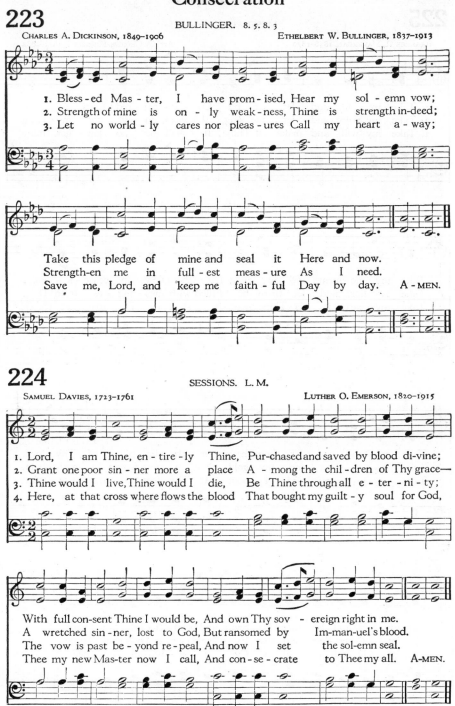

1. Bless-ed Mas - ter, I have prom-ised, Hear my sol - emn vow;
2. Strength of mine is on - ly weak-ness, Thine is strength in-deed;
3. Let no world - ly cares nor pleas-ures Call my heart a - way;

Take this pledge of mine and seal it Here and now.
Strength-en me in full - est meas - ure As I need.
Save me, Lord, and keep me faith - ful Day by day. A - MEN.

224

SESSIONS. L. M.

Samuel Davies, 1723–1761

Luther O. Emerson, 1820–1915

1. Lord, I am Thine, en - tire - ly Thine, Pur-chased and saved by blood di-vine;
2. Grant one poor sin - ner more a place A - mong the chil-dren of Thy grace—
3. Thine would I live, Thine would I die, Be Thine through all e - ter - ni - ty;
4. Here, at that cross where flows the blood That bought my guilt - y soul for God,

With full con-sent Thine I would be, And own Thy sov - ereign right in me.
A wretched sin-ner, lost to God, But ransomed by Im-man-uel's blood.
The vow is past be-yond re-peal, And now I set the sol-emn seal.
Thee my new Mas-ter now I call, And con-se - crate to Thee my all. A-MEN.

The Gospel

225

MESSIAH. 7. 7. 7. 7. D.

Frances R. Havergal, 1836-1879

Louis J. F. Herold, 1791-1833
Arr. by George Kingsley, 1811-1884

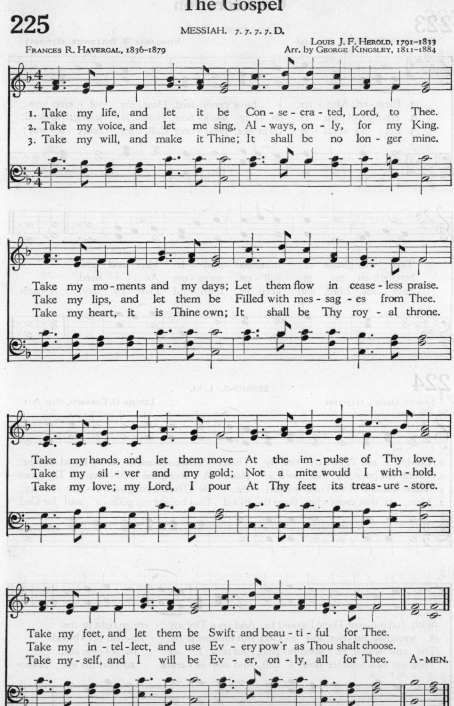

1. Take my life, and let it be Con - se - cra - ted, Lord, to Thee.
2. Take my voice, and let me sing, Al - ways, on - ly, for my King.
3. Take my will, and make it Thine; It shall be no lon - ger mine.

Take my mo - ments and my days; Let them flow in cease - less praise.
Take my lips, and let them be Filled with mes - sag - es from Thee.
Take my heart, it is Thine own; It shall be Thy roy - al throne.

Take my hands, and let them move At the im - pulse of Thy love.
Take my sil - ver and my gold; Not a mite would I with - hold.
Take my love; my Lord, I pour At Thy feet its treas - ure - store.

Take my feet, and let them be Swift and beau - ti - ful for Thee.
Take my in - tel - lect, and use Ev - ery pow'r as Thou shalt choose.
Take my - self, and I will be Ev - er, on - ly, all for Thee. A - MEN.

Consecration

226

ANGEL'S STORY. 7. 6. 7. 6. D.

JOHN E. BODE, 1816–1874   ARTHUR H. MANN, 1850–1929

1. O Je - sus, I have prom - ised To serve Thee to the end;
2. O let me feel Thee near me! The world is ev - er near;
3. O let me hear Thee speak - ing, In ac - cents clear and still,
4. O Je - sus, Thou hast prom - ised To all who fol - low Thee

Be Thou for ev - er near me, My Mas - ter and my Friend:
I see the sights that daz - zle, The tempt - ing sounds I hear;
A - bove the storms of pas - sion, The mur - murs of self - will;
That where Thou art in glo - ry There shall Thy ser - vant be;

I shall not fear the bat - tle If Thou art by my side,
My foes are ev - er near me, A - round me and with - in;
O speak to re - as - sure me, To has - ten or con - trol;
And, Je - sus, I have prom - ised To serve Thee to the end;

Nor wan - der from the path - way If Thou wilt be my guide.
But, Je - sus, draw Thou near - er, And shield my soul from sin.
O speak, and make me lis - ten, Thou guard - ian of my soul.
O give me grace to fol - low, My Mas - ter and my Friend. A - MEN.

The Gospel

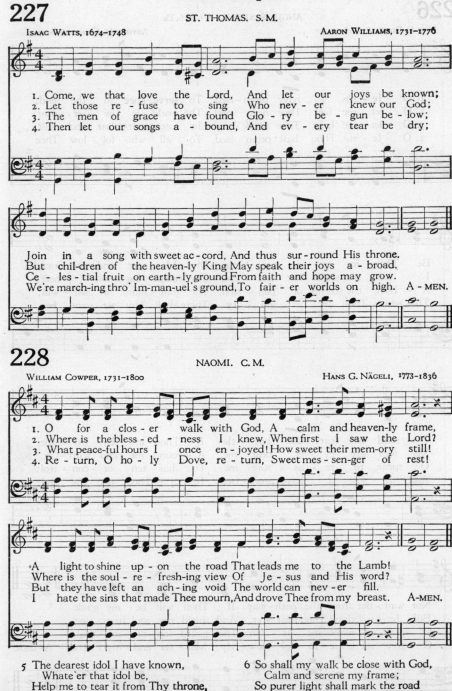

227

ST. THOMAS. S. M.

Isaac Watts, 1674–1748

Aaron Williams, 1731–1776

1. Come, we that love the Lord, And let our joys be known;
2. Let those re-fuse to sing Who nev-er knew our God;
3. The men of grace have found Glo-ry be-gun be-low;
4. Then let our songs a-bound, And ev-ery tear be dry;

Join in a song with sweet ac-cord, And thus sur-round His throne.
But chil-dren of the heaven-ly King May speak their joys a-broad.
Ce-les-tial fruit on earth-ly ground From faith and hope may grow.
We're march-ing thro' Im-man-uel's ground, To fair-er worlds on high. A-MEN.

228

NAOMI. C. M.

William Cowper, 1731–1800

Hans G. Nägeli, 1773–1836

1. O for a clos-er walk with God, A calm and heaven-ly frame,
2. Where is the bless-ed-ness I knew, When first I saw the Lord?
3. What peace-ful hours I once en-joyed! How sweet their mem-ory still!
4. Re-turn, O ho-ly Dove, re-turn, Sweet mes-sen-ger of rest!

A light to shine up-on the road That leads me to the Lamb!
Where is the soul-re-fresh-ing view Of Je-sus and His word?
But they have left an ach-ing void The world can nev-er fill.
I hate the sins that made Thee mourn, And drove Thee from my breast. A-MEN.

5 The dearest idol I have known,
Whate'er that idol be,
Help me to tear it from Thy throne,
And worship only Thee.

6 So shall my walk be close with God,
Calm and serene my frame;
So purer light shall mark the road
That leads me to the Lamb.

Songs of Salvation

229

FILLMORE. 8. 8. 8. 8. 8. 8.

CHARLES WESLEY, 1707–1788

JEREMIAH INGALLS, 1764–1828

1. And can it be that I should gain An in - terest
2. Long my im - pris - oned spir - it lay, Fast bound in
3. No con - dem - na - tion now I dread, Je - sus, with

in the Sav - iour's blood? Died He for me, who caused His pain?
sin and na - ture's night; Thine eye dif - fused a quick - ening ray,
all in Him, is mine; A - live in Him, my liv - ing Head,

For me, who Him to death pur - sued? A - maz - ing
I woke, the dun - geon flamed with light: My chains fell
And clothed in right - eous - ness di - vine, Bold I ap -

love! how can it be That Thou, my Lord, shouldst die for me?
off, my heart was free, I rose, went forth, and fol-lowed Thee.
proach th' e - ter - nal throne, And claim the crown, thro' Christ my own. A - MEN.

The Gospel

230

ST. HILDA. 7. 6. 7. 6. D.

HORATIUS BONAR, 1808–1889

JUSTIN H. KNECHT, 1752–1817
EDWARD HUSBAND, 1843–1908

1. I lay my sins on Je-sus, The spot-less Lamb of God;
2. I lay my wants on Je-sus; All full-ness dwells in Him;
3. I long to be like Je-sus, Meek, lov-ing, low-ly, mild;

He bears them all and frees us From the ac-curs-ed load:
He heal-eth my dis-eas-es, He doth my soul re-deem:
I long to be like Je-sus, The Fa-ther's ho-ly child:

I bring my guilt to Je-sus, To wash my crim-son stains
I lay my griefs on Je-sus, My bur-dens and my cares;
I long to be with Je-sus A-mid the heav'n-ly throng,

White in His blood most pre-cious, Till not a stain re-mains.
He from them all re-leas-es, He all my sor-rows shares.
To sing with saints His prais-es, And learn the an-gels' song. A-MEN.

Songs of Salvation

231

PASS ME NOT. 8. 5. 8. 5. with Refrain

FANNY J. CROSBY, 1820–1915

WILLIAM H. DOANE, 1832–1915

1. Pass me not, O gen - tle Sav - iour, Hear my hum - ble cry;
2. Let me at Thy throne of mer - cy Find a sweet re - lief;
3. Trust - ing on - ly in Thy mer - it, Would I seek Thy face;
4. Thou the Spring of all my com - fort, More than life for me;

While on oth - ers Thou art call - ing, Do not pass me by.
Kneel - ing there in deep con - tri - tion, Help my un - be - lief.
Heal my wound - ed, bro - ken spir - it, Save me by Thy grace.
Whom have I on earth be - side Thee? Whom in heaven but Thee?

REFRAIN

Sav - iour, Sav - iour, hear my hum - ble cry,

While on oth - ers Thou art call - ing, Do not pass me by. A - MEN.

The Gospel

232

I NEED THEE EVERY HOUR. 6. 4. 6. 4. with Refrain

ANNIE S. HAWKS, 1835-1918

ROBERT LOWRY, 1826-1899

1. I need Thee ev-ery hour, Most gra-cious Lord; No ten-der voice like Thine
2. I need Thee ev-ery hour; Stay Thou near by; Temp-ta-tions lose their power
3. I need Thee ev-ery hour, In joy or pain; Come quick-ly and a-bide,
4. I need Thee ev-ery hour; Teach me Thy will; And Thy rich prom-is-es

REFRAIN

Can peace af-ford.
When Thou art nigh.
Or life is vain.
In me ful-fill.

I need Thee, O I need Thee, Ev-ery hour I

need Thee; O bless me now, my Sav-iour, I come to Thee! A-MEN.

Copyright, 1914, by Mary Runyon Lowry. Renewal. Used by permission

233

GALILEE. 8. 7. 8. 7.

CECIL F. ALEXANDER, 1823-1895

WILLIAM H. JUDE, 1851-1892

1. Je-sus calls us, o'er the tu-mult Of our life's wild, rest-less sea;
2. Je-sus calls us from the wor-ship Of the vain world's gold-en store,
3. In our joys and in our sor-rows, Days of toil and hours of ease,
4. Je-sus calls us! by Thy mer-cies, Sav-iour, may we hear Thy call,

Songs of Salvation

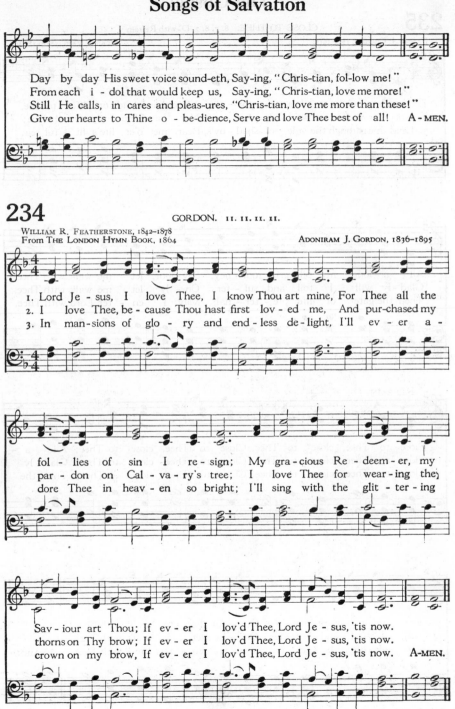

Day by day His sweet voice sound-eth, Say-ing, "Chris-tian, fol-low me!"
From each i - dol that would keep us, Say-ing, "Chris-tian, love me more!"
Still He calls, in cares and pleas-ures, "Chris-tian, love me more than these!"
Give our hearts to Thine o - be-dience, Serve and love Thee best of all! A - MEN.

234

GORDON. 11. 11. 11. 11.

WILLIAM R. FEATHERSTONE, 1842–1878
FROM THE LONDON HYMN BOOK, 1864

ADONIRAM J. GORDON, 1836–1895

1. Lord Je - sus, I love Thee, I know Thou art mine, For Thee all the
2. I love Thee, be - cause Thou hast first lov - ed me, And pur-chased my
3. In man-sions of glo - ry and end - less de-light, I'll ev - er a -

fol - lies of sin I re - sign; My gra - cious Re - deem - er, my
par - don on Cal - va - ry's tree; I love Thee for wear - ing the
dore Thee in heav - en so bright; I'll sing with the glit - ter - ing

Sav - iour art Thou; If ev - er I lov'd Thee, Lord Je - sus, 'tis now.
thorns on Thy brow; If ev - er I lov'd Thee, Lord Je - sus, 'tis now.
crown on my brow, If ev - er I lov'd Thee, Lord Je - sus, 'tis now. A-MEN.

The Gospel

235

CLOSE TO THEE. 8. 7. 8. 7. D. with Refrain

FANNY J. CROSBY, 1820-1915

SILAS J. VAIL, 1818-1884

1. Thou my ev - er - last - ing por - tion, More than friend or life to me,
2. Not for ease or world - ly pleas - ure, Nor for fame my prayer shall be;
3. Lead me through the vale of shad - ows, Bear me o'er life's fit - ful sea;

All a - long my pil - grim jour - ney, Sav - iour, let me walk with Thee.
Glad - ly will I toil and suf - fer, On - ly let me walk with Thee.
Then the gate of life e - ter - nal, May I en - ter, Lord, with Thee.

REFRAIN

Close to Thee, close to Thee, Close to Thee, close to Thee; All a -
Close to Thee, close to Thee, Close to Thee, close to Thee; Glad - ly
Close to Thee, close to Thee, Close to Thee, close to Thee; Then the

long my pil - grim jour - ney, Sav - iour, let me walk with Thee.
will I toil and suf - fer, On - ly let me walk with Thee.
gate of life e - ter - nal, May I en - ter, Lord, with Thee. A - MEN.

Songs of Salvation

EVERY DAY AND HOUR. 7. 9. 7. 9. with Refrain

FANNY J. CROSBY, 1820–1915

WILLIAM H. DOANE, 1832–1915

1. Sav - iour, more than life to me, I am cling-ing, cling-ing close to Thee;
2. Thro' this chang-ing world be -low, Lead me gen - tly, gen - tly as I go;
3. Let me love Thee more and more, Till this fleet - ing, fleet-ing life is o'er;

Let Thy pre - cious blood ap-plied, Keep me ev - er, ev - er near Thy side.
Trust-ing Thee, I can - not stray, I can nev - er, nev - er lose my way.
Till my soul is lost in love, In a bright-er, bright-er world a - bove.

REFRAIN

Ev - ery day, ev - ery hour, Let me feel Thy cleans-ing
Ev - ery day and hour, ev - ery day and hour,

power; May Thy ten-der love to me Bind me clos-er, clos-er, Lord, to Thee. A - MEN.

The Gospel

237
I AM PRAYING FOR YOU. 11. 11. 12. 11. with Refrain

SAMUEL O'M. CLOUGH (CLUFF), 1837–1910

IRA D. SANKEY, 1840–1908

1. I have a Sav-iour, He's plead-ing in glo-ry, A dear, lov-ing
2. I have a Fa-ther; to me He has giv-en A hope for e-
3. When Je-sus finds you, tell oth-ers the sto-ry, That your lov-ing

Sav-iour, tho' earth-friends be few; And now He is watch-ing in
ter-ni-ty, bless-ed and true; And soon He will call me to
Sav-iour is their Sav-iour, too; Then pray that the Fa-ther will

ten-der-ness o'er me, But oh, that my Sav-iour were your Sav-iour, too.
meet Him in glo-ry, But oh, that He'd let me bring you with me, too!
bring them to glo-ry, And pray'r will be an-swered; 'twas an-swered for you!

REFRAIN

For you I am pray-ing, For you I am pray-ing, For
you I am pray-ing, I'm pray-ing for you. A-MEN.

Songs of Salvation

238

ASSURANCE. 9. 10. 9. 9. with Refrain

FANNY J. CROSBY, 1820-1915

Mrs. JOSEPH F. KNAPP, 1839-1908

1. Bless-ed as-sur-ance, Je-sus is mine! O what a fore-taste of glo-ry di-
2. Per-fect sub-mis-sion, per-fect de-light, Vi-sions of rap-ture now burst on my
3. Per-fect sub-mis-sion, all is at rest, I in my Sav-iour am hap-py and

vine! Heir of sal-va-tion, pur-chase of God, Born of His
sight; An-gels de-scend-ing, bring from a-bove, Ech-oes of
blest, Watch-ing and wait-ing, look-ing a-bove, Filled with His

REFRAIN

Spir-it, washed in His blood. This is my sto-ry, this is my
mer-cy, whis-pers of love.
good-ness, lost in His love.

song, Prais-ing my Sav-iour all the day long; This is my

sto-ry, this is my song, Praising my Sav-iour all the day long. A - MEN.

The Gospel

SOFTLY AND TENDERLY. 11. 7. 11. 7. with Refrain

Will L. Thompson, 1847–1909

Will L. Thompson, 1847–1909

1. Soft-ly and ten-der-ly Je-sus is call-ing,
2. Why should we tar-ry when Je-sus is plead-ing,
3. O, for the won-der-ful love He has prom-ised,

Call-ing for you and for me; Pa-tient-ly Je-sus is
Plead-ing for you and for me? Why should we lin-ger and
Prom-ised for you and for me; Tho' we have sinned, He has

wait-ing and watch-ing, Watch-ing for you and for me.
heed not His mer-cies, Mer-cies for you and for me?
mer-cy and par-don, Par-don for you and for me.

REFRAIN

Come home, Come home, Ye who are wea-ry, come home;

Come home, Come home,

Ear-nest-ly, ten-der-ly, Je-sus is call-ing, Call-ing, O sin-ner, come home! A-MEN.

Songs of Salvation

CONVERSE. 8. 7. 8. 7. D.

JOSEPH SCRIVEN, 1820–1886

CHARLES C. CONVERSE, 1832–1918

1. What a Friend we have in Je - sus, All our sins and griefs to bear!
2. Have we tri - als and temp-ta - tions? Is there trou-ble an - y - where?
3. Are we weak and heav - y la - den, Cum-bered with a load of care?

What a priv - i - lege to car - ry Ev - ery-thing to God in prayer!
We should nev - er be dis-cour - aged: Take it to the Lord in prayer.
Pre - cious Sav-iour, still our Ref - uge— Take it to the Lord in prayer.

O what peace we oft - en for - feit, O what need-less pain we bear,
Can we find a friend so faith - ful Who will all our sor-rows share?
Do thy friends de - spise, for - sake thee? Take it to the Lord in prayer!

All be-cause we do not car - ry Ev - ery-thing to God in prayer!
Je - sus knows our ev - ery weak-ness: Take it to the Lord in prayer.
In His arms He'll take and shield thee, Thou wilt find a sol-ace there. A-MEN.

The Gospel

FRIEND. 8. 7. 8. 7. D.

James G. Small, 1817–1888

George C. Stebbins, 1846–

1. I've found a Friend; O such a Friend! He loved me ere I knew Him;
2. I've found a Friend, O such a Friend! He bled, He died to save me;
3. I've found a Friend, O such a Friend! So kind, and true, and ten-der,

He drew me with the cords of love, And thus He bound me to Him.
And not a-lone the gift of life, But His own self He gave me.
So wise a Coun-sel-or and Guide, So might-y a De-fend-er!

And 'round my heart still close-ly twine Those ties which naught can sev-er,
Naught that I have my own I call, I hold it for the Giv-er;
From Him who loves me now so well, What power my soul can sev-er?

For I am His, and He is mine, For ev-er and for ev-er.
My heart, my strength, my life, my all Are His, and His for ev-er.
Shall life or death, or earth or hell? No! I am His for ev-er. A-men.

Songs of Salvation

242

HE LEADETH ME. L. M. with Refrain

JOSEPH H. GILMORE, 1834–1918

WILLIAM B. BRADBURY, 1816–1868

1. He lead-eth me: O bless-ed thought! O words with heavenly com-fort fraught!
2. Sometimes 'mid scenes of deep - est gloom, Sometimes where E-den's bow - ers bloom,
3. Lord, I would place my hand in Thine, Nor ev - er mur - mur nor re - pine;
4. And when my task on earth is done, When, by Thy grace, the vic - tory's won,

What-e'er I do, wher-e'er I be, Still 'tis God's hand that lead-eth me.
By wa - ters still, o'er trou-bled sea, Still 'tis His hand that lead-eth me.
Con - tent, what-ev - er lot I see, Since 'tis my God that lead-eth me.
E'en death's cold wave I will not flee, Since God thro' Jor - dan lead-eth me.

REFRAIN

He lead-eth me, He lead-eth me, By His own hand He lead-eth me:

His faith-ful fol-lower I would be, For by His hand He lead-eth me. A - MEN.

The Gospel

242

243

HOLY SPIRIT, FAITHFUL GUIDE. 7. 7. 7. 7. D.

MARCUS M. WELLS, 1815–1895   MARCUS M. WELLS, 1815–1895

1. Ho - ly Spir - it, faith - ful Guide, Ev - er near the Chris - tian's side;
2. Ev - er pres - ent, tru - est Friend, Ev - er near Thine aid to lend,
3. When our days of toil shall cease, Wait-ing still for sweet re - lease,

Gen - tly lead us by the hand, Pil - grims in a des - ert land;
Leave us not to doubt and fear, Grop-ing on in dark - ness drear;
Noth - ing left but heav'n and prayer, Won-dering if our names were there;

Wea - ry souls for - e'er re - joice, While they hear that sweet - est voice,
When the storms are rag - ing sore, Hearts grow faint, and hopes give o'er,
Wad - ing deep the dis - mal flood, Plead - ing naught but Je - sus' blood,

Whis-p'ring soft - ly, Wan-d'rer, come! Fol - low me, I'll guide thee home."
Whis - per soft - ly, "Wan-d'rer, come! Fol - low me, I'll guide thee home."
Whis - per soft - ly, "Wan-d'rer, come! Fol - low me, I'll guide thee home." A-MEN.

Songs of Salvation

244

THE SOLID ROCK. L. M. with Refrain

EDWARD MOTE, 1797–1874

WILLIAM B. BRADBURY, 1816–1868

1. My hope is built on noth-ing less Than Je - sus' blood and
2. When dark-ness veils His love - ly face I rest on His un -
3. His oath, His cov - e - nant, His blood, Sup - port me in the
4. When He shall come with trum-pet sound, O may I then in

right-eous - ness; I dare not trust the sweet - est frame, But
chang-ing grace; In ev - ery high and storm - y gale, My
whelm-ing flood; When all a - round my soul gives way, He
Him be found! Dressed in His right - eous - ness a - lone, Fault -

REFRAIN

whol - ly lean on Je - sus' name. On Christ, the sol - id rock, I stand; All
an - chor holds with - in the veil.
then is all my hope and stay.
less to stand be - fore the throne!

oth - er ground is sink - ing sand, All oth - er ground is sink - ing sand. A - MEN.

The Gospel

245

THE ROCK OF REFUGE. L. M. with Refrain

ERASTUS JOHNSON, 1826–1909

WILLIAM G. FISCHER, 1835–1912

1. O some-times the shad-ows are deep, And rough seems the path to the goal,
2. O some-times how long seems the day, And some-times how wea-ry my feet;
3. O near to the Rock let me keep If bless-ings or sor-rows pre-vail,

And sor-rows, sometimes how they sweep Like tem-pests down o-ver the soul!
But toil-ing in life's dust-y way, The Rock's bless-ed shad-ow, how sweet!
Or climb-ing the moun-tain way steep, Or walk-ing the shad-ow-y vale.

REFRAIN

O then to the Rock let me fly, To the
let me fly,

Rock that is high-er than I; O then to the
is high-er than I;

Rock let me fly, To the Rock that is high-er than I! A-MEN.
let me fly,

Songs of Salvation

COMING TO THE CROSS. 7. 7. 7. 7. with Refrain

WILLIAM McDONALD, 1820–1901　　　　　WILLIAM G. FISCHER, 1835–1912

1. I am com - ing to the cross; I am poor, and weak, and blind;
2. Long my heart has sighed for Thee; Long has e - vil reigned with - in;
3. Here I give my all to Thee—Friends, and time, and earth - ly store;
4. Je - sus comes! He fills my soul! Per - fect - ed in Him I am;

I am count - ing all but dross; I shall full sal - va - tion find.
Je - sus sweet - ly speaks to me, "I will cleanse you from all sin."
Soul and bod - y Thine to be, Whol - ly Thine for ev - er - more.
I am ev - ery whit made whole—Glo - ry, glo - ry to the Lamb!

REFRAIN

I am trust - ing, Lord, in Thee, Blest Lamb of Cal - va - ry;

Hum - bly at Thy cross I bow, Save me, Je - sus, save me now. A - MEN.

The Gospel

247

THE NINETY AND NINE. Irregular

Elizabeth C. Clephane, 1830–1869

Ira D. Sankey, 1840–1908

1. There were nine-ty and nine that safe-ly lay In the shel-ter of the fold, But one was out on the hills a-way, Far off from the gates of gold— A-way on the moun-tains wild and bare, A-way from the ten-der

2. "Lord, Thou hast here Thy nine-ty and nine; Are they not e-nough for Thee?" But the Shep-herd made an-swer: "This of mine Has wan-dered a-way from me; And al-though the road be rough and steep I go to the des-ert to

3. But none of the ran-somed ev-er knew How deep were the wa-ters crossed; Nor how dark was the night that the Lord passed thro' Ere He found His sheep that was lost. Out in the des-ert He heard its cry— So sick and so help-less and

4. 'Lord, whence are those blood-drops all the way That mark out the moun-tain's track?"—"They were shed for one who had gone a-stray Ere the Shep-herd could bring him back."— "Lord, whence are Thy hands so rent and torn?"—"They are pierc'd to-night by

5. But all thro' the moun-tains, thun-der-riv-en, And up from the rock-y steep, There a-rose a glad cry to the gate of heaven, "Re-joice! I have found my sheep! And the an-gels ech-oed a-round the throne, "Re-joice, for the Lord brings

Songs of Salvation

Shep-herd's care, A - way from the ten - der Shep-herd's care.
find my sheep, I go to the des-ert to find my sheep."
read-y to die, So sick and so help-less and read-y to die.
man-y a thorn, They are pierc'd to - night by man-y a thorn."
back His own, Re - joice, for the Lord brings back His own!" A-MEN.

248 NEAR THE CROSS. 7. 6. 7. 6. with Refrain

FANNY J. CROSBY, 1820–1915   WILLIAM H. DOANE, 1832–1915

1. Je - sus, keep me near the cross; There a pre-cious foun-tain, Free to all— a
2. Near the cross, a trem-bling soul, Love and mer - cy found me; There the bright and
3. Near the cross! O Lamb of God, Bring its scenes be-fore me; Help me walk from
4. Near the cross I'll watch and wait, Hop-ing, trust-ing ev - er, Till I reach the

REFRAIN

heal-ing stream—Flows from Calvary's mountain. In the cross, in the cross, Be my glo-ry
morn - ing Star Shed its beams a-round me.
day to day With its shad-ow o'er me.
gold - en strand Just be-yond the riv - er.

ev - er, Till my rap-tured soul shall find Rest be-yond the riv - er. A-MEN.

The Gospel

249

HANKEY. 7. 6. 7. 6. D. with Refrain

Katherine Hankey, 1834–1911
Refrain added

William G. Fischer, 1835–1912

1. I love to tell the story Of un-seen things a-bove, Of Je-sus and His glo-ry, Of Je-sus and His love. I love to tell the story, Be-cause I know 'tis true; It sat-is-fies my long-ings As noth-ing else can do.

2. I love to tell the story; More won-der-ful it seems Than all the gold-en fan-cies Of all our gold-en dreams. I love to tell the story, It did so much for me; And that is just the rea-son I tell it now to thee.

3. I love to tell the story; 'Tis pleas-ant to re-peat What seems, each time I tell it, More won-der-ful-ly sweet. I love to tell the story, For some have nev-er heard The mes-sage of sal-va-tion From God's own ho-ly Word.

4. I love to tell the story, For those who know it best Seem hun-ger-ing and thirst-ing To hear it like the rest. And when, in scenes of glo-ry, I sing the new, new song, 'Twill be the old, old sto-ry That I have loved so long.

Refrain

I love to tell the sto-ry, 'Twill be my theme in glo-ry, To tell the old, old sto-ry Of Je-sus and His love. A-MEN.

Songs of Salvation

250

RESCUE. 6. 5. 10. D. with Refrain

Fanny J. Crosby, 1820–1915

William H. Doane, 1832–1915

1. Res - cue the per - ish - ing, Care for the dy - ing, Snatch them in pit - y from
2. Though they are slighting Him, Still He is wait - ing, Wait - ing the pen - i - tent
3. Down in the hu - man heart, Crushed by the tempter, Feel - ings lie bur - ied that
4. Res - cue the per - ish - ing, Du - ty de - mands it; Strength for thy la - bor the

sin and the grave; Weep o'er the err - ing one, Lift up the fall - en,
child to re - ceive: Plead with them earn-est - ly, Plead with them gen - tly:
grace can re - store; Touched by a lov - ing heart, Wak - ened by kind - ness,
Lord will pro - vide: Back to the nar - row way Pa - tient - ly win them;

Refrain

Tell them of Je - sus the might - y to save. Res - cue the per - ish-ing,
He will for - give if they on - ly be - lieve.
Chords that were bro - ken will vi - brate once more.
Tell the poor wan-derer a Sav - iour has died.

Care for the dy - ing; Je - sus is mer - ci - ful, Je - sus will save. A-men.

The Gospel

251

HOLINESS. 6. 5. 6. 5. D.

WILLIAM D. LONGSTAFF, 1822-1894

GEORGE C. STEBBINS, 1846-

1. Take time to be ho - ly, Speak oft with thy Lord;
2. Take time to be ho - ly, The world rush - es on;
3. Take time to be ho - ly, Let Him be thy Guide,
4. Take time to be ho - ly, Be calm in thy soul,

A - bide in Him al - ways, And feed on His Word;
Spend much time in se - cret With Je - sus a - lone;
And run not be - fore Him, What - ev - er be - tide;
Each thought and each mo - tive Be - neath His con - trol;

Make friends of God's chil - dren, Help those who are weak,
By look - ing to Je - sus, Like Him thou shalt be;
In joy or in sor - row, Still fol - low the Lord,
Thus led by His Spir - it To foun - tains of love,

For - get - ting in noth - ing His bless - ing to seek.
Thy friends in thy con - duct His like - ness shall see.
And, look - ing to Je - sus, Still trust in His Word.
Thou soon shalt be fit - ted For serv - ice a - bove. A - MEN.

Songs of Salvation

252

I AM THINE. 10. 7. 10. 7. with Refrain

FANNY J. CROSBY, 1820–1915

WILLIAM H. DOANE, 1832–1915

1. I am Thine, O Lord, I have heard Thy voice, And it told Thy love to me; But I long to rise in the arms of faith, And be clos-er drawn to Thee.

2. Con-se-crate me now to Thy serv-ice, Lord, By the pow'r of grace di-vine; Let my soul look up with a stead-fast hope, And my will be lost in Thine.

3. O the pure de-light of a sin-gle hour That be-fore Thy throne I spend, When I kneel in prayer, and with Thee, my God, I com-mune as friend with friend!

4. There are depths of love that I can-not know Till I cross the nar-row sea; There are heights of joy that I may not reach Till I rest in peace with Thee.

REFRAIN

Draw me near-er, near-er, bless-ed Lord, To the cross where Thou hast died; Draw me near-er, near-er, near-er, bless-ed Lord, To Thy pre-cious, bleed-ing side. A-MEN.

The Gospel

PRECIOUS NAME. 8. 7. 8. 7. with Refrain

LYDIA BAXTER, 1809-1874

WILLIAM H. DOANE, 1832-1915

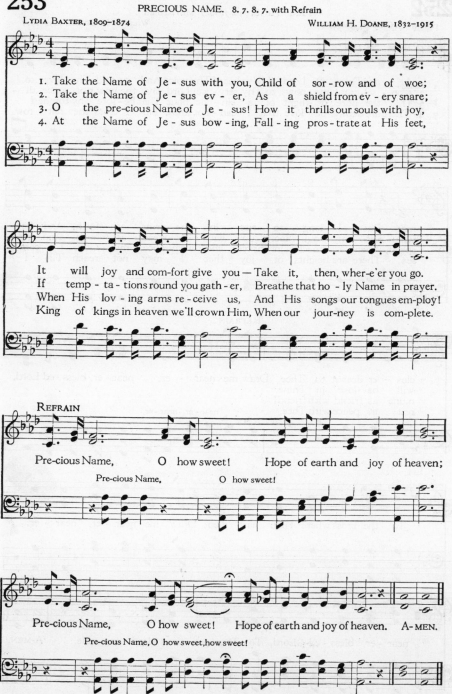

1. Take the Name of Je - sus with you, Child of sor - row and of woe;
2. Take the Name of Je - sus ev - er, As a shield from ev - ery snare;
3. O the pre-cious Name of Je - sus! How it thrills our souls with joy,
4. At the Name of Je - sus bow - ing, Fall - ing pros - trate at His feet,

It will joy and com-fort give you — Take it, then, wher-e'er you go.
If temp - ta - tions round you gath - er, Breathe that ho - ly Name in prayer.
When His lov - ing arms re - ceive us, And His songs our tongues em-ploy!
King of kings in heaven we'll crown Him, When our jour-ney is com-plete.

REFRAIN

Pre-cious Name, O how sweet! Hope of earth and joy of heaven;

Pre-cious Name, O how sweet!

Pre-cious Name, O how sweet! Hope of earth and joy of heaven. A - MEN.

Pre-cious Name, O how sweet, how sweet!

Songs of Salvation

254

LOWER LIGHTS. 8. 7. 8. 7. with Refrain

PHILIP P. BLISS, 1838–1876

PHILIP P. BLISS, 1838–1876

1. Bright-ly beams our Fa-ther's mer-cy From His light-house ev-er-more;
2. Dark the night of sin has set-tled, Loud the an-gry bil-lows roar:
3. Trim your fee-ble lamp, my broth-er! Some poor sea-man, tem-pest-tossed,

But to us He gives the keep-ing Of the lights a-long the shore.
Ea-ger eyes are watch-ing, long-ing, For the lights a-long the shore,
Try-ing now to make the har-bor, In the dark-ness may be lost.

REFRAIN

Let the low-er lights be burn-ing! Send a gleam a-cross the wave!

Some poor faint-ing, strug-gling sea-man You may res-cue, you may save. A-MEN.

The Gospel

TRUE–HEARTED, WHOLE–HEARTED. 11. 10. 11. 10. with Refrain

FRANCES R. HAVERGAL, 1836–1879

GEORGE C. STEBBINS, 1846–

1. True-heart-ed, whole-heart-ed, faith-ful and loy-al, King of our lives, by Thy
2. True-heart-ed, whole-heart-ed, full-est al-le-giance Yield-ing henceforth to our
3. True-heart-ed, whole-heart-ed, Sav-iour all-glo-rious! Take Thy great pow-er and

grace we will be; Un-der the standard ex-alt-ed and roy-al, Strong in Thy
glo-ri-ous King; Val-iant en-deav-or and lov-ing o-bedience, Free-ly and
reign there a-lone, O-ver our wills and af-fec-tions vic-to-rious, Free-ly sur-

REFRAIN

strength we will bat-tle for Thee. Peal out the watchword! Si-lence it nev-er!
joy-ous-ly now would we bring. Peal Si-lence
ren-dered and wholly Thine own.

Song of our spir-its, re-joic-ing and free; Peal out the watchword!
Song re-joic-ing and free; Peal

Loy-al for ev-er! King of our lives, By Thy grace we will be. A-MEN.
Loy-al King

Copyright, 1916. Renewal. Hope Publishing Company, owner

The Christian Life

Discipleship

256

ST. CATHERINE. 8. 8. 8. 8. 8. 8.

HENRI F. HEMY, 1818–1888
Adapted by JAMES G. WALTON, 1821–1905

FREDERICK W. FABER, 1814–1863

1. Faith of our fa - thers! liv - ing still In spite of dun - geon,
2. Faith of our fa - thers! we will strive To win all na - tions
3. Faith of our fa - thers! we will love Both friend and foe in

fire, and sword, O how our hearts beat high with joy
un - to thee, And through the truth that comes from God
all our strife, And preach thee, too, as love knows how

When-e'er we hear that glo - rious word! Faith of our fa - thers,
Man - kind shall then be tru - ly free. Faith of our fa - thers,
By kind - ly words and vir - tuous life: Faith of our fa - thers,

ho - ly faith! We will be true to thee till death.
ho - ly faith! We will be true to thee till death.
ho - ly faith! We will be true to thee till death. A - MEN.

The Christian Life

257

HOLBORN HILL. L. M.

Philip Doddridge, 1702–1751

St. Alban's Tune Book, c. 1866

1. My gra-cious Lord, I own Thy right To ev-er-y serv-ice I can pay,
2. What is my be-ing but for Thee, Its sure sup-port, its no-blest end?
3. 'Tis to my Sav-iour I would live, To Him who for my ran-som died;
4. His work my hoa-ry age shall bless, When youth-ful vig-or is no more;

And call it my su-preme de-light To hear Thy dic-tates, and o-bey.
'Tis my de-light Thy face to see, And serve the cause of such a Friend.
Nor could all world-ly hon-or give Such bliss as crowns me at His side.
And my last hour of life con-fess His dy-ing love, His sav-ing power. A-MEN.

258

FEDERAL STREET. L. M.

Joseph Grigg, c. 1720–1768
Alt. by Benjamin Francis, 1734–1799

Henry K. Oliver, 1800–1885

1. Je-sus, and shall it ev-er be, A mor-tal man a-shamed of Thee?
2. A-shamed of Je-sus! soon-er far Let eve-ning blush to own a star;
3. A-shamed of Je-sus! just as soon Let mid-night be a-shamed of noon;
4. A-shamed of Je-sus! that dear Friend On whom my hopes of heaven de-pend!

A-shamed of Thee, whom an-gels praise, Whose glo-ries shine thro' end-less days?
He sheds the beams of light di-vine O'er this be-night-ed soul of mine.
'Tis mid-night with my soul till He, Bright Morn-ing-Star, bid dark-ness flee.
No; when I blush, be this my shame, That I no more re-vere His Name. A-MEN.

5 Ashamed of Jesus! yes, I may,
When I've no guilt to wash away;
No tear to wipe, no good to crave,
No fears to quell, no soul to save.

6 Till then, nor is my boasting vain,
Till then I boast a Saviour slain;
And O may this my glory be,
That Christ is not ashamed of me!

Discipleship

259

MARYTON. L. M.

WASHINGTON GLADDEN, 1836–1918

H. PERCY SMITH, 1825–1898

1. O Mas-ter, let me walk with Thee In low-ly paths of serv-ice free;
2. Help me the slow of heart to move By some clear, win-ning word of love;
3. Teach me Thy pa-tience; still with Thee In clos-er, dear-er com-pa-ny,
4. In hope that sends a shin-ing ray Far down the fu-ture's broad-ening way;

Tell me Thy se-cret; help me bear The strain of toil, the fret of care.
Teach me the way-ward feet to stay, And guide them in the home-ward way.
In work that keeps faith sweet and strong, In trust that tri-umphs o-ver wrong;
In peace that on-ly Thou canst give, With Thee, O Mas-ter, let me live. A-MEN.

Alternative tune, Canonbury, No. 116

260

GERMANY. L. M.

CHARLES W. EVEREST, 1814–1877

WILLIAM GARDINER'S SACRED MELODIES, 1815

1. "Take up thy cross," the Sav-iour said, "If thou wouldst my dis-ci - ple be;
2. Take up thy cross; let not its weight Fill thy weak spir-it with a-larm;
3. Take up thy cross, nor heed the shame; Nor let thy fool-ish pride re-bel;
4. Take up thy cross and fol-low Christ; Nor think till death to lay it down;

De-ny thy-self, the world for-sake, And hum-bly fol-low aft-er me."
His strength shall bear thy spir-it up, And brace thy heart and nerve thine arm.
Thy Lord for thee the cross en-dured, To save thy soul from death and hell.
For on-ly he who bears the cross May hope to wear the glo-rious crown. A-MEN.

The Christian Life

ELLESDIE. 8. 7. 8. 7. D.

Henry F. Lyte, 1793-1847

Wolfgang A. Mozart (?), 1756-1791
Arr. by Hubert P. Main, 1839-1926

1. Je - sus, I my cross have tak - en, All to leave, and fol - low Thee;
2. Let the world de - spise and leave me, They have left my Sav - iour, too;
3. Man may trou - ble and dis - tress me, 'Twill but drive me to Thy breast;
4. Haste thee on from grace to glo - ry, Armed by faith, and winged by prayer;

Des - ti - tute, de - spised, for - sak - en, Thou, from hence, my all shalt be:
Hu - man hearts and looks de - ceive me; Thou art not, like man, un - true;
Life with tri - als hard may press me, Heav'n will bring me sweet - er rest.
Heaven's e - ter - nal day's be - fore thee, God's own hand shall guide thee there.

Per - ish ev - er - y fond am - bi - tion, All I've sought or hoped, or known;
And, while Thou shalt smile up - on me, God of wis - dom, love, and might,
O 'tis not in grief to harm me While Thy love is left to me;
Soon shall close thy earth - ly mis - sion; Swift shall pass thy pil - grim days;

Yet how rich is my con - di - tion: God and heav'n are still my own!
Foes may hate, and friends may shun me; Show Thy face, and all is bright.
O 'twere not in joy to charm me, Were that joy un - mixed with Thee.
Hope shall change to glad fru - i - tion, Faith to sight, and prayer to praise. A - men.

Discipleship

262

CORWIN. 8. 6. 8. 6. 6. D.

Samuel Longfellow, 1819–1892   J. W. Lerman, 1864–

1. God's trum-pet wakes the slum-b'ring world; Now each man to his post!
2. He who, no an-ger on his tongue, Nor an-y i-dle boast,
3. He who is read-y for the cross, The cause de-spised loves most,

The red-cross ban-ner is un-furl'd; Who joins the glo-rious host?
Bears stead-fast wit-ness 'gainst the wrong, He joins the sa-cred host,
And shuns not pain, nor shame, nor loss, He joins the mar-tyr host,

Who joins the glo-rious host? He who, in feal-ty to the truth,
He joins the sa-cred host. He who, with calm, un-daunt-ed will,
He joins the mar-tyr host. God's trum-pet wakes the slum-b'ring world;

And count-ing all the cost, Doth con-se-crate his gen-'rous youth—
Ne'er counts the bat-tle lost, But, though de-feat-ed, bat-tles still—
Now each man to his post; The red-cross ban-ner is un-furl'd;

He joins the no-ble host, He joins the no-ble host.
He joins the faith-ful host, He joins the faith-ful host.
We join the glo-rious host, We join the glo-rious host. A-men.

Music used by permission of D. Appleton-Century Company

The Christian Life

263

TON—Y—BOTEL. 8. 7. 8. 7. D.

James Russell Lowell, 1819-1891, alt.

Welsh hymn melody

1. Once to ev - ery man and na - tion Comes the mo - ment to de - cide,
2. Then to side with truth is no - ble, When we share her wretched crust,
3. By the light of burn-ing mar - tyrs, Christ, Thy bleed-ing feet we track,
4. Though the cause of e - vil pros - per, Yet 'tis truth a - lone is strong:

In the strife of truth with false-hood, For the good or e - vil side;
Ere her cause bring fame and prof - it, And 'tis pros-perous to be just;
Toil - ing up new Cal - varies ev - er With the cross that turns not back;
Though her por - tion be the scaf-fold, And up - on the throne be wrong;

Some great cause, God's new Mes - si - ah, Of - fering each the bloom or blight,
Then it is the brave man choos - es While the cow - ard stands a - side,
New oc - ca - sions teach new du - ties, Time makes an - cient good un - couth;
Yet that scaf-fold sways the fu - ture, And, be - hind the dim un-known,

And the choice goes by for ev - er 'Twixt that darkness and that light.
Till the mul - ti-tude make vir - tue Of the faith they had de - nied.
They must up - ward still and on - ward, Who would keep a-breast of truth.
Standeth God with-in the shad-ow Keep-ing watch a - bove His own. A - MEN.

Music used by permission of W. Gwenlyn Evans and Sons

Discipleship

264

GEORGE T. COSTER, 1835–1912

ARTHUR'S SEAT. 6. 6. 6. 6. 8. 8.

Arr. from JOHN GOSS, 1800–1880

1. March on, O soul, with strength! Like those strong men of old
2. The sons of fa-thers we By whom our faith is taught
3. March on, O soul, with strength, As strong the bat-tle rolls!
4. Not long the con-flict: soon The ho-ly war shall cease,

Who 'gainst en-thron-ed wrong Stood con-fi-
To fear no ill, to fight The ho-ly
'Gainst lies and lusts and wrongs, Let cour-age
Faith's war-fare end-ed, won The home of

dent and bold; Who, thrust in prison or cast to flame,
fight they fought: He - ro - ic war-riors, ne'er from Christ
rule our souls: In keen-est strife, Lord, may we stand,
end - less peace! Look up! the vic-tor's crown at length!

Still made their glo - - ry in Thy name.
By an - y lure or guile en - ticed.
Up - held and strength - ened by Thy hand.
March on, O soul, march on, with strength! A - MEN.

Words used by permission of V. B. Coster, 36, Abbotsford Gardens, Woodford Green, Essex, England

The Christian Life

MONK'S GATE. 6. 5. 6. 5. 6. 6. 6. 5.

JOHN BUNYAN, 1628-1688, alt.

English traditional melody

1. He who would val-iant be 'Gainst all dis-as-ter,
2. Who so be-set him round With dis-mal sto-ries,
3. Since, Lord, Thou dost de-fend Us with Thy Spir-it,

Let him in con-stan-cy Fol-low the Mas-ter.
Do but them-selves con-found— His strength the more is.
We know we at the end Shall life in-her-it.

There's no dis-cour-age-ment Shall make him once re-lent
No foes shall stay his might; Though he with gi-ants fight,
Then, fan-cies, flee a-way! I'll fear not what men say,

His first a-vowed in-tent To be a pil-grim.
He will make good his right To be a pil-grim.
I'll la-bor night and day To be a pil-grim. A-MEN.

Discipleship

266

BLAIRGOWRIE (Dykes). 13. 13. 13. 13

S. Ralph Harlow, 1885–

John B. Dykes, 1823–1876

1. O young and fear-less Proph-et of an-cient Gal-i-lee:
2. We mar-vel at the pur-pose that held Thee to Thy course
3. O help us stand un-swerv-ing a-gainst war's blood-y way,
4. Cre-ate in us the splen-dor that dawns when hearts are kind,
5. O young and fear-less Proph-et, we need Thy pres-ence here,

Thy life is still a sum-mons to serve hu-man-i-ty,
While ev-er on the hill-top be-fore Thee loomed the cross;
Where hate and lust and false-hood hold back Christ's ho-ly sway;
That knows not race nor sta-tion as boun-daries of the mind;
A-mid our pride and glo-ry to see Thy face ap-pear;

To make our thoughts and ac-tions less prone to please the crowd,
Thy stead-fast face set for-ward where love and du-ty shone,
For-bid false love of coun-try, that blinds us to His call
That learns to val-ue beau-ty, in heart, or brain, or soul,
Once more to hear Thy chal-lenge a-bove our noi-sy day,

To stand with hum-ble cour-age for Truth with hearts un-cowed.
While we be-tray so quick-ly and leave Thee there a-lone.
Who lifts a-bove the na-tion the broth-er-hood of all.
And longs to bind God's chil-dren in-to one per-fect whole.
A-gain to lead us for-ward a-long God's ho-ly way. A-men.

Words used by permission of S. Ralph Harlow

The Christian Life

267

FESTAL SONG. S. M.
(First Tune)

WILLIAM PIERSON MERRILL, 1867-   WILLIAM H. WALTER, 1825-1893

1. Rise up, O men of God! Have done with less-er things;
2. Rise up, O men of God! His king-dom tar-ries long;
3. Rise up, O men of God! The Church for you doth wait,
4. Lift high the cross of Christ! Tread where His feet have trod;

Give heart and mind and soul and strength To serve the King of kings.
Bring in the day of broth-er-hood And end the night of wrong.
Her strength un-e-qual to her task; Rise up, and make her great!
As broth-ers of the Son of man, Rise up, O men of God! A-MEN.

Words used by permission of The Presbyterian Tribune, formerly The Presbyterian Advance

267

OXNAM. S. M.
(Second Tune)

WILLIAM P. MERRILL, 1867-   ROBERT G. McCUTCHAN, 1877-

1. Rise up, O men of God! Have done with less-er things; Give
2. Rise up, O men of God! His king-dom tar-ries long; Bring
3. Rise up, O men of God! The Church for you doth wait, Her
4. Lift high the cross of Christ! Tread where His feet have trod; As

heart and mind and soul and strength To serve the King of kings.
in the day of broth-er-hood And end the night of wrong.
strength un-e-qual to her task; Rise up, and make her great!
broth-ers of the Son of man, Rise up, O men of God! A-MEN.

Words used by permission of The Presbyterian Tribune, formerly The Presbyterian Advance
Music copyright, 1930, by Robert G. McCutchan. Used by permission

Discipleship

268

BEACON HILL. Irregular

EARL MARLATT, 1892–

HARRY S. MASON, 1881–

1. "Are ye a - ble," said the Mas - ter, "To be cru - ci - fied with me?—"
2. "Are ye a - ble" to re - mem - ber, When a thief lifts up his eyes,
3. "Are ye a - ble" when the shad - ows Close a - round you with the sod,
4. "Are ye a - ble?" Still the Mas - ter Whis-pers down e - ter - ni - ty,

"Yea," the sturd - y dream-ers an-swered, "To the death we fol - low Thee."
That his par -doned soul is wor - thy Of a place in par - a - dise?
To be - lieve that spir - it tri-umphs, To com-mend your soul to God?
And he - ro - ic spir - its an - swer Now, as then, in Gal - i - lee.

REFRAIN

"Lord, we are a - ble." Our spir - its are Thine. Re - mold them,

make us, Like Thee, di - vine. Thy guid - ing ra-diance A - bove us shall

be A bea - con to God, To love and loy - al - ty. A-MEN.

Words used by permission of Earl Marlatt
Music used by permission of Harry S. Mason

The Christian Life

269

PILOT. 7. 7. 7. 7. 7. 7.

EDWARD HOPPER, 1816-1888

JOHN E. GOULD, 1822-1875

1. Je - sus, Sav - iour, pi - lot me O - ver life's tem - pest - uous sea;
2. As a moth - er stills her child, Thou canst hush the o - cean wild;
3. When at last I near the shore, And the fear - ful break - ers roar

Un-known waves be - fore me roll, Hid - ing rock and treach-erous shoal;
Boisterous waves o - bey Thy will When Thou sayest to them, "Be still!"
'Twixt me and the peace-ful rest, Then, while lean - ing on Thy breast,

Chart and com - pass came from Thee: Je - sus, Sav - iour, pi - lot me.
Won-drous Sov-ereign of the sea, Je - sus, Sav - iour, pi - lot me.
May I hear Thee say to me, "Fear not, I will pi - lot thee." A - MEN.

270

ARLINGTON. C. M.

WILLIAM H. BATHURST, 1796-1877

THOMAS A. ARNE, 1710-1778

1. O for a faith that will not shrink, Tho' pressed by ev - ery foe,
2. That will not mur - mur nor com-plain Be - neath the chas-tening rod,
3. A faith that shines more bright and clear When tem-pests rage with - out;
4. Lord, give me such a faith as this; And then, what-e'er may come,

Trials and Conflicts

That will not trem-ble on the brink Of an-y earth-ly woe!
But, in the hour of grief or pain, Will lean up-on its God;
That when in dan-ger knows no fear, In dark-ness feels no doubt:
I'll taste, e'en now, the hal-lowed bliss Of an e-ter-nal home. A-MEN.

271

BURLEIGH. 10. 10. 10. 10.

WILLIAM H. BURLEIGH, 1812–1871   JOSEPH BARNBY, 1838–1896

1. Lead us, O Fa-ther, in the paths of peace: With-out Thy
2. Lead us, O Fa-ther, in the paths of truth: Un-helped by
3. Lead us, O Fa-ther, in the paths of right: Blind-ly we
4. Lead us, O Fa-ther, to Thy heaven-ly rest, How-ev-er

guid-ing hand we go a-stray, And doubts ap-pall, and
Thee, in er-ror's maze we grope, While pas-sion stains, and
stum-ble when we walk a-lone, In-volved in shad-ows
rough and steep the path may be, Thro' joy or sor-row,

sor-rows still in-crease; Lead us thro' Christ, the true and liv-ing Way.
fol-ly dims our youth, And age comes on, un-cheered by faith or hope.
of a dark-some night; On-ly with Thee we jour-ney safe-ly on.
as Thou deem-est best, Un-til our lives are per-fect-ed in Thee. A-MEN.

The Christian Life

272

BREMEN (Neumark) Irregular

GEORG NEUMARK, 1621–1681
Tr. by CATHERINE WINKWORTH, 1829–1878

GEORG NEUMARK, 1621–1681

1. If thou but suf-fer God to guide thee, And hope in Him thro' all thy ways,
2. O - bey, thou rest-less heart, be still   And wait in cheer-ful hope, con-tent
3. Sing, pray, and swerve not from His ways; But do thine own part faith-ful-ly.

He'll give thee strength, whate'er betide thee, And bear thee thro' the e - vil days;
To take what-e'er His gra - cious will,   His all - dis - cern-ing love, hath sent;
Trust His rich prom-is - es   of   grace,   So shall they be ful-filled in thee.

Who trusts in God's unchanging love Builds on the rock that naught can move.
Nor doubt our in-most wants are known To Him who chose us for His own.
God nev - er yet for-sook at need The soul that trust-ed Him in-deed. A-MEN.

273

HESPERUS (QUEBEC). L.M.

OLIVER W. HOLMES, 1809–1894

HENRY BAKER, 1835–1910

1. O   Love di - vine, that stooped to share Our sharp-est pang, our bit-t'rest tear!
2. Though long the wea - ry way we tread, And sor - row crown each lingering year,
3. When droop-ing pleas-ure turns to grief, And trem-bling faith is changed to fear,
4. On   Thee we fling our bur-dening woe, O   Love di - vine, for ev - er dear!

Trials and Conflicts

On Thee we cast each earth-born care; We smile at pain while Thou art near.
No path we shun, no dark-ness dread, Our hearts still whis-p'ring, "Thou art near!"
The mur-muring wind, the quivering leaf, Shall soft-ly tell us Thou art near!
Con-tent to suf-fer while we know, Liv-ing and dy-ing, Thou art near! A-MEN.

274   PENITENCE. 6. 5. 6. 5. D.

JAMES MONTGOMERY, 1771-1854
Alt. by FRANCES A. HUTTON, 1811-1877   SPENCER LANE, 1843-1903

1. In the hour of tri-al, Je-sus, plead for me; Lest by base de-ni-al,
2. With for-bid-den pleas-ures Would this vain world charm, Or its sor-did treas-ures
3. Should Thy mer-cy send me Sor-row, toil, and woe, Or should pain at-tend me
4. When my last hour com-eth, Fraught with strife and pain, When my dust re-turn-eth

I de-part from Thee. When Thou see'st me wa-ver, With a look re-call,
Spread to work me harm; Bring to my re-mem-brance Sad Geth-sem-a-ne,
On my path be-low, Grant that I may nev-er Fail Thy hand to see:
To the dust a-gain; On Thy truth re-ly-ing, Thro' that mor-tal strife:

Nor for fear or fa-vor Suf-fer me to fall.
Or, in dark-er sem-blance, Cross-crowned Cal-va-ry.
Grant that I may ev-er Cast my care on Thee.
Je-sus, take me, dy-ing, To e-ter-nal life. A-MEN.

The Christian Life

275

ST. ANDREW OF CRETE. 6. 5. 6. 5. D.
(*First Tune*)

ANDREW OF CRETE, 660–732
Tr. by JOHN M. NEALE, 1818–1866, alt.

JOHN B. DYKES, 1823–1876

1. Chris-tian! dost thou see them On the ho-ly ground,
How the powers of dark-ness Rage thy steps a-round?
Chris-tian! up and smite them, Count-ing gain but loss,
In the strength that com-eth By the ho-ly cross.

2. Chris-tian! dost thou feel them, How they work with-in,
Striv-ing, tempt-ing, lur-ing, Goad-ing in-to sin?
Chris-tian! nev-er trem-ble; Nev-er be down-cast;
Gird thee for the bat-tle; Watch, and pray, and fast!

3. Chris-tian! dost thou hear them, How they speak thee fair?
"Al-ways fast and vi-gil? Al-ways watch and prayer?"
Chris-tian! an-swer bold-ly, "While I breathe I pray!"
Peace shall fol-low bat-tle, Night shall end in day.

4. "Well I know thy trou-ble, O my ser-vant true;
Thou art ver-y wea-ry— I was wea-ry too;
But that toil shall make thee Some day all mine own,
And the end of sor-row Shall be near my throne." A-MEN.

Trials and Conflicts

275

GREEK HYMN. 6. 5. 6. 5. D.
(*Second Tune*)

ANDREW OF CRETE, 660-732
Tr. by JOHN M. NEALE, 1818-1866, alt.

JOSEPH P. HOLBROOK, 1822-1888

1. Chris - tian! dost thou see them On the ho - ly ground,
2. Chris - tian! dost thou feel them, How they work with - in,
3. Chris - tian! dost thou hear them, How they speak thee fair?
4. "Well I know thy trou - ble, O my ser - vant true;

How the powers of dark - ness Rage thy steps a - round?
Striv - ing, tempt - ing, lur - ing, Goad - ing in - to sin?
"Al - ways fast and vig - il? Al - ways watch and prayer?"
Thou art ver - y wea - ry— I was wea - ry too;

Chris - tian! up and smite them, Count - ing gain but loss,
Chris - tian! nev - er trem - ble; Nev - er be down - cast;
Chris - tian! an - swer bold - ly, "While I breathe I pray!"
But that toil shall make thee Some day all mine own,

In the strength that com - eth By the ho - ly cross.
Gird thee for the bat - tle; Watch, and pray, and fast!
Peace shall fol - low bat - tle, Night shall end in day.
And the end of sor - row Shall be near my throne." A-MEN.

The Christian Life

276

MAITLAND. C. M.

Thomas Shepherd, 1665–1739, and others

George N. Allen, 1812–1877

1. Must Je - sus bear the cross a - lone, And all the world go free?
2. How hap - py are the saints a - bove, Who once went sor - row ing here!
3. The con - se - crat - ed cross I'll bear Till death shall set me free;

No, there's a cross for ev - ery one, And there's a cross for me.
But now they taste un - min - gled love And joy with - out a tear.
And then go home my crown to wear, For there's a crown for me. A - MEN.

277

LABAN. S. M.

George Heath, 1750–1822

Lowell Mason, 1792–1872

1. My soul, be on thy guard; Ten thou - sand foes a - rise;
2. O watch, and fight, and pray; The bat - tle ne'er give o'er;
3. Ne'er think the vic - tory won, Nor lay thine ar - mor down;
4. Fight on, my soul, till death Shall bring thee to thy God;

The hosts of sin are press - ing hard To draw thee from the skies.
Re - new it bold - ly ev - ery day, And help di - vine im - plore.
The work of faith will not be done Till thou ob - tain the crown.
He'll take thee, at thy part - ing breath, To His di - vine a - bode. A-MEN.

Activity and Zeal

278

LANCASHIRE. 7. 6. 7. 6. D.

ERNEST W. SHURTLEFF, 1862–1917

HENRY SMART, 1813–1879

1. Lead on, O King E - ter - nal, The day of march has come;
2. Lead on, O King E - ter - nal, Till sin's fierce war shall cease,
3. Lead on, O King E - ter - nal: We fol - low, not with fears,

Hence-forth in fields of con - quest Thy tents shall be our home:
And Ho - li - ness shall whis - per The sweet A - men of peace;
For glad - ness breaks like morn - ing Wher - e'er Thy face ap - pears;

Thro' days of prep - a - ra - tion Thy grace has made us strong,
For not with swords loud clash - ing, Nor roll of stir - ring drums;
Thy cross is lift - ed o'er us; We jour - ney in its light:

And now, O King E - ter - nal, We lift our bat - tle song.
With deeds of love and mer - cy, The heav'n-ly king-dom comes.
The crown a - waits the con - quest; Lead on, O God of might. A-MEN.

The Christian Life

279

CWM RHONDDA. 8. 7. 8. 7. 8. 7.

Welsh hymn melody
JOHN HUGHES, 1873-1932

HARRY EMERSON FOSDICK, 1878-

1. God of grace and God of glo-ry, On Thy peo-ple pour Thy power; Crown Thine an-cient Church's sto-ry; Bring her bud to glo-rious flower. Grant us wis-dom, Grant us cour-age, For the fac-ing of this hour, For the fac-ing of this hour.

2. Lo! the hosts of e-vil round us Scorn Thy Christ, as-sail His ways! Fears and doubts too long have bound us, Free our hearts to work and praise. Grant us wis-dom, Grant us cour-age, For the liv-ing of these days, For the liv-ing of these days.

3. Cure Thy chil-dren's war-ring mad-ness, Bend our pride to Thy con-trol; Shame our wan-ton, self-ish glad-ness, Rich in things and poor in soul. Grant us wis-dom, Grant us cour-age, Lest we miss Thy kingdom's goal, Lest we miss Thy king-dom's goal. A-MEN.

4 Set our feet on lofty places;
Gird our lives that they may be
Armored with all Christ-like graces
In the fight to set men free.
Grant us wisdom,
Grant us courage,
That we fail not man nor Thee!

5 Save us from weak resignation
To the evils we deplore;
Let the search for Thy salvation
Be our glory evermore.
Grant us wisdom,
Grant us courage,
Serving Thee whom we adore.

Alternative tune, Regent Square, No. 77

Words used by permission of Harry Emerson Fosdick
Music used by permission of Mrs. John Hughes, owner of copyright

Activity and Zeal

280

ST. GERTRUDE. 6. 5. 6. 5. D. with Refrain

Sabine Baring-Gould, 1834-1924

Arthur S. Sullivan, 1842-1900

1. On - ward, Chris-tian sol - diers! March-ing as to war, With the cross of
2. Like a might - y arm - y Moves the Church of God; Broth-ers, we are
3. Crowns and thrones may per - ish, King-doms rise and wane, But the Church of
4. On - ward, then, ye peo - ple, Join our hap - py throng, Blend with ours your

Je - sus Go - ing on be - fore. Christ, the roy - al Mas - ter,
tread-ing Where the saints have trod; We are not di - vid - ed,
Je - sus Con - stant will re - main; Gates of hell can nev - er
voic - es In the tri - umph-song; Glo - ry, laud, and hon - or

Leads a - gainst the foe; For-ward in - to bat - tle, See His ban - ners go!
All one bod - y we, One in hope and doc - trine, One in char - i - ty.
'Gainst that Church pre-vail; We have Christ's own prom-ise, And that can - not fail.
Un - to Christ the King; This thro' count-less a - ges Men and an - gels sing.

Refrain

On - ward, Chris - tian sol - diers, March - ing as to war,

With the cross of Je - sus Go - ing on be - fore. A - men.

The Christian Life

CALEDONIA. 7. 7. 7. 6. D.

JARED B. WATERBURY, 1799–1876

Scottish traditional melody

1. Sol-diers of the cross, a-rise! Lo! your Lead-er from the skies
2. Je-sus con-quered when He fell, Met and van-quished earth and hell;
3. On-ward, then, ye hosts of God! Je-sus points the vic-tor's rod;

Waves be-fore you glo-ry's prize, The prize of vic-to-ry.
Now He leads you on to swell The tri-umphs of His cross.
Fol-low where your Lead-er trod; You soon shall see His face.

Seize your ar-mor, gird it on; Now the bat-tle will be won;
Though all earth and hell ap-pear, Who will doubt, or who can fear?
Soon, your en-e-mies all slain, Crowns of glo-ry you shall gain;

See, the strife will soon be done; Then strug-gle man-ful-ly.
God, our strength and shield, is near; We can-not lose our cause.
Soon you'll join that glo-rious train Who shout their Sav-iour's praise. A-MEN.

Activity and Zeal

282

DIADEMATA. S. M. D.

Charles Wesley, 1707–1788

George J. Elvey, 1816–1893

1. Sol - diers of Christ, a - rise, And put your ar - mor on,
2. Stand, then, in His great might, With all His strength en - dued;
3. From strength to strength go on; Wres - tle, and fight, and pray;

Strong in the strength which God sup - plies Through His e - ter - nal Son;
But take, to arm you for the fight, The pan - o - ply of God:
Tread all the powers of dark - ness down, And win the well-fought day:

Strong in the Lord of hosts, And in His might - y power,
That, hav - ing all things done, And all your con - flicts passed,
Still let the Spir - it cry, In all His sol - diers, "Come!"

Who in the strength of Je - sus trusts Is more than con-quer - or.
Ye may o'er-come thro' Christ a - lone, And stand en - tire at last.
Till Christ the Lord who reigns on high, Shall take the con-querors home. A-MEN.

The Christian Life

283

GEIBEL. 7. 6. 7. 6. D. with Refrain

GEORGE DUFFIELD, JR., 1818–1888

ADAM GEIBEL, 1855–1933

In unison

1. Stand up, stand up for Je - sus, Ye sol - diers of the cross;
2. Stand up, stand up for Je - sus, The trum - pet call o - bey;
3. Stand up, stand up for Je - sus, Stand in His strength a - lone;
4. Stand up, stand up for Je - sus, The strife will not be long;

Lift high His roy - al ban - ner, It must not suf - fer loss:
Forth to the might - y con - flict, In this His glo - rious day;
The arm of flesh will fail you, Ye dare not trust your own;
This day the noise of bat - tle, The next, the vic - tor's song:

From vic - t'ry un - to vic - t'ry His ar - my shall He lead,
Ye that are men now serve Him A - gainst un - num-bered foes;
Put on the gos - pel ar - mor, Each piece put on with prayer;
To him that o - ver - com - eth, A crown of life shall be;

Till ev - ery foe is van - quished, And Christ is Lord in - deed.
Let cour - age rise with dan - ger, And strength to strength op - pose.
Where du - ty calls or dan - ger, Be nev - er want - ing there.
He with the King of Glo - ry Shall reign e - ter - nal - ly.

Activity and Zeal

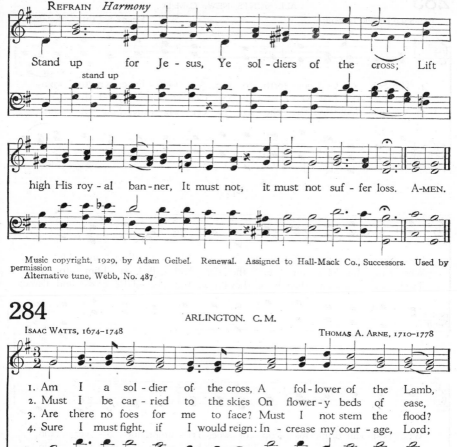

Stand up for Je-sus, Ye sol-diers of the cross; Lift
stand up

high His roy-al ban-ner, It must not, it must not suf-fer loss. A-MEN.

Alternative tune, Webb, No. 487

284

ARLINGTON. C.M.

Isaac Watts, 1674–1748

Thomas A. Arne, 1710–1778

1. Am I a sol-dier of the cross, A fol-lower of the Lamb,
2. Must I be car-ried to the skies On flower-y beds of ease,
3. Are there no foes for me to face? Must I not stem the flood?
4. Sure I must fight, if I would reign: In-crease my cour-age, Lord;

And shall I fear to own His cause, Or blush to speak His Name?
While oth-ers fought to win the prize, And sailed thro' blood-y seas?
Is this vile world a friend to grace, To help me on to God?
I'll bear the toil, en-dure the pain, Sup-port-ed by Thy word. A-MEN.

5 Thy saints in all this glorious war
  Shall conquer, though they die;
They see the triumph from afar,
  By faith they bring it nigh.

6 When that illustrious day shall rise,
  And all Thy armies shine
In robes of victory through the skies,
  The glory shall be Thine.

The Christian Life

285

ALL SAINTS, NEW. C. M. D.

REGINALD HEBER, 1783-1826

HENRY S. CUTLER, 1824-1902

1. The Son of God goes forth to war, A king-ly crown to gain;
2. The mar-tyr first, whose ea-gle eye Could pierce be-yond the grave,
3. A glo-rious band, the cho-sen few On whom the Spir-it came,

His blood-red ban-ner streams a-far: Who fol-lows in His train?
Who saw his Mas-ter in the sky, And called on Him to save:
Twelve val-iant saints, their hope they knew, And mocked the cross and flame;

Who best can drink his cup of woe, Tri-umph-ant o-ver pain,
Like Him, with par-don on His tongue, In midst of mor-tal pain,
They climbed the steep as-cent of heav'n Thro' per-il, toil, and pain:

Who pa-tient bears his cross be-low, He fol-lows in His train.
He prayed for them that did the wrong: Who fol-lows in His train?
O God, to us may grace be given To fol-low in their train! A-MEN.

Activity and Zeal

286

PENTECOST. L. M.

John S. B. Monsell, 1811–1875

William Boyd, 1847–1928

1. Fight the good fight with all thy might; Christ is thy strength, and Christ thy right:
2. Run the straight race thro' God's good grace, Lift up thine eyes, and seek His face;
3. Cast care a - side, lean on thy Guide, His bound-less mer - cy will pro - vide;
4. Faint not nor fear, for He is near, He chang-eth not and thou art dear;

Lay hold on life, and it shall be Thy joy and crown e - ter - nal - ly.
Life with its way be - fore us lies, Christ is the path, and Christ the prize.
Trust, and thy trusting soul shall prove Christ is its life, and Christ its love.
On - ly be-lieve, and thou shalt see That Christ is all in all to thee. A-MEN.

287

BOYLSTON. S. M.

Charles Wesley, 1707–1788

Lowell Mason, 1792–1872

1. A charge to keep I have, A God to glo - ri - fy,
2. To serve the pres - ent age, My call - ing to ful - fill;
3. Arm me with jeal - ous care, As in Thy sight to live,
4. Help me to watch and pray, And on Thy - self re - ly,

A nev - er - dy - ing soul to save, And fit it for the sky.
O may it all my powers en - gage To do my Mas - ter's will!
And, oh, Thy ser - vant, Lord, pre-pare A strict ac-count to give!
As - sured, if I my trust be - tray, I shall for ev - er die. A - MEN.

The Christian Life

ELLESDIE. 8 7. 8. 7. D.

Daniel March, 1816-1909

Wolfgang A. Mozart (?) 1756-1791
Arr. by Hubert P. Main, 1839-1926

1. Hark, the voice of Jesus calling, "Who will go and work to-day?
2. If you cannot cross the ocean And the heathen lands explore,
3. Let none hear you idly saying, "There is nothing I can do,"

Fields are white, and harvests waiting, Who will bear the sheaves away?"
You can find the heathen nearer, You can help them at your door:
While the souls of men are dying, And the Master calls for you:

Loud and long the Master calleth, Rich reward He offers thee;
If you cannot give your thousands, You can give the widow's mite;
Gladly take the task He gives you; Let His work your pleasure be;

Who will answer, gladly saying, "Here am I; send me, send me"?
And the least you give for Jesus Will be precious in His sight.
Answer quickly when He calleth, "Here am I, send me, send me." A-MEN.

Alternative tune, Hyfrydol, No. 11

Activity and Zeal

289

MOUNT CALVARY. C. M.

SAMUEL LONGFELLOW, 1819-1892

ROBERT P. STEWART, 1825-1894

1. O   still in   ac - cents sweet and strong Sounds forth the an - cient word,
2. We   hear the   call; in dreams no more In   self - ish ease we   lie,
3. Where proph-ets' word, and   mar - tyrs' blood, And prayers of saints were sown,
4. O   Thou whose call our hearts has stirred, To   do Thy will we come;

"More reap - ers for white har - vest fields, More la - borers for the Lord!"
But   gird - ed for our Fa - ther's work, Go forth be-neath His sky.
We,   to their la - bors en - tering in, Would reap where they have strown.
Thrust in our sick - les at Thy word, And bear our har-vest home. A-MEN.

290

KEBLE. L. M.

CHARLES WESLEY, 1707-1788

JOHN B. DYKES, 1823-1876

1. Forth in Thy name, O Lord, I go, My dai - ly la - bor to pur - sue,
2. The task Thy wis - dom hath as - signed, O let me cheer - ful - ly ful - fill;
3. Give me to bear Thy ea - sy yoke, And ev - ery mo-ment watch and pray;
4. For Thee de-light - ful - ly em - ploy What-e'er Thy boun-teous grace hath giv'n;

Thee, on - ly Thee, re-solved to know In all I think, or speak, or do.
In   all my works Thy pres-ence find, And prove Thy good and per - fect will.
And still to things e - ter - nal look, And has-ten to Thy glo-rious day;
And run my course with e - ven joy, And close-ly walk with Thee to heaven. A-MEN.

The Christian Life

291

ABENDS. L. M.

John G. Whittier, 1807–1892

Herbert S. Oakeley, 1830–1903

1. It may not be our lot to wield The sic-kle in the rip-ened field;
2. Yet where our du-ty's task is wrought In u-ni-son with God's great tho't,
3. And ours the grate-ful serv-ice whence Comes, day by day, the rec-om-pense:
4. And were this life the ut-most span, The on-ly end and aim of man,
5. But life, though fall-ing like our grain, Like that, re-vives and springs a-gain;

Nor ours to hear, on sum-mer eves, The reap-er's song a-mong the sheaves.
The near and fu-ture blend in one, And what-so-e'er is willed, is done.
The hope, the trust, the pur-pose stayed, The foun-tain, and the noon-day shade.
Bet-ter the toil of fields like these Than wak-ing dream and sloth-ful ease.
And, ear-ly called, how blest are they Who wait in heav'n their har-vest day! A-MEN.

292

ERNAN. L. M.

Horatius Bonar, 1808–1889

Lowell Mason, 1792–1872

1. Go, la-bor on! spend and be spent; Thy joy to do the Fa-ther's will:
2. Go, la-bor on! 'tis not for naught, Thine earth-ly loss is heav'n-ly gain;
3. Go, la-bor on, while it is day; The world's dark night is hasten-ing on:
4. Men die in dark-ness at your side, With-out a hope to cheer the tomb:

It is the way the Mas-ter went—Should not the ser-vant tread it still?
Men heed thee, love thee, praise thee not; The Mas-ter prais-es—what are men?
Speed, speed thy work, cast sloth a-way; It is not thus that souls are won.
Take up the torch, and wave it wide, The torch that lights time's thick-est gloom. AMEN.

Activity and Zeal

293

WORK SONG. 7. 6. 7. 6. D.

ANNIE L. COGHILL, 1836–1907

LOWELL MASON, 1792–1872

1. Work, for the night is com - ing; Work through the morn - ing hours;
2. Work, for the night is com - ing; Work through the sun - ny noon;
3. Work, for the night is com - ing, Un - der the sun - set skies;

Work while the dew is spark - ling; Work 'mid spring - ing flowers;
Fill bright - est hours with la - bor: Rest comes sure and soon.
While their bright tints are glow - ing, Work, for day - light flies.

Work when the day grows bright - er; Work in the glow - ing sun;
Give ev - ery fly - ing min - ute Some-thing to keep in store;
Work till the last beam fad - eth, Fad - eth to shine no more;

Work, for the night is com - ing, When man's work is done.
Work, for the night is com - ing, When man works no more.
Work while the night is dark - ening, When man's work is o'er. A-MEN.

The Christian Life

294

GERMANY. L. M.

RUDYARD KIPLING, 1865–1936

WILLIAM GARDINER'S SACRED MELODIES, 1815

2. Fa - ther in heaven, who lov - est all, O help Thy
3. Teach us to bear the yoke in youth, With stead - fast -
4. Teach us to rule our selves al - way, Con - trolled and
5. Teach us to look, in all our ends, On Thee for
6. Teach us the strength that can - not seek, By deed or
7. Teach us de - light in sim - ple things, And mirth that

chil - dren when they call; That they may build from age to
ness and care - ful truth; That, in our time, Thy grace may
clean - ly night and day; That we may bring, if need a -
Judge, and not our friends; That we, with Thee, may walk un -
thought, to hurt the weak; That, un - der Thee, we may pos -
has no bit - ter springs; For - give - ness free of e - vil

age, An un - de - fil - ed her - it - age.
give The truth where - by the na - tions live.
rise, No maimed or worth - less sac - ri - fice.
cowed By fear or fa - vor of the crowd.
sess Man's strength to suc - cor man's dis - tress.
done, And love to all men 'neath the sun! A - MEN.

This may be used as a children's patriotic hymn by the use of the following stanzas:

1 Land of our Birth, we pledge to thee
Our love and toil in the years to be;
When we are grown and take our place,
As men and women with our race.

8 Land of our Birth, our faith, our pride,
For whose dear sake our fathers died;
O Motherland, we pledge to thee,
Head, heart, and hand through the years
to be!

Integrity

295

SAVANNAH. 7. 7. 7. 7.

Edwin P. Parker, 1836-1925

John Wesley's Foundery Collection, 1742

1. Lord, as we Thy Name pro-fess, May our hearts Thy love con - fess,
2. Make us res - o - lute to do What Thou show-est to be true;
3. May Thy yoke be meek-ly worn, May Thy cross be brave-ly borne;
4. Gra - cious Sav-iour, heav'n-ly Friend, On Thy grace our souls de - pend;

And in all our praise of Thee May our lips and lives a-gree.
Make us hate and shun the ill, Loy - al to Thy ho - ly will.
Make us pa - tient, gen - tle, kind, Pure in life and heart and mind.
Let that grace our needs sup - ply While we live and when we die. A-MEN.

296

RHYS. L. M.

Samuel Longfellow, 1819-1892

Rhys Thomas, 1867-1932

1. Go forth to life, O child of earth! Still mind-ful of thy heav'n-ly birth;
2. Tho' pas-sion's fires are in thy soul, Thy spir - it can their flames con-trol;
3. Go on from in - no - cence of youth To man-ly pu - ri - ty and truth;
4. Then forth to life, O child of earth! Be wor-thy of thy heav'n-ly birth!

Thou art not here for ease, or sin, But man-hood's no-ble crown to win.
Tho' temp-ters strong be-set thy way, Thy spir-it is more strong than they.
God's an-gels still are near to save, And God Him-self doth help the brave.
For no-ble serv-ice thou art here: Thy broth-ers help, thy God re-vere! A-MEN.

The Christian Life

297

ST. EDMUND. 6. 4. 6. 4. 6. 6. 6. 4.

LUCY LARCOM, 1826–1893

ARTHUR S. SULLIVAN, 1842–1900

1. Draw Thou my soul, O Christ, Clos-er to Thine;
2. Lead forth my soul, O Christ, One with Thine own,
3. Not for my-self a-lone May my prayer be;

Breathe in-to ev-ery wish Thy will di-vine!
Joy-ful to fol-low Thee Through paths un-known!
Lift Thou Thy world, O Christ, Clos-er to Thee!

Raise my low self a-bove, Won by Thy death-less love;
In Thee my strength re-new; Give me my work to do!
Cleanse it from guilt and wrong; Teach it sal-va-tion's song,

Ev-er, O Christ, through mine Let Thy life shine.
Through me Thy truth be shown, Thy love made known.
Till earth, as heaven, ful-fill God's ho-ly will. A-MEN.

Music copyright, 1913, by The Methodist Book Concern

Integrity

298

COURAGE, BROTHER. 8. 7. 8. 7. D.

NORMAN MACLEOD, 1812–1872

ARTHUR S. SULLIVAN, 1842–1900

1. Cour-age, broth-er! do not stum-ble, Though thy path be dark as night;
2. Per - ish pol - i - cy and cun-ning, Per - ish all that fears the light,
3. Some will hate thee, some will love thee, Some will flat - ter, some will slight;

There's a star to guide the hum - ble: Trust in God, and do the right.
Wheth-er los - ing, wheth - er win - ning, Trust in God, and do the right.
Cease from man, and look a - bove thee: Trust in God, and do the right.

Though the road be long and drear-y, And the end be out of sight, Tread it brave-ly,
Shun all forms of guilt - y pas-sion, Fiends can look like an-gels bright; Heed no cus-tom,
Sim - ple rule and saf - est guid-ing, In-ward peace and shin-ing light, Star up-on our

strong or wea-ry: Trust in God, trust in God, trust in God, and do the right.
school, nor fash-ion: Trust in God, trust in God, trust in God, and do the right.
path a - bid - ing: Trust in God, trust in God, trust in God, and do the right. A-MEN.

The Christian Life

299

GERALD. C. M. D.

Charles Wesley, 1707-1788

Louis Spohr, 1784-1859

1. I want a prin-ci-ple with-in Of watch-ful, god-ly fear,
2. From Thee that I no more may stray, No more Thy good-ness grieve,
3. Al-might-y God of truth and love, To me Thy power im-part;

A sen-si-bil-i-ty of sin, A pain to feel it near.
Grant me the fil-ial awe, I pray, The ten-der con-science give;
The bur-den from my soul re-move, The hard-ness from my heart.

Help me the first ap-proach to feel Of pride or wrong de-sire;
Quick as the ap-ple of an eye, O God, my con-science make!
O may the least o-mis-sion pain My re-a-wak-ened soul,

To catch the wan-dering of my will, And quench the kind-ling fire.
A-wake my soul when sin is nigh, And keep it still a-wake.
And drive me to that grace a-gain, Which makes the wound-ed whole. A-men.

Integrity

300

FORTITUDE. 2. 10. 10. 10.

MALTBIE D. BABCOCK, 1858–1901

DAVID S. SMITH, 1877–

1. Be strong! We are not here to play, to dream, to drift: We have hard work to do and loads to lift; Shun not the strug-gle: face it— 'tis God's gift. Be strong, be strong!

2. Be strong! Say not the days are e-vil— who's to blame? And fold the hands and ac-qui-esce— O shame! Stand up, speak out, and brave-ly, in God's Name, Be strong, be strong!

3. Be strong! It mat-ters not how deep en-trenched the wrong, How hard the bat-tle goes, the day, how long; Faint not, fight on! To-mor-row comes the song. Be strong, be strong!

A-MEN.

Be strong, be

The Christian Life

301

CWM RHONDDA. 8. 7. 8. 7. 8. 7.

From the Welsh
WILLIAM WILLIAMS, 1717–1791
Stanza 1, tr. attributed to PETER WILLIAMS, 1722–1796
Stanzas 2, 3, tr. by WILLIAM WILLIAMS, 1717–1791

Welsh hymn melody
JOHN HUGHES, 1873–1932

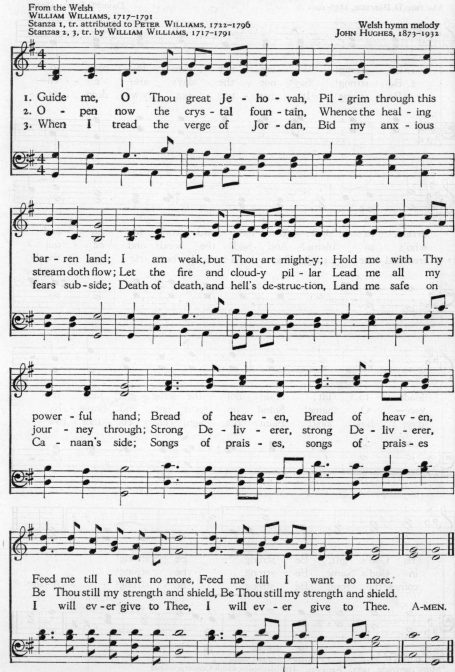

1. Guide me, O Thou great Je-ho-vah, Pil-grim through this
2. O - pen now the crys-tal foun-tain, Whence the heal-ing
3. When I tread the verge of Jor-dan, Bid my anx-ious

bar - ren land; I am weak, but Thou art might-y; Hold me with Thy
stream doth flow; Let the fire and cloud-y pil-lar Lead me all my
fears sub-side; Death of death, and hell's de-struc-tion, Land me safe on

power - ful hand; Bread of heav - en, Bread of heav - en,
jour - ney through; Strong De - liv - erer, strong De - liv - erer,
Ca - naan's side; Songs of prais - es, songs of prais - es

Feed me till I want no more, Feed me till I want no more.
Be Thou still my strength and shield, Be Thou still my strength and shield.
I will ev - er give to Thee, I will ev - er give to Thee. A-MEN.

Prayer and Guidance

302

SWEET HOUR. L. M. D.

WILLIAM W. WALFORD, ?

WILLIAM B. BRADBURY, 1816-1868

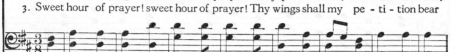

1. Sweet hour of prayer! sweet hour of prayer! That calls me from a world of care,
2. Sweet hour of prayer! sweet hour of prayer! The joys I feel, the bliss I share,
3. Sweet hour of prayer! sweet hour of prayer! Thy wings shall my pe - ti - tion bear

And bids me at my Fa - ther's throne Make all my wants and wish - es known;
Of those whose anx-ious spir - its burn With strong de-sires for thy re - turn!
To Him whose truth and faith-ful - ness En-gage the wait-ing soul to bless;

In sea-sons of dis-tress and grief, My soul has oft - en found re - lief;
With such I has - ten to the place Where God my Sav - iour shows His face,
And since He bids me seek His face, Be - lieve His Word and trust His grace,

And oft es-caped the tempt-er's snare, By thy re - turn, sweet hour of prayer!
And glad - ly take my sta - tion there, And wait for thee, sweet hour of prayer!
I'll cast on Him my ev - ery care, And wait for thee, sweet hour of prayer! A-MEN.

The Christian Life

303

CAMPMEETING. C.M.

James Montgomery, 1771–1854

Early American melody

1. Prayer is the soul's sin-cere de-sire, Un-ut-tered or ex-pressed;
2. Prayer is the bur-den of a sigh, The fall-ing of a tear,
3. Prayer is the sim-plest form of speech That in-fant lips can try;
4. Prayer is the con-trite sin-ner's voice, Re-turn-ing from his ways;

The mo-tion of a hid-den fire That trem-bles in the breast.
The up-ward glanc-ing of an eye, When none but God is near.
Prayer the sub-lim-est strains that reach The Ma-jes-ty on high.
While an-gels in their songs re-joice And cry, "Be-hold, he prays!" A-men.

5 Prayer is the Christian's vital breath,
  The Christian's native air,
  His watchword at the gates of death;
  He enters heaven with prayer.

6 O Thou, by whom we come to God,
  The Life, the Truth, the Way;
  The path of prayer Thyself hast trod:
  Lord, teach us how to pray!

Alternative tune, St. Agnes, No. 341

304

SEYMOUR. 7.7.7.7.

Alexander Clark, 1835–1879

Carl M. von Weber, 1786–1826

1. Heav'n-ly Fa-ther, bless me now; At the cross of Christ I bow;
2. Now, O Lord, this ve-ry hour, Send Thy grace and show Thy power;
3. Mer-cy now, O Lord, I plead In this hour of ut-ter need;
4. O Thou lov-ing, bless-ed One, Ris-ing o'er me like the sun,

Take my guilt and grief a-way, Hear and heal me now, I pray.
While I rest up-on Thy word, Come, and bless me now, O Lord!
Turn me not a-way un-blest, Calm my an-guish in-to rest.
Light and life art Thou with-in: Sav-iour, Thou, from ev-ery sin! A-men.

Prayer and Guidance

305

ST. MICHEL'S. C. M. D.

HENRY H. TWEEDY, 1868–

From W. GAWLER'S HYMNS AND PSALMS, 1789

1. O gra - cious Fa - ther of man-kind, Our spir - its' un - seen Friend,
2. Thou hear - est these, the good and ill, Deep bur - ied in each breast;
3. Our best is but Thy - self in us, Our high - est thought Thy will;
4. Thou seek - est us in love and truth More than our minds seek Thee;

High heav - en's Lord, our hearts' dear Guest, To Thee our prayers as - cend.
The se - cret thought, the hid - den plan, Wrought out or un - ex - pressed.
To hear Thy voice we need but love, To lis - ten, and be still.
Through o - pen gates Thy power flows in Like flood tides from the sea.

Thou dost not wait till hu - man speech Thy gifts di - vine im - plore;
O cleanse our prayers from hu - man dross, At - tune our lives to Thee,
We would not bend Thy will to ours, But blend our wills to Thine;
No more we seek Thee from a - far, Nor ask Thee for a sign,

Our dreams, our aims, our work, our lives Are prayers Thou lov-est more.
Un - til we la - bor for those gifts We ask on bend - ed knee.
Not beat with cries on heav - en's doors, But live Thy life di - vine.
Con - tent to pray in life and love And toil, till all are Thine. A - MEN.

The Christian Life

306

HANFORD. 8.8.8.4.

CHARLOTTE ELLIOTT, 1789–1871

ARTHUR S. SULLIVAN, 1842–1900

1. My God, my Fa-ther, while I stray Far from my home, on life's rough way,
2. Tho' dark my path, and sad my lot, Let me be still and mur-mur not,
3. Let but my faint-ing heart be blest With Thy sweet Spir-it for its Guest,
4. Re-new my will from day to day; Blend it with Thine, and take a-way

O teach me from my heart to say, "Thy will be done!"
Or breathe the prayer di-vine-ly taught,"Thy will be done!"
My God, to Thee I leave the rest; "Thy will be done!"
All that now makes it hard to say, "Thy will be done!" A-MEN.

307

LOUVAN. L.M.

SAMUEL F. SMITH, 1808–1895

VIRGIL C. TAYLOR, 1817–1891

1. Lord of our life, God whom we fear, Un-known,yet known; un-seen, yet near;
2. Thine eye de-tects the spar-row's fall; Thy heart of love ex-pands for all;
3. Shine in our dark-ness, Light of light, Our minds il-lume, dis-perse our night;
4. We love Thy Name; we heed Thy rod; Thy Word, our law: O gra-cious God!

Breath of our breath,in Thee we live; Life of our life, our praise re-ceive.
Our throb-bing life is full of Thee,Throned in Thy vast in-fin-i-ty.
Make us re-spon-sive to Thy will,Our souls with all Thy full-ness fill.
We wait Thy will;on Thee we call: Our light, our life, our love,our all. A-MEN.

Prayer and Guidance

308

EUDOXIA. 6. 5. 6. 5.

ALLEN EASTMAN CROSS, 1864–1943

S. BARING-GOULD, 1834–1924

1. Je - sus, kneel be - side me In the dawn of day;
2. Mas - ter, work be - side me In the shin - ing sun;
3. Sav - iour, watch be - side me In the clos - ing light;
4. Birds are wing - ing home - ward, Sun and shad - ow cease;

Thine is prayer e - ter - nal—Teach me how to pray!
Gen - tly guide Thy ser - vant Till the work be done.
Lo, the eve - ning com - eth—Watch with me this night!
Sav - iour, take my spir - it To Thy per - fect peace. A - MEN.

Words used by permission of Allen Eastman Cross
Music used by permission of A. W. Ridley and Company

309

SOHO. C. M.

CHARLES WESLEY, 1707–1788

JOSEPH BARNBY, 1838–1896

1. Talk with us, Lord, Thy - self re - veal, While here o'er earth we rove;
2. With Thee con - vers - ing, we for - get All time, and toil, and care;
3. Here, then, my God, vouch-safe to stay, And bid my heart re - joice;
4. Thou call - est me to seek Thy face—'Tis all I wish to seek;
5. Let this my ev - ery hour em - ploy, Till I Thy glo - ry see;

Speak to our hearts, and let us feel The kind-ling of Thy love.
La - bor is rest, and pain is sweet, If Thou, my God, art here.
My bound-ing heart shall own Thy sway, And ech - o to Thy voice.
To attend the whis - pers of Thy grace, And hear Thee in - ly speak.
En - ter in - to my Mas-ter's joy, And find my heaven in Thee. A - MEN.

The Christian Life

310

LIEBSTER JESU, WIR SIND HIER. 7. 8. 7. 8. 8. 8.

Tobias Clausnitzer, 1619–1684
Tr. by Catherine Winkworth, 1829–1878

Johann R. Ahle, 1625–1673

1. Bless-ed Je-sus, at Thy word We are gath-ered all to hear Thee; Let our hearts and souls be stirred Now to seek and love and fear Thee; By Thy teach-ings sweet and ho-ly, Drawn from earth to love Thee sole-ly.

2. All our know-ledge, sense, and sight Lie in deep-est dark-ness shroud-ed, Till Thy Spir-it breaks our night With the beams of truth un-cloud-ed. Thou a-lone to God canst win us, Thou must work all good with-in us.

3. Glo-rious Lord, Thy-self im-part! Light of light, from God pro-ceed-ing, O-pen Thou our ears and heart, Help us by Thy Spir-it's plead-ing, Hear the cry Thy peo-ple rais-es, Hear, and bless our prayers and prais-es. A-MEN.

Prayer and Guidance

311

CANDLER. L. M. D.

CHARLES WESLEY, 1707-1788

Scottish traditional melody
From THE HESPERIAN HARP, 1847

1. Come, O Thou Trav-el - er un-known, Whom still I hold, but can -not see;
2. I need not tell Thee who I am, My sin and mis - er - y de -clare;
3. Yield to me now, for I am weak, But con-fi - dent in self - de-spair;
4. 'Tis Love! 'tis Love! Thou diedst for me! I hear Thy whis - per in my heart;

My com-pa - ny be - fore is gone, And I am left a - lone with Thee:
Thy-self hast called me by my name — Look on Thy hands, and read it there:
Speak to my heart, in bless-ing speak; Be con-quered by my in - stant prayer:
The morn-ing breaks, the shad-ows flee; Pure, u - ni - ver - sal love Thou art:

With Thee all night I mean to stay, And wres-tle till the break of day,
But who, I ask Thee, who art Thou? Tell me Thy Name, and tell me now,
Speak, or Thou nev - er hence shalt move, And tell me if Thy Name be Love,
To me, to all, Thy mer - cies move; Thy na - ture and Thy Name is Love.

With Thee all night I mean to stay, And wres-tle till the break of day.
But who, I ask Thee, who art Thou? Tell me Thy Name, and tell me now.
Speak, or Thou nev-er hence shalt move, And tell me if Thy Name be Love.
To me, to all, Thy mer-cies move; Thy na - ture and Thy Name is Love. A - MEN.

Alternative tune, St. Catherine, No. 256

The Christian Life

312

CONSOLATION (Webbe). 11. 10. 11. 10.

THOMAS MOORE, 1779–1852
Alt. by THOMAS HASTINGS, 1784–1872

Arr. from SAMUEL WEBBE, 1740–1816

1. Come, ye dis-con-so-late, wher-e'er ye lan-guish, Come to the mer-cy seat, fer-vent-ly kneel; Here bring your wound-ed hearts, here tell your an-guish: Earth has no sor-row that heaven can-not heal.

2. Joy of the des-o-late, Light of the stray-ing, Hope of the pen-i-tent, fade-less and pure! Here speaks the Com-fort-er, ten-der-ly say-ing, "Earth has no sor-row that heaven can-not cure."

3. Here see the Bread of Life; see wa-ters flow-ing Forth from the throne of God, pure from a-bove: Come to the feast of love; come, ev-er know-ing Earth has no sor-row but heaven can re-move. A-MEN.

313

SOMERSET. C. M.

JOHN NEWTON, 1725–1807

WILLIAM H. HEWLETT, 1873–1940

1. Dear Shep-herd of Thy peo-ple, hear; Thy pres-ence now dis-play;

2. With-in these walls let ho-ly peace And love and con-cord dwell;

3. May we in faith re-ceive Thy word, In faith pre-sent our prayers,

4. The hear-ing ear, the see-ing eye, The hum-bled mind be-stow;

Prayer and Guidance

As Thou hast given a place for prayer, So give us hearts to pray.
Here give the trou-bled con-science ease, The wound-ed spir - it heal.
And in the pres-ence of our Lord Un-bos - om all our cares.
And shine up - on us from on high, To make our grac - es grow. A - MEN.

Music used by permission of William H. Hewlett

314

VINCENT. 8. 4. 8. 4. D.

SYBIL F. PARTRIDGE
(SISTER MARY XAVIER)

HORATIO R. PALMER, 1834–1907

1. Lord, for to-mor-row and its needs I do not pray; Keep me, my God, from
2. Let me be slow to do my will, Prompt to o - bey; Help me to sac-ri-
3. Let me in sea-son, Lord, be grave, In sea-son gay; Let me be faith-ful

stain of sin Just for to-day. Help me to la - bor ear-nest-ly,
fice my -self, Fa - ther, to-day. Let me no wrong or i - dle word
to Thy grace, Fa - ther, to-day. Lord, for to - mor - row and its needs

And du - ly pray; Let me be kind in word and deed, Fa-ther, to-day.
Un-think-ing say; Set Thou a seal up - on my lips Thro' all to-day.
I do not pray; Still keep me, guide me, love me, Lord, Thro' each to-day. A-MEN.

The Christian Life

ADESTE FIDELES (PORTUGUESE HYMN). 11. 11. 11. 11.

(*First Tune*)

"K" in RIPPON'S SELECTION, 1787   From JOHN F. WADE'S CANTUS DIVERSI, 1751

1. How firm a foun-da-tion, ye saints of the Lord, Is laid for your
2. "Fear not, I am with thee; O be not dis-mayed, For I am thy
3. "When thro' the deep wa-ters I call thee to go, The riv-ers of

faith in His ex-cel-lent Word! What more can He say than to
God, and will still give thee aid; I'll strength-en thee, help thee, and
woe shall not thee o-ver-flow; For I will be with thee thy

you He hath said, To you who for ref-uge to Je-sus have fled?
cause thee to stand, Up-held by my right-eous, om-nip-o-tent hand,
trou-bles to bless, And sanc-ti-fy to thee thy deep-est dis-tress,

To you who for ref-uge to Je-sus have fled?
Up-held by my right-eous, om-nip-o-tent hand.
And sanc-ti-fy to thee thy deep-est dis-tress. A-MEN.

4 "When through fiery trials thy pathway shall lie,
My grace, all-sufficient, shall be thy supply,
The flame shall not hurt thee; I only design
Thy dross to consume, and thy gold to refine.

5 "The soul that on Jesus still leans for repose,
I will not, I will not desert to his foes;
That soul, though all hell should endeavor to shake,
I'll never, no, never, no, never forsake!"

Trust and Assurance

315

FOUNDATION. 11. 11. 11. 11.

(Second Tune)

"K" in Rippon's Selection, 1787   Early American melody

1. How firm a foun-da-tion, ye saints of the Lord,
2. "Fear not, I am with thee; O be not dis-mayed,
3. "When through the deep wa-ters I call thee to go,

Is laid for your faith in His ex-cel-lent Word!
For I am thy God, and will still give thee aid;
The riv-ers of woe shall not thee o-ver-flow;

What more can He say than to you He hath said,
I'll strength-en thee, help thee, and cause thee to stand,
For I will be with thee thy trou-bles to bless,

To you who for ref-uge to Je-sus have fled?
Up-held by my right-eous, om-nip-o-tent hand.
And sanc-ti-fy to thee thy deep-est dis-tress. A-MEN.

4 "When through fiery trials thy pathway shall lie,
  My grace, all-sufficient, shall be thy supply,
  The flame shall not hurt thee; I only design
  Thy dross to consume, and thy gold to refine.

5 "The soul that on Jesus still leans for repose,
  I will not, I will not desert to his foes;
  That soul, though all hell should endeavor to shake,
  I'll never, no, never, no, never forsake!"

The Christian Life

316

PEACE. 10. 10. 10. 6.

Anonymous, c. 1904

George W. Chadwick, 1854–1931

1. I sought the Lord, and af-ter-ward I knew He moved my
2. Thou didst reach forth Thy hand and mine en-fold; I walked and
3. I find, I walk, I love, but, oh, the whole Of love is

soul to seek Him, seek-ing me; It was not I that
sank not on the storm-vexed sea; 'Twas not so much that
but my an-swer, Lord, to Thee! For Thou wert long be-

found, O Sav-iour true, No, I was found of Thee.
I on Thee took hold As Thou, dear Lord, on me.
fore-hand with my soul; Al-ways Thou lov-edst me. A - MEN.

317

RETREAT. L. M.

Hugh Stowell, 1799–1865

Thomas Hastings, 1784–1872

1. From ev-ery storm-y wind that blows, From ev-ery swell-ing tide of woes,
2. There is a place where Je-sus sheds The oil of glad-ness on our heads;
3. There is a scene where spir-its blend, Where friend holds fel-low-ship with friend;
4. Ah! there on ea-gle wings we soar, Where sin and sense mo-lest no more;

Trust and Assurance

There is a calm, a sure re-treat: 'Tis found be-neath the mer-cy seat.
A place than all be-side more sweet: It is the blood-bought mer-cy seat.
Tho' sun-dered far, by faith they meet A-round one com-mon mer-cy seat.
For heav'n comes down our souls to greet, And glo-ry crowns the mer-cy seat. A-MEN.

318

ST. MARGARET. 8. 8. 8. 8. 6.

GEORGE MATHESON, 1842–1906

ALBERT L. PEACE, 1844–1912

1. O Love that wilt not let me go, I rest my
2. O Light that fol-lowest all my way, I yield my
3. O Joy that seek-est me through pain, I can-not
4. O Cross that lift-est up my head, I dare not

wea-ry soul in Thee; I give Thee back the life I owe,
flick-ering torch to Thee; My heart re-stores its bor-rowed ray,
close my heart to Thee; I trace the rain-bow through the rain,
ask to fly from Thee; I lay in dust life's glo-ry dead,

That in Thine o-cean depths its flow May rich-er, full-er be.
That in Thy sun-shine's blaze its day May bright-er, fair-er be.
And feel the prom-ise is not vain That morn shall tear-less be.
And from the ground there blos-soms red Life that shall end-less be. A-MEN.

The Christian Life

319

TANTUM ERGO. 8. 7. 8. 7. 8. 7.

Percy Dearmer, 1867–1936

Melody from Samuel Webbe's Antiphons, 1792

1. When by fear my heart is daunt-ed, Thou dost hold me in Thy hand;
2. God, Thou art un-fail-ing treas-ure, Ref-uge Thou, and faith-ful Friend;
3. Held by love, to peace I win me, Con-fi-dent what-e'er be-tide;

Prayer-less, anx-ious, vain-ly haunt-ed, Thou dost make my cour-age stand:
Thy re-sourc-es none can meas-ure, Naught Thy stead-fast-ness can bend.
Safe in hope, Thy spir-it in me, With th'e-ter-nal power I hide;

Fool-ish wor-ries, fret-ting trou-bles Melt a-way at Thy com-mand.
Life and light and love im-mor-tal, Firm-ly we on Thee de-pend.
Strength and health are mine, and val-or— Brave-ly o-ver care I ride. A-men.

Words from Enlarged Songs of Praise. By permission of the Oxford University Press

320

MORNINGTON. S. M.

George Herbert, 1593–1632
Alt. by John Wesley, 1703–1791

Arr. from a chant by
Garret Wellesley, 1735–1781

1. Teach me, my God and King, In all things Thee to see,
2. To scorn the sens-es' sway, While still to Thee I tend;
3. All may of Thee par-take; Noth-ing so small can be
4. If done t' o-bey Thy laws, E'en ser-vile la-bors shine;
5. Thee, then, my God and King, In all things may I see;

Trust and Assurance

And what I do in an-y-thing, To do it as for Thee.
In all I do be Thou the way, In all be Thou the end.
But draws, when acted for Thy sake, Great-ness and worth from Thee.
Hal-lowed is toil, if this the cause, The mean-est work, di - vine.
And what I do, in an-y-thing, May it be done for Thee! A-MEN.

321

SELVIN. S. M.

AUGUSTUS M. TOPLADY, 1740–1778
Alt. by others

Arr. by LOWELL MASON, 1792–1872

1. If, on a qui - et sea, Toward heaven we calm - ly sail
2. But should the surg - es rise, And rest de - lay to come,
3. Soon shall our doubts and fears All yield to Thy con - trol;
4. Teach us, in ev - ery state, To make Thy will our own;

With grate - ful hearts, O God, to Thee, We'll own the fav - oring gale,
Blest be the tem - pest, kind the storm, Which drives us near - er home,
Thy ten - der mer - cies shall il - lume The mid-night of the soul,
And when the joys of sense de-part, To live by faith a - lone,

With grate-ful hearts, O God, to Thee, We'll own the fav - oring gale.
Blest be the tem-pest, kind the storm, Which drives us near-er home.
Thy ten - der mer-cies shall il - lume The mid-night of the soul.
And when the joys of sense de-part, To live by faith a - lone. A-MEN.

The Christian Life

322

FERGUSON. S. M.

WILLIAM F. LLOYD, 1791–1853

GEORGE KINGSLEY, 1811–1884

1. My times are in Thy hand: My God, I wish them there;
2. My times are in Thy hand, What-ev-er they may be;
3. My times are in Thy hand; Why should I doubt or fear?
4. My times are in Thy hand; I'll al-ways trust in Thee;

My life, my friends, my soul, I leave En-tire-ly to Thy care.
Pleas-ing or pain-ful, dark or bright, As best may seem to Thee.
My Fa-ther's hand will nev-er cause His child a need-less tear.
And, aft-er death, at Thy right hand I shall for ev-er be. A-MEN.

323

DOLOMITE CHANT. 6. 6. 6. 6.

Austrian melody

BRADFORD TORREY, 1843–1912

Harmonized by JOSEPH T. COOPER, 1819–1870

May be sung in unison

1. Not so in haste, my heart! Have faith in God and wait; Al-though He
2. He nev-er com-eth late; He know-eth what is best; Vex not thy-
3. Un-til He com-eth, rest, Nor grudge the hours that roll; The feet that
4. Are soon-est at the goal That is not gained by speed; Then hold thee

lin-ger long, He nev-er comes too late.
self in vain; Un-til He com-eth, rest.
wait for God Are soon-est at the goal.
still, my heart, For I shall wait His lead. A-MEN.

Trust and Assurance

324

AURELIA. 7. 6. 7. 6. D.

JAMES MONTGOMERY, 1771–1854

SAMUEL S. WESLEY, 1810–1876

1. God is my strong sal-va-tion: What foe have I to fear?
2. Place on the Lord re-li-ance; My soul, with cour-age wait;

In dark-ness and temp-ta-tion, My light, my help, is near:
His truth be thine af-fi-ance, When faint and des-o-late;

Though hosts en-camp a-round me, Firm in the fight I stand;
His might thy heart shall strength-en, His love thy joy in-crease;

What ter-ror can con-found me, With God at my right hand?
Mer-cy thy days shall length-en; The Lord will give thee peace. A-MEN.

The Christian Life

325

O JESU. 8. 6. 8. 6. 8. 8.

SAMUEL LONGFELLOW, 1819–1892

Melody from HIRSCHBERG GESANGBUCH, 1741

1. I look to Thee in ev - ery need,
2. Dis - cour - aged in the work of life,
3. Thy calm - ness bends se - rene a - bove,
4. Em - bos - omed deep in Thy dear love,

And nev - er look in vain; I feel Thy strong and ten - der love,
Dis - heart - ened by its load, Shamed by its fail - ures or its fears,
My rest - less - ness to still; A - round me flows Thy quick - ening life,
Held in Thy law, I stand; Thy hand in all things I be - hold,

And all is well a - gain: The thought of Thee is might - ier far
I sink be - side the road; But let me on - ly think of Thee
To nerve my fal - tering will: Thy pres - ence fills my sol - i - tude;
And all things in Thy hand; Thou lead - est me by un - sought ways,

Than sin and pain and sor - row are.
And then new heart springs up in me.
Thy prov - i - dence turns all to good.
And turn'st my mourn - ing in - to praise. A - MEN.

Trust and Assurance

326

PLEYEL'S HYMN. 7. 7. 7. 7.

John Cennick, 1718-1755

Ignace J. Pleyel, 1757-1831

1. Chil-dren of the Heaven-ly King, As we jour-ney let us sing;
2. We are travel-ing home to God, In the way our fa-thers trod;
3. Fear not, breth-ren; joy-ful stand On the bor-ders of our land:
4. Lord, o-be-dient-ly we'll go, Glad-ly leav-ing all be-low:

Sing our Sav-iour's wor-thy praise, Glo-rious in His works and ways.
They are hap-py now, and we Soon their hap-pi-ness shall see.
Je-sus Christ, our Fa-ther's Son, Bids us un-dis-mayed go on.
On-ly Thou our Lead-er be, And we still will fol-low Thee. A-men.

327

FLEMMING. 8. 8. 8. 6.

Charlotte Elliott, 1789-1871

Friedrich F. Flemming, 1778-1813

1. O Ho-ly Sav-iour, Friend un-seen, Since on Thine arm Thou bidd'st me lean,
2. What tho' the world de-ceit-ful prove, And earth-ly friends and hopes re-move;
3. Tho' oft I seem to tread a-lone Life's drear-y waste, with thorns o'er-grown,
4. Tho' faith and hope may long be tried, I ask not, need not, aught be-side;

Help me, through-out life's chang-ing scene, By faith to cling to Thee.
With pa-tient, un-com-plain-ing love, Still would I cling to Thee.
Thy voice of love, in gen-tlest tone, Still whis-pers, "Cling to me!"
How safe, how calm, how sat-is-fied, The soul that clings to Thee! A-men.

The Christian Life

328

ABERGELE. C. M.

Frederick W. Faber, 1814–1863

John A. Lloyd, 1815–1874

1. I wor-ship Thee, most gra-cious God, And all Thy ways a - dore;
2. When ob - sta - cles and tri - als seem Like pris - on walls to be,
3. I have no cares, O bless - ed Will, For all my cares are Thine;

And ev - ery day I live, I seem To love Thee more and more.
I do the lit - tle I can do, And leave the rest to Thee.
I live in tri -umph, Lord, for Thou Hast made Thy tri -umphs mine. A-MEN.

4 He always wins who sides with God;
　To him no chance is lost;
　God's will is sweetest to him when
　It triumphs at his cost.

5 Ill that He blesses is our good,
　And unblest good is ill;
　And all is right that seems most wrong,
　If it be His sweet will.

329

TRURO. L. M.

Samuel Medley, 1738–1799

From Psalmodia Evangelica, 1789

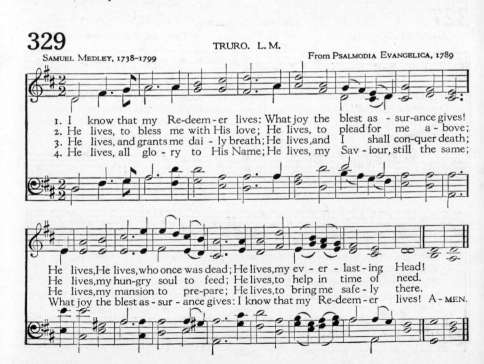

1. I know that my Re-deem - er lives: What joy the blest as - sur-ance gives!
2. He lives, to bless me with His love; He lives, to plead for me a - bove;
3. He lives, and grants me dai - ly breath; He lives, and I shall con-quer death;
4. He lives, all glo - ry to His Name; He lives, my Sav - iour, still the same;

He lives, He lives, who once was dead; He lives, my ev - er - last-ing Head!
He lives, my hun-gry soul to feed; He lives, to help in time of need.
He lives, my mansion to pre-pare; He lives, to bring me safe - ly there.
What joy the blest as - sur-ance gives: I know that my Re-deem - er lives! A - MEN.

Trust and Assurance

330

JEWETT. 6. 6. 6. 6. D.

Benjamin Schmolck, 1672-1737
Tr. by Jane Borthwick, 1813-1897

From Carl M. von Weber, 1786-1826

1. My Je - sus, as Thou wilt! O may Thy will be mine!
2. My Je - sus, as Thou wilt! Tho' seen thro' many a tear,
3. My Je - sus, as Thou wilt! All shall be well for me;

In - to Thy hand of love I would my all re - sign.
Let not my star of hope Grow dim or dis - ap - pear.
Each chang - ing fu - ture scene I glad - ly trust with Thee.

Through sor - row or thro' joy, Con - duct me as Thine own;
Since Thou on earth hast wept And sor - rowed oft a - lone,
Straight to my home a - bove I trav - el calm - ly on,

And help me still to say, "My Lord, Thy will be done."
If I must weep with Thee, My Lord, Thy will be done.
And sing, in life or death, "My Lord, Thy will be done." A - MEN.

The Christian Life

331

COPELAND. L. M.

Benjamin Copeland, 1855-1940

Karl P. Harrington, 1861-

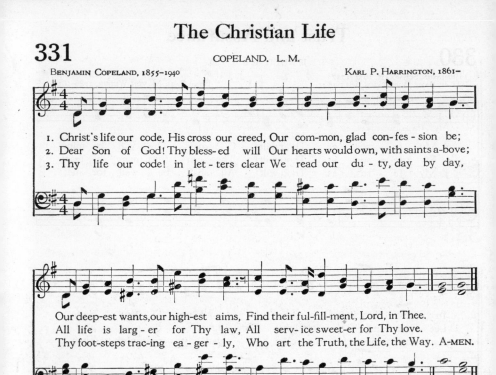

1. Christ's life our code, His cross our creed, Our com-mon, glad con-fes-sion be;
2. Dear Son of God! Thy bless-ed will Our hearts would own, with saints a-bove;
3. Thy life our code! in let-ters clear We read our du-ty, day by day,

Our deep-est wants, our high-est aims, Find their ful-fill-ment, Lord, in Thee.
All life is larg-er for Thy law, All serv-ice sweet-er for Thy love.
Thy foot-steps trac-ing ea-ger-ly, Who art the Truth, the Life, the Way. A-MEN.

4 Thy cross our creed! Thy boundless love
  A ransomed world at last shall laud,
And crown Thee their eternal King,
  O Lord of Glory! Lamb of God!

5 Till then, to Thee our souls aspire
  In ardent prayer and earnest deed,
With love like Thine, confessing, still,
  Christ's life our code! His cross our creed!

Alternative tune, Rimington, No. 345
Music copyright by Karl P. Harrington. Renewal, **1933**

332

ST. BERNARD. C. M.

George W. Doane, 1799-1859

John Richardson, 1816-1879

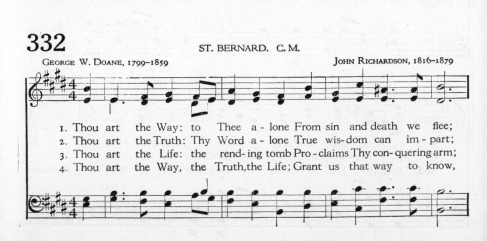

1. Thou art the Way: to Thee a-lone From sin and death we flee;
2. Thou art the Truth: Thy Word a-lone True wis-dom can im-part;
3. Thou art the Life: the rend-ing tomb Pro-claims Thy con-quering arm;
4. Thou art the Way, the Truth, the Life; Grant us that way to know,

Trust and Assurance

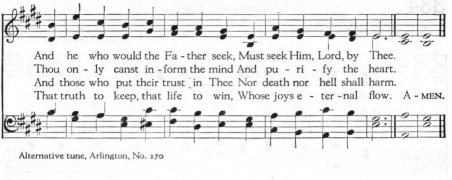

And he who would the Fa-ther seek, Must seek Him, Lord, by Thee.
Thou on-ly canst in-form the mind And pu-ri-fy the heart.
And those who put their trust in Thee Nor death nor hell shall harm.
That truth to keep, that life to win, Whose joys e-ter-nal flow. A-MEN.

Alternative tune, Arlington, No. 270

333

KEDRON. 6. 4. 6. 4. 6. 6. 4.

HORATIUS BONAR, 1808-1889

ANN B. SPRATT, 1829-?

Ped.

1. No, not de-spair-ing-ly Come I to Thee; No, not dis-
2. Ah! mine in-i-qui-ty Crim-son hath been, In-fi-nite,
3. Lord, I con-fess to Thee Sad-ly my sin; All I am

trust-ing-ly Bend I the knee: Sin hath gone o-ver me,
in-fi-nite- Sin up-on sin: Sin of not lov-ing Thee,
tell I Thee, All I have been: Purge Thou my sin a-way,

Yet is this still my plea: Je-sus hath died.
Sin of not trust-ing Thee— In-fi-nite sin.
Wash Thou my soul this day: Lord, make me clean. A-MEN.

4 Faithful and just art Thou,
   Forgiving all;
Loving and kind art Thou
   When poor ones call:
Lord, let the cleansing blood,
Blood of the Lamb of God,
   Pass o'er my soul.

5 Then all is peace and light
   This soul within;
Thus shall I walk with Thee,
   The loved Unseen;
Leaning on Thee, my God,
Guided along the road,
   Nothing between.

The Christian Life

334

HAMBURG. L. M.

Madame Guyon, 1648-1717
Tr. by William Cowper, 1731-1800
Alt. by others

From a Gregorian chant
Arr. by Lowell Mason, 1792-1872

1. My Lord, how full of sweet con - tent, I pass my
2. To me re - mains nor place nor time; My coun - try
3. While place we seek, or place we shun The soul finds
4. Could I be cast where Thou art not, That were in -

years of ban - ish - ment! Wher-e'er I dwell, I
is in ev - er - y clime: I can be calm and
hap - pi - ness in none: But with a God to
deed a dread - ful lot: But re - gions none re -

dwell with Thee, In heaven, in earth, or on the sea.
free from care On an - y shore, since God is there.
guide our way, 'Tis e - qual joy, to go or stay.
mote I call, Se - cure of find - ing God in all. A - MEN.

335

LAKE ENON. S. M.

Henry Harbaugh, 1817-1867

Isaac B. Woodbury, 1819-1858

1. Je - sus, I live to Thee, The love - li - est and best;
2. Je - sus, I die to Thee, When - ev - er death shall come;
3. Wheth-er to live or die, I know not which is best;
4. Liv - ing or dy - ing, Lord, I ask but to be Thine;

Trust and Assurance

My life in Thee, Thy life in me, In Thy blest love I rest.
To die in Thee is life to me In my e - ter - nal home.
To live in Thee is bliss to me, To die is end - less rest.
My life in Thee, Thy life in me, Makes heaven for ev - er mine. A-MEN.

336

SEELENBRAUTIGAM. 5. 5. 8. 8. 5. 5.

Nicolaus L. Zinzendorf, 1700–1760
Tr. by Jane L. Borthwick, 1813–1897

Adam Drese, 1620–1701
Harmonized by Samuel S. Wesley, 1810–1876

1. Je - sus, still lead on, Till our rest be won, And, al - though the
2. If the way be drear, If the foe be near, Let not faith - less
3. Je - sus, still lead on, Till our rest be won; Heaven-ly Lead - er,

way be cheer - less, We will fol - low, calm and fear - less;
fears o'er - take us, Let not faith and hope for - sake us;
still di - rect us, Still sup - port, con - sole, pro - tect us,

Guide us by Thy hand To our fa - ther - land.
For, through many a foe, To our home we go.
Till we safe - ly stand In our fa - ther - land. A - MEN.

The Christian Life

337

BRADBURY. 8. 7. 8. 7. D.

From Hymns for the Young, 1836
Ascribed to Dorothy A. Thrupp, 1779–1847

William B. Bradbury, 1816–1868

1. Sav - iour, like a shep - herd lead us, Much we need Thy ten - der care;
2. We are Thine, do Thou be - friend us, Be the guard - ian of our way;
3. Thou hast prom - ised to re - ceive us, Poor and sin - ful tho' we be;
4. Ear - ly let us seek Thy fa - vor, Ear - ly let us do Thy will;

In Thy pleas - ant pas - tures feed us, For our use Thy folds pre - pare:
Keep Thy flock, from sin de - fend us, Seek us when we go a - stray:
Thou hast mer - cy to re - lieve us, Grace to cleanse, and power to free:
Bless - ed Lord and on - ly Sav - iour, With Thy love our bos - oms fill:

Bless - ed Je - sus, Bless - ed Je - sus! Thou hast bought us, Thine we are,
Bless - ed Je - sus, Bless - ed Je - sus! Hear, O hear us, when we pray,
Bless - ed Je - sus, Bless - ed Je - sus! We will ear - ly turn to Thee,
Bless - ed Je - sus, Bless - ed Je - sus! Thou hast loved us, love us still,

Bless - ed Je - sus, Bless - ed Je - sus! Thou hast bought us, Thine we are.
Bless - ed Je - sus, Bless - ed Je - sus! Hear, O hear us, when we pray.
Bless - ed Je - sus, Bless - ed Je - sus! We will ear - ly turn to Thee.
Bless - ed Je - sus, Bless - ed Je - sus! Thou hast loved us, love us still. A-MEN.

Peace and Joy

338

MARTYN. 7. 7. 7. 7. D.

(*First Tune*)

CHARLES WESLEY, 1707–1788   SIMEON B. MARSH, 1798–1875

1. Je - sus, Lov - er of my soul, Let me to Thy bos - om fly,
2. Oth - er ref - uge have I none; Hangs my help-less soul on Thee;
3. Thou, O Christ, art all I want; More than all in Thee I find:
4. Plen-teous grace with Thee is found, Grace to cov - er all my sin;

While the near - er wa - ters roll, While the tem - pest still is high:
Leave, ah! leave me not a - lone, Still sup-port and com - fort me:
Raise the fall - en, cheer the faint, Heal the sick, and lead the blind.
Let the heal - ing streams a - bound; Make and keep me pure with - in.

Hide me, O my Sav - iour, hide, Till the storm of life is past;
All my trust on Thee is stayed, All my help from Thee I bring;
Just and ho - ly is Thy Name, I am all un - right-eous - ness;
Thou of life the Foun - tain art, Free - ly let me take of Thee:

Safe in - to the ha - ven guide; O re-ceive my soul at last!
Cov - er my de-fense - less head With the shad-ow of Thy wing.
False and full of sin I am, Thou art full of truth and grace.
Spring Thou up with-in my heart, Rise to all e - ter - ni - ty. A - MEN.

The Christian Life

338

HOLLINGSIDE. 7. 7. 7. 7. D.
(*Second Tune*)

CHARLES WESLEY, 1707–1788

JOHN B. DYKES, 1823–1876

1. Je - sus, Lov - er of my soul, Let me to Thy bos - om fly,
2. Oth - er ref - uge have I none; Hangs my help - less soul on Thee;
3. Thou, O Christ, art all I want; More than all in Thee I find:
4. Plen-teous grace with Thee is found, Grace to cov - er all my sin;

While the near - er wa - ters roll, While the tem-pest still is high:
Leave, ah! leave me not a - lone, Still sup - port and com-fort me:
Raise the fall - en, cheer the faint, Heal the sick, and lead the blind.
Let the heal - ing streams a - bound; Make and keep me pure with - in.

Hide me, O my Sav - iour, hide, Till the storm of life is past;
All my trust on Thee is stayed, All my help from Thee I bring;
Just and ho - ly is Thy Name, I am all un - right - eous-ness;
Thou of life the Foun-tain art, Free - ly let me take of Thee:

Safe in - to the ha - ven guide; O re - ceive my soul at last!
Cov - er my de-fense-less head With the shad - ow of Thy wing.
False and full of sin I am, Thou art full of truth and grace.
Spring Thou up with - in my heart, Rise to all e - ter - ni - ty. A-MEN.

Peace and Joy

338

ABERYSTWYTH. 7. 7. 7. 7. D.

(*Third Tune*)

CHARLES WESLEY, 1707–1788

JOSEPH PARRY, 1841–1903

1. Je - sus, Lov-er of my soul, Let me to Thy bos - om fly,
2. Oth - er ref - uge have I none; Hangs my help - less soul on Thee;
3. Thou, O Christ, art all I want; More than all in Thee I find:
4. Plen - teous grace with Thee is found, Grace to cov - er all my sin;

While the near - er wa - ters roll, While the tem - pest still is high:
Leave, ah! leave me not a - lone, Still sup - port and com - fort me:
Raise the fall - en, cheer the faint, Heal the sick, and lead the blind.
Let the heal - ing streams a - bound; Make and keep me pure with - in.

Hide me, O my Sav - iour, hide, Till the storm of life is past;
All my trust on Thee is stayed, All my help from Thee I bring;
Just and ho - ly is Thy Name, I am all un - right - eous-ness;
Thou of life the Foun - tain art, Free - ly let me take of Thee:

Safe in - to the ha - ven guide; O re - ceive my soul at last!
Cov - er my de - fense-less head With the shad - ow of Thy wing.
False and full of sin I am, Thou art full of truth and grace.
Spring Thou up with - in my heart, Rise to all e - ter - ni - ty. A - MEN.

Music used by permission of Hughes and Son, Publishers, Wrexham, North Wales

The Christian Life

339

ST. PETERSBURG. 8. 8. 8. 8. 8. 8.

CHARLES WESLEY, 1707-1788

DIMITRI S. BORTNIANSKY, 1752-1825

1. Thou hid - den Source of calm re - pose, Thou all - suf -
2. Thy might - y Name sal - va - tion is, And keeps my
3. Je - sus, my All - in - All Thou art: My rest in
4. In want my plen - ti - ful sup - ply, In weak - ness

fi - cient Love di - vine, My help and ref - uge from my foes,
hap - py soul a - bove: Com-fort it brings, and pow'r, and peace,
toil, my ease in pain, The heal - ing of my bro - ken heart,
my al - might - y pow'r, In bonds my per - fect lib - er - ty,

Se - cure I am while Thou art mine; And lo! from sin, and
And joy, and ev - er - last - ing love: To me, with Thy great
In war my peace, in loss my gain, My smile be - neath the
My light in Sa - tan's dark - est hour, In grief my joy un -

grief, and shame, I hide me, Je - sus, in Thy Name.
Name, are given Par - don, and ho - li - ness and heaven.
ty - rant's frown: In shame my glo - ry and my crown,
speak - a - ble, My life in death: my All - in - All. A - MEN.

Peace and Joy

STRACATHRO. C. M.

340

JOHN G. WHITTIER, 1807–1892

CHARLES HUTCHESON, 1792–1860

1. All as God wills, who wise-ly heeds To give or to with-hold,
2. E-nough that bless-ings un - de-served Have marked my err - ing track;
3. That more and more a prov - i - dence Of love is un - der-stood,

And know-eth more of all my needs Than all my pray'rs have told.
That, where-so - e'er my feet have swerved, His chas-tening turned me back;
Mak-ing the springs of time and sense Sweet with e - ter - nal good; A-MEN.

4 That death seems but a covered way
  Which opens into light,
Wherein no blinded child can stray
  Beyond the Father's sight;

5 And so the shadows fall apart,
  And so the west winds play;
And all the windows of my heart
  I open to the day.

341

ST. AGNES. C. M.

JOHN OXENHAM

JOHN B. DYKES, 1823–1876

1. 'Mid all the traf - fic of the ways—Tur-moils with-out, with - in—
2. A lit - tle shrine of qui - et - ness, All sa - cred to Thy - self,
3. A lit - tle shel - ter from life's stress, Where I may lay me prone,
4. A lit - tle place of mys - tic grace, Of self and sin swept bare,

Make in my heart a qui - et place, And come and dwell there-in:
Where Thou shalt all my soul pos-sess, And I may find my - self;
And bare my soul in lone - li - ness, And know as I am known;
Where I may look up - on Thy face, And talk with Thee in prayer A-MEN.

The Christian Life

REST (ELTON). 8. 6. 8. 8. 6.

JOHN G. WHITTIER, 1807-1892   FREDERICK C. MAKER, 1844-1927

342

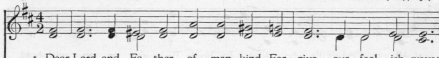

1. Dear Lord and Fa-ther of man-kind, For-give our fool-ish ways;
2. In sim-ple trust like theirs who heard, Be-side the Syr-ian sea,
3. O Sab-bath rest by Gal-i-lee! O calm of hills a-bove,
4. Drop Thy still dews of qui-et-ness, Till all our striv-ings cease;

Re-clothe us in our right-ful mind, In pur-er lives Thy
The gra-cious call-ing of the Lord, Let us, like them, with
Where Je-sus knelt to share with Thee The si-lence of e-
Take from our souls the strain and stress, And let our or-dered

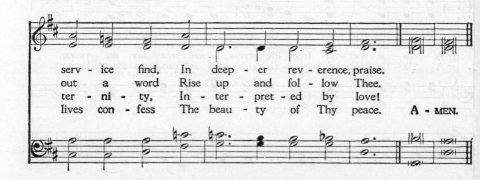

serv-ice find, In deep-er rev-er-ence, praise.
out a word Rise up and fol-low Thee.
ter-ni-ty, In-ter-pret-ed by love!
lives con-fess The beau-ty of Thy peace.   A - MEN.

5 Breathe through the heats of our desire
    Thy coolness and Thy balm;
  Let sense be dumb, let flesh retire;
  Speak through the earthquake, wind, and fire,
    O still small voice of calm!

Peace and Joy

343

RICHMOND. S. M. D.

Charles Wesley, 1707–1788

Asa B. Everett, 1828–1875

1. Je - sus, my strength, my hope, On Thee I cast my care,
2. I want a so - ber mind, A self - re - nounc - ing will,
3. I want a god - ly fear, A quick dis - cern - ing eye,
4. I want a true re - gard, A sin - gle, stead - y aim,

With hum - ble con - fi - dence look up, And know Thou hear'st my prayer.
That tram - ples down, and casts be - hind The baits of pleas - ing ill;
That looks to Thee when sin is near, And sees the tempt - er fly;
Un - moved by threat - en - ing or re - ward, To Thee and Thy great Name;

Give me on Thee to wait, Till I can all things do,
A soul in - ured to pain, To hard - ship, grief, and loss;
A spir - it still pre - pared, And armed with jeal - ous care;
A jeal - ous, just con - cern For Thine im - mor - tal praise;

On Thee, al - might - y to cre - ate, Al - might - y to re - new.
Bold to take up, firm to sus - tain, The con - se - crat - ed cross.
For ev - er stand - ing on its guard, And watch - ing un - to prayer.
A pure de - sire that all may learn And glo - ri - fy Thy grace. A - MEN.

The Christian Life

344

EISENACH. L. M.

CHARLES WESLEY, 1707–1788

JOHANN H. SCHEIN, 1586–1630
Harmonized by J. S. BACH, 1685–1750

1. O Thou who cam - est from a - bove, The
2. There let it for Thy glo - ry burn With
3. Je - sus, con - firm my heart's de - sire To
4. Read - y for all Thy per - fect will, My

pure ce - les - tial fire t'im - part, Kin - dle a flame of
in - ex - tin - guish - a - ble blaze, And trem - bling to its
work, and speak, and think for Thee; Still let me guard the
acts of faith and love re - peat, Till death Thy end - less

sa - cred love On the mean al - tar of my heart.
source re - turn, In hum - ble prayer and fer - vent praise.
ho - ly fire, And still stir up Thy gift in me:
mer - cies seal, And make the sac - ri - fice com - plete. A - MEN.

345

RIMINGTON. L. M.

Authorship uncertain
Ascribed to BERNARD OF CLAIRVAUX, 1091–1153
Tr. and arr. by RAY PALMER, 1808–1887

FRANCIS DUCKWORTH, 1862–

1. Je - sus, Thou Joy of lov - ing hearts! Thou Fount of life! Thou Light of men!
2. Thy truth un - changed hath ev - er stood; Thou sav - est those that on Thee call;
3. We taste Thee, O Thou Liv - ing Bread, And long to feast up - on Thee still;
4. Our rest - less spir - its yearn for Thee, Wher - e'er our change - ful lot is cast;
5. O Je - sus, ev - er with us stay; Make all our mo - ments calm and bright;

Peace and Joy

From the best bliss that earth im-parts, We turn un-filled to Thee a-gain.
To them that seek Thee, Thou art good; To them that find Thee, all in all.
We drink of Thee, the Foun-tain Head, And thirst our souls from Thee to fill!
Glad, when Thy gra-cious smile we see, Blest, when our faith can hold Thee fast.
Chase the dark night of sin a - way, Shed o'er the world Thy ho - ly light! A-MEN.

Alternative tune, Federal Street, No. 185
Music used by permission of Francis Duckworth

346

BELOVED. 11. 8. 11. 8.

JOSEPH SWAIN, 1761-1796

FREEMAN LEWIS, 1780-1859
Arr. by HUBERT P. MAIN, 1839-1926

1. O Thou, in whose pres - ence my soul takes de - light,
2. Where dost Thou, dear Shep - herd, re - sort with Thy sheep,
3. O why should I wan - der an a - lien from Thee,
4. Re - store, my dear Sav - iour, the light of Thy face;
5. He looks! and ten thou - sands of an - gels re - joice,

On whom in af - flic - tion I call, My com - fort by day, and my
To feed them in pas - tures of love? Say, why in the val - ley of
Or cry in the des - ert for bread? Thy foes will re - joice when my
Thy soul-cheer-ing com - fort im - part; And let the sweet to - kens of
And myr - i - ads wait for His word; He speaks! and e - ter - ni - ty,

song in the night, My hope, my sal - va - tion, my all!
death should I weep, Or a - lone in this wil - der - ness rove?
sor - rows they see, And smile at the tears I have shed.
par - don - ing grace Bring joy to my des - o - late heart.
filled with His voice, Re - ech - oes the praise of the Lord. A-MEN.

The Christian Life

347

HOLY CROSS. C.M.

JOHN NEWTON, 1725-1807

Adapted by JAMES C. WADE, 1847-

1. How sweet the name of Je - sus sounds In a be - liev - er's ear!
2. It makes the wound-ed spir - it whole, And calms the trou-bled breast;
3. Weak is the ef - fort of my heart, And cold my warm-est thought;
4. Till then, I would Thy love pro-claim With ev - ery fleet-ing breath;

It soothes his sor-rows, heals his wounds, And drives a-way his fear.
'Tis man - na to the hun - gry soul, And to the wea - ry, rest.
But when I see Thee as Thou art, I'll praise Thee as I ought.
And may the mu - sic of Thy Name Re-fresh my soul in death. A-MEN.

Alternative tune, St. Peter, No. 424

348

ST. AGNES. C.M.

Authorship uncertain
Ascribed to BERNARD OF CLAIRVAUX, 1091-1153
Tr. by EDWARD CASWALL, 1814-1878

JOHN B. DYKES, 1823-1876

1. Je - sus, the ver - y thought of Thee With sweet-ness fills the breast;
2. Nor voice can sing, nor heart can frame, Nor can the mem-ory find
3. O Hope of ev - ery con - trite heart, O Joy of all the meek,

But sweet-er far Thy face to see, And in Thy pres-ence rest.
A sweet -er sound than Thy blest Name, O Sav-iour of man-kind!
To those who ask, how kind Thou art! How good to those who seek! A - MEN.

4 But what to those who find? Ah, this
 Nor tongue nor pen can show:
 The love of Jesus, what it is
 None but His loved ones know.

5 Jesus, our only joy be Thou,
 As Thou our prize wilt be;
 Jesus, be Thou our glory now,
 And through eternity.

Peace and Joy

CONTRAST. 8. 8. 8. 8. 8. 8. 8. 8.

JOHN NEWTON, 1725–1807

Early American melody

1. How te - dious and taste-less the hours When Je - sus no lon - ger I see!
2. His Name yields the rich - est per-fume, And sweet - er than mu - sic His voice;
3. Con - tent with be - hold-ing His face, My all to His pleas-ure re - signed,
4. Dear Lord, if in - deed I am Thine, If Thou art my sun and my song,

Sweet pros-pects, sweet birds, and sweet flowers, Have all lost their sweet-ness to me;
His pres-ence dis - per - ses my gloom, And makes all with - in me re - joice;
No chang-es of sea - son or place Would make an - y change in my mind:
Say, why do I lan-guish and pine, And why are my win - ters so long?

The mid - sum-mer sun shines but dim, The fields strive in vain to look gay;
I should, were He al - ways thus nigh, Have noth-ing to wish or to fear;
While blest with a sense of His love, A pal - ace a toy would ap - pear;
O drive these dark clouds from my sky, Thy soul-cheer-ing pres-ence re - store;

But when I am hap-py in Him, De - cem-ber's as pleas-ant as May.
No mor - tal so hap-py as I, My sum-mer would last all the year.
And pri-sons would pal-a - ces prove, If Je - sus would dwell with me there.
Or take me to Thee up on high, Where win-ter and clouds are no more. A - MEN.

The Christian Life

350

ADRIAN. 11. 10. 11. 10.

(*First Tune*)

Catherine H. Esling, 1812–1897

Thomas F. Rinehart, 1860–1937

1. Come un-to Me, when sha-dows dark-ly gath-er,
2. Large are the man-sions in thy Fa-ther's dwell-ing;
3. There, like an E-den blos-som-ing in glad-ness,

When the sad heart is wea-ry and dis-tressed;
Glad are the homes that sor-rows nev-er dim:
Bloom the fair flowers the earth too rude-ly pressed;

Seek - ing for com - fort from your Heaven-ly Fa - ther,
Sweet are the harps in ho - ly mu - sic swell-ing;
Come un - to Me, all ye who droop in sad - ness,

Come un - to Me, and I will give you rest.
Soft are the tones which raise the heaven-ly hymn.
Come un - to Me, and I will give you rest. A - MEN.

Music used by permission of Thomas F. Rinehart

Peace and Joy

350

HENLEY. 11. 10. 11. 10
(*Second Tune*)

CATHERINE H. ESLING, 1812–1897   LOWELL MASON, 1792–1872

1. Come un-to Me, when shad-ows dark-ly gath-er,
2. Large are the man-sions in thy Fa-ther's dwell-ing;
3. There, like an E-den blos-som-ing in glad-ness,

When the sad heart is wea-ry and dis-tressed;
Glad are the homes that sor-rows nev-er dim;
Bloom the fair flowers the earth too rude-ly pressed;

Seek-ing for com-fort from your Heaven-ly Fa-ther,
Sweet are the harps in ho-ly mu-sic swell-ing;
Come un-to Me, all ye who droop in sad-ness,

Come un-to Me, and I will give you rest.
Soft are the tones which raise the heaven-ly hymn.
Come un-to Me, and I will give you rest. A-MEN.

The Christian Life

351

PETITION. 7. 6. 7. 6. D.

WILLIAM COWPER, 1731-1800

FRANCIS J. HAYDN, 1732-1809

1. Some-times a light sur-pris-es The Chris-tian while he sings;
2. In ho-ly con-tem-pla-tion We sweet-ly then pur-sue
3. It can bring with it noth-ing But He will bear us through;
4. Though vine nor fig tree nei-ther Their wont-ed fruit should bear,

It is the Lord, who ris-es With heal-ing in His wings:
The theme of God's sal-va-tion, And find it ev-er new;
Who gives the lil-ies cloth-ing Will clothe His peo-ple, too;
Though all the field should with-er, Nor flocks nor herds be there;

When com-forts are de-clin-ing, He grants the soul a-gain
Set free from pres-ent sor-row, We cheer-ful-ly can say,
Be-neath the spread-ing heav-ens, No crea-ture but is fed;
Yet God the same a-bid-ing, His praise shall tune my voice,

A sea-son of clear shin-ing, To cheer it af-ter rain.
Let the un-known to-mor-row Bring with it what it may.
And He who feeds the ra-vens Will give His chil-dren bread.
For while in Him con-fid-ing, I can-not but re-joice. A-MEN.

Peace and Joy

352

DAY OF REST. 7. 6. 7. 6. D.

ANNA L. WARING, 1823–1910

JAMES W. ELLIOTT, 1833–1915

1. In heaven-ly love a - bid - ing, No change my heart shall fear;
2. Wher - ev - er He may guide me, No want shall turn me back;
3. Green pas - tures are be - fore me, Which yet I have not seen;

And safe is such con - fid - ing, For noth - ing chan - ges here.
My Shep - herd is be - side me, And noth - ing can I lack.
Bright skies will soon be o'er me, Where dark - est clouds have been.

The storm may roar with - out me, My heart may low be laid;
His wis - dom ev - er wak - eth, His sight is nev - er dim;
My hope I can - not mea - sure, My path to life is free;

In unison   *In harmony*

But God is round a - bout me, And can I be dis-mayed?
He knows the way He tak - eth, And I will walk with Him.
My Sav - iour has my treas - ure, And He will walk with me. A - MEN.

The Christian Life

353

DOMINUS REGIT ME. 8. 7. 8. 7.

HENRY W. BAKER, 1821–1877

JOHN B. DYKES, 1823–1876

1. The King of love my Shep-herd is, Whose good-ness fail-eth nev-er;
2. Where streams of liv-ing wa-ter flow, My ran-somed soul He lead-eth,
3. Per-verse and fool-ish oft I strayed, But yet in love He sought me,

I noth-ing lack if I am His And He is mine for ev-er.
And, where the ver-dant pas-tures grow, With food ce-les-tial feed-eth.
And on His shoul-der gen-tly laid, And home, re-joic-ing, brought me. A-MEN.

4 In death's dark vale I fear no ill
  With Thee, dear Lord, beside me;
Thy rod and staff my comfort still,
  Thy cross before to guide me.

5 And so through all the length of days
  Thy goodness faileth never:
Good Shepherd, may I sing Thy praise
  Within Thy house for ever.

354

PAX TECUM. 10. 10.

EDWARD H. BICKERSTETH, 1825–1906

GEORGE T. CALDBECK, 1852–1912 (?)
Arr. by CHARLES J. VINCENT, 1852–1934

1. Peace, per - fect peace, in this dark world of sin?
2. Peace, per - fect peace, by throng - ing du - ties pressed?
3. Peace, per - fect peace, with sor - rows surg - ing round?
4. Peace, per - fect peace, with loved ones far a - way?
5. Peace, per - fect peace, our fu - ture all un - known?

The blood of Je - sus whis - pers peace with - in.
To do the will of Je - sus: this is rest.
On Je - sus' bos - om naught but calm is found.
In Je - sus' keep - ing we are safe, and they.
Je - sus we know, and He is on the throne. A - MEN.

The Christian Life

355

MIT FREUDEN ZART. 8. 7. 8. 7. 8. 8. 7.

JOHANN J. SCHÜTZ, 1640–1690
Tr. by FRANCES E. COX, 1812–1897

From the Bohemian Brethren's GESANGBUCH, 1566

In unison

1. Sing praise to God who reigns a - bove, The God of all cre - a - tion,
2. What God's al-might-y power hath made, His gra-cious mer - cy keep - eth;
3. The Lord is nev - er far a - way, But, through all grief dis - tress - ing,
4. Thus, all my toil - some way a - long, I sing a - loud Thy prais - es,

The God of power, the God of love, The God of our sal -
By morn-ing glow or eve - ning shade His watch-ful eye ne'er
An ev - er - pres - ent help and stay, Our peace, and joy, and
That men may hear the grate-ful song My voice un - wea - ried

va - tion; With heal-ing balm my soul He fills, And ev - ery faith - less
sleep - eth; With-in the king-dom of His might, Lo! all is just and
bless - ing; As with a moth - er's ten - der hand, He leads His own, His
rais - es; Be joy - ful in the Lord, my heart, Both soul and bod - y

mur-mur stills: To God all praise and glo - ry.
all is right: To God all praise and glo - ry.
cho - sen band: To God all praise and glo - ry.
bear your part: To God all praise and glo - ry. A - MEN.

The Christian Life

RAPTURE. 6. 6. 9. D.

CHARLES WESLEY, 1707–1788

R. D. HUMPHREYS (?), 1826–?

1. O how hap-py are they Who the Sav-iour o-bey, And have
2. That sweet com-fort was mine, When the fa-vor di-vine I first
3. 'Twas a heav-en be-low My Re-deem-er to know, And the
4. Je-sus all the day long Was my joy and my song: O that
5. O the rap-tur-ous height Of that ho-ly de-light Which I

laid up their treas-ure a-bove! Tongue can nev-er ex-press The sweet
found in the blood of the Lamb; When my heart first be-lieved, What a
an-gels could do noth-ing more, Than to fall at His feet, And the
all His sal-va-tion might see! "He hath loved me," I cried, "He hath
felt in the life-giv-ing blood! By my Sav-iour pos-sessed, I was

com-fort and peace Of a soul in its ear-li-est love.
joy I re-ceived, What a heav-en in Je-sus' Name!
sto-ry re-peat, And the Lov-er of sin-ners a-dore.
suf-fered and died, To re-deem a poor reb-el like me."
per-fect-ly blest, As if filled with the full-ness of God. A-MEN.

357

ELIZABETHTOWN. C. M.

JOHN NEWTON, 1725–1807

GEORGE KINGSLEY, 1811–1884

1. Joy is a fruit that will not grow In na-ture's bar-ren soil;
2. But where the Lord has plant-ed grace, And made His glo-ries known,
3. A bleed-ing Sav-iour seen by faith, A sense of par-d'ning love,
4. To take a glimpse with-in the veil, To know that God is mine—
5. These are the joys which sat-is-fy And sanc-ti-fy the mind;

Peace and Joy

All we can boast, till Christ we know, Is van-i-ty and toil.
There fruits of heavenly joy and peace Are found—and there a-lone.
A hope that tri-umphs o-ver death— Give joys like those a-bove.
Are springs of joy that nev-er fail, Un-speak-a-ble, di-vine!
Which make the spir-it mount on high, And leave the world be-hind. A-MEN.

358

MARION. S. M. with Refrain

EDWARD H. PLUMPTRE, 1821-1891   ARTHUR H. MESSITER, 1831-1916

1. Re-joice, ye pure in heart, Re-joice, give thanks and sing;
2. Bright youth and snow-crowned age, Strong men and maid-ens fair,
3. Yes, on through life's long path, Still chant-ing as ye go;
4. Still lift your stan-dard high, Still march in firm ar-ray,

Your glo-rious ban-ner wave on high, The cross of Christ your King.
Raise high your free, ex-ult-ing song, God's won-drous praise de-clare.
From youth to age, by night and day, In glad-ness and in woe.
As war-riors thro' the dark-ness toil Till dawns the gold-en day.

REFRAIN

Re-joice, re-joice, Re-joice, give thanks and sing. A-MEN.
Re-joice, re-joice,

The Christian Life

359

CHRISTMAS. C. M.

PHILIP DODDRIDGE, 1702-1751

Arr. from GEORGE F. HANDEL, 1685-1759

1. A - wake, my soul, stretch ev - ery nerve, And
2. A cloud of wit - ness - es a - round Hold
3. 'Tis God's all - an - i - mat - ing voice That
4. Blest Sav - iour, in - tro - duced by Thee, Have

press with vig - or on; A heaven-ly race de - mands thy zeal,
thee in full sur - vey; For - get the steps al - read - y trod,
calls thee from on high; 'Tis His own hand pre - sents the prize
I my race be - gun; And, crowned with vic - tory, at Thy feet,

And an im - mor - tal crown, And an im - mor - tal crown.
And on - ward urge thy way, And on - ward urge thy way.
To thine as - pir - ing eye, To thine as - pir - ing eye.
I'll lay my hon - ors down, I'll lay my hon - ors down. A - MEN.

360

BERA. L. M.

NICOLAUS L. ZINZENDORF, 1700-1760
Tr. by JOHN WESLEY, 1703-1791

JOHN E. GOULD, 1822-1875

1. O Thou, to whose all - search-ing sight The dark-ness shin-eth as the light:
2. If in this dark-some wild I stray, Be Thou my Light, be Thou my Way:
3. When ris - ing floods my soul o'er - flow, When sinks my heart in waves of woe,
4. Sav - iour, wher - e'er Thy steps I see, Daunt-less, un-tired, I fol - low Thee;

Hope and Aspiration

Search, prove my heart, it yearns for Thee; O burst these bonds, and set it free!
No foes, no vi - o - lence I fear, No fraud, while Thou, my God, art near.
Je - sus, Thy time-ly aid im - part, And raise my head, and cheer my heart.
O let Thy hand sup-port me still, And lead me to Thy ho - ly hill! A-MEN.

361

DEEPER LIFE. 11. 10. 11. 10.

KATHARINE LEE BATES, 1859–1929

LINDSAY B. LONGACRE, 1870–

1. Dear God, our Fa - ther, at Thy knee con - fess - ing Our sins and
2. Not for more beau - ty would our eyes en - treat Thee, Flood-ed with
3. The stars and rain - bows are Thy won - drous wear-ing, Sun - light and
4. Not for more love our crav - ing hearts im-plore Thee, But for more
5. In souls most sul - len Thou art soft - ly dream-ing Of saints and

fol - lies, close in Thine em-brace, Chil - dren for - giv - en,
beau - ty, beau - ty ev - ery-where; On - ly for keen - er
shad - ow mov - ing on the hills; Ho - ly the mead - ow
power to love un - til they glow Like hearths of com - fort,
he - roes wrought from Thy di - vine Pit - y and pa - tience,

hap - py in Thy bless-ing, Deep-en our spir - its to re-ceive Thy grace.
vi - sion that may greet Thee, In all Thy ves-tures of the earth and air.
where Thy feet are far - ing, Ho - ly the brook-let that Thy laugh-ter fills.
ea - ger to re - store Thee, Hid-den in hu-man wretch-ed-ness and woe.
still the lost re - deem - ing, Deep-en our spir-its for a love like Thine. A-MEN.

Words used by permission of Houghton Mifflin Company
Music used by permission of Earl E. Harper

The Christian Life

362

BETHANY. 6. 4. 6. 4. 6. 6. 4.

Sarah F. Adams, 1805–1848

Lowell Mason, 1792–1872

1. Near - er, my God, to Thee, Near - er to Thee! E'en though it be a cross
2. Though like the wan-der - er, The sun gone down, Dark-ness be o - ver me,
3. There let the way ap - pear, Steps un - to heaven; All that Thou send-est me,

That rais - eth me; Still all my song shall be, Near - er, my
My rest a stone; Yet in my dreams I'd be Near - er, my
In mer - cy given; An - gels to beck - on me Near - er, my

God, to Thee, Near - er, my God, to Thee, Near - er to Thee!
God, to Thee, Near - er, my God, to Thee, Near - er to Thee!
God, to Thee, Near - er, my God, to Thee, Near - er to Thee! A - MEN.

4 Then, with my waking thoughts
  Bright with Thy praise,
Out of my stony griefs
  Bethel I'll raise;
So by my woes to be
Nearer, my God, to Thee,
  Nearer to Thee!

5 Or if, on joyful wing
  Cleaving the sky,
Sun, moon, and stars forgot,
  Upward I fly,
Still all my song shall be,
Nearer, my God, to Thee,
  Nearer to Thee!

363

SPOHR. C. M.

Anonymous

Adapted from Louis Spohr, 1784–1859

1. O for a heart of calm re - pose A - mid the world's loud roar,
2. Come, Ho - ly Spir - it! still my heart With gen - tle - ness di - vine;
3. A - bove these scenes of storm and strife There spreads a re - gion fair;
4. Come, Ho - ly Spir - it! breathe that peace, That vic - t'ry make me win;

Hope and Aspiration

A life that like a riv - er flows A - long a peace-ful shore!
In-dwell-ing peace Thou canst im-part; O make that bless-ing mine!
Give me to live that high - er life, And breathe that heaven-ly air.
Then shall my soul her con - flict cease, And find a heaven with-in. A-MEN.

364 MORE LOVE TO THEE. 6. 4. 6. 4. 6. 6. 4

ELIZABETH P. PRENTISS, 1818-1878   WILLIAM H. DOANE, 1832-1915

1. More love to Thee, O Christ, More love to Thee! Hear Thou the
2. Once earth-ly joy I craved, Sought peace and rest; Now Thee a -
3. Then shall my lat - est breath Whis - per Thy praise; This be the

prayer I make On bend - ed knee; This is my ear - nest plea,
lone I seek, Give what is best: This all my prayer shall be,
part - ing cry My heart shall raise; This still its prayer shall be,

More love, O Christ, to Thee, More love to Thee, More love to Thee!
More love, O Christ, to Thee, More love to Thee, More love to Thee!
More love, O Christ, to Thee, More love to Thee, More love to Thee! A-MEN.

The Christian Life

365

RESIGNATION. S. M.

Marianne Hearn, 1834-1909   Moses S. Cross, 1854-1911

1. We hope in Thee, O God! The day wears on to night; Thick
2. We hope in Thee, O God! Our joys go one by one, But
3. We hope in Thee, O God! Hope fails us oth-er-where; But
4. We hope in Thee, O God! In whom none hope in vain; We

shad-ows lie a-cross our world, In Thee a-lone is light.
lone-ly hearts can rest in Thee, When all be-side is gone.
since Thou art in all that is, Peace takes the hand of care.
cling to Thee in love and trust, And joy suc-ceeds to pain. A-MEN.

366

SPOHR. C. M.

Psalm XLII
Tate and Brady, 1696
Alt. by Henry F. Lyte, 1793-1847   Adapted from Louis Spohr, 1784-1859

1. As pants the hart for cool-ing streams, When heat-ed in the chase,
2. For Thee, my God, the liv-ing God, My thirst-y soul doth pine;
3. I sigh to think of hap-pier days, When Thou, O Lord, wast nigh;
4. Why rest-less, why cast down, my soul? Hope still, and thou shalt sing

So longs my soul, O God, for Thee, And Thy re-fresh-ing grace.
O when shall I be-hold Thy face, Thou Ma-jes-ty di-vine!
When ev-ery heart was tuned to praise, And none more blest than I.
The praise of Him who is thy God, Thy Sav-iour, and thy King. A-MEN.

Alternative tune, Martyrdom (Avon), No. 70

Hope and Aspiration

367

LEOMINSTER. S. M. D.

George Matheson, 1842–1906

George W. Martin, 1828–1881
Arr. by Arthur S. Sullivan, 1842–1900

1. Make me a cap-tive, Lord, And then I shall be free;
2. My heart is weak and poor Un-til it mas-ter find;
3. My power is faint and low Till I have learned to serve;
4. My will is not my own Till Thou hast made it Thine;

Force me to ren-der up my sword, And I shall con-queror be.
It has no spring of ac-tion sure— It va-ries with the wind.
It wants the need-ed fire to glow, It wants the breeze to nerve;
If it would reach a mon-arch's throne It must its crown re-sign;

I sink in life's a-larms When by my-self I stand;
It can-not free-ly move Till Thou hast wrought its chain;
It can-not drive the world, Un-til it-self be driven;
It on-ly stands un-bent, A-mid the clash-ing strife,

Im-pris-on me with-in Thine arms, And strong shall be my hand.
En-slave it with Thy match-less love, And death-less it shall reign.
Its flag can on-ly be un-furled When Thou shalt breathe from heaven.
When on Thy bos-om it has leant And found in Thee its life. A-men.

The Christian Life

368

CROSSING THE BAR. Irregular

ALFRED TENNYSON, 1809–1892

JOSEPH BARNBY, 1838–1896

Sun - set and eve - ning star, And one clear call for me! And may there

be no moan-ing of the bar When I put out to sea, But such a

tide as mov - ing seems a - sleep, Too full for sound and foam,

When that which drew from out the bound-less deep Turns a - gain home.

home. Twi-

Twi - light and eve - ning bell, And aft - er that the dark!

- - - light and eve - ning bell,

Hope and Aspiration

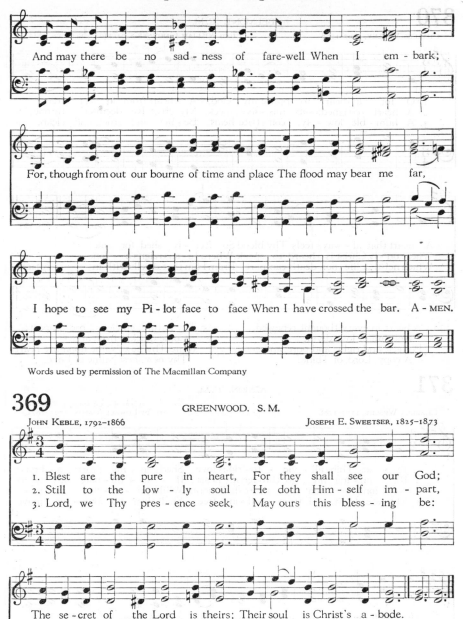

And may there be no sad-ness of fare-well When I em-bark;

For, though from out our bourne of time and place The flood may bear me far,

I hope to see my Pi-lot face to face When I have crossed the bar. A-MEN.

369

GREENWOOD. S. M.

JOHN KEBLE, 1792–1866　　　　　JOSEPH E. SWEETSER, 1825–1873

1. Blest are the pure in heart, For they shall see our God;
2. Still to the low-ly soul He doth Him-self im-part,
3. Lord, we Thy pres-ence seek, May ours this bless-ing be:

The se-cret of the Lord is theirs; Their soul is Christ's a-bode.
And for His tem-ple and His throne Se-lects the pure in heart.
O give the pure and low-ly heart, A tem-ple meet for Thee! A-MEN.

The Christian Life

370

BELMONT. C. M.

CHARLES WESLEY, 1707-1788

From WILLIAM GARDINER'S SACRED MELODIES, 1812

1. O for a heart to praise my God, A heart from sin set free,
2. A heart re-signed, sub-mis-sive, meek, My great Re-deem-er's throne;
3. A hum-ble, low-ly, con-trite heart, Be-liev-ing, true, and clean,

A heart that al-ways feels Thy blood So free-ly shed for me!
Where on-ly Christ is heard to speak, Where Je-sus reigns a-lone;
Which nei-ther life nor death can part From Him that dwells with-in; A-MEN.

4 A heart in every thought renewed,
And full of love divine;
Perfect, and right, and pure, and good,
A copy, Lord, of Thine!

5 Thy nature, gracious Lord, impart;
Come quickly from above,
Write Thy new Name upon my heart,
Thy new, best Name of Love.

371

AZMON. C. M.

CARL G. GLÄSER, 1784-1829
Arr. by LOWELL MASON, 1792-1872

CHARLES WESLEY, 1707-1788

1. Je-sus, Thine all-vic-to-rious love Shed in my heart a-broad:
2. Re-fin-ing fire, go through my heart; Il-lu-mi-nate my soul;
3. No long-er then my heart shall mourn, While, pu-ri-fied by grace,
4. My stead-fast soul, from fall-ing free, Shall then no long-er move,

Then shall my feet no lon-ger rove, Root-ed and fixed in God.
Scat-ter Thy life thro' ev-ery part, And sanc-ti-fy the whole.
I on-ly for His glo-ry burn, And al-ways see His face.
While Christ is all the world to me, And all my heart is love. A-MEN.

Christian Perfection

372

LOVE DIVINE. 8. 7. 8. 7. D.

CHARLES WESLEY, 1707-1788

JOHN ZUNDEL, 1815-1882

1. Love di-vine, all loves ex-cell-ing, Joy of heaven, to earth come down;
2. Breathe, O breathe Thy lov-ing Spir-it In-to ev-ery trou-bled breast!
3. Come, Al-might-y to de-liv-er, Let us all Thy grace re-ceive;
4. Fin-ish, then, Thy new cre-a-tion; Pure and spot-less let us be;

Fix in us Thy hum-ble dwell-ing, All Thy faith-ful mer-cies crown!
Let us all in Thee in-her-it, Let us find the prom-ised rest;
Sud-den-ly re-turn, and nev-er, Nev-er more Thy tem-ples leave.
Let us see Thy great sal-va-tion Per-fect-ly re-stored in Thee:

Je-sus, Thou art all com-pas-sion, Pure, un-bound-ed love Thou art;
Take a-way our bent to sin-ning; Al-pha and O-me-ga be;
Thee we would be al-ways bless-ing, Serve Thee as Thy hosts a-bove,
Changed from glo-ry in-to glo-ry, Till in heaven we take our place,

Vis-it us with Thy sal-va-tion, En-ter ev-ery trem-bling heart.
End of faith, as its be-gin-ning, Set our hearts at lib-er-ty.
Pray, and praise Thee with-out ceas-ing, Glo-ry in Thy per-fect love.
Till we cast our crowns be-fore Thee, Lost in won-der, love, and praise. A-MEN.

The Christian Life

373

MARTYRDOM (AVON). C. M.

CHARLES WESLEY, 1707-1788

HUGH WILSON, 1766-1824

1. For ev - er here my rest shall be, Close to Thy bleed-ing side;
2. My dy - ing Sav - iour, and my God, Foun-tain for guilt and sin,
3. Wash me, and make me thus Thine own; Wash me, and mine Thou art;
4. Th' a-tone-ment of Thy blood ap - ply, Till faith to sight im - prove,

This all my hope and all my plea: For me the Sav- iour died.
Sprin-kle me ev - er with Thy blood, And cleanse and keep me clean.
Wash me, but not my feet a - lone: My hands, my head, my heart.
Till hope in full fru - i - tion die, And all my soul be love. A-MEN.

374

SAWLEY. C. M.

FREDERICK W. FABER, 1814-1863

JAMES WALCH, 1837-1901

1. O how the thought of God at - tracts And draws the heart from earth,
2. 'Tis not e - nough to save our souls, To shun th' e - ter - nal fires;
3. God on - ly is the crea-ture's home, Tho' rough and strait the road;
4. O ut - ter but the Name of God Down in your heart of hearts,
5. A trust - ing heart, a yearn-ing eye, Can win their way a - bove;

And sick - ens it of pass - ing shows And dis - si - pat - ing mirth!
The tho't of God will rouse the heart To more sub - lime de - sires.
Yet noth-ing less can sat - is - fy The love that longs for God.
And see how from the world at once All tempt-ing light de-parts!
If moun-tains can be moved by faith, Is there less power in love? A-MEN.

Christian Perfection

375

NEW 113TH. 8. 8. 8. 8. 8. 8.

GERHARD TERSTEEGEN, 1607–1769
Tr. by JOHN WESLEY, 1703–1791

WILLIAM HAYES, 1706–1777

1. Thou hid-den Love of God, whose height, Whose depth un-fath-omed, no man knows, I see from far Thy beau-teous light, And in-ly sigh for Thy re-pose; My heart is pained, nor can it be At rest till it finds rest in Thee.

2. Is there a thing be-neath the sun, That strives with Thee my heart to share? Ah, tear it thence, and reign a-lone, The Lord of ev-ery mo-tion there! Then shall my heart from earth be free, When it hath found re-pose in Thee.

3. O Love, Thy sov-ereign aid im-part, To save me from low-thought-ed care; Chase this self-will from all my heart, From all its hid-den maz-es there; Make me Thy du-teous child, that I Cease-less may, "Ab-ba, Fa-ther," cry.

4. Each mo-ment draw from earth a-way My heart, that low-ly waits Thy call; Speak to my in-most soul, and say, "I am thy Love, thy God, thy All!" To feel Thy power, to hear Thy voice, To taste Thy love, be all my choice. A-MEN.

The Christian Life

376

HURSLEY. L. M.

JOHN HUNTER, 1848-1917

Adapted from KATHOLISCHES GESANGBUCH, 1774

1. Dear Mas - ter, in whose life I see All that I
2. Though what I dream and what I do In my weak

would, but fail to be; Let Thy clear light for
days are al - ways two, Help me, op - pressed by

ev - er shine, To shame and guide this life of mine.
things un - done, O Thou, whose deeds and dreams were one! A - MEN.

Words used by permission of Canon L. S. Hunter

377

OLD 134TH (ST. MICHAEL). S. M.

CHARLES WESLEY, 1707-1788

Adapted from the GENEVAN PSALTER, 1551

1. O come, and dwell in me, Spir - it of power with - in!
2. Has - ten the joy - ful day Which shall my sins con - sume;
3. I want the wit - ness, Lord, That all I do is right,
4. I ask no high - er state; In - dulge me but in this,

Christian Perfection

And bring the glo-rious lib-er-ty From sor-row, fear, and sin.
When old things shall be done a-way, And all things new be-come.
Ac-cord-ing to Thy will and Word, Well pleas-ing in Thy sight.
And soon or la-ter then trans-late To my e-ter-nal bliss. A-MEN.

378

MANOAH. C. M.

BERNARD BARTON, 1784–1849

From HENRY W. GREATOREX'S COLLECTION, 1851

1. Walk in the light! so shalt thou know That
2. Walk in the light! and thou shalt find Thy
3. Walk in the light! and thou shalt own Thy
4. Walk in the light! and thine shall be A

fel-low-ship of love His Spir-it on-ly
heart made tru-ly His, Who dwells in cloud-less
dark-ness passed a-way, Be-cause that light hath
path, though thorn-y, bright: For God, by grace, shall

can be-stow, Who reigns in light a-bove.
light en-shrined, In whom no dark-ness is.
on thee shone, In which is per-fect day.
dwell in thee, And God Him-self is light. A-MEN.

The Living Church

379

ST. THOMAS. S. M.

Timothy Dwight, 1752–1817

From Williams' Psalmody, 1770

1. I love Thy king-dom, Lord, The house of Thine a-bode,
2. I love Thy Church, O God! Her walls be-fore Thee stand,
3. For her my tears shall fall, For her my prayers as-cend,

The Church our blest Re-deem-er saved With His own pre-cious blood.
Dear as the ap-ple of Thine eye, And grav-en on Thy hand.
To her my cares and toils be given, Till toils and cares shall end. A-MEN.

4 Beyond my highest joy
    I prize her heavenly ways,
  Her sweet communion, solemn vows,
    Her hymns of love and praise.

5 Sure as Thy truth shall last,
    To Zion shall be given
  The brightest glories earth can yield,
    And brighter bliss of heaven.

380

LITANY (Hervey). 7. 7. 7. 6.

Thomas B. Pollock, 1836–1896

Melody by Frederick A. J. Hervey, 1846–1910

1. Je-sus, with Thy Church a-bide; Be her Sav-iour, Lord, and Guide,
2. May her voice be ev-er clear, Warn-ing of a Judg-ment near,
3. May she guide the poor and blind, Seek the lost un-til she find,
4. May her lamp of truth be bright; Bid her bear a-loft its light

While on earth her faith is tried: We be-seech Thee, hear us.
Tell-ing of a Sav-iour dear: We be-seech Thee, hear us.
And the bro-ken-heart-ed bind: We be-seech Thee, hear us.
Thro' the realms of pa-gan night: We be-seech Thee, hear us. A-MEN.

5 Judge her not for work undone,
  Judge her not for fields unwon,
  Bless her works in Thee begun:
    We beseech Thee, hear us.

6 May she holy triumphs win,
  Overthrow the hosts of sin,
  Gather all the nations in:
    We beseech Thee, hear us.

The Church

381

AURELIA. 7. 6. 7. 6. D.

SAMUEL J. STONE, 1839–1900

SAMUEL S. WESLEY, 1810–1876

1. The Church-'s one foun-da-tion Is Je-sus Christ her Lord;
2. E-lect from ev-ery na-tion, Yet one o'er all the earth,
3. 'Mid toil and trib-u-la-tion, And tu-mult of her war,
4. Yet she on earth hath un-ion With God the Three in One,

She is His new cre-a-tion By wa-ter and the word:
Her char-ter of sal-va-tion, One Lord, one faith, one birth;
She waits the con-sum-ma-tion Of peace for ev-er-more;
And mys-tic sweet com-mun-ion With those whose rest is won:

From heaven He came and sought her To be His ho-ly bride;
One ho-ly Name she bless-es, Par-takes one ho-ly food,
Till, with the vi-sion glo-rious, Her long-ing eyes are blest,
O hap-py ones and ho-ly! Lord, give us grace that we,

With His own blood He bought her, And for her life He died.
And to one hope she press-es, With ev-ery grace en-dued.
And the great Church vic-to-rious Shall be the Church at rest.
Like them, the meek and low-ly, On high may dwell with Thee. A-MEN.

The Living Church

382

AUSTRIAN HYMN. 8. 7. 8. 7. D.

JOHN NEWTON, 1725-1807

FRANCIS J. HAYDN, 1732-1809

1. Glo-rious things of thee are spo-ken, Zi-on, cit-y of our God;
2. See, the streams of liv-ing wa-ters, Spring-ing from e-ter-nal Love,
3. Round each hab-i-ta-tion hov-ering, See the cloud and fire ap-pear

He, whose word can-not be bro-ken, Formed thee for His own a-bode:
Well sup-ply thy sons and daugh-ters, And all fear of want re-move:
For a glo-ry and a cov-ering, Show-ing that the Lord is near!

On the Rock of A-ges found-ed, What can shake thy sure re-pose?
Who can faint, while such a riv-er Ev-er flows their thirst t'as-suage?
Glo-rious things of thee are spo-ken, Zi-on, cit-y of our God;

With sal-va-tion's walls sur-round-ed, Thou may'st smile at all thy foes.
Grace which, like the Lord, the Giv-er, Nev-er fails from age to age.
He, whose word can-not be bro-ken, Formed thee for His own a-bode. A-MEN.

The Church

383

SALZBURG. C. M.

From PSALM LXXXIV
SCOTTISH PSALTER, 1650

Adapted from JOHANN M. HAYDN, 1737–1806

1. How love - ly is Thy dwell - ing-place, O Lord of hosts, to me!
2. My thirst - y soul longs ar - dent - ly, Yea, faints Thy courts to see:
3. Be - hold, the spar - row find - eth out An house where-in to rest;

The tab - er - na - cles of Thy grace How pleas-ant, Lord, they be!
My ver - y heart and flesh cry out, O liv - ing God, for Thee.
The swal-low al - so for her-self Pro - vid - ed hath a nest; A-MEN.

4 Even Thine own altars, where she safe
   Her young ones forth may bring,
   O Thou Almighty Lord of hosts,
   Who art my God and King.

5 Blest are they in Thy house that dwell,
   They ever give Thee praise.
   Blest is the man whose strength Thou art,
   In whose heart are Thy ways.

384

ST. ANNE. C. M.

A. CLEVELAND COXE, 1818–1896

Probably by WILLIAM CROFT, 1678–1727

1. O where are kings and em - pires now, Of old that went and came?
2. We mark her good - ly bat - tle-ments And her foun - da - tions strong;
3. For not like king-doms of the world Thy ho - ly Church, O God!
4. Un - sha - ken as e - ter - nal hills, Im - mov - a - ble she stands,

But, Lord, Thy Church is pray - ing yet, A thou-sand years the same.
We hear with - in the sol - emn voice Of her un - end - ing song.
Tho' earth-quake shocks are threatening her, And tem-pests are a - broad;
A moun-tain that shall fill the earth, A house not made with hands. A - MEN.

The Living Church

385

LUTHER. 8. 7. 8. 7. 8. 8. 7.

THOMAS H. GILL, 1819–1906

FROM KLUG'S GESANGBUCH, 1535

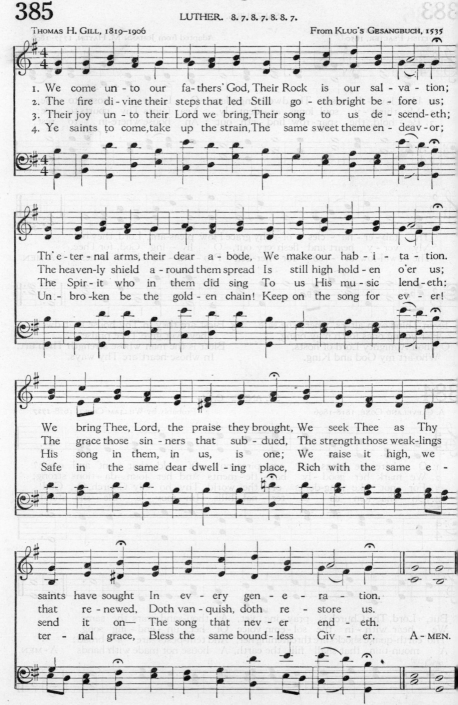

1. We come un-to our fa-thers' God, Their Rock is our sal-va-tion;
2. The fire di-vine their steps that led Still go-eth bright be-fore us;
3. Their joy un-to their Lord we bring, Their song to us de-scend-eth;
4. Ye saints to come, take up the strain, The same sweet theme en-deav-or;

Th' e-ter-nal arms, their dear a-bode, We make our hab-i-ta-tion.
The heaven-ly shield a-round them spread Is still high hold-en o'er us;
The Spir-it who in them did sing To us His mu-sic lend-eth;
Un-bro-ken be the gold-en chain! Keep on the song for ev-er!

We bring Thee, Lord, the praise they brought, We seek Thee as Thy
The grace those sin-ners that sub-dued, The strength those weak-lings
His song in them, in us, is one; We raise it high, we
Safe in the same dear dwell-ing place, Rich with the same e-

saints have sought In ev-ery gen-e-ra-tion.
that re-newed, Doth van-quish, doth re-store us.
send it on— The song that nev-er end-eth.
ter-nal grace, Bless the same bound-less Giv-er. A-MEN.

The Holy Scriptures

386

MUNICH. 7. 6. 7. 6. D.

WILLIAM W. HOW, 1823–1897

NEUVERMEHRTES MEININGISCHES GESANGBUCH, 1693
Arr. by FELIX MENDELSSOHN-BARTHOLDY, 1809–1847

1. O Word of God In - car - nate, O Wis - dom from on high,
2. The Church from Thee, her Mas - ter, Re - ceived the gift di - vine,
3. It float - eth like a ban - ner Be - fore God's host un - furled;
4. O make Thy Church, dear Sav - iour, A lamp of pur - est gold,

O Truth un - changed, un - chang - ing, O Light of our dark sky:
And still that light she lift - eth O'er all the earth to shine.
It shin - eth like a bea - con A - bove the dark - ling world.
To bear be - fore the na - tions Thy true light as of old.

We praise Thee for the ra - diance That from the hal - lowed page,
It is the sa - cred cas - ket, Where gems of truth are stored;
It is the chart and com - pass That o'er life's surg - ing sea,
O teach Thy wan - dering pil - grims By this their path to trace,

A lan - tern to our foot - steps, Shines on from age to age.
It is the heaven-drawn pic - ture Of Thee, the liv - ing Word.
'Mid mists and rocks and quick-sands, Still guides, O Christ, to Thee.
Till, clouds and dark - ness end - ed, They see Thee face to face. A - MEN.

Alternative tune, Aurelia, No. 324

The Living Church

387

BREAD OF LIFE. 6. 4. 6. 4. D.

MARY A. LATHBURY, 1841-1913

WILLIAM F. SHERWIN, 1826-1888

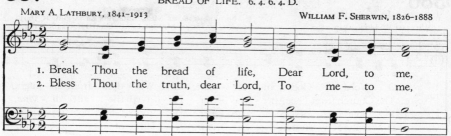

1. Break Thou the bread of life, Dear Lord, to me,
2. Bless Thou the truth, dear Lord, To me — to me,

As Thou didst break the loaves Be - side the sea;
As Thou didst bless the bread By Gal - i - lee;

Be - yond the sa - cred page I seek Thee, Lord;
Then shall all bond - age cease, All fet - ters fall;

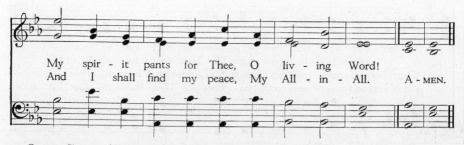

My spir - it pants for Thee, O liv - ing Word!
And I shall find my peace, My All - in - All. A - MEN.

Courtesy Chautauqua Institution, Chautauqua, New York

The Holy Scriptures

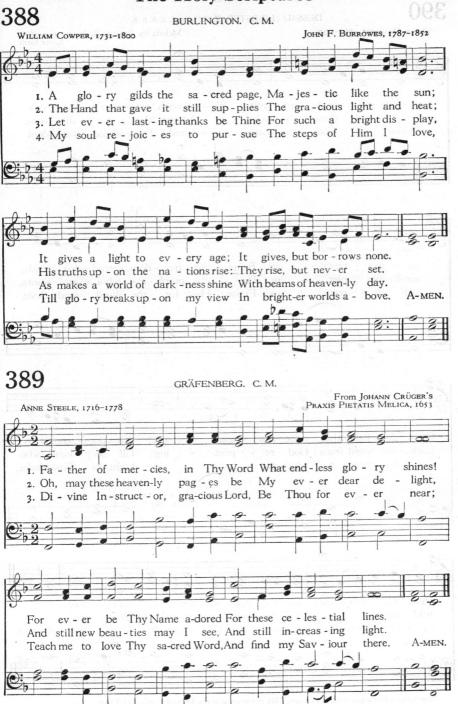

388

BURLINGTON. C. M.

WILLIAM COWPER, 1731-1800

JOHN F. BURROWES, 1787-1852

1. A glo-ry gilds the sa-cred page, Ma-jes-tic like the sun;
2. The Hand that gave it still sup-plies The gra-cious light and heat;
3. Let ev-er-last-ing thanks be Thine For such a bright dis-play,
4. My soul re-joic-es to pur-sue The steps of Him I love,

It gives a light to ev-ery age; It gives, but bor-rows none.
His truths up-on the na-tions rise: They rise, but nev-er set.
As makes a world of dark-ness shine With beams of heaven-ly day.
Till glo-ry breaks up-on my view In bright-er worlds a-bove. A-MEN.

389

GRÄFENBERG. C. M.

ANNE STEELE, 1716-1778

From JOHANN CRÜGER'S
PRAXIS PIETATIS MELICA, 1653

1. Fa-ther of mer-cies, in Thy Word What end-less glo-ry shines!
2. Oh, may these heaven-ly pag-es be My ev-er dear de-light,
3. Di-vine In-struct-or, gra-cious Lord, Be Thou for ev-er near;

For ev-er be Thy Name a-dored For these ce-les-tial lines.
And still new beau-ties may I see, And still in-creas-ing light.
Teach me to love Thy sa-cred Word, And find my Sav-iour there. A-MEN.

The Living Church

390

DESSAU (LIEBSTER JESU). 7. 8. 7. 8. 8. 8.

PERCY DEARMER, 1867–1936

Melody by JOHANN R. AHLE. 1625–1673
Later form

1. Book of books, our peo - ple's strength, States-man's, teach - er's, he - ro's treas - ure, Bring - ing free - dom, spread - ing truth, Shed - ding light that none can meas - ure: Wis - dom comes to those who know thee, All the best we have we owe thee.

2. Thank we those who toiled in thought, Man - y di - verse scrolls com - plet - ing: Po - ets, proph - ets, schol - ars, saints, Each his word from God re - peat - ing; Till they came, who told the sto - ry Of the Word, and showed His glo - ry.

3. Praise we God, who hath in - spired Those whose wis - dom still di - rects us; Praise Him for the Word made flesh, For the Spir - it which pro - tects us. Light of Knowledge, ev - er burn - ing, Shed on us Thy death - less learn - ing. A - MEN.

The Holy Scriptures

BETHLEHEM. C. M. D.

Washington Gladden, 1836-1918

Gottfried W. Fink, 1783-1846

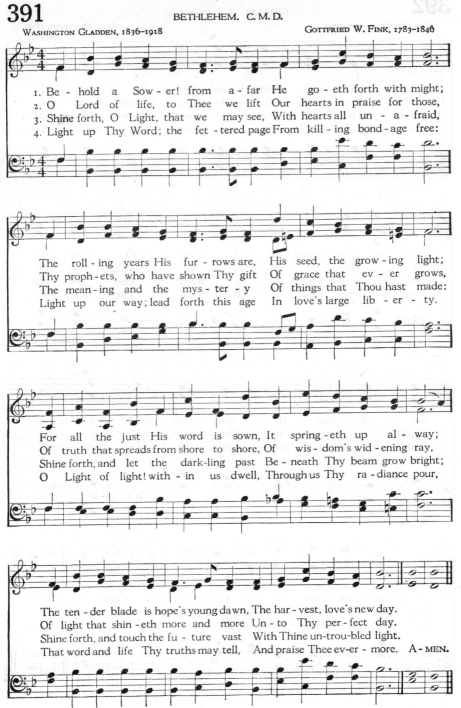

1. Be - hold a Sow - er! from a - far He go - eth forth with might;
2. O Lord of life, to Thee we lift Our hearts in praise for those,
3. Shine forth, O Light, that we may see, With hearts all un - a - fraid,
4. Light up Thy Word; the fet - tered page From kill - ing bond - age free:

The roll - ing years His fur - rows are, His seed, the grow - ing light;
Thy proph - ets, who have shown Thy gift Of grace that ev - er grows,
The mean - ing and the mys - ter - y Of things that Thou hast made:
Light up our way; lead forth this age In love's large lib - er - ty.

For all the just His word is sown, It spring - eth up al - way;
Of truth that spreads from shore to shore, Of wis - dom's wid - ening ray,
Shine forth, and let the dark - ling past Be - neath Thy beam grow bright;
O Light of light! with - in us dwell, Through us Thy ra - diance pour,

The ten - der blade is hope's young dawn, The har - vest, love's new day.
Of light that shin - eth more and more Un - to Thy per - fect day.
Shine forth, and touch the fu - ture vast With Thine un - trou - bled light.
That word and life Thy truths may tell, And praise Thee ev - er - more. A - MEN.

The Living Church

392

STOWELL. 6. 6. 4. 6. 6. 6. 4.

HUGH STOWELL, 1799–1865

I. H. MEREDITH, 1872–

1. Lord of all power and might, Fa-ther of
love and light, Speed on Thy Word! O let the
gos-pel sound All the wide world a-round,
Wher-ev-er man is found! God speed His Word!

2. Hail, bless-ed Ju-bi-lee! Thine, Lord, the
glo-ry be; Al-le-lu-ia! Thine was the
might-y plan; From Thee the work be-gan;
A-way with praise of man! Glo-ry to God!

3. Lo, what em-bat-tled foes, Stern in their
hate, op-pose God's ho-ly Word! One for His
truth we stand, Strong in His own right hand,
Firm as a mar-tyr-band: God shield His Word!

4. On-ward shall be our course, De-spite all
fraud and force; God is be-fore. His words ere
long shall run Free as the noon-day sun;
His pur-pose must be done: God bless His Word! A-MEN.

Music used by permission of I. H. Meredith

The Lord's Day

393

SABBATH. 7. 7. 7. 7. D.

John Newton, 1725–1807

Lowell Mason, 1792–1872

1. Safe - ly through an - oth - er week God has brought us on our way;
2. While we pray for par-doning grace, Thro' the dear Re-deem-er's Name,
3. Here we come Thy Name to praise; May we feel Thy pres-ence near:
4. May Thy gos-pel's joy - ful sound Con-quer sin - ners, com - fort saints;

Let us now a bless-ing seek, Wait-ing in His courts to - day:
Show Thy rec - on - cil - ed face, Take a - way our sin and shame;
May Thy glo - ry meet our eyes, While we in Thy house ap - pear:
Make the fruits of grace a-bound, Bring re - lief for all com-plaints:

Day of all the week the best, Em - blem of e - ter - nal rest;
From our world - ly cares set free, May we rest this day in Thee;
Here af - ford us, Lord, a taste Of our ev - er - last - ing feast;
Thus may all our Sab-baths prove, Till we join the Church a - bove;

Day of all the week the best, Em - blem of e - ter - nal rest.
From our world - ly cares set free, May we rest this day in Thee.
Here af - ford us, Lord, a taste Of our ev - er - last - ing feast.
Thus may all our Sab-baths prove, Till we join the Church a - bove. A-MEN.

The Living Church

LISCHER. 6. 6. 6. 6. 8. 8.

"Hayward," in John Dobell's Selection, 1806

Friedrich Schneider, 1786–1853

1. Wel - come, de - light - ful morn, Thou day of sa - cred rest!
2. Now may the King de - scend, And fill His throne with grace;
3. De - scend, ce - les - tial Dove, With all Thy quick - ening powers;

I hail thy kind re - turn; Lord, make these mo - ments blest:
Thy scep - ter, Lord, ex - tend, While saints ad - dress Thy face:
Dis - close a Sav - iour's love, And bless the sa - cred hours:

From the low plane of mor - tal toys I soar to reach im -
Let sin - ners feel Thy quick - ening word, And learn to know and
Then shall my soul new life ob - tain, Nor Sab - baths be en -

mor - tal joys I soar to reach im - mor - tal joys.
fear the Lord, And learn to know and fear the Lord.
joyed in vain, Nor Sab - baths be en - joyed in vain. A - MEN.

The Lord's Day

395

WELCOME. Irregular

Percy Dearmer, 1867-1936

Rowland Leach, 1885–

1. Wel - come, day of the Lord, the first and the best of the sev - en, Day where - on Christ a - rose, brought us the prom - ise of life.
2. Day of re - fresh - ing and rest, that was won by the Church for the wea - ry Work - ing at la - bor un - blest, slaves, with no break in their toil.
3. Day that we set a - part for all that is high - est with - in us, Freed from the work-shop and mart, find - ing the love - ly and true. A - MEN.

4 Day for the worship of God, in fellowship sacred and joyful,
Prayer and the heavenly food, comfort and knowledge and praise.

Words from Enlarged Songs of Praise. By permission of the Oxford University Press
Music copyright, 1935, by Rowland Leach. Used by permission

The Living Church

396

MENDEBRAS. 7. 6. 7. 6. D.

CHRISTOPHER WORDSWORTH, 1807–1885

Arr. by LOWELL MASON, 1792–1872

1. O day of rest and glad - ness, O day of joy and light,
2. On thee, at the cre - a - tion, The light first had its birth;
3. To - day on wea - ry na - tions The heaven-ly man - na falls;
4. New grac - es ev - er gain-ing From this our day of rest,

O balm of care and sad - ness, Most beau - ti - ful, most bright:
On thee, for our sal - va - tion, Christ rose from depths of earth;
To ho - ly con - vo - ca - tions The sil - ver trum - pet calls,
We reach the rest re - main - ing To spir - its of the blest.

On thee, the high and low - ly, Through a - ges joined in tune,
On thee, our Lord, vic - to - rious, The Spir - it sent from heaven;
Where gos - pel light is glow - ing With pure and ra - diant beams,
To Ho - ly Ghost be prais - es, To Fa - ther, and to Son;

Sing Ho - ly, ho - ly, ho - ly, To the great God Tri - une.
And thus on thee, most glo - rious, A tri - ple light was given.
And liv - ing wa - ter flow - ing With soul - re - fresh-ing streams.
The Church her voice up - rais - es To Thee, blest Three in One.

A - MEN.

The Lord's Day

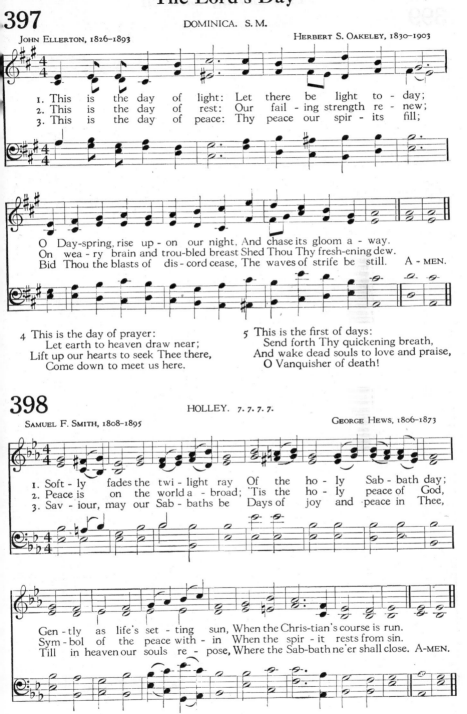

397

DOMINICA. S. M.

JOHN ELLERTON, 1826–1893

HERBERT S. OAKELEY, 1830–1903

1. This is the day of light: Let there be light to - day;
2. This is the day of rest: Our fail - ing strength re - new;
3. This is the day of peace: Thy peace our spir - its fill;

O Day-spring, rise up - on our night, And chase its gloom a - way.
On wea - ry brain and trou-bled breast Shed Thou Thy fresh-ening dew.
Bid Thou the blasts of dis - cord cease, The waves of strife be still. A - MEN.

4 This is the day of prayer:
   Let earth to heaven draw near;
   Lift up our hearts to seek Thee there,
   Come down to meet us here.

5 This is the first of days:
   Send forth Thy quickening breath,
   And wake dead souls to love and praise,
   O Vanquisher of death!

398

HOLLEY. 7. 7. 7. 7.

SAMUEL F. SMITH, 1808–1895

GEORGE HEWS, 1806–1873

1. Soft - ly fades the twi - light ray Of the ho - ly Sab - bath day;
2. Peace is on the world a - broad; 'Tis the ho - ly peace of God,
3. Sav - iour, may our Sab - baths be Days of joy and peace in Thee,

Gen - tly as life's set - ting sun, When the Chris-tian's course is run.
Sym - bol of the peace with - in When the spir - it rests from sin.
Till in heaven our souls re - pose, Where the Sab-bath ne'er shall close. A-MEN.

The Living Church

399

ARLINGTON. C. M.

PHILIP DODDRIDGE, 1702–1751

THOMAS A. ARNE, 1710–1778

1. Let Zi-on's watch-men all a-wake, And heed the call they give;
2. 'Tis not a cause of small im-port The pas-tor's care de-mands;
3. They watch for souls for whom the Lord Did heaven-ly bliss fore-go;
4. May they in Je-sus, whom they preach, Their own Re-deem-er see;

Now let them from the mouth of God Their sol-emn charge re-ceive.
But what might fill an an-gel's heart, And filled a Sav-iour's hands.
For souls that must for ev-er live In rap-ture or in woe.
And watch Thou dai-ly o'er their souls, That they may watch for Thee. A-MEN.

400

GRÄFENBERG. C. M.

CHARLES WESLEY, 1707–1788

From JOHANN CRÜGER'S
PRAXIS PIETATIS MELICA, 1653

1. Je-sus! the Name high o-ver all, In hell, or earth, or sky;
2. Je-sus! the Name to sin-ners dear, The Name to sin-ners given;
3. O that the world might taste and see The rich-es of His grace!
4. His on-ly right-eous-ness I show, His sav-ing grace pro-claim;
5. Hap-py, if with my lat-est breath I may but gasp His Name;

An-gels and men be-fore it fall, And dev-ils fear and fly.
It scat-ters all their guilt-y fear; It turns their hell to heaven.
The arms of love that com-pass me Would all man-kind em-brace.
'Tis all my busi-ness here be-low, To cry, "Be-hold the Lamb!"
Preach Him to all, and cry in death, "Be-hold, be-hold the Lamb!" A-MEN.

Alternative tune, Azmon, No. 162

The Ministry

401

MISSIONARY HYMN. 7. 6. 7. 6. D.

John S. B. Monsell, 1811–1875

Lowell Mason, 1792–1872

1. Lord of the liv-ing har-vest That whi-tens o'er the plain,
2. As la-borers in Thy vine-yard, Send us, O Christ, to be
3. Be with us, God the Fa-ther, Be with us, God the Son,

Where an-gels soon shall gath-er Their sheaves of gold-en grain;
Con-tent to bear the bur-den Of wea-ry days for Thee;
Be with us, God the Spir-it, E-ter-nal Three in One!

Ac-cept these hands to la-bor, These hearts to trust and love,
We ask no oth-er wa-ges, When Thou shalt call us home,
Make us a roy-al priest-hood, Thee right-ly to a-dore,

And deign with them to has-ten Thy king-dom from a-bove.
But to have shared the tra-vail Which makes Thy king-dom come.
And fill us with Thy full-ness Now and for ev-er-more. A-MEN.

The Living Church

402

DENNIS. S. M.

CHARLES WESLEY, 1707-1788

From HANS G. NÄGELI, 1773-1836
Arr. by LOWELL MASON, 1792-1872

1. And are we yet a - live, And see each oth - er's face?
2. What trou - bles have we seen, What con - flicts have we passed,
3. But out of all the Lord Hath brought us by His love;
4. Then let us make our boast Of His re - deem - ing power,

Glo - ry and praise to Je - sus give, For His re - deem - ing grace.
Fight-ings with-out, and fears with-in, Since we as - sem - bled last!
And still He doth His help af - ford, And hides our life a - bove,
Which saves us to the ut - ter-most, Till we can sin no more. A - MEN.

Alternative tune, Boylston, No. 403

403

BOYLSTON. S. M.

CHARLES WESLEY, 1707-1788

LOWELL MASON, 1792-1872

1. And let our bod - ies part, To dif - ferent climes re - pair;
2. O let us still pro - ceed In Je - sus' work be - low;
3. The vine - yard of the Lord Be - fore His la - borers lies;
4. O let our heart and mind Con - tin - u - ally as - cend,

In - sep - a - ra - bly joined in heart The friends of Je - sus are.
And, fol-lowing our tri - umph-ant Head, To fur - ther con - quests go!
And lo! we see the vast re - ward Which waits us in the skies.
That ha - ven of re - pose to find, Where all our la - bors end! A - MEN.

Alternative tune, Dennis, No. 402

The Ministry

404

TIPLADY. C. M.

CHARLES WESLEY, 1707–1788

JOHN PORTER, 1877–

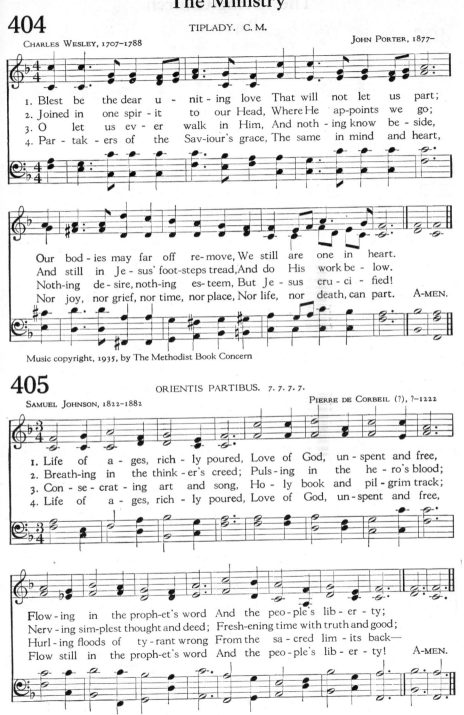

1. Blest be the dear u – nit – ing love That will not let us part;
2. Joined in one spir - it to our Head, Where He ap-points we go;
3. O let us ev - er walk in Him, And noth - ing know be - side,
4. Par - tak - ers of the Sav-iour's grace, The same in mind and heart,

Our bod - ies may far off re-move, We still are one in heart.
And still in Je - sus' foot-steps tread, And do His work be - low.
Noth-ing de - sire, noth-ing es - teem, But Je - sus cru - ci - fied!
Nor joy, nor grief, nor time, nor place, Nor life, nor death, can part. A-MEN.

Music copyright, 1935, by The Methodist Book Concern

405

ORIENTIS PARTIBUS. 7. 7. 7. 7.

SAMUEL JOHNSON, 1822–1882

PIERRE DE CORBEIL (?), ?–1222

1. Life of a - ges, rich - ly poured, Love of God, un - spent and free,
2. Breath-ing in the think - er's creed; Puls-ing in the he - ro's blood;
3. Con - se - crat - ing art and song, Ho - ly book and pil - grim track;
4. Life of a - ges, rich - ly poured, Love of God, un - spent and free,

Flow-ing in the proph-et's word And the peo - ple's lib - er - ty;
Nerv - ing sim-plest thought and deed; Fresh-ening time with truth and good;
Hurl - ing floods of ty - rant wrong From the sa - cred lim - its back—
Flow still in the proph-et's word And the peo - ple's lib - er - ty! A-MEN.

The Living Church
Baptism

FFIGYSBREN. 10. 10. 10. 10.

406

Howell E. Lewis, 1860-

Welsh hymn melody

1. Friend of the home: as when in Gal - i - lee
2. Thine are they, by Thy love's e - ter - nal claim,
3. Lord, may Thy Church, as with a moth - er's care,
4. Draw through the child the par - ents near - er Thee,

The moth - ers brought their lit - tle ones to Thee,
Thine we bap - tize them in the three - fold Name;
For Thee the lambs with - in her bo - som bear;
En - due their home with grow - ing sanc - ti - ty;

So we, dear Lord, would now the chil - dren bring,
Yet not the sign we trust, Lord, but the grace
And grant, as morn - ing grows to noon, that they
And gath - er all, by earth - ly homes made one,

And seek for them the shel - ter of Thy wing.
That in Thy fold pre - pared the lambs a place.
Still in her love and ho - ly serv - ice stay.
In heaven, O Christ, when earth - ly days are done. A - MEN.

The Sacraments
Baptism

407

MEDITATION (Gower). C. M.

Philip Doddridge, 1702-1751

John H. Gower, 1855-1922

1. See Is-rael's gen-tle Shep-herd stand With all-en-gag-ing charms;
2. "Per-mit them to ap-proach," He cries, "Nor scorn their hum-ble name;
3. We bring them, Lord, in thank-ful hands, And yield them up to Thee;

Hark, how He calls the ten-der lambs, And folds them in His arms!
For 'twas to bless such souls as these The Lord of an-gels came."
Joy-ful that we our-selves are Thine, Thine let our off-spring be. A-men.

Music used by permission of Mrs. John H. Gower

The Lord's Supper

408

DUNDEE (FRENCH). C. M.

James Montgomery, 1771-1854

Scottish Psalter, 1615

1. Be known to us in break-ing bread, But do not then de-part;
2. There sup with us in love di-vine; Thy bod-y and Thy blood,

Sav-iour, a-bide with us, and spread Thy ta-ble in our heart,
That liv-ing bread, that heaven-ly wine, Be our im-mor-tal food. A-men.

The Living Church

409

DUNDEE (FRENCH). C. M.

PHILIP DODDRIDGE, 1702–1751

SCOTTISH PSALTER, 1615

1. The King of heaven His ta - ble spreads, And bless-ings crown the board;
2. Par - don and peace to dy - ing men, And end - less life are given,
3. Mil - lions of souls, in glo - ry now, Were fed and feast - ed here;
4. All things are rea - dy, come a - way, Nor weak ex - cus - es frame;

Not par - a - dise, with all its joys, Could such de - light af - ford.
Thro' the rich blood that Je - sus shed To raise our souls to heaven.
And mil - lions more, still on the way, A - round the board ap - pear.
Come to your plac - es at the feast, And bless the Found-er's Name. A-MEN.

410

ST. JOHN'S, WESTMINSTER. C. M.

JAMES MONTGOMERY, 1771–1854

JAMES TURLE, 1802–1882

1. Ac - cord - ing to Thy gra - cious word, In meek hu - mil - i - ty,
2. Thy bod - y, bro - ken for my sake, My bread from heaven shall be;
3. Re - mem - ber Thee, and all Thy pains, And all Thy love to me;
4. And when these fail - ing lips grow dumb, And mind and mem - ory flee,

This will I do, my dy - ing Lord, I will re - mem - ber Thee.
Thy tes - ta - men - tal cup I take, And thus re - mem - ber Thee.
Yea, while a breath, a pulse re - mains, Will I re - mem - ber Thee!
When Thou shalt in Thy king-dom come, Then, Lord, re - mem - ber me! A - MEN.

Alternative tune, Naomi, No. 202

The Sacraments
The Lord's Supper

411

AUTUMN. 8. 7. 8. 7. D.

Roswell Park, 1807–1869

Arr. from François H. Barthélémon, 1741–1808

1. Je - sus spreads His ban - ner o'er us, Cheers our fam - ished souls with food;
2. In Thy ho - ly in - car - na - tion, When the an - gels sang Thy birth;

He the ban - quet spreads be - fore us, Of His mys - tic flesh and blood.
In Thy fast - ing and temp - ta - tion, In Thy la - bors on the earth,

Pre - cious ban - quet, bread of heav - en, Wine of glad - ness, flow - ing free;
In Thy tri - al and re - jec - tion, In Thy suf - ferings on the tree,

May we taste it, kind - ly giv - en, In re - mem - brance, Lord, of Thee.
In Thy glo - rious res - ur - rec - tion, May we, Lord, re - mem - ber Thee. A - MEN.

The Living Church

AGAPÉ. 8. 7. 8. 7.

412

Louis F. Benson, 1855-1930

Charles J. Dickinson, 1822-1883

1. For the bread, which Thou hast bro - ken; For the
2. By this pledge that Thou dost love us, By Thy
3. With our saint - ed ones in glo - ry Seat - ed
4. In Thy serv - ice, Lord, de - fend us; In our

wine, which Thou hast poured; For the words, which Thou hast
gift of peace re - stored, By Thy call to heaven a -
at our Fa - ther's board, May the Church that wait - eth
hearts keep watch and ward; In the world where Thou dost

spo - ken; Now we give Thee thanks, O Lord.
bove us, Hal - low all our lives, O Lord.
for Thee Keep love's tie un - bro - ken, Lord.
send us Let Thy King - dom come, O Lord. A - men.

Words used by permission of Mrs. Robert E. Jefferys

413

SALZBURG. C. M.

Thomas Cotterill, 1779-1823

Adapted from Johann M. Haydn, 1737-1806

1. In mem-ory of the Sav-iour's love, We keep the sa - cred feast,
2. By faith we take the bread of life With which our souls are fed,
3. In faith and mem-ory thus we sing The won-ders of His love,

The Sacraments
The Lord's Supper

Where ev - ery hum-ble, con-trite heart Is made a wel-come guest.
The cup in to - ken of His blood That was for sin - ners shed.
And thus an - tic - i - pate by faith The heaven-ly feast a - bove. A-MEN.

414

EUCHARISTIC HYMN. 9. 8. 9. 8.

REGINALD HEBER, 1783–1826

JOHN S. B. HODGES, 1830–1915

1. Bread of the world in mer - cy bro - ken, Wine of the
2. Look on the heart by sor - row bro - ken, Look on the

soul in mer - cy shed, By whom the words of
tears by sin - ners shed; And be Thy feast to

life were spo - ken, And in whose death our sins are dead;
us the to - ken That by Thy grace our souls are fed. A - MEN.

The Living Church

415

PENITENTIA. 10. 10. 10. 10.

HORATIUS BONAR, 1808–1889

EDWARD DEARLE, 1806–1891

1. Here, O my Lord, I see Thee face to face;
   Here would I touch and han - dle things un - seen,
   Here grasp with firm - er hand e - ter - nal grace,
   And all my wea - ri - ness up - on Thee lean.

2. Here would I feed up - on the bread of God,
   Here drink with Thee the roy - al wine of heaven,
   Here would I lay a - side each earth - ly load,
   Here taste a - fresh the calm of sin for - given.

3. Too soon we rise: the sym - bols dis - ap - pear;
   The feast, though not the love, is past and gone;
   The bread and wine re - move: but Thou art here,
   Near - er than ev - er — still my shield and sun.

4. Feast aft - er feast thus comes, and pass - es by;
   Yet, pass - ing, points to the glad feast a - bove,
   Giv - ing sweet fore - taste of the fes - tal joy,
   The Lamb's great bri - dal feast of bliss and love. A - MEN.

Fellowship

416

DENNIS. S. M.

JOHN FAWCETT, 1740-1817

From HANS G. NÄGELI, 1773-1836
Arr. by LOWELL MASON, 1792-1872

1. Blest be the tie that binds Our hearts in Chris-tian love:
2. Be - fore our Fa-ther's throne We pour our ar - dent prayers;
3. We share each oth - er's woes, Each oth - er's bur - dens bear,
4. When we are called to part, It gives us in - ward pain;

The fel - low - ship of kin - dred minds Is like to that a - bove.
Our fears, our hopes, our aims are one, Our com-forts and our cares.
And of - ten for each oth - er flows The sym - pa - thiz - ing tear.
But we shall still be joined in heart, And hope to meet a - gain. A-MEN.

417

ARMENIA. C. M.

CHARLES WESLEY, 1707-1788

SYLVANUS B. POND, 1792-1871

1. All praise to our re - deem-ing Lord, Who joins us by His grace,
2. He bids us build each oth - er up; And, gath-ered in - to one,
3. We all par-take the joy of one; The com-mon peace we feel:
4. And if our fel - low - ship be - low In Je - sus be so sweet,

And bids us, each to each re-stored, To - geth-er seek His face.
To our high call-ing's glo - rious hope, We hand in hand go on.
A peace to world-ly minds un-known, A joy un - speak-a - ble.
What height of rap-ture shall we know When round His throne we meet! A-MEN.

The Living Church

418

LLANGOEDMOR. 8. 8. 8. 8. 8. 8.

HENRY C. SHUTTLEWORTH, 1850-1900

Welsh hymn melody

1. Fa - ther of men, in whom are one All hu - man - kind be - neath Thy sun, Stab - lish our work in Thee be - gun. Ex - cept the house be built of Thee, In vain the build - er's toil must be: O strength - en our in - firm - i - ty!

2. Man lives not for him - self a - lone, In oth - ers' good he finds his own; Life's worth in fel - low - ship is known. We, friends and com - rades on life's way, Gath - er with - in these walls to pray: Bless Thou our fel - low - ship to - day.

3. O Christ, our Eld - er Broth - er, who By serv - ing man God's will didst do, Help us to serve our breth - ren, too. Guide us to seek the things a - bove, The base to shun, the pure ap - prove, To live by Thy free law of love.

4. In all our work, in all our play, Be with us, Lord, our Friend, our Stay; Lead on - ward to the per - fect day: Then may we know, earth's les - son o'er, With com - rades missed or gone be - fore, Heav'n's fel - low - ship for ev - er - more. A - MEN.

Fellowship

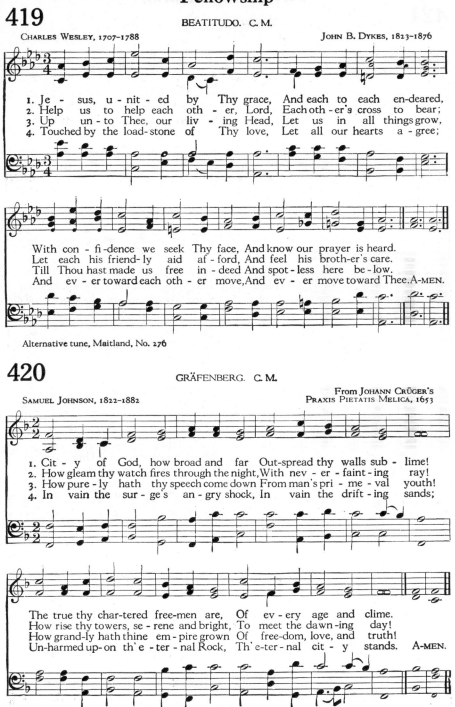

The Living Church

421

ALFORD. 7. 6. 8. 6. D.

Henry van Dyke, 1852–1933

John B. Dykes, 1823–1876

1. No form of hu-man fram-ing, No bond of out-ward might,
2. The mind that is in Je-sus Will guide us in-to truth,
3. Wher-ev-er men a-dore Thee, Our souls with them would kneel;
4. For-give us, Lord, the fol-ly That quar-rels with Thy friends,

Can bind Thy Church to-geth-er, Lord, And all her flocks u-nite;
The hum-ble, o-pen, joy-ful mind Of ev-er-learn-ing youth;
Wher-ev-er men im-plore Thy help, Their trou-ble we would feel;
And draw us near-er to Thy heart, Where ev-ery dis-cord ends;

But, Je-sus, Thou hast told us How u-ni-ty must be:
The heart that is in Je-sus Will lead us out of strife,
And where men do Thy serv-ice, Though know-ing not Thy sign,
Thou art the crown of man-hood, And Thou of God the Son:

Thou art with God the Fa-ther one, And we are one in Thee.
The giv-ing and for-giv-ing heart That fol-lows love in life.
Our hand is with them in good work, For they are al-so Thine.
O Mas-ter of our man-y lives, In Thee our life is one. A-men.

The Communion of Saints

DUNDEE (FRENCH). C. M.

CHARLES WESLEY, 1707–1788

SCOTTISH PSALTER, 1615

1. Come, let us join our friends a - bove Who have ob-tained the prize,
2. Let saints on earth u - nite to sing With those to glo - ry gone;
3. One fam - i - ly we dwell in Him, One Church a - bove, be - neath,

And on the ea - gle wings of love To joys ce - les - tial rise.
For all the ser-vants of our King, In earth and heaven, are one:
Tho' now di - vid - ed by the stream, The nar-row stream of death; A-MEN.

4 One army of the living God,
   To His command we bow:
Part of His host have crossed the flood,
And part are crossing now.

5 E'en now by faith we join our hands
   With those that went before,
And greet the blood-redeemèd bands
   On the eternal shore.

ST. FLAVIAN. C. M.

FREDERICK L. HOSMER, 1840–1929

Adapted from DAY'S PSALTER, 1562

1. We can - not think of them as dead Who walk with us no more
2. The Fa - ther's house is man-sioned fair Be - yond our vi - sion dim;
3. And still their si - lent min - is - tries With - in our hearts have place,
4. Ours are they by an own - er - ship Nor time nor death can free;

A - long the path of life we tread; They have but gone be - fore.
All souls are His, and here or there Are • liv - ing un - to Him.
As when on earth they walked with us And met us face to face.
For God hath given to love to keep Its own e - ter - nal - ly. A - MEN.

The Living Church

424

ST. PETER. C. M.

Isaac Watts, 1674-1748

Alexander R. Reinagle, 1799-1877

1. Give me the wings of faith to rise With-in the veil, and see
2. I ask them whence their vic-tory came: They, with u - nit - ed breath,
3. They marked the foot - steps that He trod; His zeal in-spired their breast;
4. Our glo - rious Lead - er claims our praise For His own pat - tern given,

The saints a - bove, how great their joys, How bright their glo-ries be.
As - cribe their con-quest to the Lamb, Their tri-umph to His death.
And, fol-low-ing their in - car-nate God, They gained the prom-ised rest.
While the long cloud of wit - ness - es Show the same path to heaven. A - MEN.

425

MEYER (ES IST KEIN TAG). 8. 8. 8. 4.

William Charter Piggott, 1872-

From Johann D. Meyer's
Geistliche Seelenfreud, 1692

1. For those we love with-in the veil, Who once were com-rades of our way,
2. And life for them is life in-deed, The splen-did goal of earth's strait race;
3. Not as we knew them an - y more, Toil-worn, and sad with bur-dened care—
4. Free from the fret of mor-tal years, And know-ing now Thy per-fect will,

We thank Thee, Lord; for they have won To cloud - less day;
And where no shad-ows in - ter - vene, They see Thy face.
E - rect, clear - eyed, up - on their brows Thy name they bear.
With quick-ened sense and height-ened joy They serve Thee still. A - MEN.

Words used by permission of William C. Piggott

The Christian Home and Family

426

SICILIAN MARINERS' HYMN. 8. 7. 8. 7. 8. 7.

CHRISTIAN BURKE, 1859–

Arr. from a Sicilian melody

1. Lord of life and King of glo - ry, Who didst deign a
2. Since the day the bless - ed moth-er Thee, the world's Re -
3. Grant us, then, pure hearts and pa - tient, That in all we

child to be, Cra - dled on a moth - er's bo - som,
deem - er, bore, Thou hast crowned us with an hon - or
do or say Lit - tle ones our deeds may cop - y

Throned up - on a moth - er's knee: For the chil - dren
Wo - men nev - er knew be - fore; And that we may
And be nev - er led a - stray; Lit - tle feet our

Thou hast giv - en We must an - swer un - to Thee.
bear it meet - ly, We must seek Thine aid the more.
steps may fol - low In a safe and nar - row way. A - MEN.

4 When our growing sons and daughters
   Look on life with eager eyes,
Grant us then a deeper insight
   And new powers of sacrifice:
Hope to trust them, faith to guide them,
   Love that nothing good denies.

5 May we keep our holy calling
   Stainless in its fair renown,
That, when all the work is over
   And we lay the burden down,
Then the children Thou hast given
   Still may be our joy and crown.

Words used by permission of The Mothers' Union

The Christian Home and Family

427

ALVERSTOKE. 11. 10. 11. 10.

CARL J. P. SPITTA, 1801–1859
Adapted from a tr. by SARAH B. FINDLATER, 1823–1907

JOSEPH BARNBY, 1838–1896

1. O hap-py home, where Thou art loved the dear-est, Thou lov-ing
2. O hap-py home, where each one serves Thee, low-ly, What-ev-er
3. O hap-py home, where Thou art not for-got-ten When joy is
4. Un-til at last, when earth's day's work is end-ed All meet Thee

Friend, and Sav-iour of our race, And where a-mong the guests there nev-er
his ap-point-ed work may be, Till ev-ery com-mon task seems great and
o-ver-flow-ing, full, and free; O hap-py home, where ev-ery wound-ed
in the bless-ed home a-bove, From whence Thou cam-est, where Thou hast as-

com-eth One who can hold such high and hon-ored place!
ho-ly, When it is done, O Lord, as un-to Thee!
spir-it Is brought, Phy-si-cian, Com-fort-er, to Thee—
cend-ed, Thy ev-er-last-ing home of peace and love! A-MEN.

428

ST. AGNES. C. M.

HENRY WARE, the younger, 1794–1843

JOHN B. DYKES, 1823–1876

1. Hap-py the home when God is there, And love fills ev-ery breast;
2. Hap-py the home where Je-sus' Name Is sweet to ev-ery ear;
3. Hap-py the home where prayer is heard, And praise is wont to rise;
4. Lord, let us in our homes a-gree This bless-ed peace to gain;

The Christian Home and Family

When one their wish, and one their prayer, And one their heaven-ly rest.
Where chil-dren ear - ly lisp His fame, And par-ents hold Him dear.
Where par-ents love the sa - cred Word And all its wis - dom prize.
U - nite our hearts in love to Thee, And love to all will reign. A - MEN.

429

KIRBY BEDON. 6. 6. 4. 6. 6. 6. 4.

CLEMENT OF ALEXANDRIA, (?) c. 200
Tr. by HENRY M. DEXTER, 1821–1890

EDWARD BUNNETT, 1834–1923

1. Shep - herd of ten - der youth, Guid - ing in love and truth,
2. Thou art our ho - ly Lord, The all - sub - du - ing Word,
3. Thou art the great High Priest; Thou hast pre - pared the feast
4. Ev - er be Thou our Guide, Our Shep - herd and our Pride,
5. So now, and till we die, Sound we Thy prais - es high,

Through de - vious ways; Christ our tri - umph - ant King,
Heal - er of strife; Thou didst Thy - self a - base,
Of heaven - ly love; While in our mor - tal pain
Our Staff and Song; Je - sus, Thou Christ of God,
And joy - ful sing; In - fants and the glad throng

We come Thy name to sing, Hith-er our chil-dren bring To shout Thy praise.
That from sin's deep dis-grace Thou might-est save our race, And give us life.
None calls on Thee in vain; Help Thou dost not dis-dain, Help from a - bove.
By Thy per - en-nial word, Lead us where Thou hast trod, Make our faith strong.
Who to Thy Church be-long, U-nite to swell the song To Christ our King! A - MEN.

The earliest Christian hymn extant

The Christian Home and Family

430

BLAIRGOWRIE (Dykes). 7. 6. 7. 6. D.

John S. B. Monsell, 1811–1875   John B. Dykes, 1823–1876

1. O Love divine and golden, Mysterious depth and height,
   To Thee the world beholden Looks up for life and light;
   O Love divine and gentle, The Blesser and the Blest,
   Beneath Thy care parental The world lies down in rest.

2. O Love divine and tender, That through our homes dost move,
   Veiled in the softened splendor Of holy household love,
   A throne without Thy blessing Were labor without rest,
   And cottages possessing Thy blessedness are blest.

3. God bless these hands united; God bless these hearts made one!
   Unsevered and unblighted May they through life go on,
   Here in earth's home preparing For the bright home above,
   And there for ever sharing Its joy where God is Love. A-MEN.

The Christian Home and Family

431

O PERFECT LOVE. 11. 10. 11. 10

DOROTHY B. GURNEY, 1858-1932

Arr. from JOSEPH BARNBY, 1838-1896

1. O per-fect Love, all hu-man thought tran-scend-ing,
2. O per-fect Life, be Thou their full as-sur-ance
3. Grant them the joy which bright-ens earth-ly sor-row;

Low-ly we kneel in prayer be-fore Thy throne,
Of ten-der char-i-ty and stead-fast faith,
Grant them the peace which calms all earth-ly strife,

That theirs may be the love which knows no end-ing,
Of pa-tient hope and qui-et, brave en-dur-ance,
And to life's day the glo-rious un-known mor-row

Whom Thou for ev-er-more dost join in one.
With child-like trust that fears nor pain nor death.
That dawns up-on e-ter-nal love and life. A-MEN.

The Christian Home and Family

432
RIMINGTON. L. M.

Oliver W. Holmes, 1809-1894

Francis Duckworth, 1862-

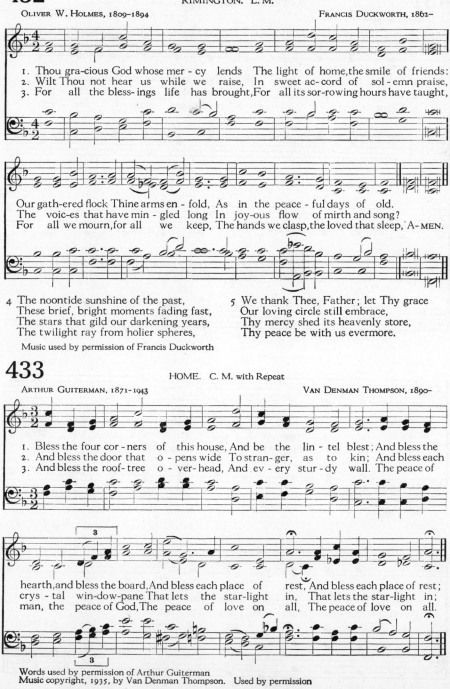

1. Thou gra-cious God whose mer-cy lends The light of home, the smile of friends:
2. Wilt Thou not hear us while we raise, In sweet ac-cord of sol-emn praise,
3. For all the bless-ings life has brought, For all its sor-rowing hours have taught,

Our gath-ered flock Thine arms en-fold, As in the peace-ful days of old.
The voic-es that have min-gled long In joy-ous flow of mirth and song?
For all we mourn, for all we keep, The hands we clasp, the loved that sleep, A-MEN.

4 The noontide sunshine of the past,
These brief, bright moments fading fast,
The stars that gild our darkening years,
The twilight ray from holier spheres,

5 We thank Thee, Father; let Thy grace
Our loving circle still embrace,
Thy mercy shed its heavenly store,
Thy peace be with us evermore.

Music used by permission of Francis Duckworth

433
HOME. C. M. with Repeat

Arthur Guiterman, 1871-1943

Van Denman Thompson, 1890-

1. Bless the four cor-ners of this house, And be the lin-tel blest; And bless the
2. And bless the door that o-pens wide To stran-ger, as to kin; And bless each
3. And bless the roof-tree o-ver-head, And ev-ery stur-dy wall. The peace of

hearth, and bless the board, And bless each place of rest, And bless each place of rest;
crys-tal win-dow-pane That lets the star-light in, That lets the star-light in;
man, the peace of God, The peace of love on all, The peace of love on all.

Hymns for Children

MÜLLER. 11. 11. 11. 11.

Anonymous

CARL MÜLLER(?), ?

1. A - way in a man - ger, no crib for a bed, The lit - tle Lord
2. The cat - tle are low - ing, the Ba - by a - wakes, But lit - tle Lord
3. Be near me, Lord Je - sus, I ask Thee to stay Close by me for

Je - sus laid down His sweet head. The stars in the sky looked
Je - sus, no cry - ing He makes. I love Thee, Lord Je - sus, look
ev - er, and love me, I pray. Bless all the dear chil - dren in

down where He lay, The lit - tle Lord Je - sus, a - sleep on the hay.
down from the sky, And stay by my cra - dle till morn - ing is nigh.
Thy ten - der care, And fit us for heav - en to live with Thee there.

Hymns for Children

435

GLADNESS (Bliss). 10. 10. 10. 10. with Refrain

Ascribed to EMILY S. OAKEY, 1829–1883

PHILIP P. BLISS, 1838–1876

1. I am so glad that our Fa-ther in heaven Tells of His love in the
2. Though I for-get Him, and wan-der a - way, Still He doth love me wher-
3. O if there's on - ly one song I can sing, When in His beau-ty I

Book He has given: Won-der-ful things in the Bi - ble I see;
ev - er I stray; Back to His dear lov-ing arms do I flee,
see the great King, This shall my song in e - ter - ni-ty be,

REFRAIN

This is the dear-est, that Je-sus loves me. I am so glad that
When I re-mem-ber that Je-sus loves me.
"O what a won-der that Je-sus loves me!"

Je - sus loves me, Je - sus loves me, Je - sus loves me,

Hymns for Children

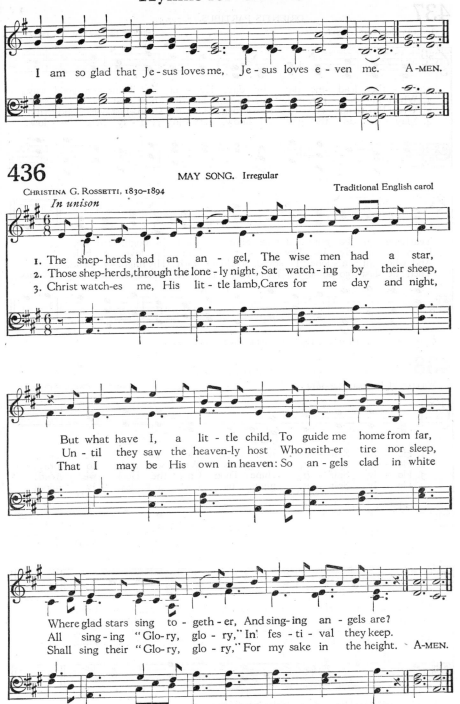

I am so glad that Je-sus loves me, Je-sus loves e-ven me. A-MEN.

436

MAY SONG. Irregular

CHRISTINA G. ROSSETTI, 1830-1894

Traditional English carol

In unison

1. The shep-herds had an an - gel, The wise men had a star,
2. Those shep-herds, through the lone - ly night, Sat watch-ing by their sheep,
3. Christ watch-es me, His lit - tle lamb, Cares for me day and night,

But what have I, a lit - tle child, To guide me home from far,
Un - til they saw the heaven-ly host Who neith-er tire nor sleep,
That I may be His own in heaven: So an - gels clad in white

Where glad stars sing to - geth - er, And sing-ing an - gels are?
All sing - ing "Glo - ry, glo - ry," In fes - ti - val they keep.
Shall sing their "Glo - ry, glo - ry," For my sake in the height. A-MEN.

Hymns for Children

437

ORIENTIS PARTIBUS. 7. 7. 7. 7.

JOHN P. HOPPS, 1834–1911

PIERRE DE CORBEIL (?), ?–1222

1. Fa - ther, lead me day by day, Ev - er in Thine own good way;
2. When in dan - ger, make me brave, Make me know that Thou canst save;
3. When I'm tempt - ed to do wrong, Make me stead - fast, wise, and strong;
4. May I do the good I know, Serv - ing glad - ly here be - low;

Teach me to be pure and true, Show me what I ought to do.
Keep me safe - ly by Thy side; Let me in Thy love a - bide.
And when all a - lone I stand, Shield me with Thy might - y hand.
Then at last go home to Thee, Ev - er - more Thine own to be. A-MEN.

438

ERNSTEIN. 6. 5. 6. 5.

WILLIAM H. PARKER, 1845–1929

JAMES F. SWIFT, 1847–1931

1. Ho - ly Spir - it, hear us; Help us while we sing;
2. Ho - ly Spir - it, prompt us When we kneel to pray;
3. Ho - ly Spir - it, shine Thou On the Book we read;
4. Ho - ly Spir - it, give us Each a low - ly mind;

Breathe in - to the mu - sic Of the praise we bring.
Near - er come and teach us What we ought to say.
Gild its ho - ly pa - ges With the light we need.
Make us more like Je - sus, Gen - tle, pure, and kind. A - MEN.

Hymns for Children

439

ELLON. 7. 6. 7. 6. D.

Anonymous
From THE BOOK OF PRAISE FOR CHILDREN, 1881

GEORGE F. ROOT, 1820-1895

1. The wise may bring their learn-ing, The rich may bring their wealth,
And some may bring their great-ness, And some bring strength and health;
We, too, would bring our treas-ures To of-fer to the King;
We have no wealth or learn-ing: What shall we chil-dren bring?

2. We'll bring Him hearts that love Him; We'll bring Him thank-ful praise,
And young souls meek-ly striv-ing To walk in ho-ly ways:
And these shall be the treas-ures We of-fer to the King,
And these are gifts that e-ven The poor-est child may bring.

3. We'll bring the lit-tle du-ties We have to do each day;
We'll try our best to please Him, At home, at school, at play:
And bet-ter are these treas-ures To of-fer to our King,
Than rich-est gifts with-out them; Yet these a child may bring. A-MEN.

Hymns for Children

440

SWEET STORY. Irregular

A Greek melody
Arr. by William B. Bradbury, 1816-1868

Jemima T. Luke, 1813-1906

1. I think when I read that sweet sto - ry of old,
2. I wish that His hands had been placed on my head,
3. Yet still to His foot - stool in prayer I may go,

When Je - sus was here a - mong men,
That His arms had been thrown a - round me,
And ask for a share in His love;

How He called lit - tle chil - dren as lambs to His fold,
And that I might have seen His kind look when He said,
And if I thus ear - nest - ly seek Him be - low,

I should like to have been with them then.
"Let the lit - tle ones come un - to me."
I shall see Him and know Him a - bove. A - men.

Hymns for Children

441

STORIES OF JESUS. 8. 4. 8. 4. 5. 4. 5. 4.

WILLIAM H. PARKER, 1845-1929

FREDERIC A. CHALLINOR, 1866-

Unison or Duet

1. Tell me the sto-ries of Je-sus I love to hear;
2. First let me hear how the chil-dren Stood round His knee,
3. In-to the cit-y I'd fol-low The chil-dren's band,

Things I would ask Him to tell me If He were here:
And I shall 'fan-cy His bless-ing Rest-ing on me;
Wav-ing a branch of the palm-tree High in my hand;

Scenes by the way-side, Tales of the sea,
Words full of kind-ness, Deeds full of grace,
One of His her-alds, Yes, I would sing

Sto-ries of Je-sus, Tell them to me.
All in the love-light Of Je-sus' face.
Loud-est ho-san-nas, "Je-sus is King!" A-MEN.

Hymns for Children

IRBY. Irregular

CECIL F. ALEXANDER, 1823–1895

HENRY J. GAUNTLETT, 1805–1876

1. Once in roy - al Da - vid's cit - y Stood a
2. He came down to earth from heav - en, Who is
3. Je - sus is our child - hood's pat - tern, Day by
4. And our eyes at last shall see Him, Through His

low - ly cat - tle shed, Where a moth - er laid her
God and Lord of all, And His shel - ter was a
day like us He grew; He was lit - tle, weak and
own re - deem - ing love; For that Child so dear and

Ba - by In a man - ger for His bed: Ma - ry
sta - ble, And His cra - dle was a stall: With the
help - less, Tears and smiles like us He knew: And He
gen - tle Is our Lord in heav'n a - bove: And He

was that moth - er mild, Je - sus Christ her lit - tle Child.
poor, and mean, and low - ly, Lived on earth our Sav - iour ho - ly.
feel - eth for our sad - ness, And He shar - eth in our glad - ness.
leads His chil - dren on To the place where He is gone. A - MEN.

Hymns for Children

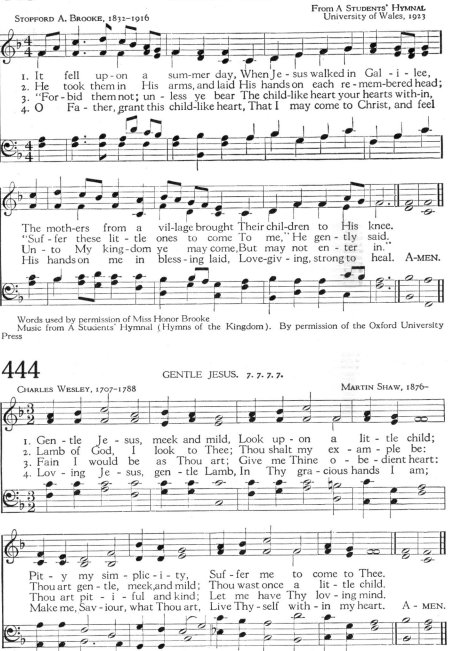

443

CHILDHOOD. 8. 8. 8. 6.

STOPFORD A. BROOKE, 1832–1916

From A STUDENTS' HYMNAL
University of Wales, 1923

1. It fell up-on a sum-mer day, When Je-sus walked in Gal-i-lee,
2. He took them in His arms, and laid His hands on each re-mem-bered head;
3. "For-bid them not; un-less ye bear The child-like heart your hearts with-in,
4. O Fa-ther, grant this child-like heart, That I may come to Christ, and feel

The moth-ers from a vil-lage brought Their chil-dren to His knee.
"Suf-fer these lit-tle ones to come To me," He gen-tly said.
Un-to My king-dom ye may come, But may not en-ter in."
His hands on me in bless-ing laid, Love-giv-ing, strong to heal. A-MEN.

Words used by permission of Miss Honor Brooke
Music from A Students' Hymnal (Hymns of the Kingdom). By permission of the Oxford University Press

444

GENTLE JESUS. 7. 7. 7. 7.

CHARLES WESLEY, 1707–1788

MARTIN SHAW, 1876–

1. Gen-tle Je-sus, meek and mild, Look up-on a lit-tle child;
2. Lamb of God, I look to Thee; Thou shalt my ex-am-ple be:
3. Fain I would be as Thou art; Give me Thine o-be-dient heart:
4. Lov-ing Je-sus, gen-tle Lamb, In Thy gra-cious hands I am;

Pit-y my sim-plic-i-ty, Suf-fer me to come to Thee.
Thou art gen-tle, meek, and mild; Thou wast once a lit-tle child.
Thou art pit-i-ful and kind; Let me have Thy lov-ing mind.
Make me, Sav-iour, what Thou art, Live Thy-self with-in my heart. A-MEN.

Music by permission, from Curwen Edition No. 6300, published by J. Curwen and Sons, Ltd., 24 Berners Street, London, W. 1. England

Hymns for Children

445

EMILY H. MILLER, 1833-1913

DEVA. 6. 5. 6. 5. D. with Refrain

EDWARD J. HOPKINS, 1818-1901

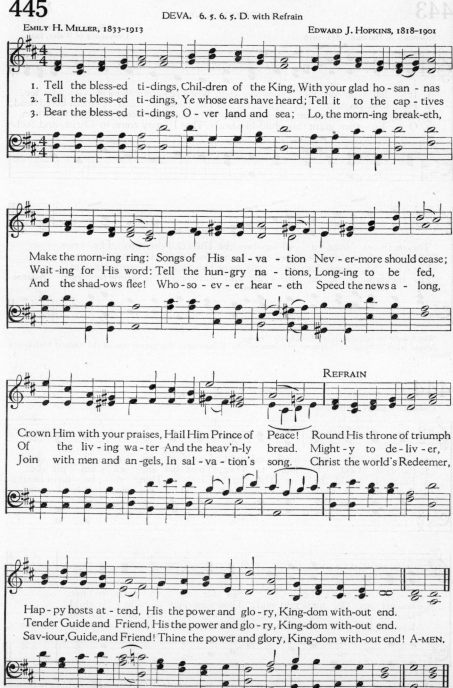

1. Tell the bless-ed ti-dings, Chil-dren of the King, With your glad ho-san-nas
2. Tell the bless-ed ti-dings, Ye whose ears have heard; Tell it to the cap-tives
3. Bear the bless-ed ti-dings, O-ver land and sea; Lo, the morn-ing break-eth,

Make the morn-ing ring: Songs of His sal-va-tion Nev-er-more should cease;
Wait-ing for His word: Tell the hun-gry na-tions, Long-ing to be fed,
And the shad-ows flee! Who-so-ev-er hear-eth Speed the news a-long,

REFRAIN

Crown Him with your praises, Hail Him Prince of Peace! Round His throne of triumph
Of the liv-ing wa-ter And the heav'n-ly bread. Might-y to de-liv-er,
Join with men and an-gels, In sal-va-tion's song. Christ the world's Redeemer,

Hap-py hosts at-tend, His the power and glo-ry, King-dom with-out end.
Tender Guide and Friend, His the power and glo-ry, King-dom with-out end.
Sav-iour, Guide, and Friend! Thine the power and glory, King-dom with-out end! A-MEN.

Hymns for Children

446

ST. THERESA. 6. 5. 6. 5. D. with Refrain

Thomas J. Potter, 1827–1873
Altered and abridged

Arthur S. Sullivan, 1842–1900

In unison

1. Bright-ly gleams our ban - ner, Point - ing to the sky,
2. Je - sus, Lord and Mas - ter, At Thy sa - cred feet,
3. Pat - tern of our child-hood, Once Thy-self a child,

Wav - ing on Christ's sol - diers To their home on high. March-ing thro' the
Here, with hearts re - joic - ing, See Thy chil-dren meet. Of - ten have we
Make our child-hood ho - ly, Pure, and meek, and mild. In the hour of

des - ert, Glad - ly thus we pray, Still with hearts u - nit - ed,
left Thee, Of - ten gone a - stray; Keep us, might - y Sav - iour,
dan - ger Whith-er can we flee, Save to Thee, dear Sav - iour,

REFRAIN

Sing-ing on our way. Bright-ly gleams our ban - ner, Point - ing to the
In the nar - row way.
On - ly un - to Thee?

sky, Wav - ing on Christ's sol - diers To their home on high. A - MEN.

Hymns for Children

447

ROYAL OAK. 7. 6. 7. 6. with Refrain

CECIL F. ALEXANDER, 1823-1895

Old English melody

In unison

Stanza 1 to be sung as refrain after stanzas 2-5

1. All things bright and beau-ti-ful, All crea-tures great and small,

All things wise and won-der-ful: The Lord God made them all. *Fine*

2. Each lit-tle flower that o-pens, Each lit-tle bird that sings:
3. The pur-ple-head-ed moun-tain, The riv-er run-ning by,
4. The cold wind in the win-ter, The pleas-ant sum-mer sun,
5. He gave us eyes to see them, And lips that we might tell

He made their glow-ing col-ors, He made their ti-ny wings.
The sun-set, and the morn-ing That bright-ens up the sky,
The ripe fruits in the gar-den: He made them ev-ery one.
How great is God Al-might-y, Who has made all things well. A-MEN.

Hymns for Children

448

ROSSLYN. 7. 7. 7. 7. 7. 7.

Whitfield G. Wills, 1841–1891

English melody

1. In our work and in our play, Je - sus, ev - er
2. May we in Thy strength sub - due E - vil tem - pers,
3. Chil - dren of the King are we! May we loy - al

with us stay; May we al - ways strive to be
words un - true, Thoughts im - pure, and deeds un - kind,
to Him be; Try to please Him ev - ery day,

True and faith - ful un - to Thee. Then we truth - ful -
All things hate - ful to Thy mind. Then we truth - ful -
In our work and in our play. Then we truth - ful -

ly can sing, We are chil - dren of the King.
ly can sing, We are chil - dren of the King.
ly can sing, We are chil - dren of the King.

Hymns for Children

449

INNOCENTS 7. 7. 7. 7.

JANE E. LEESON, 1807–1882

From THE PARISH CHOIR, 1850

1. Sav - iour, teach me, day by day, Love's sweet les - son to o - bey;
2. With a child's glad heart of love At Thy bid - ding may I move,
3. Teach me thus Thy steps to trace, Strong to fol - low in Thy grace,
4. Thus may I re - joice to show That I feel the love I owe;

Sweet - er les - son can - not be, Lov - ing Him who first loved me.
Prompt to serve and fol - low Thee, Lov - ing Him who first loved me.
Learn - ing how to love from Thee, Lov - ing Him who first loved me.
Sing - ing, till Thy face I see, Of His love who first loved me. A-MEN.

Another arrangement of this tune will be found at No. 81.

450

CAPEL. C. M.

MATILDA B. BETHAM–EDWARDS, 1836–1919

English traditional melody

1. God make my life a lit - tle light With - in the world to glow;
2. God make my life a lit - tle flower That giv - eth joy to all,
3. God make my life a lit - tle song That com - fort - eth the sad,

A lit - tle flame that burn - eth bright, Wher - ev - er I may go.
Con - tent to bloom in na - tive bower, Al - though the place be small.
That help - eth oth - ers to be strong, And makes the sing - er glad. A-MEN.

4 God make my life a little staff
   Whereon the weak may rest,
That so what health and strength I have
   May serve my neighbors best.

5 God make my life a little hymn
   Of tenderness and praise,
Of faith, that never waxeth dim,
   In all His wondrous ways.

Hymns for Children

451

SAMUEL. 6. 6. 6. 6. 8. 8.

James D. Burns, 1823-1864

Arthur S. Sullivan, 1842-1900

1. Hushed was the eve-ning hymn, The tem-ple courts were dark,
The lamp was burn-ing dim Be-fore the sa-cred ark; When sud-den-ly a
Voice di-vine Rang through the si-lence of the shrine.

2. The old man, meek and mild, The priest of Is-rael, slept;
His watch the tem-ple-child, The lit-tle Le-vite, kept; And what from E-li's
sense was sealed, The Lord to Han-nah's son re-vealed.

3. O give me Sam-uel's ear: The o-pen ear, O Lord,
A-live and quick to hear Each whis-per of Thy word! Like him to an-swer
at Thy call, And to o-bey Thee first of all. A-men.

4 O give me Samuel's heart!
A lowly heart, that waits
Where in Thy house Thou art,
Or watches at Thy gates!
By day and night, a heart that still
Moves at the breathing of Thy will.

5 O give me Samuel's mind:
A sweet, unmurmuring faith,
Obedient and resigned
To Thee in life and death!
That I may read with childlike eyes
Truths that are hidden from the wise.

Hymns for Children

452

DIJON. 8. 7. 8. 7.

MARY L. DUNCAN, 1814–1840

Old German melody

1. Je - sus, ten - der Shep-herd, hear me; Bless Thy lit - tle lamb to -night;
2. All this day Thy hand hath led me, And I thank Thee for Thy care;
3. Let my sins be all for-giv - en; Bless the friends I love so well;

Through the dark-ness be Thou near me, Watch my sleep till morn-ing light.
Thou hast clothed me, warmed and fed me; Lis - ten to my eve-ning prayer.
Take me, when I die, to heav - en, Hap - py there with Thee to dwell. A - MEN.

453

LYTHAM. C. M.

ANNIE MATHESON, 1853–1924

JAMES T. LIGHTWOOD, 1856–1944

1. Lord, when we have not an - y light, And moth-ers are a - sleep;
2. When shad-ows haunt the qui - et room, Help us to un - der - stand
3. And though we do not al - ways see The ho - ly an - gels near,
4. So in the morn-ing may we wake, When wakes the kind-ly sun,

Then through the still-ness of the night, Thy lit - tle chil-dren keep.
That Thou art with us through the gloom, To hold us by the hand.
O may we trust our-selves to Thee, Nor have one fool - ish fear.
More lov - ing for our Fa - ther's sake To each un - lov - ing one. A - MEN.

Service

454

MEIRIONYDD. 7.6.7.6.D.

John Haynes Holmes, 1879–

Welsh hymn melody

1. The voice of God is call-ing Its sum-mons un-to men;
2. I hear my peo-ple cry-ing In cot and mine and slum;
3. We heed, O Lord, Thy sum-mons, And an-swer: Here are we!
4. From ease and plen-ty save us; From pride of place ab-solve;

As once He spake in Zi-on, So now He speaks a-gain.
No field or mart is si-lent, No cit-y street is dumb.
Send us up-on Thine er-rand, Let us Thy serv-ants be.
Purge us of low de-sire; Lift us to high re-solve;

Whom shall I send to suc-cor My peo-ple in their need?
I see my peo-ple fall-ing In dark-ness and de-spair.
Our strength is dust and ash-es, Our years a pass-ing hour;
Take us, and make us ho-ly; Teach us Thy will and way.

Whom shall I send to loos-en The bonds of shame and greed?
Whom shall I send to shat-ter The fet-ters which they bear?
But Thou canst use our weak-ness To mag-ni-fy Thy power.
Speak, and, be-hold! we an-swer; Com-mand, and we o-bey! A-men.

Words used by permission of John Haynes Holmes

The Kingdom of God

455

SHELTERED DALE. 8. 6. 8. 6. 8. 6.

GEOFFREY A. STUDDERT-KENNEDY, 1883–1929

German traditional melody

1. A - wake, a - wake to love and work, The lark is in the sky,
2. Come, let thy voice be one with theirs, Shout with their shout of praise;
3. To give and give, and give a - gain, What God hath giv - en thee;

The fields are wet with dia - mond dew, The worlds a - wake to cry
See how the gi - ant sun soars up, Great lord of years and days!
To spend thy - self nor count the cost, To serve right glo - rious - ly

Their bless-ings on the Lord of Life, As He goes meek-ly by.
So let the love of Je - sus come And set thy soul a - blaze;
The God who gave all worlds that are, And all that are to be. A-MEN.

Words used by permission of Hodder and Stoughton

456

SCHUMANN. S. M.

WILLIAM W. HOW, 1823–1897

From CANTICA LAUDIS, 1850

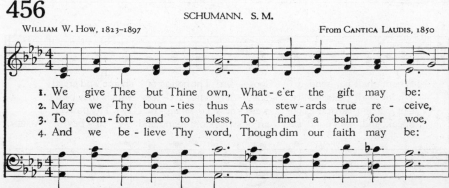

1. We give Thee but Thine own, What - e'er the gift may be;
2. May we Thy boun - ties thus As stew - ards true re - ceive,
3. To com - fort and to bless, To find a balm for woe,
4. And we be - lieve Thy word, Though dim our faith may be;

Service

All that we have is Thine a - lone, A trust, O Lord, from Thee.
And glad - ly, as Thou bless-est us, To Thee our first fruits give.
To tend the lone and fa - ther - less, Is an - gels' work be - low.
What-e'er for Thine we do, O Lord, We do it un - to Thee. A - MEN.

457

GODWIN. L. M.

RICHARD W. GILDER, 1844–1909   WILLIAM G. BLANCHARD, 1905–

1. God of the strong, God of the weak, Lord of all
2. In suf - fering Thou hast made us one, In might - y
3. Teach us, great Teach-er of man - kind, The sac - ri -
4. Teach Thou, and we shall know in - deed The truth di -

lands and our own land, Light of all souls: from Thee we seek
bur - dens one are we: Teach us that low - liest du - ty done
fice that brings Thy balm: The love, the work that bless and bind;
vine that mak - eth free; And know-ing, we may sow the seed

Light from Thy light, strength from Thy hand.
Is high - est serv - ice un - to Thee.
Teach us Thy maj - es - ty, Thy calm.
That blos - soms through e - ter - ni - ty. A - MEN.

Music copyright, 1935, by Whitmore & Smith, Nashville, Tenn.

The Kingdom of God

458

FIELD. 10. 10. 10. 10.

Calvin W. Laufer, 1874-1938

Calvin W. Laufer, 1874-1938

1. We thank Thee, Lord, Thy paths of serv-ice lead
2. We've sought and found Thee in the se-cret place
3. We've felt Thy touch in sor-row's dark-ened way
4. We've seen Thy glo-ry like a man-tle spread

To bla-zoned heights and down the slopes of need;
And mar-veled at the ra-diance of Thy face;
A-bound with love and sol-ace for the day;
O'er hill and dale in saf-fron flame and red;

They reach Thy throne, en-com-pass land and sea,
But of-ten in some far-off Gal-i-lee
And, 'neath the bur-dens there, Thy sov-reign-ty
But in the eyes of men, re-deemed and free,

And he who jour-neys in them walks with Thee.
Be-held Thee fair-er yet while serv-ing Thee.
Has held our hearts en-thralled while serv-ing Thee.
A splen-dor great-er yet while serv-ing Thee. A-men.

Service

459

ST. AGNES. C. M.

JOHN ELLERTON, 1826–1893

JOHN B. DYKES, 1823–1876

1. Be - hold us, Lord, a lit - tle space From dai - ly tasks set free,
2. A - round us rolls the cease-less tide Of busi - ness, toil, and care,
3. Yet these are not the on - ly walls Where-in Thou mayst be sought:
4. Thine is the loom, the forge, the mart, The wealth of land and sea;

And met with - in Thy ho - ly place To rest a - while with Thee.
And scarce-ly can we turn a - side For one brief hour of prayer.
On home-liest work Thy bless-ing falls, In truth and pa - tience wrought.
The worlds of sci - ence and of art, Re-vealed and ruled by Thee. A-MEN.

5 Then let us prove our heavenly birth
  In all we do and know,
  And claim the kingdom of the earth
  For Thee, and not Thy foe.

6 Work shall be prayer, if all be wrought
  As Thou wouldst have it done;
  And prayer, by Thee inspired and taught,
  Itself with work be one.

460

GRATITUDE. L. M.

FRANCES R. HAVERGAL, 1836–1879

PAUL A. I. D. BOST, 1790–1874

1. Lord, speak to me, that I may speak In liv - ing ech - oes of Thy tone;
2. O teach me, Lord, that I may teach The pre-cious things Thou dost im-part;
3. O fill me with Thy full-ness, Lord, Un - til my ver - y heart o'er-flow
4. O use me, Lord, use ev - en me, Just as Thou wilt, and when, and where;

As Thou hast sought, so let me seek Thine err-ing chil - dren lost and lone.
And wing my words, that they may reach The hid-den depths of man-y a heart.
In kind-ling tho't and glow-ing word, Thy love to tell, Thy praise to show.
Un - til Thy bless - ed face I see, Thy rest, Thy joy, Thy glo - ry share. A-MEN.

Alternative tune, Canonbury, No. 116

The Kingdom of God

461

AUSTRIAN HYMN. 8. 7. 8. 7. D.

JOHN G. ADAMS, 1810-1887

FRANCIS J. HAYDN, 1732-1809

1. Heaven is here, where hymns of glad-ness Cheer the toil-ers' rug-ged way,
2. Where the sad, the poor, de-spair-ing, Are up-lift-ed, cheered, and blest,

In this world where clouds of sad-ness Oft-en change to night our day:
Where in oth-ers' la-bors shar-ing, We can find our sur-est rest;

Heaven is here, where mis-ery light-ened Of its heav-y load is seen,
Where we heed the voice of du-ty, Tread the path that Je-sus trod:

Where the face of sor-row bright-ened, By the deed of love hath been.
This is heaven, its peace, its beau-ty, Ra-diant with the love of God. A-MEN.

Service

GRÄFENBERG. C. M.

Charles Kingsley, 1819–1875

From Johann Crüger's
Praxis Pietatis Melica, 1653

1. From Thee all skill and sci-ence flow, All pit-y, care, and love,
2. And part them, Lord, to each and all, As each and all shall need,
3. And has-ten, Lord, that per-fect day When pain and death shall cease,
4. When ev-er blue the sky shall gleam, And ev-er green the sod,

All calm and cour-age, faith and hope: O pour them from a - bove.
To rise like in-cense, each to Thee, In no - ble thought and deed.
And Thy just rule shall fill the earth With health, and light, and peace;
And man's rude work de - face no more The Par-a-dise of God. A-MEN.

463

IRISH. C. M.

Frederick L. Hosmer, 1840–1929

Melody from A Collection of
Hymns and Sacred Poems, 1749

1. "Thy King-dom come," on bend-ed knee The pass-ing a - ges pray;
2. But the slow watch-es of the night Not less to God be-long,
3. And lo! al-read-y on the hills The flags of dawn ap-pear;

And faith-ful souls have yearned to see On earth that King-dom's day.
And for the ev-er-last - ing right The si - lent stars are strong.
Gird up your loins, ye proph - et souls, Pro-claim the day is near: A-MEN.

4 The day in whose clear-shining light
All wrong shall stand revealed,
When justice shall be clothed with might,
And every hurt be healed;

5 When knowledge, hand in hand with peace,
Shall walk the earth abroad —
The day of perfect righteousness,
The promised day of God.

The Kingdom of God

464

LOVE'S OFFERING. 6. 4. 6. 4. 6. 6. 4. 4.

EDWIN P. PARKER, 1836-1925

EDWIN P. PARKER, 1836-1925

1. Mas - ter, no of - fer - ing Cost - ly and sweet
2. Dai - ly our lives would show Weak - ness made strong,
3. Some word of hope for hearts Bur - dened with fears,
4. Thus in Thy serv - ice, Lord, Till e - ven - tide

May we, like Mag - da - lene, Lay at Thy feet;
Toil - some and gloom - y ways Bright - ened with song;
Some balm of peace for eyes Blind - ed with tears,
Clos - es the day of life, May we a - bide.

Yet may love's in - cense rise, Sweet - er than sac - ri - fice,
Some deeds of kind - ness done, Some souls by pa - tience won,
Some dews of mer - cy shed, Some way - ward foot - steps led,
And when earth's la - bors cease, Let us de - part in peace,

Dear Lord, to Thee, Dear Lord, to Thee. A - MEN.

Brotherhood

GERMANY. L. M.

465

FRANK MASON NORTH, 1850–1935

From WILLIAM GARDINER'S
SACRED MELODIES, 1815

1. Where cross the crowd-ed ways of life, Where sound the
2. In haunts of wretch-ed-ness and need, On shad-owed
3. From ten-der child-hood's help-less-ness, From wo-man's
4. The cup of wa-ter given for Thee Still holds the

cries of race and clan, A-bove the noise of
thresh-olds dark with fears, From paths where hide the
grief, man's bur-dened toil, From fam-ished souls, from
fresh-ness of Thy grace; Yet long these mul-ti-

self-ish strife, We hear Thy voice, O Son of man!
lures of greed, We catch the vi-sion of Thy tears.
sor-row's stress, Thy heart has nev-er known re-coil.
tudes to see The sweet com-pas-sion of Thy face. A-MEN.

5 O Master, from the mountain side,
  Make haste to heal these hearts of pain;
Among these restless throngs abide,
  O tread the city's streets again,

6 Till sons of men shall learn Thy love
  And follow where Thy feet have trod;
Till, glorious from Thy heaven above,
  Shall come the city of our God!

The Kingdom of God

466

ILONA. 11. 10. 11. 10.

John G. Whittier, 1807-1892

J. W. Lerman, 1864-

1. O broth-er man, fold to thy heart thy broth-er!
2. For he whom Je-sus loved hath tru-ly spo-ken:
3. Fol-low with rev-erent steps the great ex-am-ple

Where pit-y dwells, the peace of God is there;
The ho-lier wor-ship which He deigns to bless
Of Him whose ho-ly work was do-ing good;

To wor-ship right-ly is to love each oth-er,
Re-stores the lost, and binds the spir-it bro-ken,
So shall the wide earth seem our Fa-ther's tem-ple,

Each smile a hymn, each kind-ly deed a prayer.
And feeds the wid-ow and the fa-ther-less.
Each lov-ing life a psalm of grat-i-tude. A-MEN.

Brotherhood

467

LLANGLOFFAN. 7. 6. 7. 6. D.

JOHN HAY, 1838-1905

Welsh hymn melody
From D. EVANS' HYMNAU A THONAU, 1865

1. Not in dumb res - ig - na - tion We lift our hands on high;
2. Thy will! It strength-ens weak - ness, It bids the strong be just;

Not like the nerve-less fa - tal - ist Con - tent to trust and die:
No lip to fawn, no hand to beg, No brow to seek the dust.

Our faith springs like the ea - gle, That soars to meet the sun,
Wher - ev - er man op - press-es man Be - neath Thy lib - eral sun,

And cries ex - ult - ing un - to Thee, "O Lord, Thy will be done!"
O Lord, be there, Thine arm made bare, Thy right-eous will be done! A - MEN.

The Kingdom of God

468

LAUFER. 7. 6. 7. 6. D.

LOUIS F. BENSON, 1855–1930

EMILY S. PERKINS, 1866–1941

1. The light of God is fall - ing Up - on life's com - mon way;
2. Who shares his life's pure pleas - ures, And walks the hon - est road,
3. Where hu - man lives are throng - ing In toil and pain and sin,
4. Thy ran - somed host in glo - ry, All souls that sin and pray,

The Mas - ter's voice still call - ing, "Come, walk with me to - day;"
Who trades with heap - ing meas - ures, And lifts his broth - er's load,
While clois - tered hearts are long - ing To bring the king - dom in,
Turn toward the cross that bore Thee; "Be - hold the man!" they say;

No du - ty can seem low - ly To him who lives with Thee,
Who turns the wrong down blunt - ly, And lends the right a hand,
O Christ, the Eld - er Broth - er Of proud and beat - en men,
And while Thy Church is plead - ing For all who would do good,

And all of life grows ho - ly, O Christ of Gal - i - lee!
He dwells in God's own coun - try, He tills the Ho - ly Land.
When they have found each oth - er, Thy king - dom will come then.
We hear Thy true voice lead - ing Our song of broth - er - hood. A - MEN.

Words used by permission of Mrs. Robert E. Jefferys
Music copyright, 1924, by Emily S. Perkins. Used by permission

Brotherhood

469

ST. MICHEL'S. C. M. D.

Ozora S. Davis, 1866–1931

From W. Gawler's Hymns and Psalms, 1789

1. At length there dawns the glo - rious day By proph-ets long fore - told;
2. For what are sun-dering strains of blood, Or an - cient caste and creed?
3. One com - mon faith u - nites us all, We seek one com-mon goal,

At length the cho - rus clear - er grows That shep - herds heard of old.
One claim u - nites all men in God To serve each hu - man need.
One ten - der com - fort broods up - on The strug - gling hu - man soul.

The day of dawn - ing Broth - er - hood Breaks on our ea - ger eyes,
Then here to - geth - er, broth - er - men, We pledge the Lord a - new
To this clear call of Broth - er - hood Our hearts re - spon - sive ring;

And hu - man ha - treds flee be - fore The ra - diant east-ern skies.
Our loy - al love, our stal - wart faith, Our serv - ice strong and true.
We join the glo - rious new cru - sade Of our great Lord and King. A-men.

The Kingdom of God

470

BELOIT. L. M.

Charles S. Newhall, 1842–1935

Carl G. Reissiger, 1798–1859

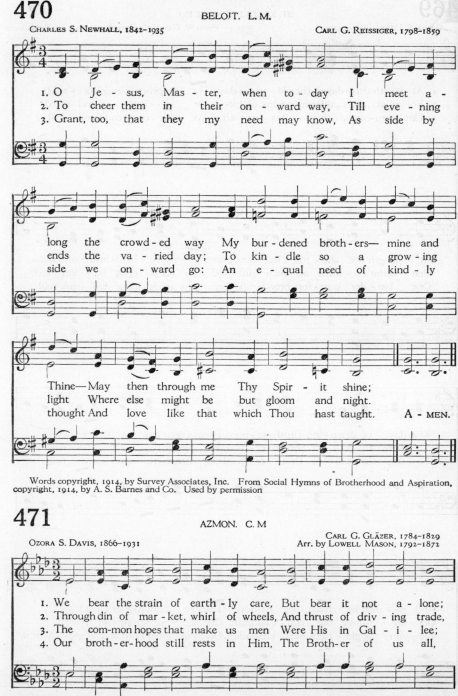

1. O Je - sus, Mas - ter, when to - day I meet a -
2. To cheer them in their on - ward way, Till eve - ning
3. Grant, too, that they my need may know, As side by

long the crowd - ed way My bur - dened broth - ers— mine and
ends the va - ried day; To kin - dle so a grow - ing
side we on - ward go: An e - qual need of kind - ly

Thine—May then through me Thy Spir - it shine;
light Where else might be but gloom and night.
thought And love like that which Thou hast taught. A - men.

471

AZMON. C. M

Ozora S. Davis, 1866–1931

Carl G. Gläzer, 1784–1829
Arr. by Lowell Mason, 1792–1872

1. We bear the strain of earth - ly care, But bear it not a - lone;
2. Through din of mar - ket, whirl of wheels, And thrust of driv - ing trade,
3. The com - mon hopes that make us men Were His in Gal - i - lee;
4. Our broth - er - hood still rests in Him, The Broth - er of us all,

Brotherhood

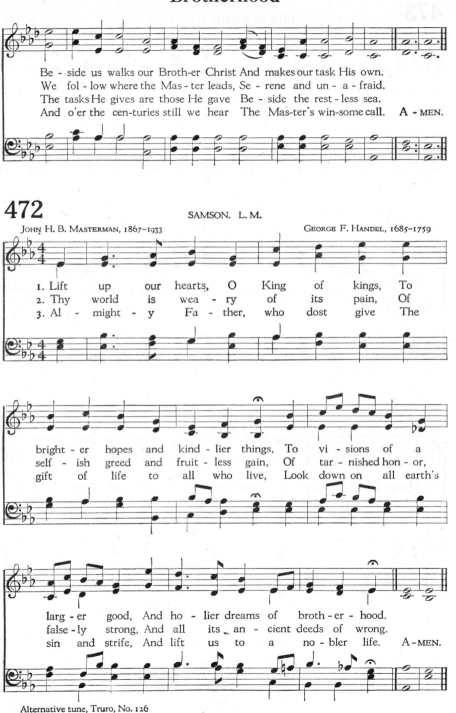

Be - side us walks our Broth-er Christ And makes our task His own.
We fol - low where the Mas - ter leads, Se - rene and un - a - fraid.
The tasks He gives are those He gave Be - side the rest - less sea.
And o'er the cen-turies still we hear The Mas-ter's win-some call. A - MEN.

472

SAMSON. L. M.

John H. B. Masterman, 1867-1933   George F. Handel, 1685-1759

1. Lift up our hearts, O King of kings, To
2. Thy world is wea - ry of its pain, Of
3. Al - might - y Fa - ther, who dost give The

bright - er hopes and kind - lier things, To vi - sions of a
self - ish greed and fruit - less gain, Of tar - nished hon - or,
gift of life to all who live, Look down on all earth's

larg - er good, And ho - lier dreams of broth - er - hood.
false - ly strong, And all its an - cient deeds of wrong.
sin and strife, And lift us to a no - bler life. A - MEN.

Alternative tune, Truro, No. 126

The Kingdom of God

473

CITY OF LIGHT. 7. 6. 7. 6. 7. 4.

GEORGE T. COSTER, 1835–1912

A. V. COSTER, 1864–1931

1. King of the Cit - y Splen - did, E - ter - nal in the height,
2. Teach love to glad - den chil - dren That know not child-hood's mirth,
3. Give joy to all the joy - less, Song's voice to sor - rows dumb,

May all our coun-try's cit - ies Grow ho - ly in Thy sight:
Wronged of their rights—no beau - ty In their scant reach of earth;
May light in - vade with bless - ing Each dark and death - ly slum;

Cleansed from the deeds of dark - ness— Cit - ies of light.
To hope's large sun - shine give them A sec - ond birth.
In - to earth's realms of hor - ror Thy King - dom come! A -MEN.

Used by permission of V. B. Coster, 36 Abbotsford Gardens, Woodford Green, Essex, England

4 Soon may our country's cities
Thy robe of glory wear;
Each place of toil a temple,
Each house a home of prayer:
Each city's name of beauty—
The Lord is there!

Brotherhood

474

FORD COTTAGE. 8. 6. 8. 6. 8. 6.

WALTER RUSSELL BOWIE, 1882–

F. C. MAKER, 1844-1927

1. O ho - ly cit - y, seen of John, Where Christ, the Lamb, doth reign,
2. Hark, how from men whose lives are held More cheap than mer - chan-dise,
3. O shame to us who rest con - tent While lust and greed for gain

With - in whose four-square walls shall come No night, nor need, nor pain,
From wo - men strug-gling sore for bread, From lit - tle chil - dren's cries,
In street and shop and ten - e - ment Wring gold from hu - man pain,

And where the tears are wiped from eyes That shall not weep a - gain!
There swells the sob-bing hu - man plaint That bids thy walls a - rise!
And bit - ter lips in blind de-spair Cry, "Christ hath died in vain!" A - MEN.

4 Give us, O God, the strength to build
   The city that hath stood
Too long a dream, whose laws are love,
   Whose ways are brotherhood,
And where the sun that shineth is
   God's grace for human good.

5 Already in the mind of God
   That city riseth fair:
Lo, how its splendor challenges
   The souls that greatly dare —
Yea, bids us seize the whole of life
   And build its glory there.

The Kingdom of God

475

TIDINGS. 11. 10. 11. 10. with Refrain

MARY A. THOMSON, 1834-1923

JAMES WALCH, 1837-1901

1. O Zi - on, haste, thy mis-sion high ful - fill - ing, To tell to all the
2. Be - hold how man - y thou-sands still are ly - ing Bound in the dark-some
3. Pro -claim to ev - ery peo - ple, tongue, and na - tion That God, in whom they
4. Give of thy sons to bear the mes-sage glo - rious; Give of thy wealth to

world that God is Light, That He who made all na-tions is not will - ing
pris - on-house of sin, With none to tell them of the Sav-iour's dy - ing,
live and move, is Love; Tell how He stooped to save His lost cre - a - tion,
speed them on their way; Pour out thy soul for them in prayer vic - to - rious;

REFRAIN

One soul should per - ish, lost in shades of night. Pub - lish glad tid - ings;
Or of the life He died for them to win.
And died on earth that man might live a - bove.
O Zi - on, haste to bring the bright-er day.

Tid - ings of peace; Tid - ings of Je - sus, Re-demp-tion and re-lease. A - MEN.

Missions

476

EVERYLAND, No. 1. C. M. D.

HENRY H. TWEEDY, 1868–

LILY RENDLE, 1875–

1. E - ter - nal God, whose power up-holds Both flower and flam - ing star,
2. O God of love, whose spir - it wakes In ev - ery hu - man breast,
3. O God of truth, whom sci - ence seeks And rev - erent souls a - dore,

To whom there is no here nor there, No time, no near nor far,
Whom love, and love a - lone can know, In whom all hearts find rest:
Who light - est ev - ery earn - est mind Of ev - ery clime and shore:

No a - lien race, no for - eign shore, No child un-sought, un - known:
Help us to spread Thy gra - cious reign Till greed and hate shall cease,
Dis - pel the gloom of er - ror's night, Of ig - no - rance and fear,

O send us forth, Thy proph-ets true, To make all lands Thine own!
And kind-ness dwell in hu - man hearts, And all the earth find peace!
Un - til true wis - dom from a - bove Shall make life's path-way clear! A-MEN.

4 O God of beauty, oft revealed
    In dreams of human art,
In speech that flows to melody,
    In holiness of heart:
Teach us to ban all ugliness
    That blinds our eyes to Thee,
Till all shall know the loveliness
    Of lives made fair and free.

5 O God of righteousness and grace,
    Seen in the Christ, Thy Son,
Whose life and death reveal Thy face,
    By whom Thy will was done:
Inspire Thy heralds of good news
    To live Thy life divine,
Till Christ is formed in all mankind
    And every land is Thine!

The Kingdom of God

477

RIGHINI. 6. 6. 4. 6. 6. 6. 4.

JOHN MARRIOTT, 1780–1825

VINCENZO RIGHINI, 1756–1812

1. Thou, whose al-might-y word Cha-os and dark-ness heard,
2. Thou who didst come to bring On Thy re-deem-ing wing,
3. Spir-it of truth and love, Life-giv-ing, ho-ly Dove,
4. Ho-ly and bless-ed Three, Glo-ri-ous Trin-i-ty,

And took their flight; Hear us, we hum-bly pray, And where the
Heal-ing and sight, Health to the sick in mind, Sight to the
Speed forth Thy flight; Move o'er the wa-ters' face Bear-ing the
Grace, Love, and Might! Bound-less as o-cean's tide Roll-ing in

gos-pel's day Sheds not its glo-rious ray, Let there be light!
in-ly blind: O now, to all man-kind, Let there be light!
lamp of grace; And in earth's dark-est place, Let there be light!
full-est pride, Through the world far and wide, Let there be light! A-MEN.

478

TALLIS' ORDINAL. C. M.

HARDWICKE D. RAWNSLEY, 1851–1920

THOMAS TALLIS, c. 1520–1585

1. Fa-ther, whose will is life and good For all of mor-tal breath
2. Em-power the hands and hearts and wills Of friends in lands a-far,
3. Wher-e'er they heal the maimed and blind, Let love of Christ at-tend:
4. For still His love works won-drous charms, And, as in days of old,
5. O Fa-ther, look from heaven and bless, Wher-e'er Thy ser-vants be,

Missions

Bind strong the bond of broth-er-hood Of those who fight with death.
Who bat-tle with the bod-y's ills, And wage Thy ho-ly war.
Pro-claim the good Phy-si-cian's mind, And prove the Sav-iour friend.
He takes the wound-ed to His arms, And bears them to the fold.
Their works of pure un-self-ish-ness, Made con-se-crate to Thee! A-MEN.

479

DUKE STREET. L. M.

From Psalm LXXII
Isaac Watts, 1674–1748

John Hatton, d. 1793

1. Je-sus shall reign wher-e'er the sun Does his suc-
2. To Him shall end-less prayer be made, And end-less
3. Peo-ple and realms of ev-ery tongue Dwell on His
4. Let ev-ery crea-ture rise, and bring His grate-ful

ces-sive jour-neys run; His king-dom spread from shore to shore,
prais-es crown His head; His name, like sweet per-fume, shall rise
love with sweet-est song, And in-fant voic-es shall pro-claim
hon-ors to our King; An-gels de-scend with songs a-gain,

Till moons shall wax and wane no more.
With ev-ery morn-ing sac-ri-fice.
Their ear-ly bless-ings on His Name.
And earth re-peat the loud A-men! A-MEN.

Alternative tune, Rimington, No. 345

The Kingdom of God

480

MELITA. 8. 8. 8. 8. 8. 8.

Frank Mason North, 1850–1935

John B. Dykes, 1823–1876

1. O Mas-ter of the wak-ing world, Who hast the na-tions in Thy heart— The heart that bled and broke to send God's love to earth's re-mot-est part: Show us a-new in Cal-va-ry The won-drous power that makes men free.

2. On ev-ery side the walls are down, The gates swing wide to ev-ery land, The rest-less tribes and rac-es feel The pres-sure of Thy pierc-ed hand; Thy way is in the sea and air, Thy world is o-pen ev-ery-where.

3. We hear the throb of surg-ing life, The clank of chains, the curse of greed, The moan of pain, the fu-tile cries Of su-per-sti-tion's cru-el creed; The peo-ples hun-ger for Thee, Lord, The isles are wait-ing for Thy word.

4. Thy wit-ness in the souls of men, Thy Spir-it's cease-less, brood-ing power, In lands where shad-ows hide the light, A-wait a new cre-a-tive hour: O might-y God, set us a-flame To show the glo-ry of Thy Name. A-MEN.

Missions

481

KIRBY BEDON. 6. 6. 4. 6. 6. 6. 4.

SAMUEL WOLCOTT, 1813–1886

EDWARD BUNNETT, 1834–1923

1. Christ for the world we sing! The world to Christ we bring, With lov - ing
2. Christ for the world we sing! The world to Christ we bring, With fer - vent
3. Christ for the world we sing! The world to Christ we bring, With one ac -

zeal; The poor, and them that mourn, The faint and o - ver - borne,
prayer; The way - ward and the lost, By rest - less pas - sions tossed,
cord; With us the work to share, With us re - proach to dare,

Sin - sick and sor - row - worn, Whom Christ doth heal.
Re - deemed at count - less cost, From dark de - spair.
With us the cross to bear, For Christ our Lord. A - MEN.

4 Christ for the world we sing!
The world to Christ we bring,
With joyful song;
The newborn souls, whose days,
Reclaimed from error's ways,
Inspired with hope and praise,
To Christ belong.

Alternative tune, Italian Hymn, No. 2

The Kingdom of God

NATIONAL HYMN. 10. 10. 10. 10.

LAURA S. COPENHAVER, 1868-1941

GEORGE W. WARREN, 1828-1902

Trumpets, before each stanza

1. Her - alds of Christ, who bear the King's com-mands,
2. Thro' des - ert ways, dark fen, and deep mo - rass,
3. Lord, give us faith and strength the road to build,

Im - mor - tal ti - dings in your mor - tal hands,
Through jun - gles, slug - gish seas, and moun - tain pass,
To see the prom - ise of the day ful - filled,

Pass on and car - ry swift the news ye bring:
Build ye the road, and fal - ter not, nor stay;
When war shall be no more and strife shall cease

Make straight, make straight the high - way of the King.
Pre - pare a - cross the earth the King's high - way.
Up - on the high - way of the Prince of Peace. Á - MEN.

Words used by permission of Mrs. H. W. Parker

Missions

483

THE KINGDOM COMING. 6. 6. 8. 6. 6. 8. with Refrain

MARY B. C. SLADE, 1826–1882

EMILIUS LAROCHE (R. M. McINTOSH)

1. From all the dark pla - ces Of earth's need - y ra - ces,
2. The sun - light is glanc - ing O'er arm - ies ad - vanc - ing
3. With shout - ing and sing - ing, And ju - bi - lant ring - ing,

O see how the thick shad - ows fly! The voice of sal - va - tion
To con - quer the king - doms of sin; Our Lord shall pos - sess them,
Their arms in sur - ren - der cast down, At last ev - ery na - tion,

A - wakes ev - ery na - tion; "Come o - ver and help us," they cry.
His pres - ence shall bless them, His beau - ty shall en - ter them in.
The Lord of sal - va - tion Their King and Re - deem - er shall crown!

REFRAIN

The king - dom is com - ing, O tell ye the sto - ry, God's ban - ner ex - alt - ed shall be!

The earth shall be full of His know - ledge and glo - ry, As wa - ters that cov - er the sea! A - MEN.

The Kingdom of God

MISSIONARY HYMN. 7. 6. 7. 6. D.

REGINALD HEBER, 1783-1826

LOWELL MASON, 1792-1872

1. From Green-land's i - cy moun-tains, From In - dia's cor - al strand;
2. Can men, whose souls are light - ed With wis-dom from on high,
3. Waft, waft, ye winds, His sto - ry; And you, ye wa - ters, roll,

Where Af - ric's sun - ny foun - tains Roll down their gold - en sand:
Can they to men be - night - ed The lamp of life de - ny?
Till, like a sea of glo - ry, It spreads from pole to pole:

From ma - ny an an - cient riv - er, From ma - ny a palm - y plain,
Sal - va - tion! O sal - va - tion! The joy - ful sound pro - claim,
Till o'er our ran - somed na - ture The Lamb for sin - ners slain,

They call us to de - liv - er Their land from er - ror's chain.
Till earth's re - mot - est na - tion Has learned Mes - si - ah's Name.
Re - deem - er, King, Cre - a - tor, In bliss re - turns to reign. A - MEN.

Missions

485

WATCHMAN. 7. 7. 7. 7. D.

John Bowring, 1792–1872

Lowell Mason, 1792–1872

1. Watch-man, tell us of the night, What its signs of prom-ise are.
2. Watch-man, tell us of the night; High-er yet that star as-cends.
3. Watch-man, tell us of the night, For the morn-ing seems to dawn.

Trav-eler, o'er yon moun-tain's height See that glo-ry-beam-ing star!
Trav-eler, bless-ed-ness and light, Peace and truth, its course por-tends.
Trav-eler, dark-ness takes its flight; Doubt and ter-ror are with-drawn.

Watch-man, doth its beau-teous ray Aught of joy or hope fore-tell?
Watch-man, will its beams a-lone Gild the spot that gave them birth?
Watch-man, let thy wan-dering cease; Hie thee to thy qui-et home!

Trav-eler, yes; it brings the day, Prom-ised day of Is-ra-el.
Trav-eler, a-ges are its own; See, it bursts o'er all the earth!
Trav-eler, lo, the Prince of Peace, Lo, the Son of God is come! A-men.

The Kingdom of God

486

LANCASHIRE. 7. 6. 7. 6. D.

Robert Murray, 1832–1910

Henry Smart, 1813–1879

1. From o-cean un-to o-cean Our land shall own Thee Lord,
2. O Christ, for Thine own glo-ry, And for our coun-try's weal,
3. Our Sav-iour King, de-fend us, And guide where we should go;

And, filled with true de-vo-tion, O-bey Thy sov-ereign word.
We hum-bly plead be-fore Thee, Thy-self in us re-veal;
Forth with Thy mes-sage send us, Thy love and light to show;

Our prai-ries and our moun-tains, For-est and fer-tile field,
And may we know, Lord Je-sus, The touch of Thy dear hand;
Till, fired with true de-vo-tion, En-kin-dled by Thy Word,

Our riv-ers, lakes, and foun-tains, To Thee shall trib-ute yield.
And, healed of our dis-eas-es, The tempt-er's power with-stand.
From o-cean un-to o-cean Our land shall own Thee Lord. A-MEN.

Missions

487

WEBB. 7. 6. 7. 6. D.

SAMUEL F. SMITH, 1808-1895

GEORGE J. WEBB, 1803-1887

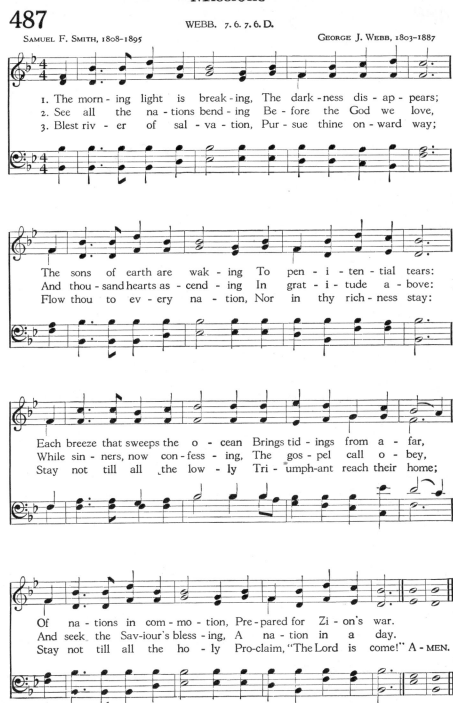

1. The morn - ing light is break-ing, The dark-ness dis - ap - pears;
2. See all the na - tions bend-ing Be - fore the God we love,
3. Blest riv - er of sal - va - tion, Pur - sue thine on - ward way;

The sons of earth are wak - ing To pen - i - ten - tial tears:
And thou-sand hearts as - cend - ing In grat - i - tude a - bove:
Flow thou to ev - ery na - tion, Nor in thy rich - ness stay:

Each breeze that sweeps the o - cean Brings tid - ings from a - far,
While sin - ners, now con - fess - ing, The gos - pel call o - bey,
Stay not till all the low - ly Tri - umph-ant reach their home;

Of na - tions in com - mo - tion, Pre - pared for Zi - on's war.
And seek the Sav-iour's bless - ing, A na - tion in a day.
Stay not till all the ho - ly Pro-claim, "The Lord is come!" A - MEN.

The Kingdom of God

488

WESLEY. 11. 10. 11. 10.

Thomas Hastings, 1784–1872

Lowell Mason, 1792–1872

1. Hail to the bright-ness of Zi-on's glad morn-ing,
2. Hail to the bright-ness of Zi-on's glad morn-ing,
3. Lo, in the des-ert rich flow-ers are spring-ing,
4. See, from all lands, from the isles of the o-cean,

Joy to the lands that in dark-ness have lain!
Long by the proph-ets of Is-rael fore-told;
Streams ev-er co-pious are flow-ing a-long;
Praise to the Sav-iour as-cend-ing on high;

Hushed be the ac-cents of sor-row and mourn-ing,
Hail to the mil-lions from bond-age re-turn-ing!
Loud from the moun-tain-tops ech-oes are ring-ing,
Fall-en the wea-pons of war and com-mo-tion,

Zi-on in tri-umph be-gins her mild reign.
Gen-tiles and Jews the blest vi-sion be-hold.
Wastes rise in ver-dure and min-gle in song.
Shouts of sal-va-tion are rend-ing the sky. A-MEN.

National and International Life

489

AMERICA. 6. 6. 4. 6. 6. 6. 4.

SAMUEL F. SMITH, 1808–1895   HENRY CAREY, c. 1690–1743

1. My coun - try, 'tis of thee, Sweet land of lib - er - ty,
2. My na - tive coun - try, thee, Land of the no - ble, free,
3. Let mu - sic swell the breeze, And ring from all the trees
4. Our fa - thers' God, to Thee, Au - thor of lib - er - ty,

Of thee I sing: Land where my fa - thers died, Land of the
Thy name I love; I love thy rocks and rills, Thy woods and
Sweet free - dom's song: Let mor - tal tongues a - wake; Let all that
To Thee we sing: Long may our land be bright With free - dom's

pil - grims' pride, From ev - ery moun - tain side Let free - dom ring!
tem - pled hills; My heart with rap - ture thrills, Like that a - bove.
breathe par - take; Let rocks their si - lence break, The sound pro - long.
ho - ly light; Pro - tect us by Thy might, Great God, our King. A - MEN.

490

SIEGFRIED A. MAHLMANN, 1771–1826
Tr. by CHARLES T. BROOKS, 1813–1883, and JOHN S. DWIGHT, 1813–1893
Stanza 3, WILLIAM E. HICKSON, 1803–1870

1 God bless our native land!
Firm may she ever stand,
  Through storm and night:
When the wild tempests rave,
Ruler of wind and wave,
Do Thou our country save
  By Thy great might!

2 For her our prayer shall rise
To God, above the skies;
  On Him we wait:
Thou who art ever nigh,
Guarding with watchful eye,
To Thee aloud we cry,
  God save the state!

3 Not for this land alone,
But be God's mercies shown
  From shore to shore;
And may the nations see
That men should brothers be,
And form one family
  The wide world o'er.

The Kingdom of God

491

MATERNA. C. M. D.

KATHARINE LEE BATES, 1859-1929

SAMUEL A. WARD, 1847-1903

1. O beau-ti-ful for spa-cious skies, For am-ber waves of grain,
2. O beau-ti-ful for pil-grim feet, Whose stern, im-pas-sioned stress
3. O beau-ti-ful for he-roes proved In lib-er-at-ing strife,
4. O beau-ti-ful for pa-triot dream That sees, be-yond the years,

For pur-ple moun-tain maj-es-ties A-bove the fruit-ed plain!
A thor-ough-fare for free-dom beat A-cross the wil-der-ness!
Who more than self their coun-try loved, And mer-cy more than life!
Thine al-a-bas-ter cit-ies gleam, Un-dimmed by hu-man tears!

A-mer-i-ca! A-mer-i-ca! God shed His grace on thee,
A-mer-i-ca! A-mer-i-ca! God mend thine ev-ery flaw,
A-mer-i-ca! A-mer-i-ca! May God thy gold re-fine,
A-mer-i-ca! A-mer-i-ca! God shed His grace on thee,

And crown thy good with broth-er-hood From sea to shin-ing sea.
Con-firm thy soul in self-con-trol, Thy lib-er-ty in law.
Till all suc-cess be no-ble-ness, And ev-ery gain di-vine.
And crown thy good with broth-er-hood From sea to shin-ing sea. A-MEN.

National and International Life

CORMAC. Irregular

CHARLES SILVESTER HORNE, 1865-1914

Irish traditional melody

In unison

1. For the might of Thine arm we bless Thee, our God, our fa - thers' God;
2. For the love of Christ con - strain - ing, that bound their hearts as one;
3. We are watch-ers of a bea - con whose light must nev - er die;

Thou hast kept Thy pil - grim peo - ple by the strength of Thy staff and rod;
For the faith in truth and free - dom in which their work was done;
We are guard - ians of an al - tar that shows Thee ev - er nigh;

Thou hast called us to the jour - ney which faith - less feet ne'er trod;
For the peace of God's e - van - gel where-with their feet were shod;
We are chil - dren of Thy free - men who sleep be - neath the sod;

For the might of Thine arm we bless Thee: our God, our fa - thers' God.
For the might of Thine arm we bless Thee: our God, our fa - thers' God.
For the might of Thine arm we bless Thee: our God, our fa - thers' God. A - MEN.

Music from Enlarged Songs of Praise. By permission of the Oxford University Press

The Kingdom of God

493

DUKE STREET. L. M.

LEONARD BACON, 1802–1881

JOHN HATTON, d. 1793

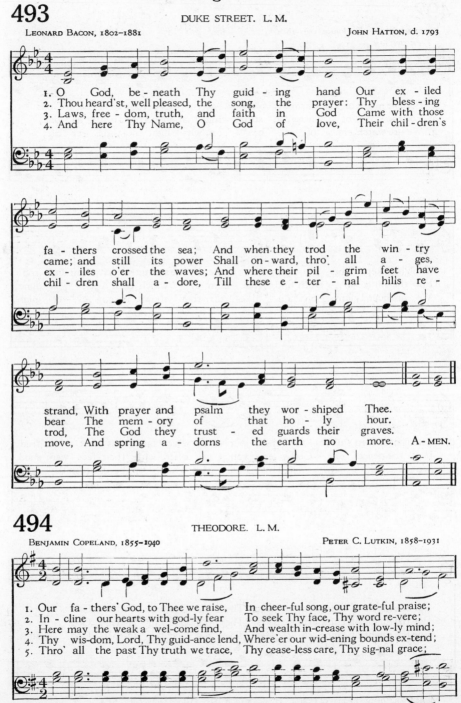

1. O God, be-neath Thy guid-ing hand Our ex-iled
2. Thou heard'st, well pleased, the song, the prayer: Thy bless-ing
3. Laws, free-dom, truth, and faith in God Came with those
4. And here Thy Name, O God of love, Their chil-dren's

fa-thers crossed the sea; And when they trod the win-try
came; and still its power Shall on-ward, thro' all a-ges,
ex-iles o'er the waves; And where their pil-grim feet have
chil-dren shall a-dore, Till these e-ter-nal hills re-

strand, With prayer and psalm they wor-shiped Thee.
bear The mem-ory of that ho-ly hour.
trod, The God they trust-ed guards their graves.
move, And spring a-dorns the earth no more. A-MEN.

494

THEODORE. L. M.

BENJAMIN COPELAND, 1855–1940

PETER C. LUTKIN, 1858–1931

1. Our fa-thers' God, to Thee we raise, In cheer-ful song, our grate-ful praise;
2. In-cline our hearts with god-ly fear To seek Thy face, Thy word re-vere;
3. Here may the weak a wel-come find, And wealth in-crease with low-ly mind;
4. Thy wis-dom, Lord, Thy guid-ance lend, Where'er our wid-ening bounds ex-tend;
5. Thro' all the past Thy truth we trace, Thy cease-less care, Thy sig-nal grace;

National and International Life

From shore to shore the an-thems rise : Ac - cept a na-tion's sac-ri - fice.
Cause Thou all wrongs, all strife to cease, And lead us in the paths of peace.
A ref - uge, still, for all op-pressed, O be our land for - ev - er blest!
In - spire our wills to speed Thy plan : The king-dom of the Son of man!
O may our chil-dren's children prove Thy sov-ereign, ev-er-last-ing love. A-MEN.

Words used by permission of Benjamin Copeland
Music used by permission of Mrs. Peter C. Lutkin

495

LANGRAN. 10. 10. 10. 10.

JOHN S. ARKWRIGHT, 1872–

JAMES LANGRAN, 1835–1909

1. O val - iant hearts, who to your glo - ry came Through dust of con - flict
2. Proud - ly you gath - ered, rank on rank to war, As who had heard God's
3. Splen - did you passed, the great sur - ren - der made, In - to the light that
4. O ris - en Lord, O Shep-herd of our dead, Whose cross has bought them,

and thro' bat - tle flame; Tran - quil you lie, your knight - ly vir - tue proved,
mes - sage from a - far; All you had hoped for, all you had, you gave
nev - er - more shall fade; Deep your con - tent - ment in that blest a - bode,
and whose star has led, In glo - rious hope their proud and sor-rowing land

Your mem - ory hal - lowed in the land you loved.
To save man - kind — your - self you scorned to save.
Who wait the last clear trum - pet - call of God.
Com - mits her chil - dren to Thy gra - cious hand. A - MEN.

Alternative tune, Ellers, No. 29

The Kingdom of God

496

NATIONAL HYMN. 10. 10. 10. 10.

Daniel C. Roberts, 1841–1907

George W. Warren, 1828–1902

Trumpets, before each stanza

1. God of our fa - thers, whose al-might - y hand
2. Thy love di - vine hath led us in the past;
3. From war's a-larms, from dead -ly pes - ti -lence,
4. Re - fresh Thy peo - ple on their toil-some way;

Leads forth in beau - ty all the star - ry band
In this free land by Thee our lot is cast;
Be Thy strong arm our ev - er sure de - fense;
Lead us from night to nev - er - end - ing day;

Of shin - ing worlds in splen - dor through the skies,
Be Thou our Rul - er, Guard-ian, Guide, and Stay,
Thy true re - li - gion in our hearts in - crease,
Fill all our lives with love and grace di - vine,

Our grate - ful songs be - fore Thy throne a - rise.
Thy Word our law, Thy paths our cho - sen way.
Thy boun - teous good - ness nour - ish us in peace.
And glo - ry, laud, and praise be ev - er Thine. A - MEN.

National and International Life

497

MELITA. 8. 8. 8. 8. 8. 8.

RUDYARD KIPLING, 1865-1936

JOHN B. DYKES, 1823-1876

1. God of our fa - thers, known of old, Lord of our far - flung
2. The tu - mult and the shout - ing dies; The cap - tains and the
3. Far - called our na - vies melt a - way, On dune and head - land

bat - tle line, Be - neath whose aw - ful hand we hold Do -
kings de - part; Still stands Thine an - cient sac - ri - fice, An
sinks the fire; Lo, all our pomp of yes - ter - day Is

min - ion o - ver palm and pine: Lord God of Hosts, be
hum - ble and a con - trite heart: Lord God of Hosts, be
one with Nin - e - veh and Tyre! Judge of the na - tions,

with us yet, Lest we for - get, lest we for - get!
with us yet, Lest we for - get, lest we for - get!
spare us yet, Lest we for - get, lest we for - get! A - MEN.

4 If, drunk with sight of power, we loose
    Wild tongues that have not Thee in awe,
Such boasting as the Gentiles use
    Or lesser breeds without the law:
Lord God of Hosts, be with us yet,
Lest we forget, lest we forget!

5 For heathen heart that puts her trust
    In reeking tube and iron shard;
All valiant dust that builds on dust,
    And guarding calls not Thee to guard:
For frantic boast and foolish word,
Thy mercy on Thy people, Lord!

The Kingdom of God

498

ST. ANNE. C. M.

Psalm xliv
Tate and Brady, 1698

Probably by William Croft, 1678–1727

1. O Lord, our fa - thers oft have told, In our at - ten - tive ears,
2. 'Twas not their cour - age nor their sword To them sal - va - tion gave;
3. But Thy right hand, Thy power - ful arm, Whose suc - cor they im - plored,

Thy won - ders in their days per-formed, And in more an - cient years.
'Twas not their num - ber nor their strength That did their coun - try save;
Thy prov - i - dence pro - tect - ed them Who Thy great Name a - dored. A-MEN.

4 As Thee their God our fathers owned,
   So Thou art still our King:
O, therefore, as Thou didst to them,
   To us deliverance bring!

5 To Thee the glory we ascribe,
   From whom salvation came;
In God, our shield, we will rejoice,
   And ever bless Thy Name.

499

MANOAH. C. M.

John R. Wreford, 1800–1881

From Henry W. Greatorex's Collection, 1851

1. Lord, while for all man-kind we pray, Of ev - ery clime and coast,
2. O guard our shores from ev - ery foe; With peace our bor - ders bless,
3. U - nite us in the sa - cred love Of know-ledge, truth, and Thee;
4. Lord of the na - tions, thus to Thee Our coun - try we com - mend;

O hear us for our na - tive land, The land we love the most.
Our cit - ies with pros - per - i - ty, Our fields with plen-teous-ness.
And let our hills and val - leys shout The songs of lib - er - ty.
Be Thou her ref - uge and her trust, Her ev - er - last - ing Friend. A-MEN.

This tune will be found in a higher key at No. 542

National and International Life

500

CULFORD. 7. 7. 7. 7. D.

CHARLES WESLEY, 1707–1788

EDWARD J. HOPKINS, 1818–1901

1. See how great a flame as-pires, Kin-dled by a spark of grace!
2. When He first the work be-gun, Small and fee-ble was His day:
3. Saw ye not the cloud a - rise, Lit - tle as a hu - man hand?

Je - sus' love the na - tions fires, Sets the king-doms on a blaze:
Now the word doth swift - ly run; Now it wins its wid-ening way:
Now it spreads a - long the skies, Hangs o'er all the thirst - y land:

To bring fire on earth He came; Kin-dled in some hearts it is:
More and more it spreads and grows, Ev - er might - y to pre - vail;
Lo! the prom - ise of a shower Drops al - rea - dy from a - bove;

O that all might catch the flame, All par - take the glo-rious bliss!
Sin's strong-holds it now o'er-throws, Shakes the trem-bling gates of hell.
But the Lord will short - ly pour All the spir - it of His love. A - MEN.

The Kingdom of God

501

MESSAGE. 10. 8. 8. 7. 7. with Refrain

"Colin Sterne," 1862–1928

H. Ernest Nichol, 1862–1928
Adapted

1. We've a sto - ry to tell to the na - tions That shall
2. We've a song to be sung to the na - tions, That shall
3. We've a mes - sage to give to the na - tions, That the
4. We've a Sav - iour to show to the na - tions, Who the

turn their hearts to the right, A sto - ry of truth and mer - cy,
lift their hearts to the Lord; A song that shall con - quer e - vil
Lord who reign - eth a - bove, Hath sent us His Son to save us,
path of sor - row hath trod, That all of the world's great peo - ples

A sto - ry of peace and light, A sto - ry of peace and light.
And shat - ter the spear and sword, And shat - ter the spear and sword.
And show us that God is love, And show us that God is love.
Might come to the truth of God, Might come to the truth of God!

Refrain

For the dark-ness shall turn to dawn - ing, And the dawn-ing to noon-day bright,

National and International Life

And Christ's great king-dom shall come on earth, The king-dom of love and light. A-MEN.

502

DOANE. L. M.

GEORGE W. DOANE, 1799-1859

JOHN B. CALKIN, 1827-1905

1. Fling out the ban - ner! let it float Sky
2. Fling out the ban - ner! an - gels bend In
3. Fling out the ban - ner! sin - sick souls That
4. Fling out the ban - ner! let it float Sky

ward and sea - ward, high and wide; The sun, that lights its
anx - ious si - lence o'er the sign, And vain - ly seek to
sink and per - ish in the strife Shall touch in faith its
ward and sea - ward, high and wide, Our glo - ry, on - ly

shin - ing folds, The cross, on which the Sav - iour died.
com - pre-hend The won - der of the love di - vine.
ra - diant hem, And spring im - mor - tal in - to life.
in the cross; Our on - ly hope, the Cru - ci - fied! A - MEN.

The Kingdom of God

503

HEREFORD. Irregular

James L. Milligan, 1876–

Francis D. Heins, 1878–

1. There's a voice in the wil-der-ness cry-ing, A call from the ways un-trod: Pre-pare in the des-ert a high-way, A high-way for our God! The val-leys shall be ex-alt-ed, The loft-y hills brought low; Make straight all the

2. O Zi-on, that bring-est good ti-dings, Get thee up to the heights and sing! Pro-claim to a des-o-late peo-ple The com-ing of their King: Like the flowers of the field they per-ish, The works of men de-cay, The power and

3. But the word of our God en-dur-eth, The arm of the Lord is strong; He stands in the midst of na-tions, And He will right the wrong: He shall feed His flock like a shep-herd, And fold the lambs to His breast; In pas-tures of

4. There's a voice in the wil-der-ness cry-ing, A call from the ways un-trod: Pre-pare in the des-ert a high-way, A high-way for our God! The val-leys shall be ex-alt-ed, The loft-y hills brought low; Make straight all the

National and International Life

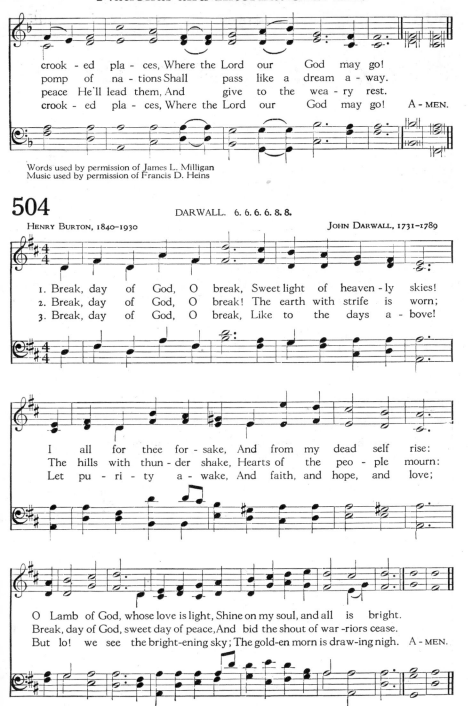

crook - ed pla - ces, Where the Lord our God may go!
pomp of na - tions Shall pass like a dream a - way.
peace He'll lead them, And give to the wea - ry rest.
crook - ed pla - ces, Where the Lord our God may go! A - MEN.

Words used by permission of James L. Milligan
Music used by permission of Francis D. Heins

504

DARWALL. 6. 6. 6. 6. 8. 8.

HENRY BURTON, 1840–1930   JOHN DARWALL, 1731–1789

1. Break, day of God, O break, Sweet light of heaven - ly skies!
2. Break, day of God, O break! The earth with strife is worn;
3. Break, day of God, O break, Like to the days a - bove!

I all for thee for - sake, And from my dead self rise:
The hills with thun - der shake, Hearts of the peo - ple mourn:
Let pu - ri - ty a - wake, And faith, and hope, and love;

O Lamb of God, whose love is light, Shine on my soul, and all is bright.
Break, day of God, sweet day of peace, And bid the shout of war - riors cease.
But lo! we see the bright-ening sky; The gold-en morn is draw-ing nigh. A - MEN.

The Kingdom of God

505

RUSSIAN HYMN. 11. 10. 11. 9.

Henry F. Chorley, 1808-1872
John Ellerton, 1826-1893

Alexis F. Lvov, 1799-1870 or 1871

1. God the Om - nip - o - tent! King, who or - dain - est
2. God the All - mer - ci - ful! earth hath for - sak - en
3. God the All - right - eous One! man hath de - fied Thee;
4. So shall Thy peo - ple, with thank - ful de - vo - tion,

Thun - der Thy clar - ion, the light - ning Thy sword;
Meek - ness and mer - cy, and slight - , ed Thy word;
Yet to e - ter - ni - ty stand - eth Thy word;
Praise Him who saved them from per - il and sword,

Show forth Thy pit - y on high where Thou reign - est;
Let not Thy wrath in its ter - rors a - wak - en;
False - hood and wrong shall not tar - ry be - side Thee;
Sing - ing in cho - rus from o - cean to o - cean

Give to us peace in our time, O Lord.'
Give to us peace in our time, O Lord.
Give to us peace in our time, O Lord.
Peace to the na - tions, and praise to the Lord. A - MEN.

National and International Life

506

BELOIT. L. M.

JOHN G. WHITTIER, 1807–1892

CARL G. REISSIGER, 1798–1859

1. Our thought of thee is glad with hope, Dear coun-try of our love and prayer!
2. Tried as by fur-nace fires, and yet By God's grace on-ly strong-er made;
3. Great, with-out seek-ing to be great By fraud or con-quest; rich in gold,
4. With peace that comes of pu-ri-ty, And strength to sim-ple jus-tice due,

Thy way is down no fa-tal slope, But up to free-er sun and air.
In fu-ture tasks be-fore thee set Thou shalt not lack the old-time aid.
But rich-er in the large es-tate Of vir-tue which thy chil-dren hold.
So runs our loy-al dream of thee. God of our fa-thers! make it true. A-MEN.

507

ST. PETER. C. M.

JOHN OXENHAM

ALEXANDER R. REINAGLE, 1799–1877

1. In Christ there is no East or West, In Him no South or North;
2. In Him shall true hearts ev-ery-where Their high com-mun-ion find;
3. Join hands, then, broth-ers of the faith, What-e'er your race may be.
4. In Christ now meet both East and West, In Him meet South and North;

But one great fel-low-ship of love Through-out the whole wide earth.
His serv-ice is the gold-en cord Close bind-ing all man-kind.
Who serves my Fa-ther as a son Is sure-ly kin to me.
All Christ-ly souls are one in Him Through-out the whole wide earth. A-MEN.

Words from "Bees in Amber." Used by permission of the American Tract Society, owner of the copyright

The Kingdom of God

508

HYMN OF NATIONS. 6. 6. 4. 6. 6. 6. 4.

Leonard B. McWhood, 1870-1939

Leonard B. McWhood, 1870-1939

1. All peo - ple of the earth Share but one com - mon birth,
2. Great God of all the earth, Lead us to know the worth

One des - ti - ny; One sun shines o'er us all, A - like we
Of sym - pa - thy; May fel - low - ship in - crease, May all con -

rise and fall, One night will spread its pall E - ter - nal - ly.
ten - tion cease, O may we dwell in peace And u - ni - ty. A-men.

509

MENDON. L. M.

Alfred A. Woodhull, 1810-1836

German traditional melody
Arr. by Samuel Dyer, 1785-1835

1. Great God of na - tions, now to Thee Our hymn of grat - i - tude we raise;
2. Thy Name we bless, Al - might - y God, For all the kind - ness Thou hast shown
3. Here free - dom spreads her ban - ner wide And casts her soft and hal - lowed ray;
4. Great God, pre - serve us in Thy fear; In dan - ger still our guard - ian be:

National and International Life

Copyright, 1935, by Whitmore & Smith, Nashville, Tenn.

The Kingdom of God

511

THEODORE. L. M.

HENRY W. BAKER, 1821–1877   PETER C. LUTKIN, 1858–1931

1. O God of love, O King of peace, Make wars thro'-out the world to cease;
2. Re-mem-ber, Lord, Thy works of old, The won-ders that our fa-thers told;
3. Whom shall we trust but Thee, O Lord? Where rest but on Thy faith-ful word?
4. Where saints and an-gels dwell a-bove, All hearts are knit in ho-ly love;

The wrath of sin-ful man re-strain: Give peace, O God, give peace a-gain!
Re-mem-ber not our sin's dark stain: Give peace, O God, give peace a-gain!
None ev-er called on Thee in vain: Give peace, O God, give peace a-gain!
O bind us in that heaven-ly chain: Give peace, O God, give peace a-gain! A-MEN.

Music used by permission of Mrs. Peter C. Lutkin

512

TRURO. L. M.

J. ADDINGTON SYMONDS, 1840–1893   From T. WILLIAMS' PSALMODIA EVANGELICA, 1789

1. These things shall be: a loft-ier race Than e'er the world hath known shall rise
2. They shall be gen-tle, brave, and strong, To spill no drop of blood, but dare
3. Na-tion with na-tion, land with land, In-armed shall live as com-rades free;
4. New arts shall bloom of loft-ier mold, And might-ier mu-sic thrill the skies,

With flame of free-dom in their souls And light of knowl-edge in their eyes.
All that may plant man's lord-ship firm On earth, and fire, and sea, and air.
In ev-ery heart and brain shall throb The pulse of one fra-ter-ni-ty.
And ev-ery life shall be a song, When all the earth is par-a-dise. A-MEN.

Alternative tune, DePauw, No. 82
Words used by permission of John Murray

The Eternal Life

513

OLD 113TH (LUCERNE). 8. 8. 8. 8. 8. 8.

ISAAC WATTS, 1674-1748
Alt. by JOHN WESLEY, 1703-1791

From a melody in THE STRASSBURG PSALTER, 1542
Arr. by ERNEST MACMILLAN, 1893-

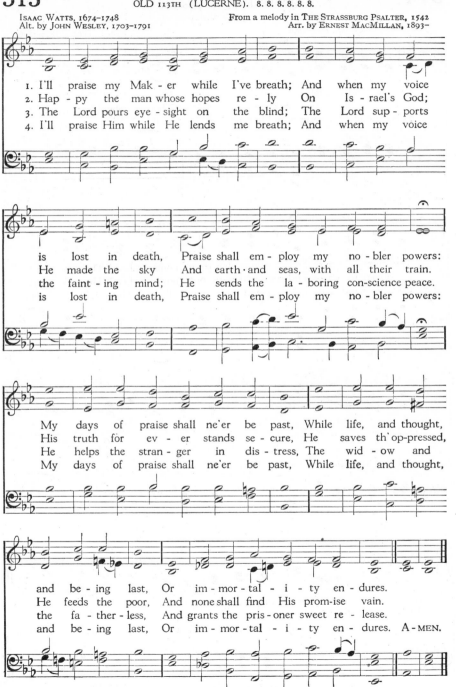

1. I'll praise my Mak-er while I've breath; And when my voice
2. Hap-py the man whose hopes re-ly On Is-rael's God;
3. The Lord pours eye-sight on the blind; The Lord sup-ports
4. I'll praise Him while He lends me breath; And when my voice

is lost in death, Praise shall em-ploy my no-bler powers:
He made the sky And earth-and seas, with all their train.
the faint-ing mind; He sends the la-boring con-science peace.
is lost in death, Praise shall em-ploy my no-bler powers:

My days of praise shall ne'er be past, While life, and thought,
His truth for ev-er stands se-cure, He saves th'op-pressed,
He helps the stran-ger in dis-tress, The wid-ow and
My days of praise shall ne'er be past, While life, and thought,

and be-ing last, Or im-mor-tal-i-ty en-dures.
He feeds the poor, And none shall find His prom-ise vain.
the fa-ther-less, And grants the pris-oner sweet re-lease.
and be-ing last, Or im-mor-tal-i-ty en-dures. A-MEN.

The Eternal Life

514

LUX BENIGNA. 10. 4. 10. 4. 10. 10.
(*First Tune*)

JOHN HENRY NEWMAN, 1801-1890

JOHN B. DYKES, 1823-1876

1. Lead, kind-ly Light, a-mid th' en-cir-cling gloom, Lead Thou me on!
2. I was not ev-er thus, nor prayed that Thou Shouldst lead me on;
3. So long Thy power hath blest me, sure it still Will lead me on,

The night is dark, and I am far from home; Lead Thou me on!
I loved to choose and see my path; but now Lead Thou me on!
O'er moor and fen, o'er crag and tor-rent, till The night is gone,

Keep Thou my feet; I do not ask to see
I loved the gar-ish day, and, spite of fears,
And with the morn those an-gel fac-es smile;

The dis-tant scene—one step e-nough for me.
Pride ruled my will: re-mem-ber not past years.
Which I have loved long since, and lost a-while! A-MEN.

The Eternal Life

SANDON. 10. 4. 10. 4. 10. 10.
(*Second Tune*)

JOHN HENRY NEWMAN, 1801-1890

CHARLES H. PURDAY, 1799-1885

514

1. Lead, kind - ly Light, a - mid th' en - cir - cling gloom, Lead Thou me on!
2. I was not ev - er thus, nor prayed that Thou Shouldst lead me on;
3. So long Thy power hath blest me, sure it still Will lead me on,

The night is dark, and I am far from home; Lead Thou me on!
I loved to choose and see my path; but now Lead Thou me on!
O'er moor and fen, o'er crag and tor - rent, till The night is gone,

Keep Thou my feet; I do not ask to see
I loved the gar - ish day, and, spite of fears,
And with the morn those an - gel fa - ces smile;

The dis - tant scene — one step e - nough for me.
Pride ruled my will: re - mem - ber not past years.
Which I have loved long since, and lost a - while! A - MEN.

The Eternal Life

515

DULCE DOMUM. Irregular

PHOEBE CARY, 1824–1871

ROBERT S. AMBROSE, 1824–1908

1. One sweet-ly sol-emn thought Comes to me o'er and o'er;
2. Near-er my Fa-ther's house, Where man-y man-sions be;
3. Near-er the bound of life, Where bur-dens are laid down;
4. Fa-ther, per-fect my trust! Strength-en my power of faith!

Near-er my home to-day am I Than e'er I've been be-fore.
Near-er, to-day, the great white throne, Near-er the crys-tal sea.
Near-er to leave the heav-y cross, Near-er to gain the crown.
Nor let me stand, at last, a-lone Up-on the shore of death. A-MEN.

516

ST. AGNES. C. M.

RICHARD BAXTER, 1615–1691

JOHN B. DYKES, 1823–1876

1. Lord, it be-longs not to my care Wheth-er I die or live;
2. If life be long, I will be glad That I may long o-bey;
3. Christ leads me through no dark-er rooms Than He went through be-fore;

To love and serve Thee is my share, And this Thy grace must give.
If short, yet why should I be sad To soar to end-less day?
He that in-to God's king-dom comes Must en-ter by this door. A-MEN.

4 Come, Lord, when grace hath made me
  Thy blessèd face to see; [meet
For, if Thy work on earth be sweet,
  What will Thy glory be?

5 My knowledge of that life is small;
  The eye of faith is dim;
But 'tis enough that Christ knows all,
  And I shall be with Him.

The Eternal Life

517

COOLING. C. M.

JOHN G. WHITTIER, 1807–1892

ALONZO J. ABBEY, 1825–1887

1. I know not what the fu-ture hath Of mar-vel or sur-prise,
2. And if my heart and flesh are weak To bear an un-tried pain,
3. And Thou, O Lord, by whom are seen Thy crea-tures as they be,

As-sured a-lone that life and death God's mer-cy un-der-lies.
The bruis-ed reed He will not break, But strength-en and sus-tain.
For-give me if too close I lean My hu-man heart on Thee. A-MEN.

Words used by permission of Houghton Mifflin Co.

4 And so beside the silent sea
  I wait the muffled oar:
No harm from Him can come to me
  On ocean or on shore.

5 I know not where His islands lift
  Their fronded palms in air;
I only know I cannot drift
  Beyond His love and care.

518

MORNINGTON. S. M.

CHARLES WESLEY, 1707–1788

Arr. from a chant by GARRET WELLESLEY, 1735–1781

1. Ser-vant of God, well done! Thy glo-rious war-fare's past;
2. With saints en-throned on high, Thou dost thy Lord pro-claim,
3. O hap-py, hap-py soul! In ec-sta-sies of praise,
4. Re-deemed from earth and pain, Ah! when shall we as-cend,

The bat-tle's fought, the race is won, And thou art crowned at last.
And still to God sal-va-tion cry, Sal-va-tion to the Lamb!
Long as e-ter-nal a-ges roll, Thou seest thy Sav-iour's face.
And all in Je-sus' pres-ence reign Through a-ges with-out end? A-MEN.

The Eternal Life

519

JOURNEY'S END. 11. 10. 11. 6.

JOHN G. WHITTIER, 1807-1892   WILLIAM K. ANDERSON, 1888–

1. When on my day of life the night is fall - ing,
   And, in the wind from un-sunned spac-es blown, I hear far
   voic - es out of dark-ness call-ing My feet to paths un-known;

2. Thou, who hast made my home of life so pleas - ant,
   Leave not its ten - ant when its walls de - cay; O Love Di-
   vine, O Help-er ev - er pres-ent, Be Thou my strength and stay.

3. I have but Thee, my Fa - ther! let Thy Spir - it
   Be with me then to com-fort and up - hold; No gate of
   pearl, no branch of palm I mer - it, Nor street of shin - ing gold.

4. Suf - fice it if— my good and ill un - reck-oned,
   And both for - given thro' Thine a - bound-ing grace— I find my-
   self by hands fa-mil - iar beck-oned Un - to my fit-ting place,— A - MEN.

5 Some humble door among Thy many mansions,
   Some sheltering shade where sin and striving cease,
   And flows for ever through heaven's green expansions
   The river of Thy peace.

6 There, from the music round about me stealing,
   I fain would learn the new and holy song,
   And find at last, beneath Thy trees of healing,
   The life for which I long.

Alternative tune, Flemming, No. 327
Words used by permission of Houghton Mifflin Co.
Music copyright, 1935, by The Methodist Book Concern

The Eternal Life

520

EVENTIDE. 10. 10. 10. 10.

HENRY F. LYTE, 1793–1847

WILLIAM H. MONK, 1823–1889

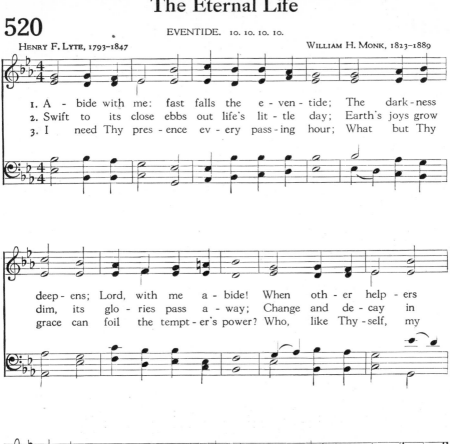

1. A - bide with me: fast falls the e - ven - tide; The dark - ness
2. Swift to its close ebbs out life's lit - tle day; Earth's joys grow
3. I need Thy pres - ence ev - ery pass - ing hour; What but Thy

deep - ens; Lord, with me a - bide! When oth - er help - ers
dim, its glo - ries pass a - way; Change and de - cay in
grace can foil the tempt - er's power? Who, like Thy - self, my

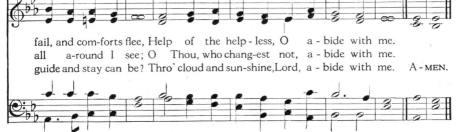

fail, and com-forts flee, Help of the help - less, O a - bide with me.
all a-round I see; O Thou, who chang-est not, a - bide with me.
guide and stay can be? Thro' cloud and sun-shine, Lord, a - bide with me. A - MEN.

4 I fear no foe, with Thee at hand to bless;
  Ills have no weight, and tears no bitterness.
  Where is death's sting? where, grave, thy victory?
  I triumph still, if Thou abide with me.

5 Hold Thou Thy cross before my closing eyes;
  Shine through the gloom and point me to the skies;
  Heaven's morning breaks, and earth's vain shadows flee;
  In life, in death, O Lord, abide with me.

The Eternal Life

521

AULD LANG SYNE. C. M. D.

JOHN W. CHADWICK, 1840-1904

Scottish melody
WILLIAM SHIELD, 1748-1829

1. It sing-eth low in ev-ery heart, We hear it each and all;
2. 'Tis hard to take the bur-den up, When these have laid it down;
3. More home-like seems the vast un-known Since they have en-tered there;

A song of those who an-swer not, How-ev-er we may call.
They bright-ened all the joy of life, They soft-ened ev-ery frown.
To fol-low them were not so hard, Wher-ev-er they may fare.

They throng the si-lence of the breast; We see them as of yore,
But, Oh, 'tis good to think of them When we are trou-bled sore;
They can-not be where God is not, On an-y sea or shore;

The kind, the true, the brave, the sweet, Who walk with us no more.
Thanks be to God that such have been, Tho' they are here no more!
What-e'er be-tides, Thy love a-bides, Our God, for ev-er-more. A-MEN.

The Eternal Life

522

ALIDA. C. M. D.

CHARLES WESLEY, 1707–1788

Early American melody
D. B. THOMPSON?

1. How hap-py ev-ery child of grace, Who knows his sins for-given!
2. O what a bless-ed hope is ours! While here on earth we stay:

"This earth," he cries, "is not my place, I seek my place in heaven:
We more than taste the heaven-ly powers, And an-te-date that day,

A coun-try far from mor-tal sight, Which yet by faith I see,
We feel the res-ur-rec-tion near, Our life in Christ con-cealed,

The land of rest, the saints' de-light, The heaven pre-pared for me."
And with His glo-rious pres-ence here His life in us re-vealed. A-MEN.

The Eternal Life

VARINA. C. M. D.

SAMUEL STENNETT, 1727-1795

GEORGE F. ROOT, 1820-1895

1. On Jor-dan's storm-y banks I stand, And cast a wish-ful eye
2. O'er all those wide-ex-tend-ed plains Shines one e-ter-nal day,
3. When I shall reach that hap-py place, I'll be for ev-er blest,

To Ca-naan's fair and hap-py land, Where my pos-ses-sions lie.
There God the Son for ev-er reigns, And scat-ters night a-way.
For I shall see my Fa-ther's face, And in His bos-om rest.

O the trans-port-ing, rap-turous scene That ris-es-to my sight;
No chill-ing winds, or poi-sonous breath, Can reach that health-ful shore;
Filled with de-light my rap-tured soul Lives out its earth-ly day,

Sweet fields ar-rayed in liv-ing green, And riv-ers of de-light!
Sick-ness and sor-row, pain and death, Are felt and feared no more.
And then, though Jor-dan's waves may roll, I'll fear-less launch a-way. A-MEN.

The Eternal Life

524

AMSTERDAM. 7. 6. 7. 6. D.

ROBERT SEAGRAVE, 1693–1759

From THE FOUNDERY COLLECTION, 1742

1. Rise, my soul, and stretch thy wings, Thy bet - ter por - tion trace;
2. Riv - ers to the o - cean run, Nor stay in all their course;
3. Cease, ye pil - grims, cease to mourn, Press on - ward to the prize;

Rise from tran - si - to - ry things Toward heaven, thy na - tive place:
Fire as - cend - ing seeks the sun; Both speed them to their source:
Soon our Sav - iour will re - turn, Tri - umph - ant in the skies:

Sun, and moon, and stars de - cay; Time shall soon this earth re - move;
So a soul that's born of God, Longs to view His glo - rious face,
Yet a sea - son, and you know Hap - py en - trance will be given,

Rise, my soul, and haste a - way To seats pre - pared a - bove.
For - ward tends to His a - bode, To rest in His em - brace.
All our sor - rows left be - low, And earth ex-changed for heaven. A -MEN.

The Eternal Life

HOME OF THE SOUL. Irregular

ELLEN H. GATES, 1835-1920

PHILIP PHILLIPS, 1834-1875

1. I will sing you a song of that beau-ti-ful land, The far - a - way home of the soul, Where no storms ev - er beat on the glit - ter - ing strand, While the years of e - ter - ni - ty roll, While the years of e - ter - ni - ty roll; Where no storms ev - er beat on the

2. O that home of the soul! In my vi - sions and dreams Its bright, jas - per walls I can see; Till I fan - cy but thin - ly the veil in - ter-venes Be - tween the fair cit - y and me, Be - tween the fair cit - y and me; Till I fan - cy but thin - ly the

3. That un-change-a-ble home is for you and for me, Where Je - sus of Naz - a - reth stands; The King of all king-doms for ev - er is He, And He hold - eth our crowns in His hands, And He hold - eth our crowns in His hands; The King of all king-doms for

4. O how sweet it will be in that beau-ti-ful land, So free from all sor - row and pain, With songs on our lips and with harps in our hands, To meet one an - oth - er a - gain, To meet one an - oth - er a - gain; With songs on our lips and with

The Eternal Life

glit - ter -ing strand, While the years of e - ter - ni - ty roll.
veil in - ter - venes Be - tween the fair cit - y and me.
ev - er is He, And He hold -eth our crowns in His hands.
harps in our hands, To meet one an - oth - er a - gain. A - MEN.

526

REQUIESCAT. 7. 7. 7. 7. 8. 8.

JOHN ELLERTON, 1826–1893

JOHN B. DYKES, 1823–1876

1. Now the la-borer's task is o'er; Now the bat - tle day is past;
2. There the tears of earth are dried; There its hid - den things are clear;
3. "Earth to earth, and dust to dust;" Calm - ly now the words we say;

Now up - on the far - ther shore Lands the voy - a - ger at last.
There the work of life is tried By a just - er Judge than here.
Left be - hind, we wait in trust, For the res - ur - rec - tion day.

Fa - ther, in Thy gra-cious keep-ing Leave we now Thy ser-vant sleep - ing.
Fa - ther, in Thy gra-cious keep-ing Leave we now Thy ser-vant sleep - ing.
Fa - ther, in Thy gra-cious keep-ing Leave we now Thy ser-vant sleep - ing. A-MEN.

The Eternal Life

527

SARUM. 10. 10. 10. with Alleluias

(First Tune)

WILLIAM W. HOW, 1823-1897

JOSEPH BARNBY, 1838-1896

1. For all the saints, who from their la - bors rest, Who Thee by
2. Thou wast their Rock, their Fort-ress, and their Might; Thou, Lord, their
3. O may Thy sol - diers, faith-ful, true, and bold, Fight as the
4. O blest com - mun - ion, fel - low-ship di - vine! We fee - bly

faith be - fore the world con - fessed, Thy Name, O Je - sus,
Cap - tain in the well - fought fight; Thou, in the dark - ness
saints who no - bly fought of old, And win with them the
strug - gle, they in glo - ry shine; Yet all are one in

be for - ev - er blessed, Al - le - lu - ia! Al - le - lu - ia!
drear, their one true Light. Al - le - lu - ia! Al - le - lu - ia!
vic - tor's crown of gold. Al - le - lu - ia! Al - le - lu - ia!
Thee, for all are Thine. Al - le - lu - ia! Al - le - lu - ia! A-MEN.

5 And when the strife is fierce, the warfare long,
   Steals on the ear the distant triumph song,
   And hearts are brave again, and arms are strong.
        Alleluia! Alleluia!

6 From earth's wide bounds, from ocean's farthest coast,
   Through gates of pearl streams in the countless host,
   Singing to Father, Son, and Holy Ghost,
        "Alleluia! Alleluia!"

The Eternal Life

527

SINE NOMINE. 10. 10. 10. with Alleluias

(Second Tune)

WILLIAM W. HOW, 1823-1897

RALPH VAUGHAN WILLIAMS, 1872—

In unison

1. For all the saints who from their la-bors rest, Who Thee by faith be-
2. Thou wast their Rock, their For-tress, and their Might; Thou, Lord, their Cap-tain
3. O may Thy sol - diers, faith-ful, true, and bold, Fight as the saints who
4. O blest com-mun - ion, fel-low-ship di - vine! We fee-bly strug-gle,
5. And when the strife is fierce, the war-fare long, Steals on the ear the
6. From earth's wide bounds, from o-cean's far-thest coast, Through gates of pearl streams

fore the world con-fessed, Thy Name, O Je - sus, be for ev - er blest.
in the well-fought fight; Thou, in the dark - ness drear, their one true Light.
no - bly fought of old, And win with them the vic-tor's crown of gold.
dis - tant tri - umph song, And hearts are brave a - gain, and arms are strong.
in the count-less host, Sing - ing to Fa - ther, Son, and Ho - ly Ghost,

Harmony

Al - le-lu - ia! Al - le-lu - ia! A-MEN.

The Eternal Life

528

VARINA. C. M. D.

Isaac Watts, 1674-1748

George F. Root, 1820-1895

1. There is a land of pure de-light Where saints im-mor - tal reign;
2. Sweet fields be - yond the swell - ing flood Stand dressed in liv - ing green;

In - fi - nite day ex - cludes the night, And pleas-ures ban - ish pain.
So to the Jews old Ca - naan stood, While Jor - dan rolled be - tween.

There ev - er - last - ing spring a - bides, And nev - er - with-ering flowers;
Could we but climb where Mo - ses stood, And view the land-scape o'er,

Death, like a nar - row sea, di - vides This heaven-ly land from ours.
Not Jor-dan's stream, nor death's cold flood, Should fright us from the shore. A-MEN.

The Eternal Life

529

EWING. 7. 6. 7. 6. D.

BERNARD OF CLUNY, 12th century
Tr. by JOHN M. NEALE, 1818–1866

ALEXANDER EWING, 1830–1895

1. Je - ru - sa - lem the gold - en, With milk and hon - ey blest!
2. They stand, those halls of Zi - on, All ju - bi - lant with song,
3. O sweet and bless - ed coun - try, The home of God's e - lect!

Be - neath thy con - tem - pla - tion Sink heart and voice op - pressed:
And bright with many an an - gel, And all the mar - tyr throng;
O sweet and bless - ed coun - try That ea - ger hearts ex - pect!

I know not, oh, I know not, What joys a - wait us there;
The Prince is ev - er in them, The day - light is se - rene;
Je - sus, in mer - cy bring us To that dear land of rest;

What ra - dian - cy of glo - ry, What light be - yond com - pare.
The pas - tures of the bless - ed Are decked in glo - rious sheen.
Who art, with God the Fa - ther, And Spir - it, ev - er blest. A-MEN.

The Eternal Life

530

HOMELAND. 7. 6. 7. 6. D.

HUGH R. HAWEIS, 1838–1901

ARTHUR S. SULLIVAN, 1842–1900

1. The Home-land, O the Home-land, The land of souls free-born!
2. My Lord is in the Home-land, With an-gels bright and fair;
3. For loved ones in the Home-land Are wait-ing me to come

No gloom-y night is known there, But aye the fade-less morn:
No sin-ful thing nor e-vil, Can ev-er en-ter there;
Where neith-er death nor sor-row In-vades their ho-ly home:

I'm sigh-ing for that coun-try, My heart is ach-ing here;
The mu-sic of the ran-somed Is ring-ing in my ears,
O dear, dear na-tive coun-try! O rest and peace a-bove!

There is no pain in the Home-land To which I'm draw-ing near.
And when I think of the Home-land, My eyes are wet with tears.
Christ bring us all to the Home-land Of His e-ter-nal love. A-MEN.

The Eternal Life

531

ALFORD. 7. 6. 8. 6. D.

Henry Alford, 1810–1871

John B. Dykes, 1823–1876

1. Ten thou - sand times ten thou - sand In spar - kling rai - ment bright,
2. O then what rap - tured greet - ings On Ca - naan's hap - py shore,
3. What rush of al - le - lu - ias Fills all the earth and sky!

The ar - mies of the ran-somed saints Throng up the steeps of light:
What knit - ting sev - ered friend-ships up Where part-ings are no more!
What ring - ing of a thou-sand harps Be - speaks the tri - umph nigh!

'Tis fin - ished, all is fin - ished, Their fight with death and sin:
Then eyes with joy shall spar - kle, That brimmed with tears of late;
O day, for which cre - a - tion And all its tribes were made;

Fling o - pen wide the gold - en gates, And let the vic - tors in!
Or - phans no long - er fa - ther - less, Nor wid - ows des - o - late.
O joy, for all its for - mer woes A thou-sand-fold re - paid! A - MEN.

The Eternal Life

532

PILGRIMS. 11. 10. 11. 10. with Refrain

FREDERICK W. FABER, 1814–1863   HENRY SMART, 1812–1879

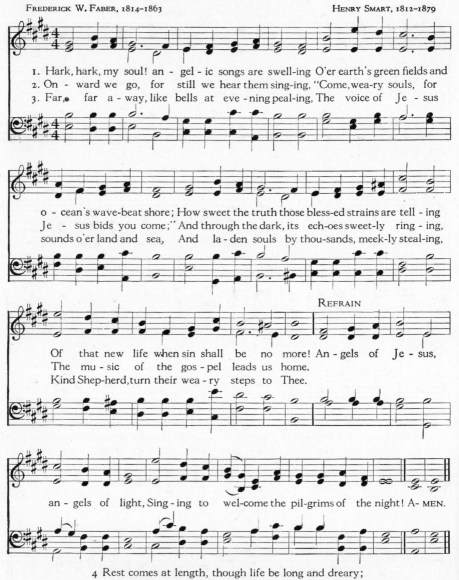

1. Hark, hark, my soul! an - gel - ic songs are swell-ing O'er earth's green fields and o - cean's wave-beat shore; How sweet the truth those bless-ed strains are tell - ing Of that new life when sin shall be no more! An - gels of Je - sus,

2. On - ward we go, for still we hear them sing-ing, "Come, wea-ry souls, for Je - sus bids you come;" And through the dark, its ech-oes sweet-ly ring - ing, The mu - sic of the gos - pel leads us home.

3. Far, far a - way, like bells at eve - ning peal-ing, The voice of Je - sus sounds o'er land and sea, And la - den souls by thou-sands, meek-ly steal-ing, Kind Shep-herd, turn their wea - ry steps to Thee.

REFRAIN

an - gels of light, Sing - ing to wel-come the pil-grims of the night! A- MEN.

4 Rest comes at length, though life be long and dreary;
   The day must dawn, and darksome night be past;
   All journeys end in welcome to the weary,
   And heaven, the heart's true home, will come at last.

5 Angels, sing on! your faithful watches keeping;
   Sing us sweet fragments of the songs above;
   Till morning's joy shall end the night of weeping,
   And life's long shadows break in cloudless love.

Special Seasons and Services
The Changing Year

533

ST. ANNE. C. M.

ISAAC WATTS, 1674–1748

Probably by WILLIAM CROFT, 1678–1727

1. O God, our help in a - ges past, Our hope for years to come,
2. Un - der the shad - ow of Thy throne Still may we dwell se - cure;
3. Be - fore the hills in or - der stood, Or earth re - ceived her frame,
4. A thou - sand a - ges, in Thy sight, Are like an eve - ning gone;
5. O God, our help in a - ges past, Our hope for years to come;

Our shel - ter from the storm - y blast, And our e - ter - nal home!
Suf - fi - cient is Thine arm a - lone, And our de - fense is sure.
From ev - er - last - ing Thou art God, To end - less years the same.
Short as the watch that ends the night, Be - fore the ris - ing sun.
Be Thou our guide while life shall last, And our e - ter - nal home! A-MEN.

534

BREMEN. 7. 6. 7. 6.

FRANCES R. HAVERGAL, 1836–1879

MELCHOIR VULPIUS, 1560–1616

1. An - oth - er year is dawn - ing, Dear Mas - ter, let it be,
2. An - oth - er year of mer - cies, Of faith - ful - ness and grace;
3. An - oth - er year of prog - ress, An - oth - er year of praise,
4. An - oth - er year of serv - ice, Of wit - ness for Thy love;
5. An - oth - er year is dawn - ing, Dear Mas - ter, let it be,

In work - ing or in wait - ing, An - oth - er year with Thee.
An - oth - er year of glad - ness In the shin - ing of Thy face.
An - oth - er year of prov - ing Thy pres - ence all the days.
An - oth - er year of train - ing For ho - lier work a - bove.
On earth, or else in heav - en, An - oth - er year for Thee! A-MEN.

Special Seasons and Services

535

DEDICATION. 7. 5. 7. 5. D.

Lawrence Tuttiett, 1825–1897

George A. Macfarren, 1813–1887

1. Fa - ther, let me ded - i - cate   All this year to Thee,
2. Can a child pre - sume to choose   Where or how to live?
3. If in mer - cy Thou wilt spare   Joys that yet are mine;
4. If Thou call - est to the cross,   And its shad - ow come,

In what - ev - er world - ly state   Thou wilt have me be:
Can a Fa - ther's love re - fuse   All the best to give?
If on life, se - rene and fair,   Bright - er rays may shine;
Turn-ing all my gain to loss,   Shroud - ing heart and home;

Not from sor - row, pain, or care,   Free - dom dare I claim;
More Thou giv - est ev - ery day   Than the best can claim,
Let my glad heart, while it sings,   Thee in all pro - claim,
Let me think how Thy dear Son   To His glo - ry came,

This a - lone shall be my prayer: "Glo - ri - fy Thy Name."
Nor with-hold - est aught that may   Glo - ri - fy Thy Name.
And, what-e'er the fu - ture brings,   Glo - ri - fy Thy Name.
And in deep - est woe pray on: "Glo - ri - fy Thy Name." A - men.

The Changing Year

536

LUCAS. Irregular

CHARLES WESLEY, 1707-1788

Early American melody
JAMES LUCAS, 1762 (?)

1. Come, let us a-new our jour-ney pur-sue, Roll
2. Our life is a dream; our time, as a stream, Glides
3. O that each in the day of His com-ing may say, "I have

round with the year, And nev-er stand still till the Mas-ter ap-pear.
swift-ly a-way, And the fu-gi-tive mo-ment re-fus-es to stay."
fought my way thro'; I have fin-ished the work Thou didst give me to do!"

His a-dor-a-ble will let us glad-ly ful-fill, And our
The ar-row is flown, the mo-ment is gone; The mil-
O that each from his Lord may re-ceive the glad word, "Well and

tal-ents im-prove, By the pa-tience of hope, and the la-bor of love,
len-ni-al year Rush-es on to our view, and e-ter-ni-ty's here,
faith-ful-ly done! En-ter in-to my joy, and sit down on my throne!

By the pa-tience of hope, and the la-bor of love.
Rush-es on to our view, and e-ter-ni-ty's here.
En-ter in-to my joy, and sit down on my throne!" A-MEN.

537

WILD BELLS. L. M. D.

ALFRED TENNYSON, 1809-1892

HENRY LAHEE, 1826-1912

1. Ring out, wild bells, to the wild, wild sky, The fly-ing cloud, the frost-y light: The year is dy-ing in the night; Ring out, wild bells, and let him die. Ring out the old, ring in the new, Ring, hap-py bells, a-cross the snow; The year is go-ing,

2. Ring out a slow-ly dy-ing cause, And an-cient forms of par-ty strife; Ring in the no-bler modes of life, With sweet-er man-ners, pur-er laws. Ring out false pride in place and blood, The civ-ic slan-der and the spite; Ring in the love of

3. Ring out old shapes of foul dis-ease; Ring out the nar-r'wing lust of gold; Ring out the thou-sand wars of old, Ring in the thou-sand years of peace. Ring in the val-iant man and free, The larg-er heart, the kind-lier hand; Ring out the dark-ness

The Changing Year

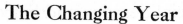

let him go; Ring out the false, ring in the true.
truth and right, Ring in the com-mon love of good.
of the land, Ring in the Christ that is to be. A-MEN.

538

EVANGELIST. C. M.

CHARLES WESLEY, 1707–1788

FELIX MENDELSSOHN-BARTHOLDY, 1809–1847

1. Sing to the great Je-ho-vah's praise! All praise to
2. His prov-i-dence hath brought us through An-oth-er
3. Fa-ther, Thy mer-cies past we own, And Thy con-
4. Our lips and lives shall glad-ly show The won-ders

Him be-longs; Who kind-ly length-ens out our
va-rious year; We all, with vows and an-thems
tin-ued care; To Thee pre-sent-ing, through Thy
of Thy love, While on in Je-sus' steps we

days, In-spires our choic-est songs.
new, Be-fore our God ap-pear.
Son, What-e'er we have or are.
go To see Thy face a-bove. A-MEN.

Special Seasons and Services

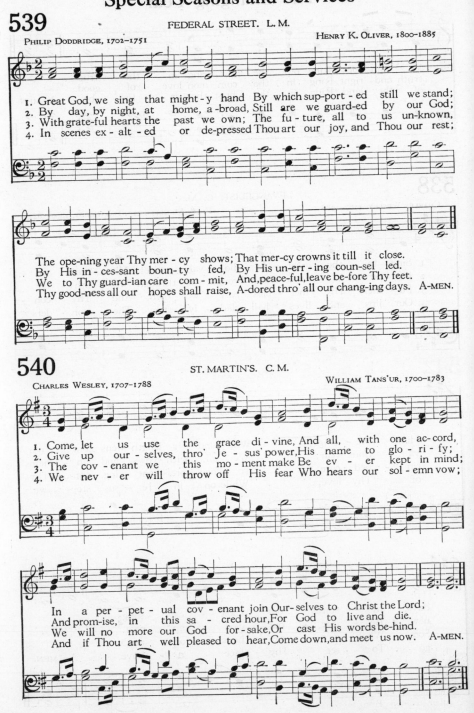

539

FEDERAL STREET. L. M.

PHILIP DODDRIDGE, 1702-1751

HENRY K. OLIVER, 1800-1885

1. Great God, we sing that might-y hand By which sup-port-ed still we stand;
2. By day, by night, at home, a-broad, Still are we guard-ed by our God;
3. With grate-ful hearts the past we own; The fu-ture, all to us un-known,
4. In scenes ex-alt-ed or de-pressed Thou art our joy, and Thou our rest;

The ope-ning year Thy mer-cy shows; That mer-cy crowns it till it close.
By His in-ces-sant boun-ty fed, By His un-err-ing coun-sel led.
We to Thy guard-ian care com-mit, And, peace-ful, leave be-fore Thy feet.
Thy good-ness all our hopes shall raise, A-dored thro' all our chang-ing days. A-MEN.

540

ST. MARTIN'S. C. M.

CHARLES WESLEY, 1707-1788

WILLIAM TANS'UR, 1700-1783

1. Come, let us use the grace di-vine, And all, with one ac-cord,
2. Give up our-selves, thro' Je-sus' power, His name to glo-ri-fy;
3. The cov-e-nant we this mo-ment make Be ev-er kept in mind;
4. We nev-er will throw off His fear Who hears our sol-emn vow;

In a per-pet-ual cov-e-nant join Our-selves to Christ the Lord;
And prom-ise, in this sa-cred hour, For God to live and die.
We will no more our God for-sake, Or cast His words be-hind.
And if Thou art well pleased to hear, Come down, and meet us now. A-MEN.

Thanksgiving

541

OLDBRIDGE. 8. 8. 8. 4.

CHRISTOPHER WORDSWORTH, 1807-1885

ROBERT N. QUAILE, 1867-

1. O Lord of heaven and earth and sea, To Thee all praise and glo - ry be!
2. The gold-en sun - shine, ver - nal air, Sweet flowers and fruit Thy love de - clare;
3. For peace-ful homes, and health-ful days, For all the bless - ings earth dis - plays,

How shall we show our love to Thee, Who giv - est all?
When har - vests rip - en, Thou art there, Who giv - est all.
We owe Thee thank - ful - ness and praise, Who giv - est all. A - MEN.

4 For souls redeemed, for sins forgiven,
For means of grace and hopes of heaven:
What can to Thee, O Lord, be given,
    Who givest all?

5 To Thee, from whom we all derive
Our life, our gifts, our power to give:
O may we ever with Thee live,
    Who givest all!

542

MANOAH. C. M.

JOSEPH ADDISON, 1672-1719

From HENRY W. GREATOREX'S COLLECTION, 1851

1. When all Thy mer-cies, O my God, My ris - ing soul sur - veys,
2. Un - num-bered com-forts to my soul Thy ten - der care be - stowed,
3. When worn with sick-ness, oft hast Thou With health renewed my face;
4. Thro' ev - ery pe - riod of my life Thy good-ness I'll pur - sue;

Trans-port - ed with the view, I'm lost In won-der, love, and praise.
Be - fore my in - fant heart could know From whom those com-forts flowed.
And, when in sins and sor-rows bowed, Re-vived my soul with grace.
And aft - er death, in dis - tant worlds, The glo-rious theme re-new. A-MEN.

This tune will be found in a lower key at No. 499
Alternative tune, Belmont, No. 28

Special Seasons and Services

543

HYFRYDOL. 8. 7. 8. 7. D.

William P. Merrill, 1867–

Melody by Rowland H. Prichard, 1811–1887

1. Not a-lone for might-y em-pire, Stretch-ing far o'er land and sea;
2. Not for bat-tle-ship and for-tress, Not for con-quests of the sword;
3. For the ar-mies of the faith-ful, Souls that passed and left no name;
4. God of jus-tice, save the peo-ple From the clash of race and creed,

Not a-lone for boun-teous har-vests, Lift we up our hearts to Thee.
But for con-quests of the spir-it Give we thanks to Thee, O Lord;
For the glo-ry that il-lu-mines Pa-triot lives of death-less fame;
From the strife of class and fac-tion: Make our na-tion free in-deed.

Stand-ing in the liv-ing pres-ent, Mem-o-ry and hope be-tween,
For the price-less gift of free-dom, For the home, the church, the school;
For our proph-ets and a-pos-tles, Loy-al to the liv-ing Word;
Keep her faith in sim-ple man-hood Strong as when her life be-gan,

Lord, we would with deep thanks-giv-ing Praise Thee most for things un-seen.
For the o-pen door to man-hood In a land the peo-ple rule.
For all he-roes of the Spir-it, Give we thanks to Thee, O Lord.
Till it find its full fru-i-tion In the broth-er-hood of man. A-men.

Alternative tune, Austrian Hymn, No. 382
Words used by permission of William P. Merrill

Thanksgiving

544

ST. ANSELM. 7. 6. 7. 6. D.

MATTHIAS CLAUDIUS, 1740–1815
Tr. by JANE M. CAMPBELL, 1817–1878

JOSEPH BARNBY, 1838–1896

1. We plow the fields and scat-ter The good seed on the land, But
2. He on-ly is the Ma-ker Of all things near and far; He
3. We thank Thee, then, O Fa-ther, For all things bright and good, The

it is fed and wa-tered By God's al-might-y hand;
paints the way-side flow-er, He lights the eve-ning star;
seed-time and the har-vest, Our life, our health, our food;

He sends the snow in win-ter, The warmth to swell the grain,
The winds and waves o-bey Him, By Him the birds are fed;
Ac-cept the gifts we of-fer For all Thy love im-parts,

The breez-es and the sun-shine, And soft re-fresh-ing rain.
Much more to us, His chil-dren, He gives our dai-ly bread.
And, what Thou most de-sir-est, Our hum-ble, thank-ful hearts. A-MEN.

Special Seasons and Services

545

ST. GEORGE'S, WINDSOR. 7. 7. 7. 7. D.

HENRY ALFORD, 1810–1871

GEORGE J. ELVEY, 1816–1893

1. Come, ye thank-ful peo-ple, come, Raise the song of har-vest-home:
2. All the world is God's own field, Fruit un-to His praise to yield;
3. For the Lord our God shall come, And shall take His har-vest home;
4. E - ven so, Lord, quick-ly come Bring Thy fi - nal har-vest home;

All is safe-ly gath-ered in, Ere the win-ter storms be-gin;
Wheat and tares to-geth-er sown, Un-to joy or sor-row grown;
From His field shall in that day All of-fens-es purge a-way;
Gath-er Thou Thy peo-ple in, Free from sor-row, free from sin;

God, our Ma-ker, doth pro-vide For our wants to be sup-plied:
First the blade, and then the ear, Then the full corn shall ap-pear:
Give His an-gels charge at last In the fire the tares to cast;
There, for ev-er pu-ri-fied, In Thy pres-ence to a-bide:

Come to God's own tem-ple, come, Raise the song of har-vest-home.
Lord of har-vest, grant that we Whole-some grain and pure may be.
But the fruit-ful ears to store In His gar-ner ev-er-more.
Come, with all Thine an-gels, come, Raise the glo-rious har-vest-home. A-MEN.

Thanksgiving

546

OLDBRIDGE. 8. 8. 8. 4.

ALBERT H. HUTCHINSON, ?

ROBERT N. QUAILE, 1867-

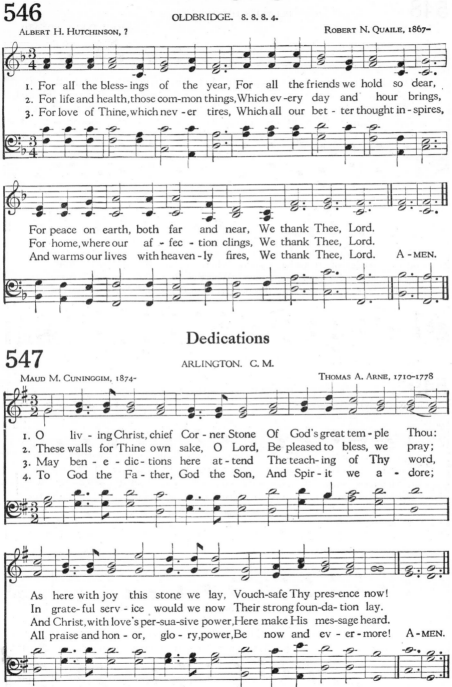

1. For all the bless-ings of the year, For all the friends we hold so dear,
2. For life and health, those com-mon things, Which ev-ery day and hour brings,
3. For love of Thine, which nev-er tires, Which all our bet-ter thought in-spires,

For peace on earth, both far and near, We thank Thee, Lord.
For home, where our af-fec-tion clings, We thank Thee, Lord.
And warms our lives with heaven-ly fires, We thank Thee, Lord. A-MEN.

Dedications

547

ARLINGTON. C. M.

MAUD M. CUNINGGIM, 1874-

THOMAS A. ARNE, 1710-1778

1. O liv-ing Christ, chief Cor-ner Stone Of God's great tem-ple Thou:
2. These walls for Thine own sake, O Lord, Be pleased to bless, we pray;
3. May ben-e-dic-tions here at-tend The teach-ing of Thy word,
4. To God the Fa-ther, God the Son, And Spir-it we a-dore;

As here with joy this stone we lay, Vouch-safe Thy pres-ence now!
In grate-ful serv-ice would we now Their strong foun-da-tion lay.
And Christ, with love's per-sua-sive power, Here make His mes-sage heard.
All praise and hon-or, glo-ry, power, Be now and ev-er-more! A-MEN.

Special Seasons and Services

548

PLEYEL'S HYMN. 7. 7. 7. 7.

JOHN PIERPONT, 1785–1866

IGNACE J. PLEYEL, 1757–1831

1. On this stone now laid with prayer Let Thy church rise, strong and fair;
2. May Thy Spir-it here give rest To the heart by sin op-pressed,
3. O-pen wide, O God, Thy door For the out-cast and the poor;
4. By wise mas-ter build-ers squared, Here be liv-ing stones pre-pared

Ev-er, Lord, Thy Name be known, Where we lay this cor-ner stone.
And the seeds of truth be sown, Where we lay this cor-ner stone.
May they know this house their own, Where we lay this cor-ner stone.
For the tem-ple near Thy throne, Je-sus Christ its Cor-ner Stone. A-MEN.

549

DUNDEE (FRENCH). C. M.

WILLIAM C. BRYANT, 1794–1878

From the SCOTTISH PSALTER, 1615

1. Thou, whose un-meas-ured tem-ple stands, Built o-ver earth and sea,
2. And let the Com-fort-er and Friend, Thy Ho-ly Spir-it, meet
3. May they who err be guid-ed here To find the bet-ter way;
4. May faith grow firm, and love grow warm, And pure de-vo-tion rise,

Ac-cept the walls that hu-man hands Have raised, O God, to Thee.
With those who here in wor-ship bend Be-fore Thy mer-cy-seat.
And they who mourn, and they who fear, Be strength-ened as they pray.
While round these hal-lowed walls the storm Of earth-born pas-sion dies. A-MEN.

550

ITALIAN HYMN (TRINITY). 6.6.4.6.6.6.4.

WILLIAM E. EVANS, 1851–1915

FELICE GIARDINI, 1716–1796

1. Come, O Thou God of grace, Dwell in this ho - ly place,
2. Be in each song of praise Which here Thy peo - ple raise
3. Speak, O e - ter - nal Lord, Out of Thy liv - ing Word,

E'en now de - scend! This tem - ple, reared to Thee, O may it
With hearts a - flame! Let ev - ery an - them rise Like in - cense
O give suc - cess! Do Thou the truth im - part Un - to each

ev - er be Filled with Thy maj - es - ty, Till time shall end!
to the skies, A joy - ful sac - ri - fice, To Thy blest Name!
wait-ing heart; Source of all strength Thou art; Thy gos - pel bless! A - MEN.

4 To the great One in Three
Glory and praises be
In love now given!
Glad songs to Thee we sing,
Glad hearts to Thee we bring,
Till we our God and King
Shall praise in heaven!

551

WEBB. 7. 6. 7. 6. D.

Frederick W. Goadby, 1845–1880

George J. Webb, 1803–1887

1. O Thou, whose hand hath brought us Un-to this joy-ful day,
2. For this new house we praise Thee, Reared at Thine own com-mand,
3. And oft as here we gath-er, And hearts in wor-ship blend,

Ac-cept our glad thanks-giv-ing, And lis-ten as we pray;
For ev-ery gen-erous spir-it, And ev-ery will-ing hand;
May truth re-veal its pow-er, And fer-vent prayer as-cend;

And may our prep-a-ra-tion For this day's serv-ice be
And now with-in Thy tem-ple Thy glo-ry let us see,
Here may the bus-y toil-er Rise to the things a-bove;

With one ac-cord to of-fer Our-selves, O Lord, to Thee.
For all its strength and beau-ty Are noth-ing with-out Thee.
The young, the old, be strength-ened, And all men learn Thy love. A-MEN.

4 And as the years roll onward,
　　And strong affections twine,
And tender memories gather
　　About this sacred shrine,
May this its chiefest honor,
　　Its glory, ever be,
That multitudes within it
　　Have found their way to Thee.

5 Lord God, our fathers' helper,
　　Our joy, and hope, and stay:
Grant now a gracious earnest
　　Of many a coming day.
Our yearning hearts Thou knowest;
　　We wait before Thy throne:
O come, and by Thy presence
　　Make this new house Thine own.

Dedications

552

BETHLEHEM. C. M. D.

HENRY WARE, Jr., 1794-1843

GOTTFRIED W. FINK, 1783-1846

1. All na-ture's works His praise de-clare, To whom they all be - long;
2. To God the tribes of o - cean cry, And birds up - on the wing;
3. Great God, to Thee we con - se-crate Our voic - es and our skill;

There is a voice in ev - ery star, In ev - ery breeze a song.
To God the powers that dwell on high Their tune - ful trib - ute bring.
We bid the peal - ing or - gan wait To speak a - lone Thy will.

Sweet mu - sic fills the world a - broad With strains of love and power;
Like them, let man the throne sur - round, With them loud cho - rus raise,
Lord, while the mu - sic round us floats May earth-born pas - sions die;

The storm - y sea sings praise to God, The thun-der and the shower.
While in - stru-ments of loft - ier sound As - sist his fee - ble praise.
O grant its rich and swell - ing notes May lift our souls on high! A-MEN.

Special Seasons and Services

553

MELITA. 8. 8. 8. 8. 8. 8.

WILLIAM WHITING, 1825–1878

JOHN B. DYKES, 1823–1876

1. E - ter - nal Fa - ther, strong to save, Whose arm hath bound the rest - less wave, Who bidd'st the might - y o - cean deep Its own ap - point - ed lim - its keep: O hear us when we cry to Thee For those in per - il on the sea.

2. O Christ, whose voice the wa - ters heard, And hushed their rag - ing at Thy word, Who walk - edst on the foam - ing deep, And calm a - mid the storm didst sleep: O hear us when we cry to Thee For those in per - il on the sea.

3. O Ho - ly Spir - it, who didst brood Up - on the wa - ters dark and rude, And bid their an - gry tu - mult cease, And give, for wild con - fu - sion, peace: O hear us when we cry to Thee For those in per - il on the sea.

4. O Trin - i - ty of love and power, Our breth - ren shield in dan - ger's hour; From rock and tem - pest, fire and foe, Pro - tect them where - so - e'er they go: Thus ev - er - more shall rise to Thee Glad hymns of praise from land and sea. A - MEN.

Travel

554

SAMUEL. 6. 6. 6. 6. 8. 8,

EDITH JONES ?
HOME HYMN BOOK, 1885

ARTHUR S. SULLIVAN, 1842-1900

1. Fa - ther, who art a - lone Our help - er and our
2. O com - pass with Thy love The dai - ly path they
3. Guard them from ev - ery harm When dan - gers shall as -

stay: O hear us! as we plead For loved ones
tread! And may Thy light and truth Up - on their
sail, And teach them that Thy power Can nev - er,

far a - way; And shield with Thine al - might - y hand
hearts be shed; That, one in all things with Thy will,
nev - er fail; We can - not with our loved ones be,

Our wan - der - ers by sea and land.
Heaven's peace and joy their souls may fill.
But trust them, Fa - ther, un - to Thee. A - MEN.

Special Seasons and Services

BYRD. C. M.

HARRY WEBB FARRINGTON, 1880–1931

ROB ROY PEERY, 1900–

1. O God Cre - a - tor, in whose hand
2. Strong Spir - it, burn - ing with man - kind

The roll - ing plan - ets lie, Give skill to those who
On mis - sions high to dare, Safe pi - lot all who

now com - mand The ships that brave the sky. A - MEN.
seek to find Their ha - ven through the air.

3 Enfolding Life, bear on Thy wing
Through storm, and dark, and sun,
The men in air who closer bring
The nations into one.

Travel

556

MARINERS. 11. 11. 11. 11.

May Rowland, 1870–

Lily Rendle, 1875–

1. Where the great ships, pass - ing, cleave the o - cean wave,
2. Grant that they may see Thy won - ders in the deep,
3. When, in mists ob - scur - ing, si - ren sig - nals sound,
4. On the foam - ing fur - rows of the rest - less sea

Where the lone - ly fish - ers near - er dan - gers brave,
Feel Thy pres - ence with them in the watch they keep,
And the un - seen per - ils com - pass them a - round,
There Thine un - known foot - steps, Son of God, may be;

Where the state - ly fleets go swift - ly out to sea:
May the stars pro - claim Thee in the si - lent night
When the rag - ing tem - pest brings its wild a - larm—
Com - rade of the faith - ful, in the storm and strife,

For all souls who voy - age, Lord, we pray to Thee.
And the sun - lit wa - ters in the morn - ing light.
Keep, O Lord, our broth - ers safe from ev - ery harm.
Lord of seas un - chart - ed, Sav - iour still of life. A - MEN.

5 When the tide, receding, ebbs across the bar
And the weary seamen sight a Land Afar,
Heavenly Master, bring these mariners in peace
To the Shore Eternal—where the breakers cease.

Special Seasons and Services

557

GOD BE WITH YOU. 9. 8. 8. 9. with Refrain

JEREMIAH E. RANKIN, 1828–1904

WILLIAM G. TOMER, 1833–1896

1. God be with you till we meet a - gain! By His coun - sels guide, up -
2. God be with you till we meet a - gain! 'Neath His wings se - cure - ly
3. God be with you till we meet a - gain! When life's per - ils thick con -
4. God be with you till we meet a - gain! Keep love's ban - ner float - ing

hold you, With His sheep se - cure - ly fold you; God be with you till we
hide you, Dai - ly man - na still pro - vide you; God be with you till we
found you, Put His arms un - fail - ing round you; God be with you till we
o'er you, Smite death's threat - 'ning wave be - fore you; God be with you till we

REFRAIN

meet a - gain! Till we meet! Till we meet!
Till we meet! Till we meet a - gain!

Till we meet at Je - sus' feet; Till we meet! . . .
Till we meet! Till we meet!

Till we meet! God be with you till we meet a - gain! A - MEN.
Till we meet a - gain!

May be sung without the Refrain

Schools and Colleges

558

PATTEN. C. M.

M. Woolsey Stryker, 1851–1929

Peter C. Lutkin, 1858–1931

1. Al - might-y Lord, with one ac - cord We of - fer Thee our youth,
2. Thy cause doth claim our souls by name, Be - cause that we are strong;
3. Let fall on ev - ery col - lege hall The lus - ter of Thy cross,
4. Our hearts be ruled, our spir - its schooled A - lone Thy will to seek;

And pray that Thou would'st give us now The war - fare of the truth.
In all the land, one stead-fast band, May we to Christ be - long.
That love may dare Thy work to share And count all else as loss.
And when we find Thy bless - ed mind, In - struct our lips to speak. A-MEN.

Alternative tune, Azmon, No. 162
Music used by permission of Mrs. Peter C. Lutkin

559

ST. MAGNUS. C. M.

Louis F. Benson, 1855–1930

Jeremiah Clark, 1670–1707

1. O Thou whose feet have climbed life's hill, And trod the path of youth,
2. The call is Thine: be Thou the Way, And give us men, to guide;
3. Who learn of Thee the truth shall find, Who fol - low, gain the goal;
4. A - wake the pur - pose high which strives, And, fall - ing, stands a - gain;
5. Thy life the bond of fel - low - ship, Thy love the law that rules,

Our Sav-iour and our Broth-er still, Now lead us in - to truth.
Let wis-dom broad-en with the day, Let hu - man faith a - bide.
With rev-erence crown the ear-nest mind, And speak with-in the soul.
Con-firm the will of ea - ger lives To quit them-selves like men:
Thy Name, pro-claimed by ev - ery lip, The Mas-ter of our schools. A-MEN.

Words used by permission of Mrs. Robert E. Jefferys

Special Seasons and Services

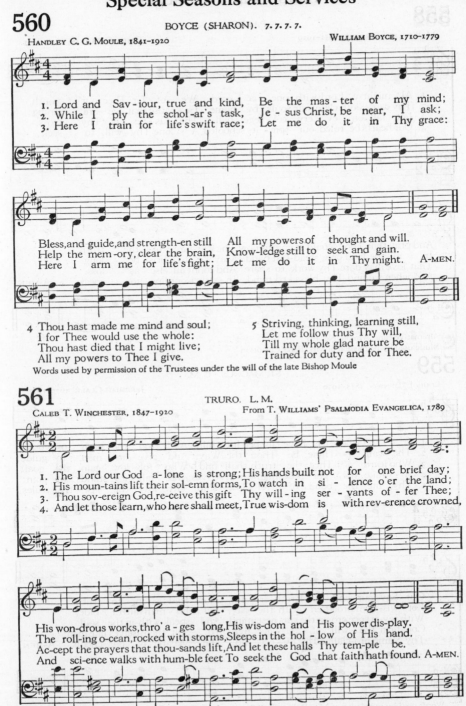

560

BOYCE (SHARON). 7. 7. 7. 7.

HANDLEY C. G. MOULE, 1841-1920

WILLIAM BOYCE, 1710-1779

1. Lord and Sav-iour, true and kind, Be the mas-ter of my mind;
2. While I ply the schol-ar's task, Je-sus Christ, be near, I ask;
3. Here I train for life's swift race; Let me do it in Thy grace:

Bless, and guide, and strength-en still All my powers of thought and will.
Help the mem-ory, clear the brain, Know-ledge still to seek and gain.
Here I arm me for life's fight; Let me do it in Thy might. A-MEN.

4 Thou hast made me mind and soul;
  I for Thee would use the whole:
  Thou hast died that I might live;
  All my powers to Thee I give.

5 Striving, thinking, learning still,
  Let me follow thus Thy will,
  Till my whole glad nature be
  Trained for duty and for Thee.

Words used by permission of the Trustees under the will of the late Bishop Moule

561

TRURO. L. M.

CALEB T. WINCHESTER, 1847-1920

From T. WILLIAMS' PSALMODIA EVANGELICA, 1789

1. The Lord our God a-lone is strong; His hands built not for one brief day;
2. His moun-tains lift their sol-emn forms, To watch in si-lence o'er the land;
3. Thou sov-ereign God, re-ceive this gift Thy will-ing ser-vants of-fer Thee;
4. And let those learn, who here shall meet, True wis-dom is with rev-erence crowned,

His won-drous works, thro' a-ges long, His wis-dom and His power dis-play.
The roll-ing o-cean, rocked with storms, Sleeps in the hol-low of His hand.
Ac-cept the prayers that thou-sands lift, And let these halls Thy tem-ple be.
And sci-ence walks with hum-ble feet To seek the God that faith hath found. A-MEN.

Schools and Colleges

562

ALL SAINTS, NEW. C. M. D.

FRANK MASON NORTH, 1850–1935

HENRY S. CUTLER, 1824–1902

1. The world's a-stir! The clouds of storm Have melt-ed in-to light
2. Where lies our path? We seek to know, To meas-ure life, to find]
3. But Thou, O Christ, art Mas-ter here! Re-deemed by Thee we stand;
4. Give us the wis-dom from a-bove; We pledge our loy-al-ty;

Whose streams, a-glow from foun-tains warm, Have driv-en back the night.
The hid-den springs of truth whence flow The joys of heart and mind.
We chal-lenge life with-out a fear; We wait for Thy com-mand;
Change flash of hope to flame of love, And doubt to cer-tain-ty.

Now bright-ens dawn toward gold-en day; The earth is full of song,
We dream of days be-yond these walls, The lure of gold we feel,
For Thy com-mand is vic-to-ry, And glo-ry crowns the task;
In Thy great will, O Mas-ter Mind, In Thee, O Mas-ter Heart,

Far stretch the shin-ing paths a-way, Spring for-ward! Hearts, be strong!
Life beck-ons us and learn-ing calls, Loud sounds the world's ap-peal.
We fol-low Thee and on-ly Thee, Thy will a-lone we ask.
Our guer-don and our guide we find: Our Lord, our King, Thou art. A-MEN.

The Wesley Graces

563

UXBRIDGE. L. M.

JOHN CENNICK, 1718-1755

LOWELL MASON, 1792-1872

May be sung to Old 100th, No. 3

Be present at our table, Lord;
Be here and everywhere adored;
Thy creatures bless; and grant that we
May feast in paradise with Thee. AMEN.

564

HURSLEY. L. M.

JOHN CENNICK, 1718-1755

Adapted from
KATHOLISCHES GESANGBUCH, c. 1774

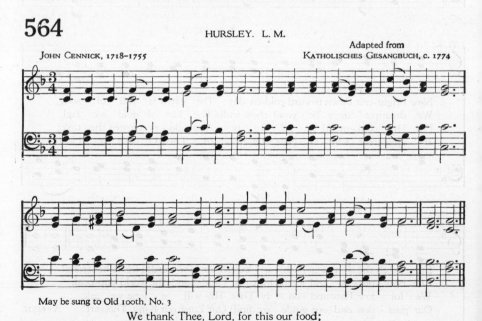

May be sung to Old 100th, No. 3

We thank Thee, Lord, for this our food;
But more because of Jesus' blood;
Let manna to our souls be given,
The bread of life sent down from heaven. AMEN.

MUSIC FOR THE HOLY COMMUNION
RESPONSES   DOXOLOGIES
ANCIENT HYMNS AND CANTICLES

The Holy Communion

565 GLORIA DEO
John Merbecke, 1523-c. 1585

Glo-ry be to God on high.

566 GLORIA DEO
Marie Briel, 1896-

Glo-ry be to God on high.

567 GLORIA DEO
Composer unknown

Glo-ry be to God on high.

568 GRATIA TIBI
Thomas Tallis, c. 1520-1585

Thanks be to Thee, O Christ, for this Thy ho-ly gos-pel.

569 GLORIA PATRI
Charles Meineke, 1782-1850

Glo-ry be to the Fa-ther, and to the Son, and to the Ho-ly Ghost; As it was in the be-gin-ning, is now, and ev-er shall be, world with-out end. A-men, A-men.

The Holy Communion

570

GLORIA PATRI

Henry W. Greatorex, 1811–1858

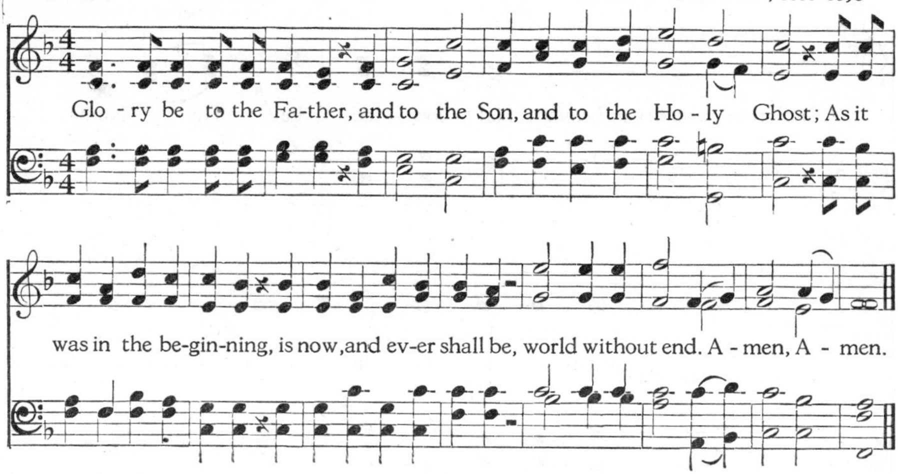

Glo - ry be to the Fa-ther, and to the Son, and to the Ho - ly Ghost; As it
was in the be-gin-ning, is now, and ev-er shall be, world without end. A - men, A - men.

571

GLORIA PATRI

Parisian Tone

In free rhythm

Glo - ry be to the Fa - ther, and to the Son, and to the
Ho - ly Ghost; As it was in the beginning, is now, and
ev - er shall be, world with - out end. A - men.

The Holy Communion

THE LORD'S PRAYER

Gregorian

Our Father, who art in heaven: Hal - low - ed be Thy Name,

{ Thy kingdom come, } earth as it is in heaven. Give us this day our
{ Thy will be done, on }

dai - - ly bread. { And forgive us our trespasses } those who
{ as we forgive }

tres - pass a - gainst us. { And lead us not into } liv - er
{ temptation, but de- }

us from e - vil. { For Thine is the king- } ev - er. A - MEN.
{ dom, and the power, }
{ and the glory, for }

The Holy Communion

THE LORD'S PRAYER

C. A. WICKES, ?

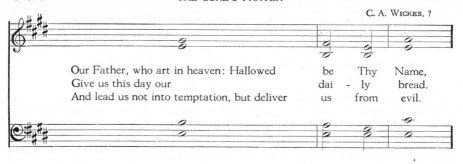

Our Father, who art in heaven: Hallowed be Thy Name,
Give us this day our dai - ly bread.
And lead us not into temptation, but deliver us from evil.

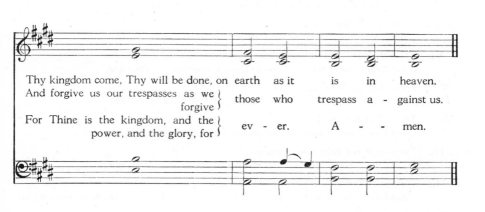

Thy kingdom come, Thy will be done, on earth as it is in heaven.
And forgive us our trespasses as we forgive those who trespass a - gainst us.
For Thine is the kingdom, and the power, and the glory, for ev - er. A - - men.

THE LORD'S PRAYER

VINCENT NOVELLO, 1781–1861

The Holy Communion

575

[The Commandments are to be read by the Minister; the Responses are to be sung or said by the People.]
Exodus xx.

God spake these words and said:

I.   I am the Lord thy God: thou shalt have no other gods before me.
Lord, have mercy upon us, and incline our hearts to keep this law.

II.   Thou shalt not make unto thee any graven image, or any likeness of anything that is in heaven above, or that is in the earth beneath, or that is in the water under the earth: thou shalt not bow down thyself to them, nor serve them.
Lord, have mercy upon us, and incline our hearts to keep this law.

III.   Thou shalt not take the Name of the Lord thy God in vain.
Lord, have mercy upon us, and incline our hearts to keep this law.

IV.   Remember the Sabbath day to keep it holy. Six days shalt thou labor, and do all thy work: but the seventh is the Sabbath of the Lord thy God.
Lord, have mercy upon us, and incline our hearts to keep this law.

V.   Honor thy father and thy mother.
Lord, have mercy upon us, and incline our hearts to keep this law.

VI.   Thou shalt not kill.
Lord, have mercy upon us, and incline our hearts to keep this law.

VII.   Thou shalt not commit adultery.
Lord, have mercy upon us, and incline our hearts to keep this law.

VIII.   Thou shalt not steal.
Lord, have mercy upon us, and incline our hearts to keep this law.

IX.   Thou shalt not bear false witness.
Lord, have mercy upon us, and incline our hearts to keep this law.

X.   Thou shalt not covet.
Lord, have mercy upon us, and write all these Thy laws in our hearts, we beseech Thee.

OUR LORD'S SUMMARY OF THE LAW

St. Mark xii. 29; St. John xiii. 34.

Our Lord Jesus Christ said: The first of all the commandments is, Hear, O Israel; the Lord our God is one Lord: And thou shalt love the Lord thy God with all thy heart, and with all thy soul, and with all thy mind, and with all thy strength: this is the first commandment.
Lord, have mercy upon us, and incline our hearts to keep this law.

And the second is like, namely, this, Thou shalt love thy neighbor as thyself.
Lord, have mercy upon us, and incline our hearts to keep this law.

A new commandment I give unto you, That ye love one another; as I have loved you, that ye also love one another.
Lord, have mercy upon us, and write all these Thy laws in our hearts, we beseech Thee.

The Responses may be sung or said after each of the Commandments

The Holy Communion

Let the congregation unite in singing at the close of the commandments

Composer unknown

Lord, have mer-cy up-on us, and write all these Thy laws in our hearts, we be-seech Thee.

CHARLES F. GOUNOD, 1818–1893

May be sung after each Commandment except the tenth

Lord, have mer-cy up-on us, and in-cline our hearts to keep this law.

After the tenth Commandment

us, and write all these Thy laws in our hearts, we be-seech Thee.

THOMAS TALLIS, c. 1520–1585

May be sung after each Commandment except the tenth

Lord, have mer-cy up-on us, and in-cline our hearts to keep this law.

After the tenth Commandment

Lord, have mercy up-on us, and write all these Thy laws in our hearts, we be-seech Thee.

The Holy Communion

576

KYRIE

J. MERBECKE, 1523–1585

In unison

Lord, have mer-cy up-on us; Christ, have mer-cy up-on us; Lord, have mer-cy up-on us.

Each of the parts of the three-fold Kyrie may be sung three times

577

KYRIE

From a Lutheran Service of 1528

In unison

Lord, have mer-cy up-on us; Christ, have mer-cy up-on us; Lord, have mer-cy up-on us.

578

RESPONSES TO THE BEATITUDES OF OUR LORD

Ancient Tone, as in CHURCH HYMNARY, 1927

May be sung after each Beatitude

Grant us this grace, we be-seech Thee, O Lord.

May be sung at the close of the Reading

Write these words in our hearts, we be-seech Thee, O Lord. A-MEN.

The Holy Communion

579

ROBERT G. McCUTCHAN, 1877–

May be sung after each Beatitude

Lord, be gra-cious un-to us, and help us to ob-tain this bless-ing.

May be sung at the close of the Reading

ROBERT G. McCUTCHAN, 1877–

Grant us Thy Ho-ly Spir-it, O God, and en-a-ble us to ob-tain all these

bless-ings, through Je-sus Christ our Lord. A-MEN.

Music copyright, 1935, by Whitmore & Smith, Nashville, Tenn.

580

VAN DENMAN THOMPSON, 1890–

May be sung after each Beatitude

Lord, be gracious un-to us, and help us to ob-tain this blessing.

May be sung at the close of the Reading

VAN DENMAN THOMPSON, 1890–

Grant us Thy Holy Spirit, O God, { and enable us to / obtain all these / blessings, through } Je-sus Christ our Lord. A-MEN.

Music copyright, 1935, by Van Denman Thompson. Used by permission

The Holy Communion

581

PRESENTATION OF THE OFFERING FOR THE NEEDY

LUDWIG VAN BEETHOVEN, 1770-1827

All things come of Thee, O Lord; and of Thine own have we giv-en Thee. A-MEN.

582

JONATHAN BATTISHILL, 1738-1891

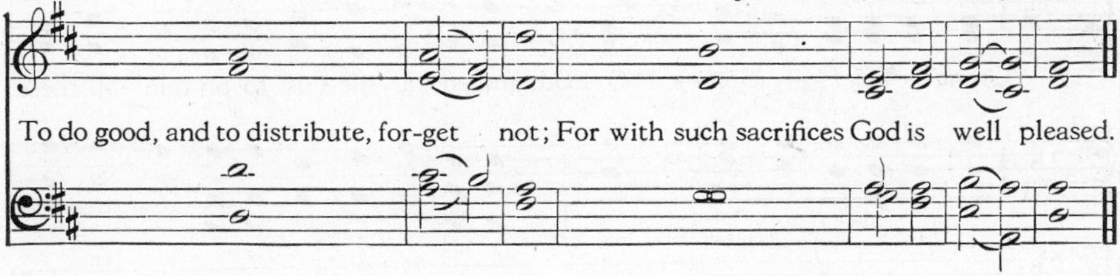

To do good, and to distribute, for-get not; For with such sacrifices God is well pleased.

583

SURSUM CORDA

JOHN CAMIDGE, 1735-1803

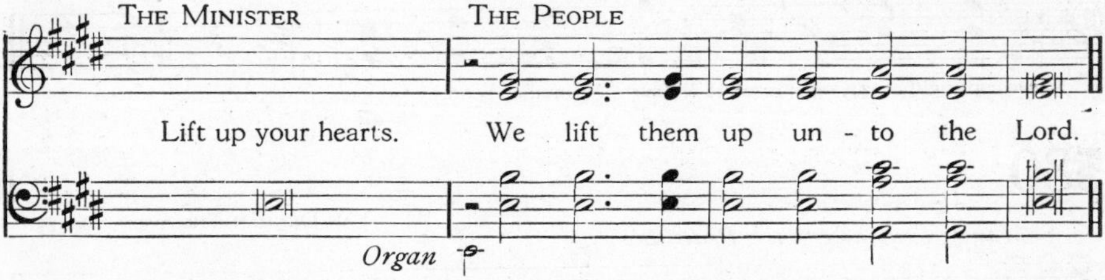

THE MINISTER THE PEOPLE

Lift up your hearts. We lift them up un-to the Lord.

Organ

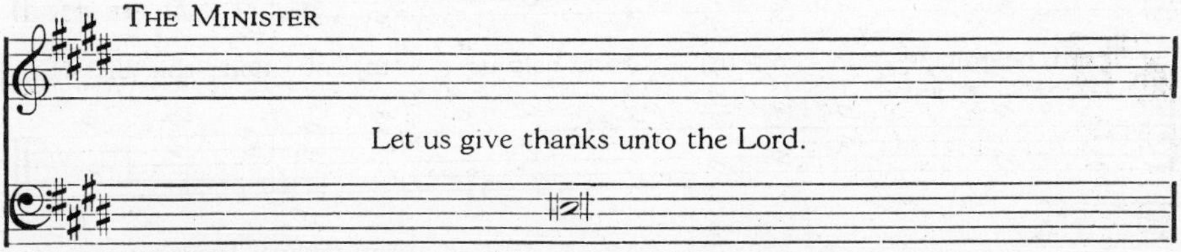

THE MINISTER

Let us give thanks unto the Lord.

THE PEOPLE

It is meet and right so to do.

The Holy Communion

SANCTUS WITH PREFACE

Composer unknown

Therefore with angels and arch-angels, and with all the company of heaven, We laud and magnify Thy glorious Name, Ev-er-more prais-ing Thee, and say-ing: Ho-ly, ho-ly, ho-ly Lord God of Hosts, Heaven and earth are full of Thy glo-ry: Glo-ry be to Thee, O Lord, Most High. A-MEN.

585

SANCTUS

ALEXANDER S. COOPER, 1835–

Ho-ly, ho-ly, ho-ly Lord God of Hosts, Heaven and earth are full of Thy glo-ry: Glo-ry be to Thee, O Lord, Most High. A-MEN.

The Holy Communion

AGNUS DEI

JOHN MERBECKE, 1523–1585

Unison *In free rhythm*

O Lamb of God, that tak-est a-way the sins of the world, have mer-cy up-on us.

O Lamb of God, that tak-est a-way the sins of the world, have mer-cy up-on us.

O Lamb of God, that tak-est a-way the sins of the world, grant us Thy peace.

587

AGNUS DEI

GIOVANNI P. DA PALESTRINA, 1525–1594

O Lamb of God, that tak-est a-way the sins of the world,

have mer-cy up-on us. O Lamb of God, that tak-est a-

way the sins of the world, Grant us Thy peace.

The Holy Communion

GLORIA IN EXCELSIS

(Enlarged Form)

Old Scottish chant

1. Glory be to God on high, and on earth peace, good
2. { We praise Thee, / we bless Thee, we } wor - ship Thee, { we glorify Thee, we / give thanks to } Thee for

will toward men. 3. O Lord God, Heaven - ly King;
Thy great glory. 4. O Lord, the only-begotten Son, Je - sus Christ,

God, the Fa - ther Al - mighty. 5. That takest away the
O Lord God, Lamb of { God, } Son . . of the Father, 6. Thou that takest away the
7. Thou that takest away the
8. { Thou that sittest at the / right hand of

Slowly

sins of the world, have mercy up - on us. 9. For Thou only
sins of the world, have mercy up - on us. 10. { Thou only, O
sins of the world, re - ceive our prayer. { Christ, with the
God the Fa - ther, have mercy up - on us.

art . . holy; Thou on - ly art the Lord.
Ho - ly Ghost, art most high in the glory of God the Father. A - men.

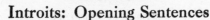

Responses
Introits: Opening Sentences

589

KARL P. HARRINGTON, 1861–

In unison or harmony

The Lord is in His ho-ly tem-ple; let all the earth keep si-lence be-fore Him.

Music copyright by Karl P. Harrington.   Renewal, 1933

590

CALVIN W. LAUFER, 1874–1938

The Lord is in His ho - ly tem - ple; let all the

earth keep si-lence be-fore Him, keep si - lence be - fore Him.

Music copyright, 1927, by Calvin W. Laufer.   Used by permission

591

KARL P. HARRINGTON, 1861–

In unison

The Lord is in His ho - ly tem - ple; let all the

earth keep si - lence be - fore Him.

Music copyright, 1935, by Karl P. Harrington.   Used by permission

Responses

592

WELWYN. 11. 10. 11. 10.

Elizabeth Wilson, 1867– and
Helen Thoburn, 1885–1932

Alfred Scott-Gatty, 1847–1918

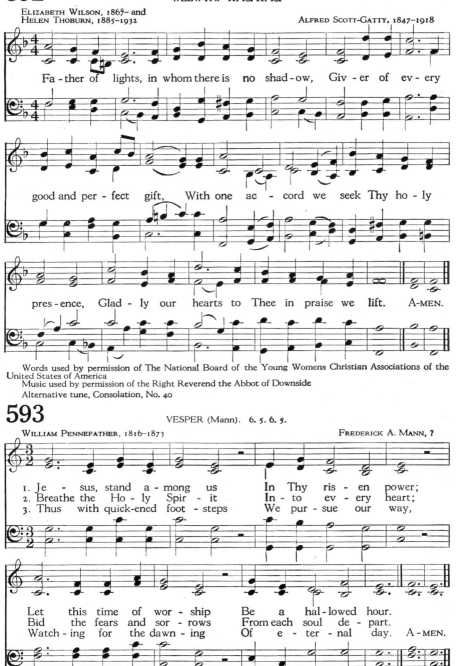

Fa-ther of lights, in whom there is no shad-ow, Giv-er of ev-ery
good and per-fect gift, With one ac-cord we seek Thy ho-ly
pres-ence, Glad-ly our hearts to Thee in praise we lift. A-men.

Words used by permission of The National Board of the Young Womens Christian Associations of the United States of America
Music used by permission of the Right Reverend the Abbot of Downside
Alternative tune, Consolation, No. 40

593

VESPER (Mann). 6. 5. 6. 5.

William Pennefather, 1816–1873

Frederick A. Mann, ?

1. Je - sus, stand a - mong us In Thy ris - en power;
2. Breathe the Ho - ly Spir - it In - to ev - ery heart;
3. Thus with quick-ened foot - steps We pur - sue our way,

Let this time of wor - ship Be a hal - lowed hour.
Bid the fears and sor - rows From each soul de - part.
Watch - ing for the dawn - ing Of e - ter - nal day. A - men.

Music used by permission of National Children's Home and Orphanage, London

Responses

594

PICARDY. 8. 7. 8. 7. 8. 7.

LITURGY OF ST. JAMES
Tr. by GERARD MOULTRIE, 1829–1885

French traditional carol

In unison

Let all mor-tal flesh keep si-lence, And with fear and trem-bling stand;

Pon-der noth-ing earth-ly mind-ed, For with bless-ing in His hand,

Christ our God to earth de-scend-eth, Our full hom-age to de-mand. A-MEN.

595

JOHN PORTER, 1877–

O wor-ship the Lord in the beau-ty of

ho-li-ness; Serve Him with glad-ness, all the earth. A-MEN.

596

Responses After Prayer

GEORGE WHELPTON, 1847–1930

Hear our prayer, O Lord, Hear our prayer, O Lord;

In - cline Thine ear to us, And grant us Thy peace. A - MEN.

Copyright, 1903, by George Whelpton. Used by permission

597

From Psalm XIX

ADOLPH BAUMBACH, 1830–1880

Let the words of my mouth and the med - i - ta - tion of my heart be ac -

cept - a - ble in Thy sight, O Lord, my Strength and my Re-deem-er. A - MEN.

598

Arr. from FELIX MENDELSSOHN-BARTHOLDY, 1809–1847

Al-might-y Fa-ther, hear our prayer, and bless all souls that wait be-fore Thee. A-MEN.

Responses

599

FINLANDIA. 10. 10. 10. 10. 10. 12.

RICHARD W. GILDER, 1844–1909

JEAN SIBELIUS, 1865–
Arr. for THE HYMNAL, 1932

Through love to light! O won-der-ful the way That leads from

dark - ness to the per - fect day; From dark - ness and from

sor-row of the night To morn-ing that comes sing-ing o'er the sea!

Through love to light! Through light, O God, to Thee,

Who art the Love of love, th'e - ter - nal Light of light! A-MEN.

Responses

600

LUCY. 6. 6. 6. 6. with Refrain

W. W. Ellsworth, ?

Arr. from Johannes Brahms, 1833–1897

1. Sav - iour, hear us, we pray: Keep us safe through this day; Keep our lives free from sin And our hearts pure with - in.

2. Be our Guard - ian and Guide; May we walk by Thy side Till the eve - ning shades fall O - ver us— o - ver all.

REFRAIN

Je - sus, Lord, hear our prayer: May we rest in Thy care,

Je - sus, Lord, hear our prayer: May we rest in Thy care. A - MEN.

601

From Felix Mendelssohn-Bartholdy, 1809–1847

Hear Thou in love, O Lord, our cry, In heaven, Thy dwell- ing place on high.

Responses
Responses After Scripture.

602

Arr. from CHARLES F. GOUNOD, 1818–1893

Ho - san - na in the high - est!
in ex - cel - sis!

603

Composer unknown

God be merciful unto us and bless us, And cause His face to shine up-on us.

That Thy way } known up-on earth, Thy saving health a - mong all nations. A-MEN.
may be }

604

ROBERT G. McCUTCHAN, 1877–

Thy testimonies are very sure: } Lord, for ever. A - MEN.
holiness becometh Thy house, O }

605

JOHN CAMIDGE, 1735-1803

O Lord, o - pen Thou our eyes,

That we may be-hold won - drous things out of Thy law.

Responses
Offertory Sentences

606

Arr. from LUDWIG VAN BEETHOVEN, 1770–1827

All things come of Thee, O Lord, and of Thine own have we giv-en Thee. A-MEN.

607

PELHAM HUMFREY, 1647–1674

All things come of Thee, O Lord, and of Thine own have we giv-en Thee. A-MEN.

608

GEORGE A. MacFARRAN, 1813–1887

All things come of Thee, O Lord, and of Thine own have we giv-en Thee. A-MEN.

609

CANONBURY. L. M.

SAMUEL LONGFELLOW, 1819–1892

ROBERT SCHUMANN, 1810–1856

Bless Thou the gifts our hands have brought; Bless
Thou the work our hearts have planned; Ours is the faith, the
will, the thought; The rest, O God, is in Thy hand. A-MEN.

610

ST. ANDREW. 6. 6. 8. 6.

WILLIAM W. HOW, 1823–1897

JOSEPH BARNBY, 1838–1896

We give Thee but Thine own, What-e'er the gift may be; All
that we have is Thine a-lone, A trust, O Lord, from Thee. A-MEN.

611

HERR JESU CHRIST. L. M.

JOHN G. WHITTIER, 1807–1892

From PENSUM SACRUM, 1648
Arr. by J. S. BACH, 1685–1750

In unison

All things are Thine: no gift have we, Lord of all gifts, to
of - fer Thee; And hence with grate-ful hearts to-day,
Thine own be-fore Thy feet we lay. A-MEN.

Responses

Responses for Closing

612

SOLITUDE. 7. 7. 7. 7.

JOHN NEWTON, 1725–1807

LEWIS T. DOWNES, 1824–1910

Now may He who from the dead Brought the Shep-herd of the sheep,

Je-sus Christ, our King and Head, All our souls in safe-ty keep. A-MEN.

613

NUMBERS vi. 24–26

LUCY RIDER MEYER, 1849–1922

The Lord bless thee and keep thee; The Lord make His face shine up-on thee, and be

gra-cious un-to thee, And be gra-cious un-to thee; The Lord lift up His

And give thee peace. . . . .

coun-te-nance, His coun-te-nance up-on thee, and give thee peace.

Responses

THE LORD BLESS YOU AND KEEP YOU

Arr. from NUMBERS VI. 24–26

PETER C. LUTKIN, 1858–1931

The Lord bless you and keep you; The Lord lift His coun-te-nance up-

the

on you,   and give you peace,   and give you peace; The Lord

and give you peace, ... and give you peace; . . . . . the Lord

Lord make His face   and be gra - - cious un - to

make His   face to shine up - on   you,   and be gra-cious,

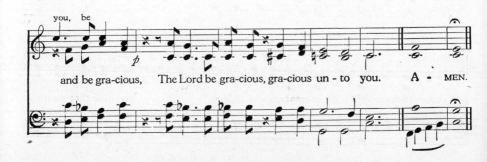

you, be

and be gra-cious,   The Lord be gra-cious, gra-cious un - to you.   A - MEN.

Responses

615

SAMUEL LONGFELLOW, 1819–1892

ALLA TRINITA BEATA. 8. 7. 8. 7. D.]

From LAUDI SPIRITUALI, 1336 (?)

Fa - ther, give Thy ben - e - dic - tion, Give Thy peace be -

fore we part; Still our minds with truth's con - vic - tion;

Calm with trust each anx - ious heart. Let Thy voice with sweet com-mand-ing,

Bid our grief and strug - gles end; Peace which pass - eth

un - der - stand - ing On our wait - ing spir - its send. A - MEN.

Responses
Doxologies

616

OLD 100TH. L. M. (Original rhythm)

THOMAS KEN, 1637-1711

From the GENEVAN PSALTER, 1551

Praise God from whom all bless-ings flow; Praise Him, all crea-tures here be-low;

Praise Him a-bove, ye heaven-ly host: Praise Fa-ther, Son, and Ho-ly Ghost.

617

MEAR. C. M.

TATE AND BRADY, 1696

Composer unknown

To Fa-ther, Son, and Ho-ly Ghost, The God whom we a-dore,

Be glo-ry, as it was, is now, And shall be ev-er-more. A-MEN.

618

OLD 134TH (ST. MICHAEL). S. M.

ISAAC WATTS, 1674-1748

Adapted from GENEVAN PSALTER, 1551

1. To God the on-ly wise, Our Sav-iour and our King,
2. To our Re-deem-er God Wis-dom and power be-long,

Let all the saints be-low the skies Their hum-ble prais-es bring.
Im-mor-tal crowns of ma-jes-ty, And ev-er-last-ing song. A-MEN.

Responses
Amens

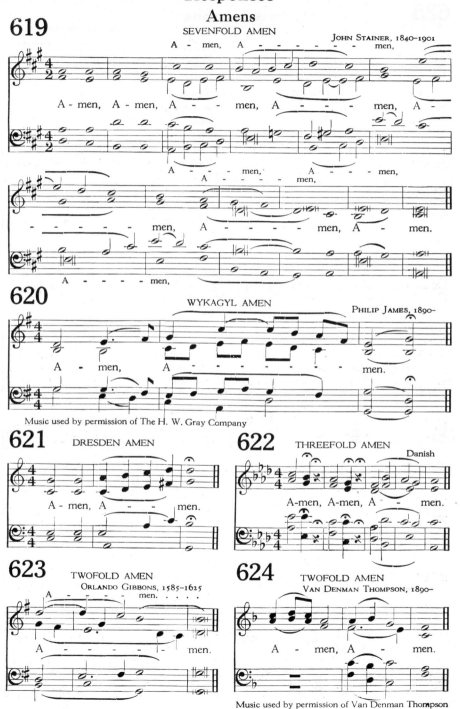

619

SEVENFOLD AMEN

John Stainer, 1840-1901

620

WYKAGYL AMEN

Philip James, 1890-

Music used by permission of The H. W. Gray Company

621 DRESDEN AMEN

622 THREEFOLD AMEN

Danish

623 TWOFOLD AMEN

Orlando Gibbons, 1585-1625

624 TWOFOLD AMEN

Van Denman Thompson, 1890-

Music used by permission of Van Denman Thompson

Ancient Hymns and Canticles

625

TE DEUM LAUDAMUS

HENRY LAWES, 1595–1662

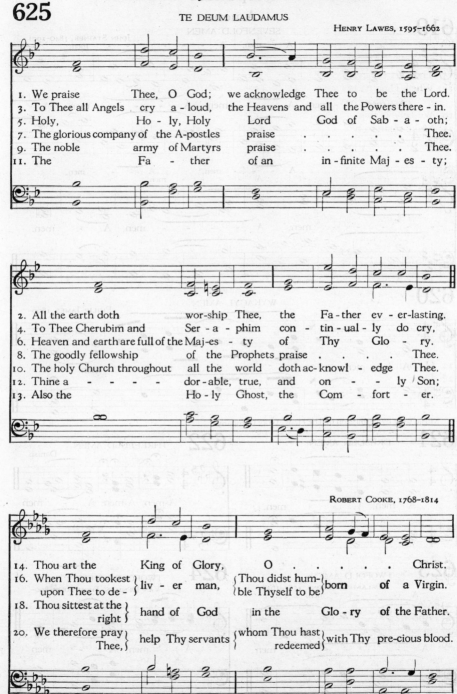

1. We praise Thee, O God; we acknowledge Thee to be the Lord.
3. To Thee all Angels cry a-loud, the Heavens and all the Powers there-in.
5. Holy, Ho-ly, Holy Lord God of Sab-a-oth;
7. The glorious company of the A-postles praise . . . . Thee.
9. The noble army of Martyrs praise . . . . Thee.
11. The Fa-ther of an in-finite Maj-es-ty;

2. All the earth doth wor-ship Thee, the Fa-ther ev-er-lasting.
4. To Thee Cherubim and Ser-a-phim con-tin-ual-ly do cry,
6. Heaven and earth are full of the Maj-es-ty of Thy Glo-ry.
8. The goodly fellowship of the Prophets praise . . . . Thee.
10. The holy Church throughout all the world doth ac-knowl-edge Thee.
12. Thine a-dor-able, true, and on-ly Son;
13. Also the Ho-ly Ghost, the Com-fort-er.

ROBERT COOKE, 1768–1814

14. Thou art the King of Glory, O . . . . Christ.
16. When Thou tookest { liv-er man, { Thou didst hum- born of a Virgin.
    upon Thee to de- } { ble Thyself to be }
18. Thou sittest at the } hand of God in the Glo-ry of the Father.
    right }
20. We therefore pray } help Thy servants { whom Thou hast } with Thy pre-cious blood.
    Thee, } { redeemed }

Ancient Hymns and Canticles

15. Thou art the ever - last - ing Son of the Fa - ther.
17. When Thou hadst overcome the { sharpness of death, { Thou didst open the Kingdom of } Heaven to all be - lievers.
19. We believe that Thou shalt come to be . our Judge.
21. Make them to be numbered } with Thy Saints in glo - ry ev - er-lasting.

HENRY LAWES, 1595–1662

22. O Lord, . . save Thy people and bless Thine her - it - age.
24. Day . . . by day, we mag - ni fy . Thee;
26. Vouch - - - safe, O Lord, to keep us this day with - out . sin.
28. O Lord, let Thy mercy be up - on us as our trust . is in Thee.

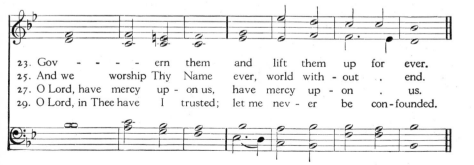

23. Gov - - - - ern them and lift them up for ever.
25. And we worship Thy Name ever, world with - out . end.
27. O Lord, have mercy up - on us, have mercy up - on . us.
29. O Lord, in Thee have I trusted; let me nev - er be con - founded.

Ancient Hymns and Canticles

626

VENITE

PSALM XCV

WILLIAM BOYCE, 1710-1799

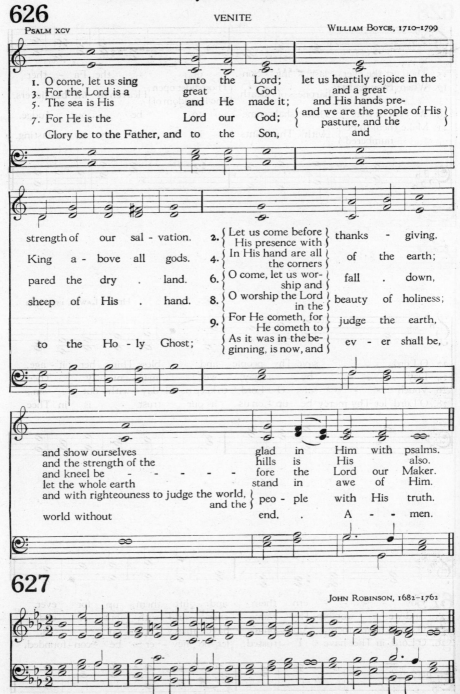

1. O come, let us sing unto the Lord; let us heartily rejoice in the
3. For the Lord is a great God and a great
5. The sea is His and He made it; and His hands pre-
7. For He is the Lord our God; { and we are the people of His
   pasture, and the }

Glory be to the Father, and to the Son, and

strength of our sal - vation. 2. { Let us come before
His presence with } thanks - giving,

King a - bove all gods. 4. { In His hand are all
the corners } of the earth;

pared the dry land. 6. { O come, let us worship and } fall down,

sheep of His hand. 8. { O worship the Lord
in the } beauty of holiness;

9. { For He cometh, for
He cometh to } judge the earth,

to the Ho - ly Ghost; { As it was in the beginning, is now, and } ev - er shall be,

and show ourselves glad in Him with psalms.
and the strength of the hills is His also.
and kneel be - - - - - fore the Lord our Maker.
let the whole earth stand in awe of Him.
and with righteouness to judge the world, { peo - ple with His truth.
and the }

world without end. A - - men.

627

JOHN ROBINSON, 1682-1762

"Glory be to the Father" may be sung at the conclusion of Canticles, as above, wherever appropriate

Ancient Hymns and Canticles

628

BENEDICTUS

LUKE I. 68–79

JOSEPH BARNBY, 1838–1896

1. Blessed be the Lord God of Israel, for He hath visited
3. As He spake by the mouth of His ho - ly Prophets, which have been
5. To perform the mercy promised to our forefathers, and to re -
7. That we, being delivered out of the hand of our enemies, might serve
9. And thou, child, shalt be called the prophet of the Highest, { for thou shalt gò before the face of the Lord, }
11. Through the tender mercy of our God, { whereby the Day-spring from on }

Glory be to the Father, and to the Son, and

and re - deemed His people, 2. And hath raised up a mighty sal -
since the world be - gan, 4. That we should be sav-ed
member His ho - ly covenant, 6. { To perform the oath which He sware to our fore- }
Him with - out fear; 8. In holiness and righteousness be -
to pre - pare His ways; 10. To give knowledge of salvation
high hath visit - ed us; 12. { To give light to them that sit in dark- ness, and in the }

to the Ho - ly Ghost; As it was in the beginning, is now, and

va - tion for us in the house of His ser - vant David:
from our enemies and from the hand of all that hate us.
fa - ther Abraham, that He would give us;
fore Him, all the days of our life.
unto His people for the re - mis - sion of their sins,
shadow of death, and to guide our feet into the way of peace.
ev - er shall be, world without end. A - men.

629

Arr. from LUDWIG VAN BEETHOVEN, 1770–1827

Ancient Hymns and Canticles

630

JUBILATE DEO

HENRY ALDRICH, 1647–1710

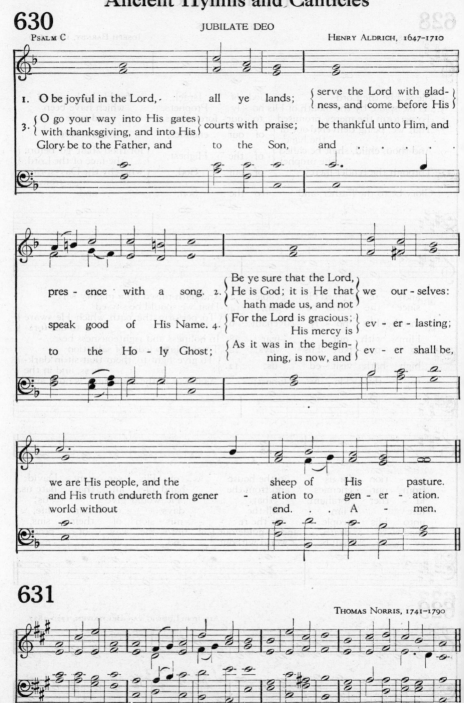

1. O be joyful in the Lord, all ye lands; { serve the Lord with gladness, and come before His }

3. { O go your way into His gates with thanksgiving, and into His } courts with praise; be thankful unto Him, and

Glory be to the Father, and to the Son, and . . . . .

pres - ence with a song. 2. { Be ye sure that the Lord, He is God; it is He that } we our - selves:

speak good of His Name. 4. { For the Lord is gracious; His mercy is } ev - er - lasting;

to the Ho - ly Ghost; { As it was in the beginning, is now, and } ev - er shall be,

we are His people, and the sheep of His pasture.

and His truth endureth from gener - ation to gen - er - ation.

world without end. . . A - men.

631

THOMAS NORRIS, 1741–1790

Ancient Hymns and Canticles

632

MAGNIFICAT

LUKE 1. 46–55   HENRY SMART, 1813–1879

1. My soul doth magni — — fy the Lord, and my spirit hath re -
3. For be — — — — — hold, from henceforth all gener - -
5. And His mercy is on them that fear Him through - -
7. He hath put down the mighty from their seat, and hath ex - -

Glory be to the Father, and to the Son, and

joiced in God my Saviour. 2. For He
ations shall call me blessed. 4. For He that is mighty hath
out all gen - er - ations. 6. He hath showed strength
alted the humble and meek. 8. He hath filled the hungry with
9. He, remembering His mercy hath holpen His

to the Ho - ly Ghost; As it was in the beginning, is now, and

hath re - garded the lowli - - - ness of His hand-maiden.
magni-fied me, and ho - ly is His Name.
with His arm; { He hath scattered the proud in the imagi- } na - tion of their hearts.
good things, and the rich He hath sent empty a - way.
ser - vant Israel { as He promised to our fore-fathers, Abraham } and his seed, for ever.
ev - er shall be, world without end. A - men.

633

SAMUEL WESLEY, 1766–1837

Ancient Hymns and Canticles

634

BONUM EST

PSALM xcii

RICHARD FARRANT, c. 1530–1580

1. It is a good thing to give thanks unto the Lord
2. To tell of Thy loving-kindness early in the morning,
3. Upon an instrument of ten strings and up on the lute;
4. For Thou, Lord, hast made me glad through Thy works;

and to sing praises unto Thy Name, O Most Highest;
and of Thy truth in the night . . season;
upon a loud instrument and up - on the harp.
and I will rejoice in giving praise for the oper - a - tions of Thy hands.

Glory be to the Father, and to the Son, and to the Ho - ly Ghost;
{ As it was in the beginning, }
{ is now, and } ev - er shall be, world with-out end. A - men.

635

JOHN ALCOCK, 1715–1806

Ancient Hymns and Canticles

636

VENI CREATOR. L. M. with Refrain
(Veni, Creator Spiritus)

Anonymous (9th or 10th century)
Tr. by JOHN COSIN, 1594–1672

Ancient plainsong

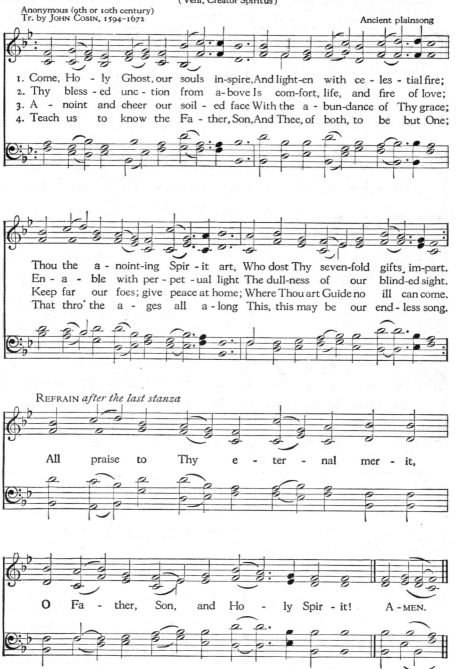

1. Come, Ho - ly Ghost, our souls in-spire, And light-en with ce - les - tial fire;
2. Thy bless - ed unc - tion from a-bove Is com-fort, life, and fire of love;
3. A - noint and cheer our soil - ed face With the a - bun-dance of Thy grace;
4. Teach us to know the Fa - ther, Son, And Thee, of both, to be but One;

Thou the a - noint-ing Spir - it art, Who dost Thy seven-fold gifts im-part.
En - a - ble with per - pet -ual light The dull-ness of our blind-ed sight.
Keep far our foes; give peace at home; Where Thou art Guide no ill can come.
That thro' the a - ges all a - long This, this may be our end - less song.

REFRAIN *after the last stanza*

All praise to Thy e - ter - nal mer - it,

O Fa - ther, Son, and Ho - ly Spir - it! A - MEN.

Ancient Hymns and Canticles

SEBASTE. Irregular

Greek hymn of the 3rd century (?)
Tr. by JOHN KEBLE, 1792-1866

JOHN STAINER, 1840-1901

In free rhythm

Hail, gladdening
Light, of His pure } glo - ry poured Who is the immortal Fa - ther, heaven-ly, blest,

Ho - li - est of ho - lies, Je - sus Christ, our Lord!

Now we come to the sun's hour of rest. The lights of eve - ning round us shine,

We hymn the Fa - ther, Son, and Ho - ly Spir - it di - vine.

Worthiest art Thou at all times to be sung With un - de - fil - ed tongue,

Son of our God, giv - er of life a - lone:

Ancient Hymns and Canticles

There - fore in all the world Thy glo - ries, Lord, they own. A-MEN.

Used by permission of J. F. R. Stainer, Esq.

638 ST. VENANTIUS. L. M.

AMBROSE OF MILAN, 340-397

Rouen church melody

1. O splen - dor of God's glo - ry bright, O Thou that
2. O Thou true Sun, on us Thy glance Let fall in
3. The Fa - ther, too, our prayers im - plore, Fa - ther of
4. To guide what - e'er we no - bly do, With love all

bring - est light from light, O Light of light, light's liv - ing spring,
roy - al ra - di - ance, The Spir - it's sanc - ti - fy - ing beam
glo - ry ev - er - more; The Fa - ther of all grace and might,
en - vy to sub - due, To make ill - for - tune turn to fair,

O Day, all days il - lu - min - ing,
Up - on our earth - ly sens - es stream.
To ban - ish sin from our de - light:
And give us grace our wrongs to bear. A - MEN.

639 THE ANGELIC SONG

Solo, if desired CHORUS From Luther's Service, 1524

Glo-ry to God in the high-est, and on earth peace to men in whom He is well pleas - ed.

Ancient Hymns and Canticles

640

DE PROFUNDIS

From HENRY PURCELL, 1658–1695
Arr. by JAMES TURLE, 1802–1882

PSALM CXXX

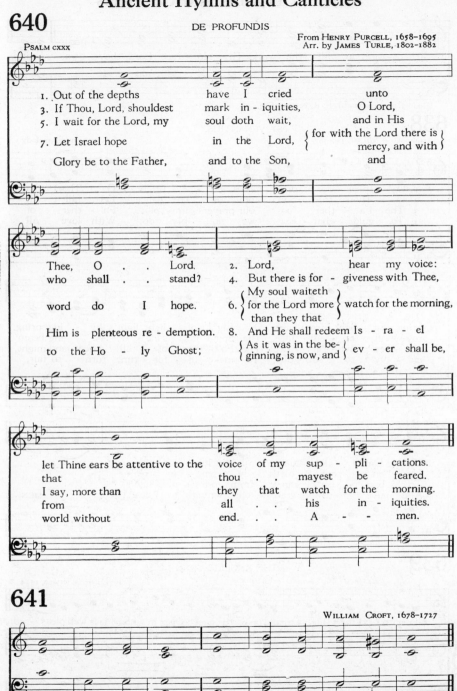

1. Out of the depths have I cried unto
3. If Thou, Lord, shouldest mark in - iquities, O Lord,
5. I wait for the Lord, my soul doth wait, and in His

7. Let Israel hope in the Lord, { for with the Lord there is mercy, and with

Glory be to the Father, and to the Son, and

Thee, O . . Lord. 2. Lord, hear my voice:
who shall . . stand? 4. But there is for - giveness with Thee,

word do I hope. 6. { My soul waiteth for the Lord more than they that } watch for the morning,

Him is plenteous re - demption. 8. And He shall redeem Is - ra - el

to the Ho - ly Ghost; { As it was in the be- ginning, is now, and } ev - er shall be,

let Thine ears be attentive to the voice of my sup - pli - cations.
that thou . . mayest be feared.
I say, more than they that watch for the morning.
from all . . his in - iquities.
world without end. . . A - men.

641

WILLIAM CROFT, 1678–1727

Ancient Hymns and Canticles

642

NUNC DIMITTIS

Luke ii. 29-32

Joseph Barnby, 1838-1896

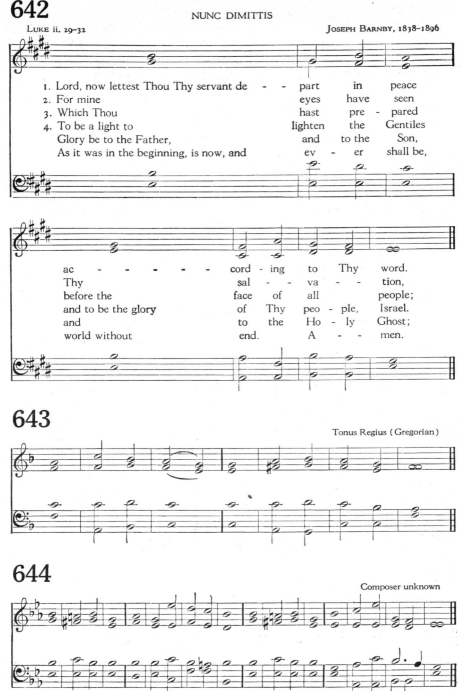

1. Lord, now lettest Thou Thy servant de - - part in peace
2. For mine eyes have seen
3. Which Thou hast pre - pared
4. To be a light to lighten the Gentiles
   Glory be to the Father, and to the Son,
   As it was in the beginning, is now, and ev - er shall be,

ac - - - - - cord - ing to Thy word.
Thy sal - - va - - tion,
before the face of all people;
and to be the glory of Thy peo - ple, Israel.
and to the Ho - ly Ghost;
world without end. A - - men.

643

Tonus Regius (Gregorian)

644

Composer unknown

ORDERS OF WORSHIP
THE RITUAL OF
THE METHODIST CHURCH
RESPONSIVE READINGS

THE USE OF THE ORDERS OF WORSHIP

In recognition of the various needs of our several congregations four Orders of Worship have been provided, which may be used according to desire. But while liberty is given in the use of these Orders of Worship, it is urged that all Ministers and Congregations make use of some one of these Orders.

Let each service proceed without announcement, as far as possible.

Choral responses may be used as desired. See Numbers 589-624, *The Methodist Hymnal.*

For Calls to Worship, Invocations and Confessions, Words of Assurance, Affirmations of Faith, Prayers, see pages 508-519.

Where there is a Junior Service or Sermon, it should immediately precede or follow the Offertory.

(The Prayer for the Church is by Walter Rauschenbusch, and is used by permission of The Pilgrim Press.)

THE SUNDAY SERVICE OF JOHN WESLEY

In commending the Sunday Service to "Our Societies in America," Mr. Wesley wrote: "I believe there is no Liturgy in the World, either in ancient or modern language, which breathes more of a solid, scriptural, rational piety than the Common Prayer of the Church of England. And though the main of it was compiled considerably more than two hundred years ago, yet is the language of it not only pure, but strong and elegant in the highest degree."

When this Service is to be used for Evening Prayer, the following changes shall be made:

The *Magnificat* shall be used in place of the *Te Deum.*
The *Nunc Dimittis* shall be used in place of the *Jubilate Deo.*

In place of the Collect for Grace shall be said the following Collects:

Lighten our darkness, we beseech Thee, O Lord; and by Thy great mercy defend us from all perils and dangers of this night; for the love of Thine only Son, our Saviour, Jesus Christ. *Amen.*

Direct us, O Lord, in all our doings, with Thy most gracious favor, and further us with Thy continual help; that in all our works, begun, continued, and ended in Thee, we may glorify Thy holy Name, and finally, by Thy mercy, obtain everlasting life; through Jesus Christ our Lord. *Amen.*

Order of Worship I[1]

Let the Services of Worship begin at the time appointed, and let the People kneel or bow in silent prayer upon entering the Sanctuary.

THE PRELUDE. The People in devout meditation.

THE CALL TO WORSHIP. Which may be said or sung.

A HYMN. If a Processional, the Hymn shall precede the Call to Worship, and the People shall then rise at the second stanza and join in singing.

THE PRAYER OF CONFESSION. To be said by all, the People seated and bowed, or kneeling. The following, or other Prayer of Confession, may be said:

Our Heavenly Father, who by Thy love hast made us, and through Thy love hast kept us, and in Thy love wouldst make us perfect, we humbly confess that we have not loved Thee with all our heart and soul and mind and strength, and that we have not loved one another as Christ hath loved us. Thy life is within our souls, but our selfishness hath hindered Thee. We have resisted Thy Spirit. We have neglected Thine inspirations.

Forgive what we have been; help us to amend what we are; and in Thy Spirit direct what we shall be; that Thou mayest come into the full glory of Thy creation, in us and in all men, through Jesus Christ our Lord. Amen.

THE SILENT MEDITATION. The People seated and bowed, or kneeling.

THE WORDS OF ASSURANCE. By the Minister.

THE LORD'S PRAYER. Which may be said or sung.

THE ANTHEM OR CHANT. Which may be the *Venite* or the *Te Deum*.

THE RESPONSIVE READING. The People to stand and remain standing until after the Affirmation of Faith.

THE GLORIA PATRI.

THE AFFIRMATION OF FAITH. To be said by the Minister and People.

THE LESSON FROM THE HOLY SCRIPTURES. The Old and New Testament.

THE PASTORAL PRAYER. The People seated and bowed, or kneeling.

THE OFFERTORY. The Dedication of Offerings. With Prayer or Offertory Sentences.

A HYMN. The People standing.

THE SERMON.

THE PRAYER. The People seated and bowed, or kneeling.

THE INVITATION TO CHRISTIAN DISCIPLESHIP.

A HYMN OR DOXOLOGY. The People standing. The closing Hymn may be a Recessional Hymn.

THE BENEDICTION. The People seated and bowed, or kneeling.

THE SILENT PRAYER.

THE POSTLUDE.

---

[1] Order of Worship II will be found on page 2.

Order of Worship III

Let the Services of Worship begin at the time appointed, and let the People kneel or bow in silent prayer upon entering the Sanctuary.

THE PRELUDE. The People in devout meditation.

THE CALL TO WORSHIP. Which may be said or sung.

A HYMN. If a Processional, the Hymn shall precede the Call to Worship, and the People shall then rise at the second stanza and join in singing.

THE PRAYER OF CONFESSION. To be said by all, the People seated and bowed, or kneeling. The following, or other Prayer of Confession, may be said:

Almighty God, from whom every good prayer cometh, and who pourest out, on all who desire it, the spirit of grace and supplication: deliver us, when we draw nigh to Thee, from coldness of heart and wanderings of mind; that with steadfast thoughts, and kindled affections, we may worship Thee in spirit and in truth; through Jesus Christ our Lord. Amen.

THE SILENT MEDITATION. The People seated and bowed, or kneeling.

THE LORD'S PRAYER. Which may be said or sung.

THE ANTHEM.

THE LESSON FROM THE HOLY SCRIPTURES. If a Responsive Reading is used, it should be followed by the *Gloria Patri,* the People standing.

THE PASTORAL PRAYER. The People seated and bowed, or kneeling.

THE PRESENTATION OF OFFERINGS.

A HYMN. The People standing.

THE SERMON.

THE INVITATION TO CHRISTIAN DISCIPLESHIP.

A HYMN OR DOXOLOGY. The People standing.

THE SILENT PRAYER.

THE BENEDICTION. The People seated and bowed, or kneeling.

THE POSTLUDE.

Order of Worship IV

AN ORDER FOR MORNING OR EVENING PRAYER

Adapted from

THE SUNDAY SERVICE OF JOHN WESLEY

(For Evening Prayer, see suggested changes in ¶ 1572, the *Methodist Discipline*, 1939.)

Suggested for Occasional Use

Let the Services of Worship begin at the time appointed, and let the People kneel or bow in silent prayer upon entering the Sanctuary.

THE PRELUDE. The People in devout meditation.

SCRIPTURE SENTENCES. One or more of them to be read by the Minister, the People standing.

The Lord is in His holy temple; let all the earth keep silence before Him.

Let the words of my mouth, and the meditation of my heart, be acceptable in Thy sight, O Lord, my strength, and my redeemer.

This is the day which the Lord hath made; we will rejoice and be glad in it.

The hour cometh, and now is, when the true worshipers shall worship the Father in spirit and in truth.

The sacrifices of God are a broken spirit: a broken and a contrite heart, O God, Thou wilt not despise.

HYMN. If a Processional, the Hymn shall precede the Scripture Sentences, and the People shall then rise at the second stanza and join in singing.

CALL TO CONFESSION. By the Minister, the People standing.

Dearly Beloved, the Scripture moveth us to acknowledge and confess our sins before Almighty God, our Heavenly Father, with a humble, lowly, penitent, and obedient heart; to the end that we may obtain forgiveness, by His infinite goodness and mercy. Wherefore I pray and beseech you, as many as are here present, to accompany me with a pure heart and a humble voice unto the throne of the Heavenly Grace. Let us pray.

GENERAL CONFESSION. To be said by all, the People seated and bowed, or kneeling.

Almighty and most merciful Father: We have erred and strayed from Thy ways like lost sheep. We have followed too much the devices and desires of our own hearts. We have offended against Thy holy laws. We have left undone those things which we ought to have done, and we have done those things which we ought not to have done. But Thou, O Lord, have mercy upon us. Spare Thou those, O God, who confess their faults. Restore Thou those who are penitent; according to Thy promises declared unto mankind in Christ Jesus our Lord. And grant, O most merciful Father, for His sake, that we may hereafter live a godly, righteous, and sober life; to the glory of Thy holy Name. Amen.

PRAYER OF PARDON. By the Minister.

O Lord, we beseech Thee, absolve Thy people from their offenses; that,

506

through Thy bountiful goodness, we may be delivered from the bonds of those sins which by our frailty we have committed. Grant this, O Heavenly Father, for Jesus Christ's sake, our blessed Lord and Saviour. **Amen.**

The People shall answer here, and at the end of all other prayers, **Amen.**

THE LORD'S PRAYER. To be said by all.

The Minister: O Lord, open Thou our lips.
The People: **And our mouth shall show forth Thy praise.**
The Minister: Praise ye the Lord.
The People: **The Lord's Name be praised.**

VENITE. To be said or sung by all, the People standing.

PSALTER. To be said by all, the People standing.

GLORIA PATRI. To be said by all, the People standing.

THE LESSON. From the Old Testament.

TE DEUM. To be said or sung by all, the People standing.

THE LESSON. From the New Testament.

JUBILATE DEO. To be said or sung by all, the People standing.

THE DECLARATION OF FAITH. Here shall be said the Apostles' **Creed.**

The Minister: The Lord be with you.
The People: **And with thy spirit.**
The Minister: Let us pray.

COLLECT FOR GRACE. To be said by all, the People seated and bowed, or kneeling.

O Lord, our Heavenly Father, Almighty and everlasting God, who hast safely brought us to the beginning of this day: defend us in the same with Thy mighty power; and grant that this day we fall into no sin; neither run into any kind of danger; but that all our doings may be ordered by Thy governance, to do always that which is righteous in Thy sight, through Jesus Christ our Lord. Amen.

PRAYER. Then may the Minister offer a Prayer, ending with:

The grace of our Lord Jesus Christ, the love of God, and the fellowship of the Holy Spirit, be with us all evermore. **Amen.**

THE OFFERTORY. Then may be sung an Anthem, and an Offering may be received.

THE SERMON. When the service is followed by a Sermon or the Holy Communion, the Minister shall make use of appropriate Hymns and Prayers. Otherwise, the service may close with a Hymn and the following Benediction:

THE BENEDICTION.

The peace of God, which passeth all understanding, keep our hearts and minds in the knowledge and love of God, and of His Son Jesus Christ our Lord: and the blessing of God Almighty, the Father, the Son, and the Holy Spirit, be among you, and remain with you always. **Amen.**

Aids to Individual and Congregational Devotion

A CALL TO HOLY SILENCE

The Lord is in His holy temple:
Let all the earth keep silence before Him.

CALLS TO WORSHIP AND PRAISE

O come, let us sing unto the Lord:
Let us make a joyful noise unto the Rock of our salvation.
Let us come before His presence with thanksgiving,
And make a joyful noise unto Him with psalms.

O praise the Lord, all ye nations:
Praise Him, all ye people.
For His merciful kindness is great toward us:
And the truth of the Lord endureth for ever.
Praise ye the Lord.

O be joyful in the Lord, all ye lands:
Serve the Lord with gladness: come before His presence with singing.
Know ye that the Lord, He is God:
It is He that hath made us, and not we ourselves;
We are His people,
And the sheep of His pasture.

The Lord is good: His mercy endureth for ever;
And His truth endureth to all generations.
This is the day which the Lord hath made,
We will rejoice and be glad in it.
Enter into His gates with thanksgiving,
And into His courts with praise.
O magnify the Lord with me, and let us exalt His Name together,
For with Him is the fountain of life, and in Him shall we see light.

The Minister: O Lord, open Thou our lips.
The People: **And our mouth shall show forth Thy praise.**

The Minister: Praise ye the Lord:
The People: **The Lord's Name be praised.**

CALLS TO PRAYER

O come, let us worship and bow down:
Let us kneel before the Lord our Maker.
For He is the Lord our God:
And we are the people of His pasture, and the sheep of His hand.

Bless the Lord, O my soul, and all that is within me bless His holy Name.
Bless the Lord, O my soul, and forget not all His benefits:
Who forgiveth all thine iniquities;
Who healeth all thy diseases;
Who redeemeth thy life from destruction;
Who crowneth thee with loving kindness and tender mercies.
What shall I render unto the Lord for all His benefits toward me?
I will pay my vows unto the Lord, in the presence of all His people.
O come, let us worship and bow down:
Let us kneel before the Lord our Maker.

Hear, O Israel; The Lord our God is one Lord: And thou shalt love the Lord thy God with all thy heart, and with all thy soul, and with all thy mind, and with all thy strength.

Give unto the Lord. O ye mighty, give unto the Lord glory and strength. Give unto the Lord the glory due unto His Name; worship the Lord in the beauty of holiness.

The hour cometh, and now is, when the true worshipers shall worship the Father in spirit and in truth. For the Father seeketh such to worship Him.

God is a Spirit. Let us worship Him in spirit and in truth.
Seek ye the Lord while He may be found; call ye upon Him while He is near.
Let the wicked forsake his way and the unrighteous man his thoughts.
And let him return unto the Lord, and He will have mercy upon him:
And to our God, for He will abundantly pardon.

INVOCATIONS

For a Devout Mind

Almighty God, from whom every good prayer cometh, and who pourest out on all who desire it the spirit of grace and supplication, deliver us, when we draw nigh to Thee, from coldness of heart and wanderings of mind: that with steadfast thoughts, and kindled affections, we may worship Thee in spirit and in truth; through Jesus Christ our Lord. **Amen.**

For the Vision of God

Gracious God, in Thee we live and move and have our being. In Thy presence is fullness of joy. Break the spell of that which blinds our minds. Purify our hearts that we may see Thee. Renew our inward life through the unseen and eternal. Visit our spirits and witness with them that we are Thy children. **Amen.**

Our Heavenly Father, we adore Thee, whose name is love, whose nature is compassion, whose presence is joy, whose word is truth, whose spirit is goodness, whose holiness is beauty, whose will is peace, whose service is perfect freedom, and in knowledge of whom standeth our eternal life. **Amen.**

FOR PURITY OF HEART

Almighty God, unto whom all hearts are open, all desires known, and from whom no secrets are hid, cleanse the thoughts of our hearts by the inspiration of Thy Holy Spirit, that we may perfectly love Thee, and worthily magnify Thy holy Name, through Jesus Christ our Lord. **Amen.**

FOR THE SPIRIT OF WORSHIP

O our God, we humbly beseech Thee to purify our hearts from all vain and worldly and sinful thoughts, and thus prepare our souls to worship Thee this day acceptably, with reverence and godly fear. O Lord, set our affection on things above, all the day long, and give us grace to receive Thy word which we shall hear this day, into honest and good hearts, and bring forth fruit with patience. Hear us, O God, for the sake of Jesus Christ, our Saviour. **Amen.**

PRAYERS OF CONFESSION

Have mercy upon us, O God, according to Thy loving kindness; according to the multitude of Thy tender mercies blot out our transgressions. Wash us thoroughly from our iniquities, and cleanse us from our sins. For we acknowledge our transgressions, and our sin is ever before us. Create in us clean hearts, O God, and renew a right spirit within us, through Jesus Christ our Lord. **Amen.**

Almighty and most merciful Father, we have erred and strayed from Thy ways like lost sheep. We have followed too much the devices and desires of our own hearts. We have offended against Thy holy laws. We have left undone those things which we ought to have done, and we have done those things which we ought not to have done. But Thou, O Lord, have mercy upon us. Spare Thou those, O God, who confess their faults. Restore Thou those who are penitent; according to Thy promises declared unto mankind in Christ Jesus our Lord. And grant, O most merciful Father, for His sake, that we may hereafter live a godly, righteous, and sober life; to the glory of Thy holy Name. **Amen.**

Our Heavenly Father, who by Thy love hast made us, and through Thy love hast kept us, and in Thy love wouldst make us perfect, we humbly confess that we have not loved Thee with all our heart and soul and mind and strength, and that we have not loved one another as Christ hath loved us. Thy life is within our souls, but our selfishness has hindered Thee. We have not lived by faith. We have resisted Thy Spirit. We have neglected Thine inspirations. Forgive what we have been; help us to amend what we are; and in Thy Spirit direct what we shall be; that Thou mayest come into the full glory of Thy creation, in us and in all men, through Jesus Christ our Lord. **Amen.**

Almighty God, Father of our Lord Jesus Christ, Maker of all things, Judge of all men, we acknowledge and bewail our manifold sins and wickedness, which we from time to time most grievously have committed, by thought, word, and deed, against Thy Divine Majesty. We do earnestly repent, and are heartily sorry for these, our misdoings; the remembrance of them is grievous unto us. Have mercy upon us, have mercy upon us, most merciful Father; for Thy Son, our Lord Jesus Christ's sake, forgive us all that is past; and grant that we may ever hereafter serve and please Thee in newness of life, to the honor and glory of Thy Name, through Jesus Christ our Lord. Amen.

WORDS OF ASSURANCE AND PROMISES OF PARDON

Hear what comfortable words our Saviour Christ saith unto all that truly turn to Him: Come unto Me, all ye that labor and are heavy laden, and I will give you rest.

Hear also the words from Saint John's Gospel: God so loved the world, that He gave His only begotten Son, that whosoever believeth in Him should not perish, but have everlasting life.

Hear also these words of Scripture:

The Lord is gracious, and full of compassion;
Slow to anger, and of great mercy.

The sacrifices of God are a broken spirit:
A broken and a contrite heart, O God, Thou wilt not despise.

If we confess our sins, God is faithful and just to forgive us our sins, and to cleanse us from all unrighteousness.

As the heaven is high above the earth, so great is His mercy toward them that fear Him. As far as the east is from the west, so far hath He removed our transgressions from us.

Like as a father pitieth his children, so the Lord pitieth them that fear Him.

Jesus said: Be of good cheer; thy sins are forgiven.

He that spared not His own Son, but delivered Him up for us all, how shall He not with Him also freely give us all things?

There is therefore now no condemnation to them who are in Christ Jesus, who walk not after the flesh, but after the Spirit.

This is the message which we have heard of Him and declare unto you, that God is light, and in Him is no darkness at all. If we walk in the light, as He is in the light, we have fellowship one with another, and the blood of Jesus Christ His Son cleanseth us from all sin.

AFFIRMATIONS OF FAITH

I. THE APOSTLES' CREED

I believe in God, the Father Almighty, Maker of heaven and earth; and in Jesus Christ, His only Son our Lord; who was conceived by the Holy Spirit, born of the Virgin Mary, suffered under Pontius Pilate, was crucified, dead, and buried; the third day He rose from the dead; He ascended into heaven, and sitteth at the right hand of God the Father Almighty; from thence He shall come to judge the quick and the dead. I believe in the Holy Spirit; the holy catholic Church, the communion of saints; the forgiveness of sins; the resurrection of the body, and the life everlasting. **Amen.**

II

The Minister: Where the Spirit of the Lord is, there is the one true Church, Apostolic and Universal, whose Holy Faith let us now reverently and sincerely declare:

The Minister and People: We believe in God the Father, infinite in wisdom, power and love, whose mercy is over all His works, and whose will is ever directed to His children's good.

We believe in Jesus Christ, Son of God and Son of man, the gift of the Father's unfailing grace, the ground of our hope and the promise of our deliverance from sin and death.

We believe in the Holy Spirit as the Divine Presence in our lives, whereby we are kept in perpetual remembrance of the truth of Christ, and find strength and help in time of need.

We believe that this faith should manifest itself in the service of love as set forth in the example of our blessed Lord, to the end that the kingdom of God may come upon the earth. **Amen.**

III

We believe in the one God, Maker and Ruler of all things, Father of all men; the source of all goodness and beauty, all truth and love.

We believe in Jesus Christ, God manifest in the flesh, our Teacher, Example, and Redeemer, the Saviour of the world.

We believe in the Holy Spirit, God present with us for guidance, for comfort and for strength.

We believe in the forgiveness of sins, in the life of love and prayer, and in grace equal to every need.

We believe in the Word of God contained in the Old and New Testaments as the sufficient rule both of faith and of practice.

We believe in the Church as the fellowship for worship and for service of all who are united to the living Lord.

We believe in the kingdom of God as the divine rule in human society; and in the brotherhood of man under the Fatherhood of God.

We believe in the final triumph of righteousness, and in the life everlasting. **Amen.**

PRAYERS AND COLLECTS

For Grace and Guidance

O Lord, our Heavenly Father, Almighty and Everlasting God, who hast safely brought us to the beginning of this day, defend us in the same with Thy mighty power; and grant that this day we fall into no sin, neither run into any kind of danger; but that all our doings may be ordered by Thy governance, to do always that which is righteous in Thy sight; through Jesus Christ our Lord. **Amen.**

For Grace to Profit by Scriptures

Blessed Lord, who hast caused all Holy Scriptures to be written for our learning; grant that we may in such wise hear them, read, mark, learn, and inwardly digest them, that by patience, and comfort of Thy Holy Word, we may embrace and ever hold fast the blessed hope of everlasting life, which Thou hast given us in our Saviour, Jesus Christ. **Amen.**

For the Spirit of Wisdom

O God, by whom the meek are guided in judgment, and light riseth up in darkness for the godly, grant us, in all doubts and uncertainties, the grace to ask what Thou wouldst have us to do, that the spirit of wisdom may save us from all false choices, and that in Thy light we may see light and in Thy straight path may not stumble; through Jesus Christ our Lord. **Amen.**

For Pardon

Almighty God, our Heavenly Father, who of Thy great mercy hast promised forgiveness of sins to all them that with hearty repentance and true faith turn unto Thee, have mercy upon us; pardon and deliver us from all our sins; confirm and strengthen us in all goodness; and bring us to everlasting life, through Jesus Christ our Lord. **Amen.**

O Lord, we beseech Thee, absolve Thy people from their offenses; that, through Thy bountiful goodness, we may be delivered from the bonds of those sins which by our frailty we have committed. Grant this, O Heavenly Father, for Jesus Christ's sake, our blessed Lord and Saviour. **Amen.**

For Love to God and Man

O Lord, grant us to love Thee with all our heart, with all our mind, and all our strength; and to love our neighbors for Thy sake, that the grace of charity and brotherly love may dwell in us, and that all envy, harshness, and ill will may die. Fill our hearts with kindness and compassion. May we constantly rejoice in the happiness and good success of others and sympathize with them in their sorrows. May we put away all harsh judgments and envious thoughts. So shall we follow Thee, who art Thyself the true and perfect Love; through Jesus Christ our Lord. **Amen.**

For God's Continual Help

Direct us, O Lord, in all our doings, with Thy most gracious favor, and is with Thy continual help, that in all our works, begun, continued, ...ed in Thee, we may glorify Thy holy Name, and finally, by Thy mercy, everlasting life, through Jesus Christ our Lord. **Amen.**

For Divine Wisdom and Strength

O Lord, we beseech Thee mercifully to receive the prayers of Thy people who call upon Thee; and grant that they may both perceive and know what things they ought to do, and that they also may have grace and power faithfully to fulfill the same; through Jesus Christ our Lord. **Amen.**

For All Conditions of Men

O God, the Creator and Preserver of all mankind, we humbly beseech Thee for all sorts and conditions of men; that Thou wouldst be pleased to make Thy ways known unto them, Thy saving health unto all nations. More especially we pray for Thy holy Church universal; that it may be so guided and governed by Thy good Spirit, that all who profess and call themselves Christians may be led into the way of truth, and hold the faith in unity of spirit, in the bond of peace, and in righteousness of life. Finally, we commend to Thy Fatherly goodness all those who are in any way afflicted or distressed in mind, body, or estate, that it may please Thee to comfort and relieve them according to their several necessities; giving them patience under their suffering, and a happy issue out of all their afflictions. And this we ask for Jesus Christ's sake. **Amen.**

General Intercession

O God, at whose word man goeth forth unto his work and to his labor until the evening, be merciful to all whose duties are difficult or burdensome, and comfort them concerning their toil. Shield from bodily accident and harm the workmen at their work. Protect the efforts of sober and honest industry, and suffer not the hire of the laborers to be kept back. Incline the hearts of employers and of those whom they employ to mutual forbearance, fairness, and good will. Give the spirit of grace and of a sound mind to all in places of authority. Bless all those who labor in works of mercy and schools of good learning. Care for all aged persons, and all little children, the sick and the afflicted, and those who travel by land or by sea. Remember all who by reason of weakness are overtasked, or because of poverty are forgotten. Let the sorrowful sighing of the prisoners come before Thee, and according to the greatness of Thy power preserve Thou those that draw nigh unto death. Give ear unto our prayer, O merciful and gracious Father, for the love of Thy dear Son our Saviour Jesus Christ. **Amen.**

General Thanksgiving

Almighty God, Father of all mercies, we, Thine unworthy servants, do give Thee most humble and hearty thanks for all Thy goodness and loving kindness to us, and to all men. We bless Thee for our creation, preservation, and all the blessings of this life; but above all, for Thine inestimable love in the redemption of the world by our Lord Jesus Christ; for the means of grace, and for the hope of glory. And we beseech Thee, give us that due sense of all Thy mercies, that our hearts may be unfeignedly thankful, and that we may show forth Thy praise, not only with our lips, but in our lives; by giving up ourselves to Thy service, and by walking before Thee in holiness and righteousness all our days, through Jesus Christ our Lord, to whom, with Thee and the Holy Spirit, be all honor and glory, world without end. **Amen.**

Prayer of Saint Chrysostom

Almighty God, who hast given us grace, at this time, with one accord to make our common supplications unto Thee; and dost promise that, when two or three are gathered together in Thy Name, Thou wilt grant their requests; fulfill now, O Lord, the desires and petitions of Thy servants, as may be most expedient for them; granting us in this world knowledge of Thy truth, and in the world to come life everlasting. **Amen.**

For a Blessing on Families

Almighty God, our Heavenly Father, who settest the solitary in families, we commend to Thy continual care the homes in which Thy people dwell. Put far from them, we beseech Thee, every root of bitterness, the desire of vainglory, and the pride of life. Fill them with faith, virtue, knowledge, temperance, patience, godliness. Knit together in constant affection those who, in holy wedlock, have been made one. Turn the hearts of the fathers to the children, and the hearts of the children to the fathers; and so kindle charity among us all, that we may ever have for each other kindly affection and brotherly love; through Jesus Christ our Lord. **Amen.**

For the Church

O God, we pray for Thy Church, which is set today amid the perplexities of a changing order, face to face with a great new task. We remember with love the nurture she gave to our spiritual life in its infancy, the tasks she set for our growing strength, the influence of the devoted hearts she gathers, the steadfast power for good she has exerted. When we compare her with all human institutions, we rejoice, for there is none like her. But when we judge her by the mind of her Master, we bow in contrition. Oh, baptize her afresh in the life-giving spirit of Jesus! Put upon her lips the ancient gospel of her Lord. Fill her with the prophet's scorn of tyranny, and with a Christlike tenderness for the heavy-laden and downtrodden. Bid her cease from seeking her own life, lest she lose it. Make her valiant to give up her life to humanity, that like her crucified Lord she may mount by the path of the cross to a higher glory. **Amen.**

For Missions

O Thou who art the Light and the Life of the world, have compassion, we pray Thee, upon those who are sitting in darkness and in the shadow of death; and as Thou didst at the first, by the preaching of Thine apostles, cause the light of Thy gospel to shine throughout the world, be pleased to make

Thy ways known upon earth, Thy saving health unto all nations. Bless Thy servants who have gone into hard fields and unto distant lands to proclaim the message of salvation. Endue them with Thy Holy Spirit, enrich them with Thy heavenly grace, prosper them in all their labors, and give them souls as their reward. And, O Thou Lord of the harvest! we pray Thee to send forth more laborers into Thy harvest. May they both sow the seed and reap the fruit of their labors! And give us grace to do our part in the great field of this world in sowing and in reaping, through the grace of Jesus Christ. **Amen.**

For Evangelism

Increase, O God, the faith and the zeal of all Thy people, that they may more earnestly desire, and more diligently seek, the salvation of their fellow men, through the message of Thy love in Jesus Christ our Lord. Send forth a mighty call unto Thy servants who labor in the gospel, granting unto them a heart of love, sincerity of speech, and the power of the Holy Spirit, that they may be able to persuade men to forsake sin and return unto Thee. And so bless and favor the work of Thine evangelists, that multitudes may be brought from the kingdom of evil into the kingdom of Thy dear Son, our Saviour, Jesus Christ. **Amen.**

For Social Service

O Lord, our Heavenly Father, who by Thy blessed Son hast taught us that Thou art Love, we beseech Thee graciously to bless all those who, following His steps, give themselves to the service of their fellow men. Grant unto them clear vision to perceive those things which in our social order are amiss; give them true judgment, courage, and perseverance to help those to right that suffer wrong, and endue them with unfailing love to minister to the poor, the suffering, and the friendless. Make us sensible of our union one with another as Thy children, that we may strive wisely to order all things among us according to Thy will; for the sake of Him who laid down His life for us, Thy Son, our Saviour, Jesus Christ. **Amen.**

For the President and Others in Authority

O God, who art the Hope of all the ends of the earth, remember us in love, and guide us by Thine infinite wisdom. Most heartily we beseech Thee to grant Thy blessing upon Thy servants, *the President of the United States, the Governor of this state,* and all others in authority. Imbue them with the spirit of wisdom, goodness, and truth; and so rule their hearts, and bless their endeavors, that law and order, justice and peace, may everywhere prevail, to the honor of Thy holy Name, through Jesus Christ our Lord. **Amen.**

For the Country

Almighty God, who in the former time didst lead our fathers forth into a wealthy place; give Thy grace, we humbly beseech Thee, to us, their children, that we may always approve ourselves a people mindful of Thy favor, and glad to do Thy will. Bless our land with honorable industry, sound learning, and pure religion. Defend our liberties, preserve our unity. Save us from violence, discord, and confusion, from pride and arrogancy, and from every evil way. Fashion into one happy people the multitudes brought hither out of many kindreds and tongues. Endue with the spirit of wisdom those whom we intrust in Thy Name with the authority of governance, to the end that there be peace at home, and that we keep a place among the nations of the earth. In the time of prosperity fill our hearts with thankfulness; and in the day of trouble suffer not our trust in Thee to fail; all of which we ask for Jesus Christ's sake. **Amen.**

Grant us peace, Thy most precious gift, O Thou eternal Source of peace. Bless our country, that it may ever be a stronghold of peace, and the advocate of peace in the councils of nations. May contentment reign within its borders, health and happiness within its homes. Strengthen the bonds of friendship and fellowship between all the inhabitants of our land. Plant virtue in every soul; and may the love of Thy Name hallow every home and every heart. Praised be Thou, O Lord, Giver of Peace. **Amen.**

FOR THE ADVANCEMENT OF THE KINGDOM

Almighty God, from whom all thoughts of truth and peace proceed; kindle, we pray Thee, in the hearts of all men the true love of peace, and guide with Thy pure and peaceable wisdom those who take counsel for the nations of the earth; that in tranquillity Thy kingdom may go forward till the earth is filled with the knowledge of Thy love; through Jesus Christ our Lord. **Amen.**

FOR QUIETNESS OF SPIRIT

O God, from whom all holy desires, all good counsels, and all just works do proceed; give unto Thy servants that peace which the world cannot give, that our hearts may be set to obey Thy commandments and that, by Thee, we may pass our time in rest and quietness; through the merits of Jesus Christ, our Saviour. **Amen.**

FOR USE AFTER THE SERMON

Grant, we beseech Thee, Almighty God, that the words which we have heard this day with our outward ears may, through Thy grace, be so grafted inwardly in our hearts that they may bring forth in us the fruit of good living, to the honor and praise of Thy Name; through Jesus Christ our Lord. **Amen.**

FOR THE COMMUNION OF SAINTS

We thank Thee for the dear and faithful dead, for those who have made the distant heavens a home for us, and whose truth and beauty are even now in our hearts. One by one Thou dost gather the scattered families out of the earthly light into the heavenly glory, from the distractions and strife and weariness of time to the peace of eternity. We thank Thee for the labors and the joys of these mortal years. We thank Thee for our deep sense of the mysteries that lie beyond our dust, and for the eye of faith which Thou hast opened for all who believe in Thy Son. May we live altogether in Thy faith and love, and in that hope which is full of immortality. **Amen.**

> O Lord, support us all the day long
> Of this troublous life,
> Until the shadows lengthen,
> And the evening comes,
> And the busy world is hushed,
> And the fever of life is over,
> And our work is done.
> Then, of Thy great mercy,
> Grant us a safe lodging
> And a holy rest,
> And peace at the last;
> Through Jesus Christ our Lord. **Amen.**

OFFERTORY SENTENCES

I

All things come of Thee, O Lord,
And of Thine own have we given Thee. **Amen.**

II

We give Thee but Thine own,
Whate'er the gift may be;
All that we have is Thine alone,
A trust, O Lord, from Thee. **Amen.**

III

The Minister: To the preaching of the good tidings of salvation
The People: **We consecrate our gifts.**

The Minister: To the teaching of Jesus' way of life
The People: **We consecrate our gifts.**

The Minister: To the healing of broken bodies and the soothing of fevered brows
The People: **We consecrate our gifts.**

The Minister: To the leading of every little child to the knowledge and love of Jesus
The People: **We consecrate our gifts.**

The Minister: To the caring for helpless age and the relief of all who look to us for help
The People: **We consecrate our gifts.**

The Minister: To the evangelization of the world and the building of the kingdom of God
The People: **We consecrate our wealth, our efforts, and our lives.**

BENEDICTIONS

The grace of the Lord Jesus Christ, and the love of God, and the communion of the Holy Spirit, be with you all. **Amen.**

The peace of God which passeth all understanding, keep your hearts and minds in the knowledge and love of God, and of His Son, Jesus Christ our Lord; and the blessing of God Almighty, the Father, the Son, and the Holy Spirit, be amongst you and remain with you always. **Amen.**

And now may the blessing of God Almighty, Father, Son, and Holy Spirit, be amongst you and abide with you, now and evermore. **Amen.**

The Lord bless you and keep you; the Lord make His face to shine upon you and be gracious unto you; the Lord lift up His countenance upon you and give you peace; both now and evermore. **Amen.**

Now unto Him that is able to keep you from falling, and to present you faultless before the presence of His glory with exceeding joy, to the only wise God our Saviour, be glory and majesty, dominion and power, both now and evermore. **Amen.**

Now the God of peace, that brought again from the dead our Lord Jesus, that great Shepherd of the sheep, through the blood of the everlasting covenant, make you perfect in every good work to do His will, working in you that which is well pleasing in His sight, through Jesus Christ; to whom be glory for ever and ever. **Amen.**

Now unto Him who is eternal, immortal, invisible, the only just and all-wise God, be glory and honor, dominion and power, now and for ever. **Amen.**

THE RITUAL OF
THE METHODIST CHURCH

We call upon all our Ministers to make faithful use of the forms and orders here provided, without other deviation than is here indicated.

We urge all Ministers to encourage and train the People to participate audibly in those portions of the service provided for this purpose, particularly in the celebration of the Lord's Supper. The portions to be used as responses are especially indicated by **bold-faced type.**

The Ritual

THE LORD'S SUPPER OR HOLY COMMUNION

THE ORDER FOR THE ADMINISTRATION OF THE SACRAMENT OF THE LORD'S SUPPER

[The Lord's Table should have upon it a fair linen cloth.

Let the pure unfermented juice of the grape be used.

It is our custom to receive the Sacrament of the Lord's Supper kneeling, but if persons so desire, they may receive the Elements while seated or standing.

Upon entering the church let the communicants bow in prayer and in the spirit of prayer and meditation approach the blessed Sacrament.

The Responses throughout may be sung if desired. See hymns 565-624 in *The Methodist Hymnal.*

The following Order has been prepared to take the place of the regular order of morning worship. Everything preceding the Invitation may be omitted if the occasion demands such brevity. If further straitened for time, as in the sickroom, the Minister may omit any part of the service except the Invitation, the Confession, the Prayer of Consecration, the usual sentences for the distribution of the Elements, and the Benediction. But it is highly to be desired that the longer form be followed for Public Worship.]

The People shall stand and join in singing the Hymn, "Holy, Holy, Holy, Lord God Almighty," or other suitable Hymn and remain standing until after the singing of the Gloria Patri.

God is a Spirit. They that worship Him must worship Him in spirit and in truth.

Glory be to God on high.

God is Light. If we walk in the light as He is in the light, we have fellowship one with another; and truly our fellowship is with the Father and with His Son, Jesus Christ.

Glory be to God on high.

God is Power. They that wait upon the Lord shall renew their strength: they shall mount up with wings as eagles: they shall run and not be weary: and they shall walk and not faint.

Glory be to God on high.

God is Love. Behold what manner of love the Father hath bestowed upon us that we should be called the sons of God. Hereby perceive we the love of God, because He laid down His life for us.

Glory be to God on high.

Then shall the Gloria Patri *be said or sung:*

Glory be to the Father, and to the Son, and to the Holy Ghost; as it was in the beginning, is now, and ever shall be, world without end. Amen.

Then shall the Minister say:

Let us pray.

Almighty God, unto whom all hearts are open, all desires

523

known, and from whom no secrets are hid, cleanse the thoughts of our hearts by the inspiration of Thy Holy Spirit, that we may perfectly love Thee, and worthily magnify Thy holy Name, through Jesus Christ our Lord. Amen.

Our Father, who art in heaven:
Hallowed be Thy Name, Thy kingdom come, Thy will be done, on earth as it is in heaven.

Give us this day our daily bread. And forgive us our trespasses, as we forgive those who trespass against us. And lead us not into temptation, but deliver us from evil.

For Thine is the kingdom, and the power, and the glory, for ever. Amen.

[Then may the Minister read the Ten Commandments, and the People, still in the attitude of prayer, shall in response ask God's mercy for their transgressions in times past and grace to keep the law in time to come.]

God spake these words, and said: I am the Lord thy God:
Thou shalt have no other gods before Me.

Thou shalt not make unto thee any graven image, or any likeness of anything that is in heaven above, or that is in the earth beneath, or that is in the water under the earth: thou shalt not bow down thyself to them, nor serve them: for I the Lord thy God am a jealous God, visiting the iniquity of the fathers upon the children unto the third and fourth generations of them that hate Me; and showing mercy unto thousands of them that love Me, and keep My commandments.

Lord, have mercy upon us, and write all these Thy laws in our hearts, we beseech Thee.

Thou shalt not take the Name of the Lord thy God in vain; for the Lord will not hold him guiltless that taketh His Name in vain.

Remember the Sabbath day, to keep it holy. Six days shalt thou labor, and do all thy work: but the seventh day is the Sabbath of the Lord thy God: in it thou shalt not do any work, thou, nor thy son, nor thy daughter, thy manservant, nor thy maidservant, nor thy cattle, nor thy stranger that is within thy gates: for in six days the Lord made heaven and earth, the sea, and all that in them is, and rested the seventh day: wherefore the Lord blessed the Sabbath day, and hallowed it.

Lord, have mercy upon us, and write all these Thy laws in our hearts, we beseech Thee.

Honor thy father and thy mother: that thy days may be long upon the land which the Lord thy God giveth thee.
Thou shalt not kill.
Thou shalt not commit adultery.
Thou shalt not steal.
Thou shalt not bear false witness against thy neighbor.
Thou shalt not covet thy neighbor's house, thou shalt not covet thy neighbor's wife, nor his manservant, nor his maidservant, nor his ox, nor his ass, nor anything that is thy neighbor's.

Lord, have mercy upon us, and write all these Thy laws in our hearts, we beseech Thee.

[In place of or in addition to the Ten Commandments the Minister may read the summary of the Divine Law in the words of Jesus, and the People, in the attitude of prayer, shall ask God's mercy and gracious aid.]

Hear what our Lord Jesus Christ saith:

Thou shalt love the Lord thy God with all thy heart, and with all thy soul, and with all thy mind. This is the first and great commandment. And the second is like unto it, Thou shalt love thy neighbor as thyself.

Lord, have mercy upon us, and write all these Thy laws in our hearts, we beseech Thee.

Then may the Minister read the Beatitudes of the Lord Jesus, and the People, still in the attitude of prayer, shall humbly ask God that they may be fulfilled in their hearts. Or here Isaiah 53: 1-10 may be used as a Responsive Scripture.

Hear the Beatitudes of our Lord Jesus Christ:

Blessed are the poor in spirit: for theirs is the kingdom of heaven.
Lord, be gracious unto us, and help us to obtain this blessing.

Blessed are they that mourn: for they shall be comforted.
Lord, be gracious unto us, and help us to obtain this blessing.

Blessed are the meek: for they shall inherit the earth.
Lord, be gracious unto us, and help us to obtain this blessing.

Blessed are they which do hunger and thirst after righteousness: for they shall be filled.
Lord, be gracious unto us, and help us to obtain this blessing.

Blessed are the merciful: for they shall obtain mercy.
Lord, be gracious unto us, and help us to obtain this blessing.

Blessed are the pure in heart: for they shall see God.
Lord, be gracious unto us, and help us to obtain this blessing.

Blessed are the peacemakers: for they shall be called the children of God.
Lord, be gracious unto us, and help us to obtain this blessing.

Blessed are they which are persecuted for righteousness' sake: for theirs is the kingdom of heaven.

Blessed are ye, when men shall revile you, and persecute you, and shall say all manner of evil against you falsely, for My sake.

Rejoice and be exceeding glad: for great is your reward in heaven: for so persecuted they the prophets which were before you.

Grant unto us Thy Holy Spirit, O God, and enable us to obtain all these blessings, through Jesus Christ our Lord. Amen.

[If desired, the following form may be used:]

Hear the Beatitudes of our Lord Jesus Christ:

Blessed are the poor in spirit: for theirs is the kingdom of heaven.
Blessed are they that mourn: for they shall be comforted.
Blessed are the meek: for they shall inherit the earth.

Lord, be gracious unto us, and help us to obtain these blessings.

Blessed are they which do hunger and thirst after righteousness: for they shall be filled.
Blessed are the merciful: for they shall obtain mercy.
Blessed are the pure in heart: for they shall see God.
Blessed are the peacemakers: for they shall be called the children of God.

Lord, be gracious unto us, and help us to obtain these blessings.

Blessed are they which are persecuted for righteousness' sake: for theirs is the kingdom of heaven.
Blessed are ye, when men shall revile you, and persecute you, and shall say all manner of evil against you falsely, for My sake.
Rejoice, and be exceeding glad: for great is your reward in heaven: for so persecuted they the prophets who were before you.

Grant unto us Thy Holy Spirit, O God, and enable us to obtain all these blessings, through Jesus Christ our Lord. Amen.

[The Responsive Scripture, Isaiah 53: 1-10:]

Who hath believed our report? and to whom is the arm of the Lord revealed?

For He shall grow up before Him as a tender plant, and as a root out of a dry ground: He hath no form nor comeliness; and when we shall see Him, there is no beauty that we should desire Him.

He is despised and rejected of men; a man of sorrows, and acquainted with grief: and we hid as it were our faces from Him; He was despised, and we esteemed Him not.

Surely He hath borne our griefs, and carried our sorrows: yet we did esteem Him stricken, smitten of God, and afflicted.

But He was wounded for our transgressions, He was bruised for our iniquities: the chastisement of our peace was upon Him; and with His stripes we are healed.

All we like sheep have gone astray; we have turned every one to his own way; and the Lord hath laid on Him the iniquity of us all.

He was oppressed, and He was afflicted, yet He opened not His mouth: He is brought as a lamb to the slaughter, and as a sheep before her shearers is dumb, so He openeth not His mouth.

526

He was taken from prison and from judgment: and who shall declare His generation? for He was cut off out of the land of the living: for the transgression of my people was He stricken.

And He made His grave with the wicked, and with the rich in His death; because He had done no violence, neither was any deceit in His mouth.

Yet it pleased the Lord to bruise Him; He hath put Him to grief: when thou shalt make His soul an offering for sin, He shall see His seed, He shall prolong His days, and the pleasure of the Lord shall prosper in His hand.

[Then may the Minister read the Epistle, to be followed by the Gospel.
Here may the Minister and People repeat the Apostles' Creed or some other of the authorized Affirmations of Faith, the People standing.
Then may follow the Sermon or Communion meditation and suitable Hymn (see Hymns 408-415, inclusive). During the singing of this Hymn the Minister shall remove the linen cloth that covers the Elements.]

After the Hymn has been sung, the Minister, standing by the Lord's Table, shall announce the Offering for the needy, using one or more of the following groups of sentences.

I

Remember the words of the Lord Jesus, how He said:

It is more blessed to give than to receive.

Let your light so shine before men, that they may see your good works, and glorify your Father which is in heaven.

Not every one that saith unto Me, Lord, Lord, shall enter into the kingdom of heaven; but he that doeth the will of My Father which is in heaven.

And the King shall answer and say unto them, Verily I say unto you, Inasmuch as ye have done it unto one of the least of these My brethren, ye have done it unto Me.

Therefore all things whatsoever ye would that men should do to you, do ye even so to them: for this is the law and the prophets.

II

They shall not appear before the Lord empty. Every man shall give as he is able, according to the blessing of the Lord thy God which He hath given thee.

Blessed is he that considereth the poor: the Lord will deliver him in time of trouble.

Thou shalt open thine hand wide unto thy brother, to thy poor, and to thy needy, in thy land.

Be merciful after thy power. If thou hast much, give plenteously: if thou hast little, do thy diligence gladly to give of that little: for so gatherest thou thyself a good reward in the day of necessity.

He that hath pity upon the poor lendeth unto the Lord; and that which he hath given will He pay him again.

III

To do good and to communicate forget not: for with such sacrifices God is well pleased.

As we have therefore opportunity, let us do good unto all men, especially unto them who are of the household of faith.

He which soweth sparingly shall reap also sparingly; and he which soweth bountifully shall reap also bountifully. Every man according as he purposeth in his heart, so let him give; not grudgingly, or of necessity: for God loveth a cheerful giver.

Whoso hath this world's good, and seeth his brother have need, and shutteth up his compassion from him, how dwelleth the love of God in him?

God is not unrighteous to forget your work and labor of love, which ye have showed toward His Name, in that ye have ministered to the saints, and do minister.

IV

Offer unto God thanksgiving; and pay thy vows unto the Most High.

Lay not up for yourselves treasures upon earth, where moth and rust doth corrupt, and where thieves break through and steal: but lay up for yourselves treasures in heaven, where neither moth nor rust doth corrupt, and where thieves do not break through nor steal: for where your treasure is, there will your heart be also.

Zacchaeus stood, and said unto Jesus, Behold, Lord, the half of my goods I give to the poor; and if I have taken anything from any man by false accusation, I restore him fourfold.

Charge them that are rich in this world, that they be rich in good works, ready to distribute, willing to communicate; laying up in store for themselves a good foundation against the time to come, that they may lay hold on eternal life.

Godliness with contentment is great gain. For we brought nothing into this world, and it is certain we can carry nothing out.

As the Minister receives the Offering, the People shall stand, and the following may be said or sung:

All things come of Thee, O Lord, and of Thine own have we given Thee.

Then may the Minister say:

Thine, O Lord, is the greatness, and the power, and the glory, and the victory, and the majesty: for all that is in the heaven and in the earth is Thine; Thine is the kingdom, O Lord, and Thou art exalted as Head above all.

The People shall remain standing while the Minister reads the Invitation.

Ye that do truly and earnestly repent of your sins, and are in love and charity with your neighbors, and intend to lead a new life, following the commandments of God, and walking from henceforth in His holy ways, draw near with faith, and take this holy Sacrament to your comfort; and devoutly kneeling make your humble confession to Almighty God.

Then shall this General Confession be made by the Minister and those who are minded to receive the Holy Communion, the Minister kneeling, facing the Lord's Table, and all the People in the attitude of prayer.

Almighty God, Father of our Lord Jesus Christ, Maker of all things, Judge of all men, we acknowledge and bewail our manifold sins and wickedness, which we from time to time most grievously have committed, by thought, word, and deed, against Thy Divine Majesty. We do earnestly repent, and are heartily sorry for these our misdoings; the remembrance of them is grievous unto us. Have mercy upon us, have mercy upon us, most merciful Father, forgive us all that is past; and grant that we may ever hereafter serve and please Thee in newness of life, to the honor and glory of Thy Name, through Jesus Christ our Lord. Amen.

Then shall the Minister offer this Prayer:

Almighty God, our Heavenly Father, who of Thy great mercy hast promised forgiveness of sins to all them that with hearty repentance and true faith turn unto Thee, have mercy upon us; pardon and deliver us from all our sins; confirm and strengthen us in all goodness; and bring us to everlasting life, through Jesus Christ our Lord. **Amen.**

Then shall the Minister say:

Hear what the Scripture saith to those of a humble and contrite heart:

If any man sin, we have an Advocate with the Father, Jesus Christ the righteous: and He is the propitiation for our sins: and not for ours only, but also for the sins of the whole world.

This is a faithful saying, and worthy of all acceptation, that Christ Jesus came into the world to save sinners.

God so loved the world, that He gave His only begotten Son, that whosoever believeth in Him should not perish, but have everlasting life.

Come unto Me, all ye that labor and are heavy laden, and I will give you rest.

After which the Minister and People may say:

Lift up your hearts.

We lift them up unto the Lord.

Let us give thanks unto the Lord.

It is meet and right so to do.

Then the Minister, still kneeling and facing the Lord's Table, shall say:

It is very meet, right, and our bounden duty that we should at all times and in all places give thanks unto Thee, O Lord, Holy Father, Almighty, Everlasting God.

Then shall be said or sung:

Therefore with angels and archangels, and with all the company of heaven, we laud and magnify Thy glorious Name, evermore praising Thee, and saying:

Holy, holy, holy, Lord God of Hosts, heaven and earth are full of Thy glory. Glory be to Thee, O Lord, most high! Amen.

Then shall the Minister offer the Prayer of Consecration:

Almighty God, our Heavenly Father, who of Thy tender mercy didst give Thine only Son Jesus Christ to suffer death upon the cross for our redemption; who made there, by the one offering of Himself, a full, perfect, and sufficient sacrifice for the sins of the whole world; and did institute, and in His holy gospel command us to continue this memorial of His precious death: hear us, O merciful Father, we most humbly beseech Thee, and grant that we, receiving this bread and wine, according to Thy Son, our Saviour Jesus Christ's holy institution, in remembrance of His death and Passion, may also be partakers of the divine nature through Him, who in the same night that He was betrayed took bread [1] and when He had given thanks, He brake it, and gave it to His disciples, saying, Take, eat; this is My body which is given for you; do this in remembrance of Me. Likewise after supper He took the cup [2] and when He had given thanks, He gave it to them, saying, Drink ye all of this, for this is My blood of the new covenant which is shed for you, and for many, for the remission of sins; do this, as oft as ye shall drink it, in remembrance of Me. Amen.

[1. Here may the Minister take the plate in his hands.]
[2. Here may the Minister take the cup in his hands.]

Then shall the Minister, kneeling before the Lord's Table, unite with the People in this Prayer:

We do not presume to come to this, Thy table, O merciful Lord, trusting in our own righteousness, but in Thy manifold and great mercies. We are not worthy so much as to gather up the crumbs under Thy table, but Thou art the same Lord, whose mercy is unfailing. Grant us, therefore, gracious Lord, so to partake of these memorials of Thy Son Jesus Christ, that we may be filled with the fullness of His life, may grow into His likeness and may evermore dwell in Him, and He in us. Amen.

Then shall the Minister first receive the Holy Communion in both kinds himself, after which he shall proceed to deliver the same to other Ministers in like manner, if any be present. After this, the Minister shall administer the Holy Communion to the People, while they are devoutly kneeling.

[Before giving the bread, the Minister shall say:]

Jesus said, "This is My body which is given for you." Take and eat this in remembrance that Christ died for you, and feed on Him in your heart by faith, with thanksgiving.

[Likewise, before giving the cup he shall say:]

Jesus said, "This cup is the new covenant in My blood, which is shed for you." Drink this in remembrance that Christ died for you, and be thankful.

[When all have communed, the Minister shall place upon the Lord's Table what remains of the consecrated Elements, covering the same with the linen cloth.]

Then shall the Minister and the People say:

O Lord, our Heavenly Father, we, Thy humble servants, desire Thy Fatherly goodness mercifully to accept this our sacrifice of praise and thanksgiving; most humbly beseeching Thee to grant, that, by the merits and death of Thy Son Jesus Christ, and through faith in His blood, we and Thy whole Church may obtain forgiveness of our sins, and all other benefits of His Passion. And here we offer and present unto Thee, O Lord, ourselves, our souls and bodies, to be a reasonable, holy, and living sacrifice unto Thee; humbly beseeching Thee that all we who are partakers of this Holy Communion may be filled with Thy grace and heavenly benediction. And although we be unworthy, through our manifold sins, to offer unto Thee any sacrifice, yet we beseech Thee to accept this our bounden duty and service; not weighing our merits, but pardoning our offenses, through Jesus Christ our Lord; by whom, and with whom, in the unity of the Holy Spirit, all honor and glory be unto Thee, O Father Almighty, world without end. Amen.

Then shall be said or sung the Gloria in Excelsis, *the People standing:*

Glory be to God on high, and on earth peace, good will toward men. We praise Thee, we bless Thee, we worship Thee, we glorify Thee, we give thanks to Thee for Thy great glory, O Lord God, Heavenly King, God the Father Almighty!

O Lord, the only-begotten Son Jesus Christ: O Lord God, Lamb of God, Son of the Father, that takest away the sins of the world, have mercy upon us. Thou that takest away the sins of the world, have mercy upon us. Thou that takest away the sins of the world, receive our prayer. Thou that sittest at the right hand of God the Father, have mercy upon us. For Thou only art holy; Thou only art the Lord; Thou only, O Christ, with the Holy Ghost, art most high in the glory of God the Father. Amen.

THE RITUAL

Then shall the Minister let the People depart with this blessing:

The peace of God, which passeth all understanding, keep your hearts and minds in the knowledge and love of God, and of His Son Jesus Christ our Lord: and the blessing of God Almighty, the Father, the Son, and the Holy Spirit, be among you and remain with you always. **Amen.**

AN ALTERNATIVE ORDER FOR THE ADMINISTRATION OF THE SACRAMENT OF THE LORD'S SUPPER

The Minister shall read one or more of these sentences, during the reading of which the Stewards shall take up the Offering for the needy.

Let your light so shine before men, that they may see your good works, and glorify your Father which is in heaven.

Lay not up for yourselves treasures upon earth, where moth and rust doth corrupt, and where thieves break through and steal: but lay up for yourselves treasures in heaven, where neither moth nor rust doth corrupt, and where thieves do not break through nor steal.

Whatsoever ye would that men should do to you, do ye even so to them: for this is the law and the prophets.

Not every one that saith unto Me, Lord, Lord, shall enter into the kingdom of heaven; but he that doeth the will of My Father which is in heaven.

Zacchaeus stood, and said unto the Lord: Behold, Lord, the half of my goods I give to the poor; and if I have taken anything from any man by false accusation, I restore him fourfold.

He which soweth sparingly shall reap also sparingly; and he which soweth bountifully shall reap also bountifully. Every man according as he purposeth in his heart, so let him give; not grudgingly, or of necessity: for God loveth a cheerful giver.

As we have therefore opportunity, let us do good unto all men, especially unto them who are of the household of faith.

Godliness with contentment is great gain. For we brought nothing into this world, and it is certain we can carry nothing out.

Charge them that are rich in this world, that they be ready to distribute, willing to communicate; laying up in store for themselves a good foundation against the time to come, that they may lay hold on eternal life.

God is not unrighteous to forget your work and labor of love, which ye have showed toward His Name, in that ye have ministered to the saints, and do minister.

To do good and to communicate forget not: for with such sacrifices God is well pleased.

Whoso hath this world's good, and seeth his brother have need, and shutteth up his bowels of compassion from him, how dwelleth the love of God in him?

He that hath pity upon the poor lendeth unto the Lord; and that which he hath given will He pay him again.

Blessed is he that considereth the poor: the Lord will deliver him in time of trouble.

Then shall the Minister read this Invitation:

Ye that do truly and earnestly repent of your sins, and are in love and charity with your neighbors, and intend to lead a new life, following the commandments of God, and walking from henceforth in His holy ways; draw near with faith, and take this holy Sacrament to your comfort; and make your humble confession to Almighty God, meekly kneeling upon your knees.

Then shall this General Confession be made by the Minister and all those who are minded to receive the Holy Communion, both he and they humbly kneeling, and saying:

Almighty God, Father of our Lord Jesus Christ, Maker of all things, Judge of all men, we acknowledge and bewail our manifold sins and wickedness, which we from time to time most grievously have committed, by thought, word, and deed, against Thy Divine Majesty, provoking most justly Thy wrath and indignation against us. We do earnestly repent, and are heartily sorry for these our misdoings; the remembrance of them is grievous unto us. Have mercy upon us, have mercy upon us, most merciful Father; for Thy Son our Lord Jesus Christ's sake, forgive us all that is past; and grant that we may ever hereafter serve and please Thee in newness of life, to the honor and glory of Thy Name, through Jesus Christ our Lord. Amen.

Then shall the Minister say:

Almighty God, our Heavenly Father, who of Thy great mercy hast promised forgiveness of sins to all them that with hearty repentance and true faith turn to Thee: have mercy upon us; pardon and deliver us from all our sins, confirm and strengthen us in all goodness, and bring us to everlasting life, through Jesus Christ our Lord. **Amen.**

The Collect

Almighty God, unto whom all hearts are open, all desires known, and from whom no secrets are hid; cleanse the thoughts of our hearts by the inspiration of Thy Holy Spirit, that we may perfectly love Thee, and worthily magnify Thy holy Name, through Christ our Lord. Amen.

Then shall the Minister say:

It is very meet, right, and our bounden duty, that we should at all times, and in all places, give thanks unto Thee, O Lord, Holy Father, Almighty, Everlasting God.

Therefore with angels and archangels, and with all the company of heaven, we laud and magnify Thy glorious Name, evermore praising Thee, and saying: Holy, holy, holy, Lord God of Hosts, heaven and earth are full of Thy glory. Glory be to Thee, O Lord, most high! Amen.

Then shall the Minister say:

We do not presume to come to this, Thy table, O merciful Lord, trusting in our own righteousness, but in Thy manifold and great mercies. We are not worthy so much as to gather up the crumbs under Thy table. But Thou art the same Lord whose property is always to have mercy: Grant us, therefore, gracious Lord, so to eat the flesh of Thy Son Jesus Christ, and to drink His blood, that our sinful souls and bodies may be made clean by His death, and washed through His most precious blood, and that we may evermore dwell in Him, and He in us. Amen.

Then shall the Minister say the Prayer of Consecration as follow-eth:

Almighty God, our Heavenly Father, who of Thy tender mercy didst give Thine only Son Jesus Christ to suffer death upon the cross for our redemption; who made there (by His oblation of Himself once offered) a full, perfect, and sufficient sacrifice, oblation, and satisfaction for the sins of the whole world; and did institute, and in His holy gospel command us to continue, a perpetual memory of His precious death until His coming again: hear us, O merciful Father, we most humbly beseech Thee, and grant that we, receiving these Thy creatures of bread and wine, according to Thy Son our Saviour Jesus Christ's holy institution, in remembrance of His death and Passion, may be partakers of His most blessed body and blood; who in the same night that He was betrayed took bread; and when He had given thanks, He brake it, and gave it to His disciples, saying, Take, eat; this is My body which is given for you; do this in remembrance of Me. Likewise after supper He took the cup; and when He had given thanks, He gave it to them, saying, Drink ye all of this; for this is My blood of the New Testament, which is shed for you and for many, for the remission of sins; do this, as oft as ye shall drink it, in remembrance of Me. Amen.

Then shall the Minister first receive the Holy Communion in both kinds himself, and then proceed to deliver the same to the other Ministers in like manner, if any be present. Then shall he say the Lord's Prayer, the People still kneeling and repeating after him every petition:

Our Father, who art in heaven:

Hallowed be Thy Name, Thy kingdom come, Thy will be done, on earth as it is in heaven.

Give us this day our daily bread. And forgive us our trespasses, as we forgive those who trespass against us. And lead us not into temptation, but deliver us from evil.

For Thine is the kingdom, and the power, and the glory, for ever. Amen.

THE LORD'S SUPPER

Then a Hymn may be sung, and the communicants shall be invited to the Lord's Table. The Minister shall deliver both kinds to the People into their hands. When he delivereth the bread, he shall say:

The body of our Lord Jesus Christ, which was given for *thee,* preserve *thy soul* and *body* unto everlasting life. Take and eat this in remembrance that Christ died for *thee,* and feed on Him in *thy heart* by faith with thanksgiving.

And the Minister that delivereth the cup shall say:

The blood of our Lord Jesus Christ, which was shed for *thee,* preserve *thy soul* and *body* unto everlasting life. Drink this in remembrance that Christ's blood was shed for *thee,* and be thankful.

[When all have communed, the Minister shall return to the Lord's Table, and place upon it what remaineth of the consecrated Elements, covering the same with a fair linen cloth.]

Then shall the Minister and the People say:

O Lord, our Heavenly Father, we, Thy humble servants, desire Thy Fatherly goodness mercifully to accept this our sacrifice of praise and thanksgiving; most humbly beseeching Thee to grant that, by the merits and death of Thy Son Jesus Christ, and through faith in His blood, we and Thy whole Church may obtain remission of our sins, and all other benefits of His Passion. And here we offer and present unto Thee, O Lord, ourselves, our souls and bodies, to be a reasonable, holy, and lively sacrifice unto Thee; humbly beseeching Thee that all we who are partakers of this Holy Communion may be filled with Thy grace and heavenly benediction. And although we be unworthy, through our manifold sins, to offer unto Thee any sacrifice, yet we beseech Thee to accept this our bounden duty and service; not weighing our merits, but pardoning our offenses, through Jesus Christ our Lord; by whom, and with whom, in the unity of the Holy Spirit, all honor and glory be unto Thee, O Father Almighty, world without end. Amen.

Then may be said or sung:

Glory be to God on high, and on earth peace, good will toward men. We praise Thee, we bless Thee, we worship Thee, we glorify Thee, we give thanks to Thee for Thy great glory, O Lord God, Heavenly King, God the Father Almighty!

O Lord, the only-begotten Son, Jesus Christ; O Lord God, Lamb of God, Son of the Father, that takest away the sins of the world, have mercy upon us. Thou that takest away the sins of the world, have mercy upon us. Thou that takest away the sins of the world, receive our prayer. Thou that sittest at the right hand of God the Father, have mercy upon us.

For Thou only art holy; Thou only art the Lord; Thou

only, O Christ, with the Holy Ghost, art most high in the glory of God the Father. Amen.

Then the Minister, if he see it expedient, may offer an extemporary Prayer; and afterward shall let the People depart with this blessing:

May the peace of God, which passeth all understanding, keep your hearts and minds in the knowledge and love of God, and of His Son Jesus Christ our Lord; and the blessing of God Almighty, the Father, the Son, and the Holy Spirit, be among you, and remain with you always. **Amen.**

BAPTISM

THE ORDER FOR THE ADMINISTRATION OF THE SACRAMENT OF BAPTISM

[Let every adult Person, and the Parents of every Child to be baptized, have the choice of sprinkling, pouring, or immersion.

It is proper and desirable that this Sacrament should not only be accompanied by prayer, admonition, and the reading of Scripture, as herein provided, but that it should be administered in the presence of the People, and most suitably in the house of God.]

THE BAPTISM OF INFANTS

Dearly Beloved, forasmuch as all men are heirs of life eternal and subjects of the saving grace of the Holy Spirit; and that our Saviour Christ saith, Suffer the little children to come unto Me, and forbid them not, for of such is the kingdom of God, I beseech you to call upon God the Father, through our Lord Jesus Christ, that of His bounteous goodness He will grant unto *this Child,* now to be baptized, the continual replenishing of His grace that *he* become *a* worthy *member* of Christ's holy Church.

Then shall the Minister say:

Let us pray.

Almighty and Everliving God, we beseech Thee, that of Thine infinite goodness Thou wilt look upon *this Child* and grant that by the aid of Thy Holy Spirit *he* may be steadfast in faith, joyful through hope, and rooted in love, and that *he* may so live the life which now is, that *he* may enter triumphantly the life which is to come; through Jesus Christ our Lord. **Amen.**

Then shall the Minister address the Parents or Sponsors, as follows:

Dearly Beloved, forasmuch as *this Child is* now presented by you for Christian Baptism, and *is* thus consecrated to God and to His Church, it is your part and duty to see that *he* be taught, as soon as *he* shall be able to learn, the meaning and purpose of this holy Sacrament; that *he* be instructed in the principles of our holy faith and the nature of the Christian life; that *he* shall be trained to give reverent attendance upon the public and private worship of God and the teaching of the Holy Scripture, and that in every way, by precept and example, you shall seek to lead *him* into the love of God and the service of our Lord Jesus Christ.

Do you solemnly promise to fulfill these duties so far as in you lies, the Lord being your helper?

We do.

Then shall the People stand and the Minister shall say:

Hear the words of the Gospel written by Saint Mark.

And they brought young children to Him, that He should touch them: and His disciples rebuked those that brought them. But when Jesus saw it, He was much displeased, and said unto them, Let the little children come unto Me, and forbid them not: for of such is the kingdom of God. Verily I say unto you, Whosoever shall not receive the kingdom of God as a little child, he shall not enter therein. And He took them up in His arms, put His hands upon them, and blessed them.

Then shall the Minister, who may here take the Child in his arms, say to the Parents or Sponsors:

What name shall be given to this Child?

And then, repeating the name, he shall baptize the Child, saying:

N., I baptize thee in the Name of the Father, and of the Son, and of the Holy Spirit. **Amen.**

Then shall the Minister say:

Let us pray.

O God, our Heavenly Father, grant that *this Child,* as *he grows* in years, may also grow in grace and in knowledge of the Lord Jesus Christ, and that by the restraining and renewing influence of Thy Holy Spirit *he* may ever be *a true Child* of God, serving Thee faithfully all *his* days, through Jesus Christ our Lord. **Amen.**

Almighty God, Fount of all love and wisdom, Source of all power, so guide and uphold the Parents [or Sponsors] of *this Child,* that, by loving care, wise counsel, and holy example, they may lead *him* into that life of faith whose strength is righteousness and whose fruit is everlasting joy and peace; through Jesus Christ our Lord. **Amen.**

Or the Minister may offer extemporary Prayer.

Then may the Minister and the People say:

Our Father, who art in heaven:
Hallowed be Thy Name, Thy kingdom come, Thy will be done, on earth as it is in heaven.
Give us this day our daily bread. And forgive us our tres-

passes, as we forgive those who trespass against us. And lead us not into temptation, but deliver us from evil.

For Thine is the kingdom, and the power, and the glory, for ever. Amen.

Then may be sung a Hymn, such as:

406—"Friend of the home: as when in Galilee."
407—"See Israel's gentle Shepherd stand."
440—"I think when I read."

Then may the Minister say:

Now unto Him that is able to keep you from falling, and to present you faultless before the presence of His glory with exceeding joy, to the only wise God our Saviour, be glory and majesty, dominion and power, now and evermore. Amen.

A BRIEFER ORDER FOR THE BAPTISM OF INFANTS

The Minister, addressing the Parents or Sponsors, shall say:

Dearly Beloved, forasmuch as *this Child is* now presented by you for Christian Baptism, it is your part and duty to see that *he* be brought up in the nurture and admonition of the Lord; and that in every way, by precept and example, you shall seek to lead *him* into the love of God and the service of our Lord Jesus Christ.

Do you solemnly engage to fulfill these duties so far as in you lies, the Lord being your helper?

We do.

The People shall stand and the Minister, who may here take the Child in his arms, shall say to the Parents or Sponsors:

What name shall be given to this Child?

Repeating the name, he shall baptize the Child, saying:

N., I baptize thee in the Name of the Father, and of the Son, and of the Holy Spirit. Amen.

Then shall the Minister say:

Let us pray.

Almighty God, Fount of all love and wisdom, Source of all power; so guide and uphold the Parents [or Sponsors] of *this Child* that, by loving care, wise counsel, and holy example, they may lead *him* into that life of faith whose strength is righteousness and whose fruit is everlasting joy and peace; through Jesus Christ our Lord. Amen.

Then may the Minister and the People say:

Our Father, who art in heaven:
Hallowed be Thy Name, Thy kingdom come, Thy will be done, on earth as it is in heaven.
Give us this day our daily bread. And forgive us our tres-

passes, as we forgive those who trespass against us. And lead us not into temptation, but deliver us from evil.

For Thine is the kingdom, and the power, and the glory, for ever. Amen.

THE ORDER FOR THE BAPTISM OF CHILDREN AND YOUTH

The Minister, coming to the Font, shall say:

Hear the words of the Gospel, written by Saint Matthew, in the twenty-eighth chapter, beginning at the sixteenth verse.

Then the eleven disciples went away into Galilee, into a mountain where Jesus had appointed them. And when they saw Him, they worshiped Him; but some doubted. And Jesus came and spake unto them, saying, All power is given unto Me in heaven and in earth. Go ye therefore, and make disciples of all nations, baptizing them in the Name of the Father, and of the Son, and of the Holy Spirit: teaching them to observe all things whatsoever I have commanded you: and lo, I am with you alway, even unto the end of the world. **Amen.**

Then shall the Minister say:

Let us pray.

Almighty and Everliving God, whose most dearly beloved Son Jesus Christ gave Himself for our salvation, and did command His disciples that they should go teach all nations, and baptize them in the Name of the Father, and of the Son, and of the Holy Spirit: regard, we beseech Thee, the supplications of Thy Congregation; and grant that *these persons* now to be baptized may so open *their hearts* to Thee that *they* may receive the fullness of Thy grace, and may ever remain in the number of Thy faithful children, through Jesus Christ our Lord. **Amen.**

Then shall the Minister say to the Persons to be baptized:

Well beloved, who *are* come hither, desiring to receive holy Baptism, you have heard how the Congregation hath prayed that God would assist you to open your hearts to His love and direction, that you may be faithful disciples of our Lord.

Wherefore, for your part, it is needful that in the presence of Almighty God and the hearing of this Congregation, you should now make known your purpose to accept the obligations of this holy Sacrament, by answering the following questions:

Will you faithfully put away from you every known sin, of thought, word, or deed, and accept and confess Jesus Christ as your Saviour and Lord?

God helping me, I will.

Will you diligently study the Bible as God's Holy Word, and in all things strive to make it the rule of your life?

God helping me, I will.

Having been taught how the Spirit of our Lord separates right from wrong, will you faithfully endeavor to live so as to be pleasing unto Him?

God helping me, I will.

Will you be baptized in this faith?

This is my desire.

Then shall the Minister ask each Person his name, and shall baptize him, saying:

N., I baptize thee in the Name of the Father, and of the Son, and of the Holy Spirit. **Amen.**

Here the Minister shall offer an extemporary Prayer.

THE ORDER FOR THE BAPTISM OF ADULTS

The Minister, addressing the People, shall say:

Dearly Beloved, forasmuch as our Saviour Jesus Christ sent forth His disciples to teach all nations and baptize them in the Name of the Father, and of the Son, and of the Holy Spirit; and wherefore *these Persons* come now to be baptized, I beseech you to call upon God the Father that of His bounteous goodness He will grant unto *them* the renewing power of the Holy Spirit and enable *them* by divine grace to attain unto the fullness of salvation in Jesus Christ our Lord.

Let us pray.

Almighty and immortal God, the aid of all that need, the helper of all that flee to Thee for succor, the life of them that believe, and the resurrection of the dead: we call upon Thee for *these Persons* now to be baptized. May *they* be filled with Thy Holy Spirit and may *they* find in Thee *their* refuge, *their* strength, *their* wisdom, and *their* joy. May *they* be faithful to Thee all the days of *their* life and finally come to the eternal kingdom which Thou hast promised, through Jesus Christ our Lord. **Amen.**

Then may the Minister read one or more of the following Lessons:

Peter said unto them, Repent, and be baptized every one of you in the Name of Jesus Christ for the remission of sins, and ye shall receive the gift of the Holy Spirit. For the promise is unto you, and to your children, and to all that are afar off, even as many as the Lord our God shall call. And with many other words did he testify and exhort, saying, Save yourselves from this untoward generation. Then they that gladly received his word were baptized: and the same day there were added unto them about three thousand souls. And they continued steadfastly in the apostles' doctrine and fellowship, and in breaking of bread, and in prayers.

And it came to pass, that, while Apollos was at Corinth, Paul having passed through the upper coasts came to Ephesus: and finding certain disciples, he said unto them, Have ye received the Holy Spirit since ye believed? And they said unto him, We have not so much as heard whether there be any Holy Spirit. And he said unto them, Unto what then were ye baptized? And they said, Unto John's baptism. Then said Paul, John verily baptized with the baptism of repentance, saying unto the people that they should believe on Him which should come after him, that is, on Christ Jesus. When they heard this, they were baptized in the Name of the Lord Jesus. And when Paul had laid his hands upon them, the Holy Spirit came on them.

There was a man of the Pharisees, named Nicodemus, a ruler of the Jews: The same came to Jesus by night, and said unto Him, Rabbi, we know that Thou art a teacher come from God: for no man can do these miracles that Thou doest, except God be with him. Jesus answered and said unto him, Verily, verily, I say unto thee, Except a man be born again, he cannot see the kingdom of God. Nicodemus saith unto Him, How can a man be born when he is old? can he enter the second time into his mother's womb, and be born? Jesus answered, Verily, verily, I say unto thee, Except a man be born of water and of the Spirit, he cannot enter into the kingdom of God. That which is born of the flesh is flesh; and that which is born of the Spirit is spirit. Marvel not that I said unto thee, Ye must be born again. The wind bloweth where it listeth, and thou hearest the sound thereof, but canst not tell whence it cometh, and whither it goeth: so is every one that is born of the Spirit.

For this cause I bow my knees unto the Father of our Lord Jesus Christ, of whom the whole family in heaven and earth is named, that He would grant you, according to the riches of His glory, to be strengthened with might by His Spirit in the inner man; that Christ may dwell in your hearts by faith; that ye, being rooted and grounded in love, may be able to comprehend with all saints what is the breadth, and length, and depth, and height; and to know the love of Christ, which passeth knowledge, that ye might be filled with all the fullness of God.

Then shall the Minister say to the Persons to be baptized:

Dearly Beloved, who have come hither desiring to receive holy Baptism, the Congregation gives thanks to God for your coming, and prays that the Holy Spirit may dwell within you, and that your faith may not fail. In the hearing of this Congregation you should now make known your purpose to accept the obligations of this holy Sacrament.

Do you truly repent of your sins and accept and confess Jesus Christ as your Saviour and Lord?

I do.

Will you earnestly endeavor to keep God's Holy Will and commandments?

I will.

Do you desire to be baptized in this faith?
I do.

Then shall the Minister pray:

O merciful God, grant that all sinful affections may die in *these Persons,* and that all things belonging to the Spirit may live and grow in *them.* **Amen.**

Almighty, Everliving God, regard, we beseech Thee, our supplications and grant that *these Persons* may receive the fullness of Thy grace, and ever remain in the number of Thy faithful and beloved children, through Jesus Christ our Lord. **Amen.**

Then the Minister, asking the name of each Person, shall baptize him, repeating the name and saying:

N., I baptize thee in the Name of the Father, and of the Son, and of the Holy Spirit. **Amen.**

Then may the Minister offer extemporary Prayer.

Then may the Minister and the People say:

· **Our Father, who art in heaven:**
Hallowed be Thy Name, Thy kingdom come, Thy will be done, on earth as it is in heaven.
Give us this day our daily bread. And forgive us our trespasses, as we forgive those who trespass against us. And lead us not into temptation, but deliver us from evil.
For Thine is the kingdom, and the power, and the glory, for ever. Amen.

Then may be sung one or more stanzas of a Hymn, such as:

223—"Blessed Master, I have promised."
226—"O Jesus, I have promised."
257—"My gracious Lord, I own Thy right."

Then may the Minister say:

Now unto Him that is able to keep you from falling, and to present you faultless before the presence of His glory with exceeding joy, to the only wise God our Saviour, be glory and majesty, dominion and power, now and evermore. **Amen.**

RECEPTION OF MEMBERS

THE ORDER FOR RECEIVING PERSONS INTO THE CHURCH

On the day appointed, all that are to be received into the Church shall be called forward, and the Minister, addressing the People, shall say:

Dearly Beloved, the Church is of God, and will be preserved to the end of time, for the promotion of His worship and the due administration of His word and ordinances, the maintenance of Christian fellowship and discipline, the edification of believers, and the conversion of the world. All, of every age and station, stand in need of the means of grace which it alone supplies.

Into this holy fellowship the *Persons* before you, who *have* received the Sacrament of Baptism, who *have* learned the nature of these privileges and these duties, and who *have* also been instructed in the teachings and the aims of The Methodist Church, *come* seeking admission. We now propose in the fear of God to question *them* as to *their* faith and purpose, that you may know that *they are* proper *Persons* to be admitted into this Church.

Then, addressing those seeking admission, the Minister shall say:

Beloved in the Lord, you are come hither seeking union with the Church of God. We rejoice that you are minded to undertake the privileges and the duties of membership in the Church. Before you are fully admitted thereto, you should here publicly renew your vows, confess your faith, and declare your purpose, by answering the following questions:

Do you here in the presence of God and this Congregation renew the solemn promise and vow that was made at your Baptism?

I do.

Do you confess Jesus Christ as your Saviour and Lord and pledge your allegiance to His kingdom?

I do.

Do you receive and profess the Christian faith as contained in the New Testament of our Lord Jesus Christ?

I do.

Will you be loyal to The Methodist Church, and uphold it by your prayers, your presence, your gifts, and your service?

I will.

Then those to be received shall kneel and the Minister, who may lay his hand upon the head of every one severally, shall say:

N., The Lord defend thee with His heavenly grace and by His Spirit confirm thee in the faith and fellowship of all true disciples of Jesus Christ. **Amen.**

Here those being received shall rise, and then the Minister, addressing the People, shall say:

Brethren, I commend to your love and care *these Persons* whom we this day recognize as *members* of the Church of Christ. What is your mind to *them?*

Then shall the People say:

We rejoice to recognize you as *members* of the Church of

Christ, and bid you welcome to all its privileges. Your peace, joy, and welfare are now our own. With you we renew our pledge to God and this Church. The Lord bless thee and keep thee, the Lord make His face to shine upon thee and be gracious unto Thee; the Lord lift up His countenance upon thee and give thee peace. Amen.

Then may be sung one or more stanzas of a Hymn, such as:

379—"I Love Thy kingdom, Lord."
380—"Jesus, with Thy Church abide."
383—"How lovely is Thy dwelling place."

Then may the Minister say:

The blessing of God Almighty, the Father, the Son, and the Holy Spirit, be among you, and remain with you always. **Amen.**

THE ORDER FOR RECEIVING CHILDREN AND YOUTH INTO THE CHURCH

After the Minister previously shall have formed the Children into a class (baptizing any whose Baptism may have been delayed or neglected), and shall have instructed them in the things necessary for them to know as to the Doctrines and Rules of the Church, he shall cause them to be conveniently placed before the Congregation, and after inviting their Parents and Teachers to stand with them on either hand, he shall say:

Brethren of the household of faith, let our hearts be lifted up in thanksgiving to Almighty God, who by the Holy Spirit hath inclined *these Children* to desire and ask for membership in the Church. Having arrived at years of discretion, and now of *their* own accord appearing before this Congregation to take upon *themselves* the vows and enter upon the privileges and duties of the Church, let us with one mind and heart most earnestly invoke in *their* behalf the blessings of Father, Son, and Holy Spirit.

Then shall the Minister say:

Let us pray.

Almighty and Everliving God, giver of every good and perfect gift, accept our hearty thanks for the *Children* whom Thou hast committed to our love and care. As Thou didst bring *them* into the world, now renew in Thy servants, *their* parents, pastors, and teachers, wisdom to train *them* in the way *they* should go. Grant unto *these* Thy *Children* that from this day forth *they* may grow in grace, and wisdom, and in favor with God and man, through Jesus Christ our Lord. **Amen.**

Then shall the Minister address the Parents or Sponsors:

Dear fathers and mothers, let this be to you a day of peculiar joy and thanksgiving, in that *these who are* of your flesh and blood have

544

also entered into a holier spiritual kinship with you in Jesus Christ. While the Church will continue to share with you the duty and privilege of bringing up *these Children* in the nurture and admonition of the Lord, it renews its solemn injunction to you as parents, by God's help, faithfully to continue both to teach and train *them,* by example and precept, in the way of the Lord. Will you accept this duty, in the fear and by the favor of God, and here and now, in the presence of Almighty God and this Congregation, renew the vows made by you as fathers and mothers in the baptism of *these Children?*

With God's help, I will.

Then shall the Minister address the Children who are candidates and say:

Beloved *Children,* our Lord Jesus, by His Holy Word, hath expressly given to everyone who believes in Him a place in His kingdom and Church. Before you are admitted into the Church, it becomes my duty to inquire of you as to your purpose of mind and heart:

Do you, each of you, believe in God as your Heavenly Father?

I do.

Do you accept Jesus Christ as your personal Saviour?

I do.

Do you believe in the Bible as God's Holy Word?

I do.

Will you be loyal to The Methodist Church and uphold it by your prayers, your presence, your gifts, and your service?

I will.

Here the Minister may offer an extemporary Prayer.

Then those to be received shall kneel and the Minister, laying his hands upon every one of them severally, shall say:

I receive you into the Church of Christ and pray God's blessing upon you.

Then shall the Minister, the People, and the Children say.

Our Father, who art in heaven:
Hallowed be Thy Name, Thy kingdom come, Thy will be done, on earth as it is in heaven.
Give us this day our daily bread. And forgive us our trespasses, as we forgive those who trespass against us. And lead us not into temptation, but deliver us from evil.
For Thine is the kingdom, and the power, and the glory, for ever. Amen.

Then may be sung one or more stanzas of a Hymn, such as:

379—"I Love Thy kingdom, Lord."
380—"Jesus, with Thy Church abide."
383—"How lovely is Thy dwelling place."

Then may the Minister say:

The blessing of God Almighty; the Father, the Son, and the Holy Spirit, be among you, and remain with you always.   **Amen.**

MATRIMONY
THE ORDER FOR THE SOLEMNIZATION OF MATRIMONY

At the time appointed, the Persons to be married—having been qualified according to the law of the State and the standards of the Church—standing together facing the Minister, the Man at the Minister's left hand and the Woman at the right, the Minister shall say:

Dearly Beloved, we are gathered together here in the sight of God and in the presence of these witnesses, to join this man and this woman in holy matrimony, which is an honorable estate, instituted by God, and signifying unto us the mystical union which exists between Christ and His Church.   It is therefore not to be entered into unadvisedly, but reverently, discreetly, and in the fear of God.   Into this holy estate these two persons come now to be joined.

Speaking to the Persons to be married, the Minister shall say:

I charge you both, as you stand in the presence of God, to remember that love and loyalty alone will avail as the foundation of a happy home. If the solemn vows which you are about to make be kept inviolate, and if steadfastly you endeavor to do the will of your Heavenly Father, your life will be full of joy, and the home which you are establishing will abide in peace.   No other human ties are more tender, no other vows more sacred than those you now assume.

Then shall the Minister say to the Man, using his Christian name:

N., wilt thou have this woman to be thy wedded wife, to live together in the holy estate of matrimony? Wilt thou love her, comfort her, honor and keep her, in sickness and in health; and forsaking all other keep thee only unto her, so long as ye both shall live?

The Man shall answer:

I will.

Then shall the Minister say to the Woman, using her Christian name:

N., wilt thou have this man to be thy wedded husband, to live together in the holy estate of matrimony? Wilt thou love him, comfort him, honor and keep him, in sickness and in health; and forsaking all other keep thee only unto him, so long as ye both shall live?

The Woman shall answer:

I will.

Then may the Minister say:

Who giveth this woman to be married to this man?

The Father of the Woman, or whoever giveth her in marriage, shall answer:

I do.

Then the Minister [receiving the hand of the Woman from her Father or other Sponsor] shall cause the Man with his right hand to take the Woman by her right hand, and say after him:

I, ———, take thee, ———, to be my wedded wife, to have and to hold, from this day forward, for better, for worse, for richer, for poorer, in sickness and in health, to love and to cherish, till death us do part, and thereto I plight thee my faith.

Then shall they loose their hands; and the Woman, with her right hand taking the Man by his right hand, shall likewise say after the Minister:

I, ———, take thee, ———, to be my wedded husband, to have and to hold, from this day forward, for better, for worse, for richer, for poorer, in sickness and in health, to love and to cherish, till death us do part, and thereto I plight thee my faith.

Then shall they again loose their hands; and the Man may give unto the Woman a ring, on this wise: the Minister, taking the ring, shall say:

The wedding ring is the outward and visible sign of an inward and spiritual bond which unites two loyal hearts in endless love.

The Minister shall then deliver the ring to the Man to put upon the third finger of the Woman's left hand. The Man, holding the ring there, shall say after the Minister:

In token and pledge of the vow between us made, with this ring I thee wed: in the Name of the Father, and of the Son, and of the Holy Spirit. **Amen.**

In case of a double ring ceremony, the Minister shall deliver the other ring to the Woman to put upon the third finger of the Man's left hand, and the Woman, holding the ring there, shall say after the Minister:

In token and pledge of the vow between us made, with this ring I thee wed: in the Name of the Father, and of the Son, and of the Holy Spirit. **Amen.**

Then shall the Minister say:

Let us pray.

O Eternal God, Creator and Preserver of all mankind, Giver of

all spiritual grace, the Author of everlasting life: send Thy blessing upon this man and this woman, whom we bless in Thy Name: that they may surely perform and keep the vow and covenant now between them made.

Look graciously upon them, that they may love, honor, and cherish each other, and so live together in faithfulness and patience, and wisdom and true godliness, that their home may be a haven of blessing and a place of peace: through Jesus Christ our Lord. **Amen.**

Then shall the Minister join their right hands together and with his hand on their united hands shall say:

Forasmuch as ———, and ———, have consented together in holy wedlock, and have witnessed the same before God and this company, and thereto have pledged their faith each to the other, and have declared the same by joining hands, and by giving and receiving a ring; I pronounce that they are husband and wife together, in the Name of the Father, and of the Son, and of the Holy Spirit. Those whom God hath joined together, let not man put asunder. **Amen.**

Then, the Husband and Wife kneeling, the Minister shall say:

Let us pray.

Our Father, who art in heaven:
Hallowed be Thy Name, Thy kingdom come, Thy will be done, on earth as it is in heaven.
Give us this day our daily bread. And forgive us our trespasses, as we forgive those who trespass against us. And lead us not into temptation, but deliver us from evil.
For Thine is the kingdom, and the power, and the glory, for ever. Amen.

Then shall the Minister add this blessing:

God the Father, the Son, and the Holy Spirit, bless, preserve, **and** keep you; the Lord graciously with His favor look upon you; and so fill you with all spiritual benediction and love that you may so live together in this life that in the world to come you may have life everlasting. **Amen.**

THE BURIAL OF THE DEAD
THE ORDER FOR THE BURIAL OF THE DEAD

The Minister shall begin the service by reading one or more of the following sentences:

Jesus said, I am the resurrection, and the life: he that believeth in Me, though he were dead, yet shall he live: and whosoever liveth and believeth in Me shall never die.

The eternal God is thy refuge, and underneath are the everlasting arms.

548

The Lord is my light and my salvation; whom shall I fear? The Lord is the strength of my life; of whom shall I be afraid?

The righteous live for ever, and the care of them is with the Most High: with His right hand He shall cover them, and with His arm shall He shield them.

For we know that if our earthly house of this tabernacle were dissolved, we have a building of God, an house not made with hands, eternal in the heavens.

Then shall the Minister say:

Let us pray.

[Here may the Minister offer one or both of the following Prayers, ending with the Lord's Prayer:]

Almighty God, Fount of all life, Thou art our refuge and strength, Thou art our help in trouble. Enable us, we pray Thee, to put our trust in Thee, that we may obtain comfort, and find grace to help in this and every time of need; through Jesus Christ our Lord. **Amen.**

Almighty God, our Father, from whom we come and unto whom our spirits return, Thou hast been our dwelling place in all generations. Thou art our refuge and strength, a very present help in trouble. Grant us Thy blessing in this hour, and enable us so to put our trust in Thee, that our spirits may grow calm and our hearts be comforted. Lift our eyes beyond the shadows of earth, and help us to see the light of eternity. So may we find grace and strength for this and every time of need; through Jesus Christ our Lord. **Amen.**

Our Father, who art in heaven:

Hallowed be Thy Name, Thy kingdom come, Thy will be done, on earth as it is in heaven.

Give us this day our daily bread. And forgive us our trespasses, as we forgive those who trespass against us. And lead us not into temptation, but deliver us from evil.

For Thine is the kingdom, and the power, and the glory, for ever. Amen.

Here may be read Lessons from the Old Testament:

The Lord is my shepherd; I shall not want.
He maketh me to lie down in green pastures:
He leadeth me beside the still waters.
He restoreth my soul:
He leadeth me in the paths of righteousness for His Name's sake.
Yea, though I walk through the valley of the shadow of death,
I will fear no evil: for Thou art with me;
Thy rod and Thy staff they comfort me.
Thou preparest a table before me in the presence of mine enemies:
Thou anointest my head with oil;
My cup runneth over.
Surely goodness and mercy shall follow me all the days of my life:
And I will dwell in the house of the Lord for ever.

Lord, Thou hast been our dwelling place in all generations.
Before the mountains were brought forth,
Or ever Thou hadst formed the earth and the world,
Even from everlasting to everlasting, Thou art God.
For a thousand years in Thy sight
Are but as yesterday when it is past,
And as a watch in the night.
Thou carriest them away as with a flood; they are as a sleep:
In the morning they are like grass which groweth up. In the
morning it flourisheth, and groweth up;
In the evening it is cut down, and withereth.
So teach us to number our days,
That we may apply our hearts unto wisdom.
Let Thy work appear unto Thy servants,
And Thy glory unto their children.
And let the beauty of the Lord our God be upon us:
And establish Thou the work of our hands upon us;
Yea, the work of our hands establish Thou it.

I will lift up mine eyes unto the hills: from whence shall my help
come?
My help cometh from the Lord, who made heaven and earth.
He will not suffer thy foot to be moved: He that keepeth thee will
not slumber.
Behold, He that keepeth Israel will neither slumber nor sleep.
The Lord is thy keeper: the Lord is thy shade upon thy right hand.
The Lord shall preserve thy going out and thy coming in, from
this time forth, and even for evermore.

The Lord is my light and my salvation; whom shall I fear?
The Lord is the strength of my life; of whom shall I be afraid?
Though an host encamp against me, my heart shall not fear;
though war should rise against me, even then will I be confident.
For in the time of trouble He shall hide me in His pavilion: in the
secret of His tabernacle shall He hide me; He shall set me up upon a
rock.
Teach me Thy way, O Lord, and lead me in a plain path.
I had fainted, unless I had believed to see the goodness of the
Lord, in the land of the living.
Wait on the Lord: be of good courage, and He shall strengthen
thine heart: wait, I say, on the Lord.

Here shall be read Lessons from the New Testament:

Let not your heart be troubled: ye believe in God, believe also in
Me. In My Father's house are many mansions: if it were not so, I
would have told you. I go to prepare a place for you. And if I go and
prepare a place for you, I will come again, and receive you unto My-
self; that where I am, there ye may be also. I am the way, the truth,

550

and the life. If ye love Me, keep My commandments. And I will pray the Father, and He shall give you another Comforter, that He may abide with you for ever; even the Spirit of truth; whom the world cannot receive, because it seeth Him not, neither knoweth Him; but ye know Him; for He dwelleth with you, and shall be in you. I will not leave you comfortless: I will come to you. Because I live, ye shall live also.

Peace I leave with you, My peace I give unto you: not as the world giveth, give I unto you. Let not your heart be troubled, neither let it be afraid.

As many as are led by the Spirit of God, they are the sons of God. For ye have not received the spirit of bondage again to fear; but ye have received the spirit of adoption, whereby we cry, Abba, Father. The Spirit itself beareth witness with our spirit, that we are the children of God: and if children, then heirs; heirs of God, and joint-heirs with Christ; if so be that we suffer with Him, that we may be also glorified together.

For I reckon that the sufferings of this present time are not worthy to be compared with the glory which shall be revealed in us.

And we know that all things work together for good to them that love God.

What shall we then say to these things? If God be for us, who can be against us? Who shall separate us from the love of Christ? shall tribulation, or distress, or persecution, or famine, or nakedness, or peril, or sword? Nay, in all these things we are more than conquerors through Him that loved us. For I am persuaded, that neither death, nor life, nor angels, nor principalities, nor powers, nor things present, nor things to come, nor height, nor depth, nor any other creature, shall be able to separate us from the love of God, which is in Christ Jesus our Lord.

Now is Christ risen from the dead, and become the first fruits of them that slept.

But some man will say, How are the dead raised up? and with what body do they come? Thou foolish one, that which thou sowest is not quickened, except it die: but God giveth it a body as it hath pleased Him.

So also is the resurrection of the dead. It is sown in corruption; it is raised in incorruption:

It is sown in dishonor; it is raised in glory: it is sown in weakness; it is raised in power:

It is sown a natural body; it is raised a spiritual body. There is a natural body, and there is a spiritual body.

And as we have borne the image of the earthy, we shall also bear the image of the heavenly.

For this corruptible must put on incorruption, and this mortal must put on immortality. So when this corruptible shall have put on incorruption, and this mortal shall have put on immortality, then shall be brought to pass the saying that is written, Death is swallowed up in victory. O death, where is thy sting? O grave, where is thy victory? The sting of death is sin; and the strength of sin is the law. But thanks be to God, who giveth us the victory, through our Lord Jesus Christ. Therefore, my beloved brethren, be ye steadfast, unmovable, always abounding in the work of the Lord, forasmuch as ye know that your labor is not in vain in the Lord.

And I John saw the holy city, new Jerusalem, coming down from God out of heaven, prepared as a bride adorned for her husband. And I heard a great voice out of heaven saying, Behold, the tabernacle of God is with men, and He will dwell with them, and they shall be His people, and God Himself shall be with them, and be their God. And God shall wipe away all tears from their eyes; and there shall be no more death, neither sorrow, nor crying, neither shall there be any more pain: for the former things are passed away.

And he showed me a river of life clear as crystal, proceeding out of the throne of God and of the Lamb. In the midst of the street of it, and on either side of the river, was there the tree of life, which bare twelve manner of fruits, and yielded her fruit every month: and the leaves of the tree were for the healing of the nations. And there shall be no more curse: but the throne of God and of the Lamb shall be in it; and His servants shall serve Him: and they shall see His face; and His name shall be in their foreheads. And there shall be no night there; and they need no candle, neither light of the sun; for the Lord God giveth them light: and they shall reign for ever and ever.

For this cause I bow my knees unto the Father of our Lord Jesus Christ, of whom the whole family in heaven and earth is named, that He would grant you, according to the riches of His glory, to be strengthened with might by His Spirit in the inner man; that Christ may dwell in your hearts by faith; that ye, being rooted and grounded in love, may be able to comprehend with all saints what is the breadth, and length, and depth, and height; and to know the love of Christ, which passeth knowledge, that ye might be filled with all the fullness of God. Now unto Him that is able to do exceeding abundantly above all that we ask or think, according to the power that worketh in us, unto Him be glory in the Church by Christ Jesus throughout all ages, world without end. **Amen.**

Here may follow music and an Address, closing with extemporary or one of the following Prayers:

Eternal God, who committest to us the swift and solemn trust of life: since we know not what a day may bring forth, but only that the hour for serving Thee is always present, may we wake to the instant claims of Thy holy will: not waiting for tomorrow, but yielding today. Consecrate with Thy presence the way our feet may go; and the humblest work will shine, and the roughest places be made plain. Lift us above unrighteous anger and mistrust into faith and hope and love by a simple and steadfast reliance on Thy sure will. In all things draw us to the mind of Christ, that Thy lost image may be traced again, and that Thou mayest own us as at one with Him and Thee. **Amen.**

O God, who art the strength of Thy saints and who redeemest the souls of Thy servants; we bless Thy Name for all those who have died in the Lord, and who now rest from their labors, having received the end of their faith, even the salvation of their souls. Especially we call to remembrance Thy loving-kindness and Thy tender mercies to this Thy servant. For all Thy goodness that withheld not *his* portion in the joys of this earthly life, and for Thy guiding hand along the way of *his* pilgrimage, we give Thee thanks and praise. Especially we bless Thee for Thy grace that kindled in *his* heart the love of Thy dear Name; that enabled *him* to fight the good fight, to endure unto the end, and to obtain the victory; yea, to become more than conqueror, through Him that loveth us. We magnify Thy holy Name that, *his* trials and temptations being ended, sickness and death being passed, with all the dangers and difficulties of this mortal life, *his* spirit is at home in Thy presence, at whose right hand dwelleth eternal peace. And grant, O Lord, we beseech Thee, that we who rejoice in the triumph of Thy saints may profit by their example, that, becoming followers of their faith and patience, we also may enter with them into an inheritance incorruptible and undefiled, and that fadeth not away; through Jesus Christ our Lord. **Amen.**

O God, the Lord of Life, the Conqueror of death, our help in every time of trouble, who dost not willingly grieve or afflict the children of men; comfort us who mourn, and give us grace, in the presence of death, to worship Thee, that we may have sure hope of eternal life and be enabled to put our whole trust in Thy goodness and mercy; through Jesus Christ our Lord. **Amen.**

Father of spirits, we have joy at this time in all who have faithfully lived, and in all who have peacefully died. We thank Thee for all fair memories and all living hopes; for the sacred ties that bind us to the unseen world; for the dear and holy dead who compass us as a cloud of witnesses, and make the distant heaven a home to our hearts. May we be followers of those who now inherit the promises, through Jesus Christ our Lord. **Amen.**

O Lord and Master, who Thyself didst weep beside the grave, and art touched with the feeling of our sorrows; fulfill now Thy promise that Thou wilt not leave Thy people comfortless, but wilt come to them. Reveal Thyself unto Thy sorrowing servants, and cause them to hear Thee say, "I am the resurrection and the life." Help them, O Lord, to turn to Thee with true discernment, and to abide in Thee through living faith; that, finding now the comfort of Thy presence, they may have also a sure confidence in Thee for all that is to come: until the day break, and the shadows flee away. Hear us for Thy great mercy's sake, O Jesus Christ our Lord. **Amen.**

O Thou who hast ordered this wondrous world and who knowest

all things in earth and heaven; so fill our hearts with trust in Thee, that by night and by day, at all times and in all seasons, we may without fear commit those who are dear to us to Thy never-failing love for this life and the life to come. **Amen.**

O Lord, we pray Thee, give us Thy strength, that we may live more bravely and faithfully for the sake of those who are no longer with us here upon earth; and grant us so to serve Thee day by day, that we may find eternal fellowship with them, through Him who died and rose again for us all, Jesus Christ our Lord. **Amen.**

Almighty God, who art leading us through the changes of time to the rest and blessedness of eternity, be Thou near to comfort and uphold. Make us to know and feel that Thy children are precious in Thy sight, that they live evermore with Thee, and that Thy mercy endureth forever. Thankful for the life which Thou hast given us for these seasons, help us now to resign it obediently unto Thee. Assist us to return to the scenes of our daily life, to obey Thy will with patience, and to bear our trials with fortitude and hope. And when the peace of death falls upon us, may we find our perfect rest in Thee: through Jesus Christ our Lord. **Amen.**

Then may the Minister say:

The grace of the Lord Jesus Christ, and the love of God, and the communion of the Holy Spirit, be with you all. **Amen.**

At the grave, when the People are assembled, the Minister shall say:

Our help is in the Name of the Lord, who made heaven and earth.

Like as a father pitieth his children, so the Lord pitieth them that fear Him.

Say to them that are of a fearful heart, Be strong, fear not: behold, your God will come and save you.

For the mercy of the Lord is from everlasting to everlasting upon them that fear Him and His righteousness unto children's children.

Then the Minister may say:

Forasmuch as Almighty God hath received unto Himself the soul of our departed *brother,* we therefore tenderly commit *his* body to the ground in the blessed hope that as *he* has borne the image of the earthly so also *he* shall bear the image of the heavenly.

[Or the Minister may say:]

Forasmuch as the spirit of the departed has entered into the life immortal, we therefore commit *his* body to its resting place, but *his* spirit we commend to God, remembering how Jesus said upon the cross, "Father, into Thy hands I commend My spirit."

[Or the Minister may say:]

Forasmuch as the spirit of the departed hath returned to the God who gave it, we therefore commit *his* body to the ground, earth to earth, ashes to ashes, dust to dust; looking for the general resurrection in the last day, and the life of the world to come, through our Lord Jesus Christ; at whose coming in glorious majesty to judge the world, the earth and the sea shall give up their dead; and the corruptible bodies of those who sleep in Him shall be changed and made like unto His own glorious body; according to the mighty working whereby He is able to subdue all things unto Himself.

Then may be said:

Blessed are the dead who die in the Lord from henceforth: yea, saith the Spirit, that they may rest from their labors; and their works do follow them.

Then shall the Minister say:

Let us pray.

Almighty God, with whom do live the spirits of those who depart hence in the Lord and with whom the souls of the faithful after death are in strength and gladness, we give Thee hearty thanks for the good examples of all those Thy servants, who, having finished their course in faith, do now rest from their labor. And we beseech Thee that we, with all those who have finished their course in faith, may have our perfect consummation and bliss in Thy eternal and everlasting glory, through Jesus Christ our Lord. **Amen.**

O Merciful God, the Father of our Lord Jesus Christ, who is the resurrection and the life; in whom whosoever believeth shall live, though he die, and whosoever liveth and believeth in Him shall not die eternally: we meekly beseech Thee, O Father, to raise us from the death of sin unto the life of righteousness; that when we shall depart this life we may rest in Him, and may receive that blessing which Thy well-beloved Son shall pronounce to all that love and fear Thee, saying, "Come, ye blessed of My Father, receive the kingdom prepared for you from the beginning of the world." Grant this, we beseech Thee, O Merciful Father, through Jesus Christ our Mediator and Redeemer. **Amen.**

Here may the Minister and the People unite in the Lord's Prayer.
Then may the Minister say:

The grace of the Lord Jesus Christ, and the love of God, and the communion of the Holy Spirit, be with you all. **Amen.**

THE ORDER FOR THE BURIAL OF A CHILD

The Minister shall begin the service by reading the following sentences:

Jesus said, I am the resurrection and the life: he that believeth in Me, though he were dead, yet shall he live: and whosoever liveth and believeth in Me shall never die.

He shall feed His flock like a shepherd: He shall gather the lambs with His arm, and carry them in His bosom.

Then shall the Minister say:

Let us pray.

Here may the Minister offer one or both of the following Prayers:

Our Loving Father, comfortingly look upon us in our sorrow and abide with us in our loneliness. O Thou who makest no life in vain and who lovest all that Thou hast made, lift upon us the light of Thy countenance and give us peace. **Amen.**

We pray that Thou wilt keep in tender love the life which we shall hold in blessed memory. Help us who continue here to serve Thee with constancy, trusting in Thy promise of eternal life, that hereafter we may be united with Thy blessed children in glory everlasting, through Jesus Christ our Lord. **Amen.**

Here may be read these Psalms:

The Lord is my shepherd; I shall not want.
He maketh me to lie down in green pastures:
He leadeth me beside the still waters.
He restoreth my soul:
He leadeth me in the paths of righteousness for His Name's sake.
Yea, though I walk through the valley of the shadow of death,
I will fear no evil: for Thou art with me;
Thy rod and Thy staff, they comfort me.
Thou preparest a table before me in the presence of mine enemies;
Thou anointest my head with oil;
My cup runneth over.
Surely goodness and mercy shall follow me all the days of my life:
And I will dwell in the house of the Lord for ever.

I will lift up mine eyes unto the hills.
From whence shall my help come?
My help cometh from the Lord,
Who made heaven and earth.
He will not suffer thy foot to be moved:
He that keepeth thee will not slumber.
Behold, He that keepeth Israel
Shall neither slumber nor sleep.
The Lord is thy keeper:
The Lord is thy shade upon thy right hand.
The Lord shall preserve thy going out and thy coming in
From this time forth, and even for evermore.

Here shall be read these Lessons from the Gospels:

At the same time came the disciples unto Jesus, saying, Who is the greatest in the kingdom of heaven? And Jesus called a little child unto Him, and set him in the midst of them, and said, Verily I say unto you, Except ye be converted, and become as little children, ye shall not enter into the kingdom of heaven. Whosoever therefore shall humble himself as this little child, the same is greatest in the kingdom of heaven. And whoso shall receive one such little child in My Name receiveth Me.

Take heed that ye despise not one of these little ones: for I say unto you, That in heaven their angels do always behold the face of My Father which is in heaven.

Let not your heart be troubled; ye believe in God, believe also in Me. In My Father's house are many mansions: if it were not so, I would have told you. I go to prepare a place for you. And if I go and prepare a place for you, I will come again, and receive you unto Myself; that where I am, there ye may be also. I am the way, the truth, and the life. If ye love Me, keep My commandments. And I will pray the Father, and He shall give you another Comforter, that He may abide with you for ever; even the Spirit of truth; whom the world cannot receive, because it seeth Him not, neither knoweth Him: but ye know Him; for He dwelleth with you, and shall be in you. I will not leave you comfortless: I will come to you. Because I live, ye shall live also.

Peace I leave with you, My peace I give unto you: not as the world giveth, give I unto you. Let not your heart be troubled, neither let it be afraid.

Here may follow music and an Address, after which the Minister shall say:

Let us pray.

Here may the Minister offer extemporary Prayer or the following Prayer:

O God, who art the Father of the families of earth, look with compassion upon this bereaved family, and pour Thy heavenly comfort into their hearts. Help them by faith to see this child, over whom they grieve, safe in that home where sin and sorrow cannot enter. Enrich with Thy presence those who mourn; abide in their home, lift up their hearts; bless them with Thy favor, which is better than life; and so guide them through the trials and temptations of this world that their reunited family may know fullness of joy in Thy presence for evermore. Grant this through Him who loved little children and blessed them, even Thy Son Jesus Christ, our Lord. **Amen.**

Then may the Minister say:

The grace of the Lord Jesus Christ, and the love of God, and the communion of the Holy Spirit, be with you all. **Amen.**

At the grave, when the People are assembled, the Minister shall say:

Jesus saith to His disciples, Ye now therefore have sorrow: but I will see you again, and your heart shall rejoice, and your joy no man taketh from you.

Forasmuch as the departed has entered into the life immortal, we therefore commit *his* body to its resting place, but *his* spirit we commend to God, remembering how Jesus said upon the cross, "Father, into Thy hands I commend My spirit."

Then shall the Minister say:

Let us pray.

Almighty God, Father of our Lord Jesus Christ, who gave His life for our redemption and who promised the Holy Spirit, the Comforter; strengthen, we beseech Thee, the faith of these bereaved ones, that they may contemplate with peace the blessedness of that eternal home which Thou hast prepared for all who love and serve Thee. Grant that they, and all others whose joy is turned into mourning, cleaving more closely unto Him, who is the resurrection and the life, may be led by Thy Spirit through this uncertain life, till the day break and the shadows flee away. **Amen.**

Here the Minister and the People may unite in the Lord's Prayer.
Then may the Minister say:

The grace of the Lord Jesus Christ, and the love of God, and the **communion** of the Holy Spirit, be with you all. **Amen.**

THE DEDICATION OF AN ORGAN

THE ORDER FOR THE DEDICATION OF AN ORGAN

After an Organ Prelude, a Processional or Opening Hymn shall be sung, such as,

15—"Angel voices, ever singing."

Then shall the Minister say, the People responding:

Dearly Beloved, we learn from the Holy Scriptures that devout men set apart temples for the worship of God, and used musical instruments therein for His praise and adoration. We therefore assemble here for the purpose of dedicating this Organ for service in the worship of Almighty God.

The Call to Worship

Surely the Lord is in this place.

This is none other than the house of the Lord: this is the gate of heaven.

Enter into His gates with thanksgiving and into His courts with praise.

O magnify the Lord with me; let us exalt His Name together.

Then shall the Gloria Patri *be said or sung:*

Glory be to the Father, and to the Son, and to the Holy Ghost; As it was in the beginning, is now, and ever shall be, world without end. Amen.

Then shall the Minister and People say the Collect:

Let us pray.

Almighty God, unto whom all hearts are open, all desires known, and from whom no secrets are hid, cleanse the thoughts of our hearts by the inspiration of Thy Holy Spirit, that we may perfectly love Thee, and worthily magnify Thy holy Name, through Jesus Christ our Lord. Amen.

[The Organ may then be presented for Dedication by one of the Trustees, or someone designated for that purpose, in some such words as:]

We present this Organ for dedication (if a gift or memorial so stating) the gift of ——————————— for the glory of God and in loving memory of ———————————.

Then shall the Minister say these words of Dedication, all the People standing and uniting in the responses:

In the Name of the Father, and of the Son, and of the Holy Spirit, we dedicate this Organ to the praise of Almighty God.

Praise God in His sanctuary: praise Him in the firmament of His power. Praise Him with the sound of the trumpet; praise Him with psaltery and harp.

We dedicate this Organ to the cultivation of a high art: to the interpretation of the message of the masters of music, to an appreciation of the great doxologies of the Church, and to the development of the language of praise which belongeth both to earth and to heaven.

Praise Him with stringed instruments and organs. Let everything that hath breath praise the Lord. Praise ye the Lord.

We dedicate this Organ to the wedding march, to thanksgiving on festal occasions, and to such inspiration in the service of song that all people may praise the Lord.

O sing unto the Lord a new song: sing unto the Lord all the earth, in psalms and hymns and spiritual songs, singing and making melody in your heart unto the Lord.

We dedicate this Organ to the healing of life's discords, and the revealing of the hidden soul of harmony; to the lifting of the depressed and the comforting of the sorrowing; to the humbling of the heart before the eternal mysteries and the lifting of the soul to abiding beauty and joy by the gospel of infinite love and good will.

That at the Name of Jesus every knee should bow, of things in heaven, and things in earth, and things under the earth; and that every tongue should confess that Jesus Christ is Lord, to the glory of God the Father.

Then shall the Minister say:

Let us pray.

Our God and Father, whom the generations have worshiped with concord of sweet sound, be pleased to accept this Organ as a song of praise unto Thee. **Amen.**

Grant that its music, with accompanying song, may come as a blessed benediction upon all who worship here. **Amen.**

May this Organ become undying music in the world as its notes of cheer, comfort, communion, and courage are modulated into human lives for daily task and noble service. **Amen.**

To all organists who shall sound its notes, and to all worshipers who shall be lifted Godward by its voice, may there come at times the sweep of hallelujahs from the throne of the Redeemed until earth below shall be attuned to heaven above, singing hallelujah to Him who reigneth, Lord of lords, the King of kings. **Hallelujah! Amen.**

[Here may be sung a suitable Hymn or an Anthem, after which a Sermon or Address may be delivered. An Offering may then be received, followed by the singing of Hymn 552 and the Benediction.]

THE DEDICATION OF A CHURCH
AN ORDER FOR THE DEDICATION OF A CHURCH

Let the service of worship begin at the time appointed. Let the people kneel or bow in silent prayer upon entering the sanctuary.

PRELUDE *The people in devout meditation.*

HYMN *The people standing.*

CALL TO WORSHIP

Minister: Serve the Lord with gladness.

People: **Enter into his gates with thanksgiving, and into his courts with praise.**

Minister: O come, let us worship and bow down: let us kneel before the Lord our Maker.

People: **He is our God; and we are the people of his pasture, and the sheep of his hand. Amen.**

Here let the people be seated.

INVOCATION *The minister.*

Let us pray.

O God, eternal and ever blessed, who delightest in the assembling of thy people in the sanctuary; receive us graciously as we come into thy house, and grant, we entreat thee, that peace and prosperity may be found within its walls, that the glory of God may be the light thereof, and that we may be satisfied with the goodness of thy house; through Jesus Christ our Lord. **Amen.**

DEDICATION OF A CHURCH

COLLECT FOR DEDICATION DAY *Here let the people unite with the minister in prayer.*

Direct us, O Lord, in all our doings, with thy most gracious favor, and further us with thy continual help, that in all our works, begun, continued, and ended in thee, we may glorify thy holy name, and finally, by thy mercy, obtain everlasting life; through Jesus Christ our Lord. Amen.

ANTHEM

CANTICLE OF THE CHURCH *To be said responsively by the minister and the people. Here let the people stand and remain standing until after the Affirmation of Faith.*

Arise, shine; for thy light is come, and the glory of the LORD is risen upon thee.

For behold, darkness shall cover the earth, and gross darkness the people.

But the LORD shall rise upon thee, and his glory shall be seen upon thee.

And the nations shall come to thy light, and kings to the brightness of thy rising.

The abundance of the sea shall be turned unto thee; the wealth of the nations shall come unto thee.

Thy gates shall stand always open; they shall not be shut day nor night,

That men may bring unto thee the wealth of the nations, and their kings led with them.

For the nation and kingdom that will not serve thee shall perish; yea, it shall be utterly wasted.

Violence shall no more be heard in thy land, wasting nor destruction within thy borders.

But thou shalt call thy walls Salvation, and thy gates thou shalt call Praise.

The sun shall be no more thy light by day; neither for brightness shall the moon give light unto thee.

But the LORD shall be unto thee an everlasting light, and thy God thy glory.

Thy sun shall no more go down; neither shall thy moon withdraw itself.

For the LORD shall be thine everlasting light, and the days of thy mourning shall be ended.

GLORIA PATRI

AFFIRMATION OF FAITH *The minister and the people.*

I believe in God the Father Almighty, Maker of heaven and earth; and in Jesus Christ his only Son our Lord; who was conceived by the Holy Spirit, born of the Virgin Mary, suffered under Pontius Pilate, was crucified, dead, and buried; the third day he rose from the dead; he ascended into heaven, and sitteth at the right hand of God the Father Almighty; from thence he shall come to judge the quick and the dead. I believe in the Holy Spirit, the holy catholic Church, the communion of saints, the forgiveness of sins, the resurrection of the body, and the life everlasting. Amen.

THE SCRIPTURE LESSON

PRAYER

HYMN

THE SERMON *Which may be followed by prayer.*

THE DEDICATION OF GIFTS AND TITHES

OFFERTORY RESPONSE *The people standing.*

> Praise God, from whom all blessings flow;
> Praise him, all creatures here below;
> Praise him above, ye heavenly host:
> Praise Father, Son, and Holy Ghost. Amen.

Here let the people be seated.

THE ACT OF DEDICATION

Some person authorized shall say to the officiating minister:
We present this building to be dedicated to the glory of God and the service of men.

Then shall the minister say:
By what name shall this church henceforth be known?

To which shall be answered:
It shall be called the *N.—— Methodist Church.*

Then shall the minister say to all the people:
Beloved in the Lord, we rejoice that God put it into the hearts of his people to build this house to the glory of his name. I now accept this building to be known as *N.* Methodist Church, to dedicate it, and to set it apart for the worship of Almighty God and the service of all men. Let us therefore, as we are assembled, solemnly dedicate this place to its proper and sacred uses.

Then, all standing, the minister shall say, the people responding:
To the glory of God the Father, who has called us by his grace;
To the honor of his Son, who loved us and gave himself for us;
To the praise of the Holy Spirit, who illumines and sanctifies us;

560*b*

We dedicate this house.

For the worship of God in prayer and praise;
For the preaching of the everlasting gospel;
For the celebration of the holy Sacraments;

We dedicate this house.

For the comfort of all who mourn;
For strength to those who are tempted;
For light to those who seek the way;

We dedicate this house.

For the hallowing of family life;
For teaching and guiding the young;
For the perfecting of the saints;

We dedicate this house.

For the conversion of sinners;
For the promotion of righteousness;
For the extension of the Kingdom of God;

We dedicate this house.

In the unity of the faith;
In the bond of Christian brotherhood;
In charity and good will to all;

We dedicate this house.

In gratitude for the labors of all who love and serve this church;
In loving remembrance of those who have finished their course;
In the hope of a blessed immortality through Jesus Christ our
    Lord;

We dedicate this house.

Then shall the minister and people together say:

**We now, the people of this church and congregation, com-
passed about with a great cloud of witnesses, grateful for our
heritage, sensible of the sacrifice of our fathers in the faith,
confessing that apart from us their work cannot be made per-
fect, do dedicate ourselves anew to the worship and service of
Almighty God; through Jesus Christ our Lord. Amen.**

Then shall the minister say:

Accept, O God our Father, this service at our hands, and bless
it to the end that this congregation of faithful people may make
manifest the Church of the living God, the pillar and ground of truth,
and so may this house be the place where thine honor dwelleth and
the whole earth be filled with thy glory; through Jesus Christ our
Lord.

THE RITUAL

THE SANCTUS *To be sung or said responsively by the minister and the people.*

Therefore with angels and archangels, and with all the company of heaven, we laud and magnify thy glorious name, evermore praising thee, and saying:

Holy, holy, holy, Lord God of hosts, heaven and earth are full of thy glory. Glory be to thee, O Lord most high! Amen.

PRAYER *Here the minister may offer an extempore prayer or one or more of the following prayers:*

O eternal God, whom the heaven of heavens cannot contain, much less the walls of temples made with hands; graciously accept the dedication of this house to thy honor and glory. **Amen.**

Grant, O Lord, that all who here share in the Sacraments, the ministry of the Word, and the fellowship of praise and prayer may know that God is in this place, may hear thy voice within their hearts, and may go forth to extend to the uttermost bounds of life the Lord Christ's Kingdom. **Amen.**

Now therefore, O Lord, let thine eyes be open toward this house day and night; and let thine ears be ready toward the prayers of thy children, which they shall make unto thee in this place. And whensoever thy servants shall make to thee their petitions, do thou hear them, and when thou hearest, forgive. Grant, O Lord, we beseech thee, that here and elsewhere thy ministers may be clothed with righteousness, and thy saints rejoice in thy salvation. And may we all, with thy people everywhere, grow up into a holy temple in the Lord, and be at last received into the glorious temple above, the house not made with hands, eternal in the heavens. And to the Father, and the Son, and the Holy Spirit, be glory and praise, world without end. **Amen.**

HYMN

SILENT PRAYER

BENEDICTION

POSTLUDE

RESPONSIVE READINGS

"And further, that the people by daily hearing of Holy Scripture read in the Church should continually profit more and more in the knowledge of God, and be the more inflamed by the love of His true religion."

(The Liturgy of Edward VI, 1549 A.D.)

Responsive Readings

FIRST SUNDAY

FIRST READING

GOD THE COMFORTER

Comfort ye, comfort ye My people, saith your God.

Speak ye comfortably to Jerusalem, and cry unto her, that her warfare is accomplished, that her iniquity is pardoned: for she hath received of the Lord's hand double for all her sins.

The voice of Him that crieth in the wilderness, Prepare ye the way of the Lord, make straight in the desert a highway for our God.

Every valley shall be exalted, and every mountain and hill shall be made low: and the crooked shall be made straight, and the rough places plain.

The glory of the Lord shall be revealed, and all flesh shall see it together: for the mouth of the Lord hath spoken it.

The voice said, Cry. And he said, What shall I cry? All flesh is grass, and all the goodliness thereof is as the flower in the field.

The grass withereth, the flower fadeth: because the spirit of the Lord bloweth upon it: surely the people is grass.

The grass withereth, the flower fadeth: but the word of our God shall stand for ever.

O Zion, that bringest good tidings, get thee up into the high mountain; O Jerusalem, that bringest good tidings, lift up thy voice with strength;

Lift it up, be not afraid; say unto the cities of Judah, Behold your God!

Behold, the Lord God will come with strong hand, and His arm shall rule for Him: behold, His reward is with Him, and His work before Him.

He shall feed His flock like a shepherd: He shall gather the lambs with His arm, and carry them in His bosom, and shall gently lead those that are with young.

He giveth power to the faint; and to them that have no might He increaseth strength.

Even the youths shall faint and be weary, and the young men shall utterly fall:

They that wait upon the Lord shall renew their strength;

They shall mount up with wings as eagles; they shall run, and not be weary; and they shall walk, and not faint.

SECOND READING

A NEW SONG

O sing unto the Lord a new song: sing unto the Lord, all the earth.

Sing unto the Lord, bless His name; show forth His salvation from day to day.

Declare His glory among the nations, His wonders among all people.

For the Lord is great, and greatly to be praised: He is to be feared above all gods.

563

For all the gods of the nations are idols: but the Lord made the heavens.

Honor and majesty are before Him: strength and beauty are in His sanctuary.

Give unto the Lord, O ye kindreds of the people, give unto the Lord glory and strength.

Give unto the Lord the glory due unto His Name: bring an offering, and come into His courts.

O worship the Lord in the beauty of holiness: fear before Him, all the earth.

Say among the nations that the Lord reigneth: the world also shall be established that it shall not be moved: He shall judge the people righteously.

Let the heavens rejoice, and let the earth be glad; let the sea roar, and the fullness thereof.

Let the field be joyful, and all that is therein: then shall all the trees of the wood rejoice before the Lord:

For He cometh, for He cometh to judge the earth.

He shall judge the world with righteousness, and the people with His truth.

SECOND SUNDAY

FIRST READING

GOD'S CREATIVE WORD

In the beginning was the Word, and the Word was with God, and the Word was God. The same was in the Beginning with God.

All things were made by Him; and without Him was not any thing made that was made.

In Him was life; and the life was the light of men.

The light shineth in darkness; and the darkness comprehended it not.

There was a man sent from God, whose name was John.

The same came for a witness, to bear witness of the Light, that all men through him might believe.

He was not that Light, but was sent to bear witness of that Light.

That was the true Light, which lighteth every man that cometh into the world.

He was in the world, and the world was made by Him, and the world knew Him not.

He came unto His own, and His own received Him not.

As many as received Him, to them gave He power to become the sons of God, even to them that believe on His Name:

Which were born, not of blood, nor of the will of the flesh, nor of the will of man, but of God.

The Word was made flesh, and dwelt among us.

We beheld His glory, the glory as of the only begotten of the Father, full of grace and truth.

SECOND READING

GLADNESS IN THE LORD

Bless the Lord, O my soul. O Lord my God, Thou art very great; Thou art clothed with honor and majesty:

Who coverest Thyself with light as with a garment: who stretchest out the heavens like a curtain:

Who layeth the beams of His chambers in the waters: who maketh the clouds His chariot: who walketh upon the wings of the wind:

Who maketh His angels spirits; His ministers a flaming fire:

Who laid the foundations of the earth, that it should not be removed for ever.

Thou coveredst it with the deep as with a garment: the waters stood above the mountains.

At Thy rebuke they fled; at the voice of Thy thunder they hasted away.

They go up by the mountains; they go down by the valleys unto the place which Thou hast founded for them.

Thou hast set a bound that they may not pass over; that they turn not again to cover the earth.

He sendeth the springs into the valleys, which run among the hills.

They give drink to every beast of the field: the wild asses quench their thirst.

By them shall the birds of the heaven have their habitation, which sing among the branches.

He watereth the hills from His chambers: the earth is satisfied with the fruit of Thy works.

He causeth the grass to grow for the cattle, and herb for the service of man: that he may bring forth food out of the earth.

O Lord, how manifold are Thy works! in wisdom hast Thou made them all: the earth is full of Thy riches.

The glory of the Lord shall endure forever: the Lord shall rejoice in His works.

He looketh on the earth, and it

trembleth: He toucheth the hills, and they smoke.

I will sing unto the Lord as long as I live: I will sing praise to my God while I have my being.

My meditation of Him shall be sweet: I will be glad in the Lord.

Bless thou the Lord, O my soul. Praise ye the Lord.

THIRD SUNDAY

FIRST READING

SPIRIT AND LIFE

God is a Spirit: and they that worship Him must worship Him in spirit and in truth.

It is the spirit that quickeneth; the flesh profiteth nothing;

The words that I speak unto you, they are spirit and they are life.

The wind bloweth where it listeth, and thou hearest the sound thereof, but canst not tell whence it cometh, and whither it goeth.

So is every one that is born of the Spirit.

That which is born of the flesh is flesh; and that which is born of the Spirit is spirit.

Marvel not that I said unto thee, Ye must be born again.

Behold, what manner of love the Father hath bestowed upon us, that we should be called the sons of God.

Therefore the world knoweth us not, because it knew Him not.

Beloved, now are we the sons of God, and it doth not yet appear what we shall be;

But we know that, when He shall appear, we shall be like Him; for we shall see Him as He is.

Every man that hath this hope in him purifieth himself, even as He is pure.

We know that we have passed from death unto life, because we love the brethren. He that loveth not his brother abideth in death.

Hereby perceive we the love of God, because He laid down His life for us: and we ought to lay down our lives for the brethren.

My little children, let us not love in word, neither in tongue; but in deed and in truth.

He that keepeth His commandments dwelleth in Him, and He in him. And hereby we know that He abideth in us, by the Spirit which He hath given us.

SECOND READING .

THE ETERNAL PRESENCE

O Lord, Thou hast searched me, and known me.

Thou knowest my downsitting and mine uprising; Thou understandest my thought afar off.

Thou compassest my path and my lying down, and art acquainted with all my ways.

For there is not a word in my tongue, but, lo, O Lord, Thou knowest it altogether.

Thou hast beset me behind and before, and laid Thine hand upon me.

Such knowledge is too wonderful for me; it is high, I cannot attain unto it.

Whither shall I go from Thy Spirit? or whither shall I flee from Thy presence?

If I ascend into heaven, Thou art there: if I make my bed in the grave, behold, Thou art there.

If I take the wings of the morning, and dwell in the uttermost parts of the sea;

Even there shall Thy hand lead me, and Thy right hand shall hold me.

If I say, Surely the darkness shall cover me; even the night shall be light about me.

Yea, the darkness hideth not from Thee; but the night shineth as the day: the darkness and the light are both alike to Thee.

How precious also are Thy thoughts unto me, O God! how great is the sum of them!

If I should count them, they are more in number than the sand: when I awake, I am still with Thee.

Search me, O God, and know my heart: try me, and know my thoughts:

See if there be any wicked way in me, and lead me in the way everlasting.

FOURTH SUNDAY

FIRST READING

THE KINGDOM OF GOD

God, who at sundry times and in divers manners spake in time past unto the fathers by the prophets,

Hath in these last days spoken unto us by His Son, whom He hath appointed heir of all things, by whom also He made the worlds.

Unto the Son He saith, Thy throne, O God, is for ever and ever: a scepter of righteousness is the scepter of Thy kingdom.

Thou hast loved righteousness,

566

and hated iniquity; therefore God, even Thy God, hath anointed Thee with the oil of gladness above Thy fellows.

The kingdom of God is not meat and drink: but righteousness, and peace, and joy in the Holy Spirit.

Let us therefore follow after the things which make for peace, and things wherewith one may edify another.

Jesus said, Unto what is the kingdom of God like? and whereunto shall I resemble it?

It is like a grain of mustard seed, which a man took, and cast into his garden; and it grew, and waxed a great tree; and the birds of the air lodged in the branches of it.

Again He said, Whereunto shall I liken the kingdom of God?

It is like leaven, which a woman took and hid in three measures of meal, till the whole was leavened.

Again, the kingdom of heaven is like unto treasure hid in a field;

The which when a man hath found, he hideth, and for joy thereof goeth and selleth all that he hath, and buyeth that field.

Again, the kingdom of heaven is like unto a merchantman, seeking goodly pearls;

Who, when he had found one pearl of great price, went and sold all that he had, and bought it.

Seek not ye what ye shall eat, or what ye shall drink, neither be ye of doubtful mind; but rather seek ye the kingdom of God.

Fear not, little flock; for it is your Father's good pleasure to give you the kingdom.

SECOND READING
THE LORD REIGNETH

O come, let us sing unto the Lord: let us make a joyful noise to the Rock of our salvation.

Let us come before His presence with thanksgiving, and make a joyful noise unto Him with psalms.

For the Lord is a great God, and a great King above all gods. In His hand are the deep places of the earth: the strength of the hills is His also.

The sea is His, and He made it: and His hands formed the dry land.

O come, let us worship and bow down: let us kneel before the Lord our maker.

For He is our God; and we are the people of His pasture, and the sheep of His hand.

The Lord reigneth, He is clothed with majesty; the Lord is clothed with strength, wherewith He hath girded himself.

The world also is stablished, that it cannot be moved. Thy throne is established of old: Thou art from everlasting.

The floods have lifted up, O Lord, the floods have lifted up their voice; the floods lift up their waves.

The Lord on high is mightier than the noise of many waters, yea, than the mighty waves of the sea. Thy testimonies are very sure: holiness becometh Thine house, O Lord, for ever.

The Lord reigneth; let the earth rejoice; let the multitude of isles be glad thereof.

Clouds and darkness are round about Him: righteousness and

judgment are the habitation of His throne.

A fire goeth before Him; His lightnings enlightened the world; the earth saw and trembled.

The hills melted like wax at the presence of the Lord, at the presence of the Lord of the whole earth. The heavens declare His righteousness, and all the people see His glory.

Thou, O Lord, art high above all the earth. Ye that love the Lord, hate evil; He preserveth the souls of His saints; He delivereth them.

Light is sown for the righteous, and gladness for the upright in heart. Rejoice in the Lord, ye righteous; and give thanks at the remembrance of His holiness.

FIFTH SUNDAY

FIRST READING

THE BREAD OF LIFE

Jesus said unto them: I am the Bread of Life:

He that cometh to Me shall never hunger; and he that believeth on Me shall never thirst.

If any man thirst, let him come unto Me, and drink.

Whosoever drinketh of this water shall thirst again:

Whosoever drinketh of the water that I shall give him shall never thirst: but the water that I shall give him shall be in him a well of water springing up into everlasting life.

I will give unto him that is athirst of the fountain of the water of life freely.

For I came down from heaven, not to do Mine own will, but the will of Him that sent Me.

They said therefore unto Him, What sign showest Thou then, that we may see, and believe Thee? what dost Thou work?

Our fathers did eat manna in the desert; as it is written, He gave them bread from heaven to eat.

Then Jesus said unto them, Verily, verily, I say unto you, Moses gave you not that bread from heaven; but My Father giveth you the true bread from heaven.

For the bread of God is He which cometh down from heaven, and giveth life unto the world.

Then said they unto Him, Lord, evermore give us this bread.

SECOND READING

THE SATISFYING GOD

O God, Thou art my God; early will I seek Thee: my soul thirsteth for Thee, my flesh longeth for Thee in a dry and thirsty land, where no water is;

To see Thy power and Thy glory, so as I have seen Thee in the sanctuary.

Because Thy lovingkindness is better than life, my lips shall praise Thee.

Thus will I bless Thee while I live: I will lift up my hands in Thy Name.

My soul shall be satisfied as with marrow and fatness; and my mouth shall praise Thee with joyful lips:

When I remember Thee upon my bed, and meditate on Thee in the night watches.

Because Thou hast been my help,

therefore in the shadow of Thy wings will I rejoice.

My soul followeth hard after Thee: Thy right hand upholdeth me.

O give thanks unto the Lord, for He is good: for His mercy endureth for ever.

Let the redeemed of the Lord say so, whom He hath redeemed from the hand of the enemy;

And gathered them out of the lands, from the east, and from the west, from the north, and from the south.

They wandered in the wilderness in a solitary way; they found no city to dwell in.

Hungry and thirsty, their soul fainted in them.

Then they cried unto the Lord in their trouble, and He delivered them out of their distresses.

He led them forth by the right way, that they might go to a city of habitation.

O that men would praise the Lord for His goodness, and for His wonderful works to the children of men!

SIXTH SUNDAY

FIRST READING

The Good Shepherd

The Lord is my shepherd; I shall not want. He maketh me to lie down in green pastures: He leadeth me beside the still waters.

He restoreth my soul: He leadeth me in the paths of righteousness for His Name's sake.

Yea, though I walk through the valley of the shadow of death, I will fear no evil;

For Thou art with me; Thy rod and Thy staff they comfort me.

Thou preparest a table before me in the presence of mine enemies; Thou anointest my head with oil; my cup runneth over.

Surely goodness and mercy shall follow me all the days of my life: and I will dwell in the house of the Lord for ever.

Jesus said, Verily, verily, I say unto you, I am the door of the sheep.

All that ever came before Me are thieves and robbers: but the sheep did not hear them.

I am the door: by Me if any man enter in, he shall be saved, and shall go in and out, and find pasture.

The thief cometh not, but for to steal, and to kill, and to destroy.

I am come that they might have life, and that they might have it more abundantly.

I am the good shepherd: the good shepherd giveth His life for the sheep.

I am the good shepherd, and know My sheep, and am known of Mine.

As the Father knoweth Me, even so know I the Father: and I lay down My life for the sheep.

Other sheep I have, which are not of this fold: them also I must bring, and they shall hear My voice; and there shall be one fold, and one shepherd.

My sheep hear My voice, and I know them, and they follow Me; and I give unto them eternal life.

They shall never perish, neither shall any man pluck them out of My hand.

My Father, who gave them Me, is greater than all; and no man is able to pluck them out of My

Father's hand. I and My Father are one.

SECOND READING

God Seeks His Own

Thus saith the Lord God; Behold, I, even I, will both search My sheep, and seek them out.

As a shepherd seeketh out his flock in the day that he is among his sheep that are scattered;

So will I seek out My sheep, and will deliver them out of all places where they have been scattered in the cloudy and dark day.

I will bring them out from the people, and gather them from the countries.

I will bring them to their own land, and feed them upon the mountains of Israel by the rivers.

I will feed My flock, and I will cause them to lie down, saith the Lord God.

I will seek that which was lost, and bring again that which was driven away, and will bind up that which was broken, and will strengthen that which was sick:

I will make with them a covenant of peace, and will cause the evil beasts to cease out of the land; and they shall dwell safely in the wilderness, and sleep in the woods.

I will make them and the places round about My hill a blessing;

I will cause the shower to come down in his season: there shall be showers of blessing.

The tree of the field shall yield her fruit, and the earth shall yield her increase, and they shall be safe in their land, and shall know that I am the Lord, when I have broken the bands of their yoke.

Thus shall they know that I the Lord their God am with them, and that they are My people, saith the Lord God.

SEVENTH SUNDAY

FIRST READING

The Way of Peace

Happy art thou. Who is like unto thee, O people saved by the Lord, the shield of thy help?

As thy days, so shall thy strength be. The eternal God is thy refuge, and underneath are the everlasting arms.

Truly my soul waiteth upon God; from Him cometh my salvation. My soul, wait thou only upon God, for my expectation is from Him.

He only is my rock and my salvation; He is my defense; I shall not be moved.

In God is my salvation and my glory; the rock of my strength, and my refuge, is in God.

Trust in Him at all times; ye people, pour out your heart before Him; God is a refuge for us.

Thou wilt keep him in perfect peace, whose mind is stayed on Thee, because he trusteth in Thee.

Trust ye in the Lord for ever; for in the Lord our God is everlasting strength.

Thus saith the Lord, In returning and rest shall ye be saved; in quietness and in confidence shall be your strength.

Therefore will the Lord wait, that He may be gracious unto you; and therefore will He be exalted, that He may have mercy upon you.

Thus saith the Lord, Fear not, for

I have redeemed thee; I have called thee by thy name; thou art Mine.

When thou passest through the waters, I will be with thee; and through the rivers, they shall not overflow thee.

When thou walkest through the fire, thou shalt not be burned; neither shall the flame kindle upon thee.

For I am the Lord thy God, thy Saviour. Fear not for I am with thee. Ye are My witnesses, saith the Lord.

SECOND READING

God Our Salvation

Lord, how are they increased that trouble me! many are they that rise up against me.

Many there be which say of my soul, There is no help for him in God.

But Thou, O Lord, art a shield for me; my glory, and the lifter up of mine head.

I cried unto the Lord with my voice, and He heard me out of His holy hill.

I laid me down and slept; I awaked; for the Lord sustained me.

I will not be afraid of ten thousands of people, that have set themselves against me round about.

Arise, O Lord; save me, O my God:

Salvation belongeth unto the Lord: Thy blessing is upon Thy people.

Give ear to my words, O Lord; consider my meditation.

Hearken unto the voice of my cry, my King, and my God: for unto Thee will I pray.

My voice shalt Thou hear in the morning, O Lord; in the morning will I direct my prayer unto Thee, and will look up.

For Thou art not a God that hath pleasure in wickedness: neither shall evil dwell with Thee.

As for me, I will come into Thy house in the multitude of Thy mercy: and in Thy fear will I worship toward Thy holy temple.

For Thou, Lord, wilt bless the righteous; with favor wilt Thou compass him as with a shield.

EIGHTH SUNDAY

FIRST READING

A Prayer of Penitence

Have mercy upon me, O God, according to Thy loving kindness.

According unto the multitude of Thy tender mercies blot out my transgressions.

Wash me thoroughly from mine iniquity;

And cleanse me from my sin.

For I acknowledge my transgressions;

And my sin is ever before me.

Against Thee, Thee only, have I sinned, and done this evil in Thy sight;

That Thou mightest be justified when Thou speakest, and be clear when Thou judgest.

Behold, Thou desirest truth in the inward parts;

And in the hidden part Thou shalt make me to know wisdom.

Purge me with hyssop, and I shall be clean;

Wash me and I shall be whiter than snow.

Make me to hear joy and gladness,
That the bones which Thou hast broken may rejoice.

Hide Thy face from my sins;
And blot out all mine iniquities.

Create in me a clean heart, O God;
And renew a right spirit within me.

Cast me not away from Thy presence;
And take not Thy Holy Spirit from me.

Restore unto me the joy of Thy salvation;
And uphold me with Thy free Spirit.

Then will I teach transgressors Thy ways;
And sinners shall be converted unto Thee.

Deliver me from bloodguiltiness, O God, Thou God of my salvation.
And my tongue shall sing aloud of Thy righteousness.

O Lord, open Thou my lips;
And my mouth shall show forth Thy praise.

For Thou desirest not sacrifice; else would I give it;
Thou delightest not in burnt offering.

The sacrifices of God are a broken spirit;
A broken and a contrite heart, O God, Thou wilt not despise.

SECOND READING

SINCERITY AND PRAYER

Take heed that ye do not your alms before men, to be seen of them: otherwise ye have no reward of your Father who is in heaven.

Therefore when thou doest thine alms, do not sound a trumpet before thee, as the hypocrites do in the synagogues and in the streets, that they may have glory of men. Verily I say unto you, They have their reward.

When thou doest alms, let not thy left hand know what thy right hand doeth:

That thine alms may be in secret: and thy Father who seeth in secret Himself shall reward thee openly.

When thou prayest, thou shalt not be as the hypocrites are: for they love to pray standing in the synagogues and in the corners of the streets, that they may be seen of men. Verily I say unto you, They have their reward.

Thou, when thou prayest, enter into thy closet, and when thou hast shut thy door, pray to thy Father who is in secret; and thy Father who seeth in secret shall reward thee openly.

When ye pray, use not vain repetitions, as the heathen do: for they think that they shall be heard for their much speaking.

Be not ye therefore like unto them: for your Father knoweth what things ye have need of, before ye ask Him.

NINTH SUNDAY

FIRST READING

CHRIST THE LIFE

I am the true vine, and My Father is the husbandman.

Every branch in Me that beareth

not fruit He taketh away: and every branch that beareth fruit, He purgeth it, that it may bring forth more fruit.

Now ye are clean through the word which I have spoken unto you.

Abide in Me, and I in you. As the branch cannot bear fruit of itself, except it abide in the vine; no more can ye, except ye abide in Me.

I am the vine, ye are the branches. He that abideth in Me, and I in him, the same bringeth forth much fruit; for without Me ye can do nothing.

If a man abide not in Me, he is cast forth as a branch, and is withered; and men gather them, and cast them into the fire, and they are burned.

If ye abide in Me and My words abide in you, ye shall ask what ye will, and it shall be done unto you.

Herein is My Father glorified, that ye bear much fruit; so shall ye be My disciples.

As the Father hath loved Me, so have I loved you: continue ye in My love.

If ye keep My commandments, ye shall abide in My love; even as I have kept My Father's commandments, and abide in His love.

These things have I spoken unto you, that My joy might remain in you, and that your joy might be full.

This is My commandment, That ye love one another, as I have loved you.

Greater love hath no man than this, that a man lay down his life for his friends.

Ye are my friends, if ye do whatsoever I command you.

SECOND READING

The Blessed Life

Blessed is the man that walketh not in the counsel of the ungodly, nor standeth in the way of sinners, nor sitteth in the seat of the scornful.

His delight is the law of the Lord; and in His law doth he meditate day and night.

He shall be like a tree planted by the rivers of water, that bringeth forth his fruit in his season; his leaf also shall not wither; and whatsoever he doeth shall prosper.

The ungodly are not so: but are like the chaff which the wind driveth away.

Therefore the ungodly shall not stand in the judgment, nor sinners in the congregation of the righteous.

For the Lord knoweth the way of the righteous: but the way of the ungodly shall perish.

TENTH SUNDAY

FIRST READING

The Divine Consolation

Let not your heart be troubled: ye believe in God, believe also in Me.

In My Father's house are many mansions: if it were not so, I would have told you. I go to prepare a place for you.

If I go and prepare a place for you, I will come again, and receive you unto Myself; that where I am, there ye may be also.

Whither I go ye know, and the way ye know.

Thomas saith unto Him, Lord, we know not whither Thou goest; and how can we know the way?

Jesus saith unto him, I am the

way, the truth, and the life: no man cometh unto the Father, but by Me.

If ye had known Me, ye should have known My Father also: and from henceforth ye know Him, and have seen Him.

Philip saith unto Him, Lord, show us the Father, and it sufficeth us.

Jesus saith unto him, Have I been so long time with you, and yet hast thou not known Me, Philip? he that hath seen Me hath seen the Father; and how sayest thou then, Show us the Father?

Believest thou not that I am in the Father, and the Father in Me? the words that I speak unto you I speak not of Myself: but the Father that dwelleth in Me, He doeth the works.

Believe Me that I am in the Father, and the Father in Me: or else believe Me for the very works' sake.

Verily, verily, I say unto you, He that believeth on Me, the works that I do shall he do also; and greater works than these shall he do; because I go unto My Father.

Whatsoever ye shall ask in My Name, that will I do, that the Father may be glorified in the Son.

If ye shall ask anything in My Name, I will do it.

If ye love Me, keep My commandments.

I will pray the Father, and He shall give you another Comforter, that He may abide with you for ever.

SECOND READING

THE GRACIOUS INVITATION

Ho, every one that thirsteth, come ye to the waters, and he that hath no money; come ye, buy, and eat; yea, come, buy wine and milk without money and without price.

Wherefore do ye spend money for that which is not bread? and your labor for that which satisfieth not? hearken diligently unto Me, and eat ye that which is good, and let your soul delight itself in fatness.

Incline your ear, and come unto Me: hear, and your soul shall live; and I will make an everlasting covenant with you, even the sure mercies of David.

Behold, I have given Him for a witness to the people, a leader and commander to the people.

Seek ye the Lord while He may be found, call ye upon Him while He is near:

Let the wicked forsake his way, and the unrighteous man his thoughts: and let him return unto the Lord, and He will have mercy upon him; and to our God, for He will abundantly pardon.

For My thoughts are not your thoughts, neither are your ways My ways, saith the Lord.

For as the heavens are higher than the earth, so are My ways higher than your ways, and My thoughts than your thoughts.

For as the rain cometh down, and the snow from heaven, and returneth not thither, but watereth the earth, and maketh it bring forth and bud, that it may give seed to the sower, and bread to the eater:

So shall My word be that goeth forth out of My mouth: it shall not return unto Me void, but it shall accomplish that which I please, and it shall prosper in the thing whereto I sent it.

For ye shall go out with joy, and be led forth with peace: the mountains and the hills shall break forth before you into singing, and all the trees of the field shall clap their hands.

Instead of the thorn shall come up the fir tree, and instead of the brier shall come up the myrtle tree: and it shall be to the Lord for a name, for an everlasting sign that shall not be cut off.

ELEVENTH SUNDAY

FIRST READING

THE BEATITUDES

Blessed are the poor in spirit:
For theirs is the kingdom of heaven.

Blessed are they that mourn:
For they shall be comforted.

Blessed are the meek:
For they shall inherit the earth.

Blessed are they which do hunger and thirst after righteousness:
For they shall be filled.

Blessed are the merciful:
For they shall obtain mercy.

Blessed are the pure in heart:
For they shall see God.

Blessed are the peacemakers:
For they shall be called the children of God.

Blessed are they which are persecuted for righteousness' sake:
For theirs is the kingdom of heaven.

Blessed are ye, when men shall revile you, and persecute you, and shall say all manner of evil against you falsely, for My sake.

Rejoice, and be exceeding glad: for great is your reward in heaven: for so persecuted they the prophets which were before you.

Ye are the salt of the earth: but if the salt have lost its savor, wherewith shall it be salted? it is thenceforth good for nothing, but to be cast out, and to be trodden under foot of men.

Ye are the light of the world. A city that is set on a hill cannot be hid.

Neither do men light a candle, and put it under a bushel, but on a candlestick; and it giveth light unto all that are in the house.

Let your light so shine before men, that they may see your good works, and glorify your Father who is in heaven.

SECOND READING

THE GLORY OF GOD

The heavens declare the glory of God; and the firmament showeth His handiwork.

Day unto day uttereth speech, and night unto night showeth knowledge.

There is no speech nor language; their voice is not heard.

Their line is gone out through all the earth, and their words to the end of the world. In them hath He set a tabernacle for the sun.

Which is as a bridegroom coming out of his chamber, and rejoiceth as a strong man to run a race.

His going forth is from the end of the heaven, and his circuit unto the ends of it: and there is nothing hid from the heat thereof.

The law of the Lord is perfect, converting the soul: the testimony of the Lord is sure, making wise the simple.

The statutes of the Lord are right, rejoicing the heart: the commandment of the Lord is pure, enlightening the eyes.

The fear of the Lord is clean, enduring for ever: the judgments of the Lord are true and righteous altogether.

More to be desired are they than gold, yea, than much fine gold: sweeter also than honey and the honeycomb.

Moreover by them is thy servant warned: and in keeping of them there is great reward.

Who can understand his errors? cleanse Thou me from secret faults.

Keep back Thy servant also from presumptuous sins; let them not have dominion over me: then shall I be upright, and I shall be innocent from the great transgression.

Let the words of my mouth, and the meditation of my heart, be acceptable in Thy sight, O Lord, my strength, and my redeemer.

TWELFTH SUNDAY

FIRST READING

SPIRITUAL TREASURE

Lay not up for yourselves treasures upon earth, where moth and rust doth corrupt, and where thieves break through and steal:

But lay up for yourselves treasures in heaven, where neither moth nor rust doth corrupt, and where thieves do not break through nor steal:

For where your treasure is, there will your heart be also.

The light of the body is the eye: if therefore thine eye be single, thy whole body shall be full of light.

But if thine eye be evil, thy whole body shall be full of darkness.

If therefore the light that is in thee be darkness, how great is that darkness!

No man can serve two masters: for either he will hate the one, and love the other;

Or else he will hold to the one, and despise the other. Ye cannot serve God and mammon.

Therefore I say unto you, Take no thought for your life, what ye shall eat, or what ye shall drink;

Nor yet for your body, what ye shall put on. Is not the life more than meat, and the body than raiment?

Behold the birds of the air: for they sow not, neither do they reap, nor gather into barns.

Yet your Heavenly Father feedeth them. Are ye not much better than they?

Which of you by taking thought can add one cubit unto his stature? And why take ye thought for raiment? Consider the lilies of the field, how they grow; they toil not, neither do they spin:

Yet I say unto you, That even Solomon in all his glory was not arrayed like one of these.

Wherefore, if God so clothe the grass of the field, which to-day is, and to-morrow is cast into the oven, shall He not much more clothe you, O ye of little faith?

Therefore take no thought, saying, What shall we eat? or, What shall we drink? or, Wherewithal shall we be clothed?

For your Heavenly Father knoweth that ye have need of all these things.

Seek ye first the kingdom of God, and His righteousness; and all these things shall be added unto you.

SECOND READING

THE MERCY OF THE LORD

Bless the Lord, O my soul: and all that is within me, bless His holy Name.

Bless the Lord, O my soul, and forget not all His benefits.

Who forgiveth all thine iniquities; who healeth all thy diseases;

Who redeemeth thy life from destruction; who crowneth thee with loving kindness and tender mercies;

Who satisfieth thy mouth with good things; so that thy youth is renewed like the eagle's.

The Lord executeth righteousness and judgment for all that are oppressed.

He made known His ways unto Moses, His acts unto the children of Israel.

The Lord is merciful and gracious, slow to anger, and plenteous in mercy.

He will not always chide: neither will He keep His anger for ever.

He hath not dealt with us after our sins, nor rewarded us according to our iniquities.

For as the heaven is high above the earth, so great is His mercy toward them that fear Him.

As far as the east is from the west, so far hath He removed our transgressions from us.

Like as a father pitieth his children, so the Lord pitieth them that fear Him.

For He knoweth our frame; He remembereth that we are dust.

As for man, his days are as grass: as a flower of the field, so he flourisheth.

For the wind passeth over it, and it is gone; and the place thereof shall know it no more.

But the mercy of the Lord is from everlasting to everlasting upon them that fear Him, and His righteousness unto children's children;

To such as keep His covenant, and to those that remember His commandments to do them.

The Lord hath prepared His throne in the heavens; and His kingdom ruleth over all.

Bless the Lord, ye His angels, that excel in strength, that do His commandments, hearkening unto the voice of His word.

Bless ye the Lord, all ye His hosts; ye ministers of His, that do His pleasure.

Bless the Lord, all His works in all places of His dominion: bless the Lord, O my soul.

THIRTEENTH SUNDAY

FIRST READING

THE HIGHER JUSTICE

Judge not, that ye be not judged. For with what judgment ye judge, ye shall be judged;

And with what measure ye mete, it shall be measured to you again.

Why beholdest thou the mote that

is in thy brother's eye, but considerest not the beam that is in thine own eye?

Or how wilt thou say to thy brother, Let me pull out the mote out of thine eye; and, behold, a beam is in thine own eye?

Thou hypocrite, first cast out the beam out of thine own eye; and then shalt thou see clearly to cast out the mote out of thy brother's eye.

Give not that which is holy unto the dogs, neither cast ye your pearls before swine, lest they trample them under their feet, and turn again and rend you.

Ask, and it shall be given you; seek, and ye shall find; knock, and it shall be opened unto you:

For every one that asketh receiveth; and he that seeketh findeth; and to him that knocketh it shall be opened.

Or what man is there of you, whom if his son ask bread, will he give him a stone?

Or if he ask a fish, will he give him a serpent?

If ye then, being evil, know how to give good gifts unto your children, how much more shall your Father who is in heaven give good things to them that ask Him?

Therefore all things whatsoever ye would that men should do to you, do ye even so to them: for this is the law and the prophets.

SECOND READING

LIBERTY IN GOD'S LAW

Teach me, O Lord, the way of Thy statutes; and I shall keep it unto the end.

Give me understanding, and I shall keep Thy law.

Yea, I shall observe it with my whole heart.

Make me to go in the path of Thy commandments; for therein do I delight.

Incline my heart unto Thy testimonies, and not to covetousness.

Turn away mine eyes from beholding vanity; and quicken Thou me in Thy way.

Stablish Thy word unto Thy servant, who is devoted to Thy fear.

Turn away my reproach which I fear: for Thy judgments are good.

Behold, I have longed after Thy precepts: quicken me in Thy righteousness.

Let Thy mercies come also unto me, O Lord, even Thy salvation, according to Thy word.

So shall I have wherewith to answer him that reproacheth me: for I trust in Thy word.

Take not the word of truth utterly out of my mouth; for I have hoped in Thy judgments.

So shall I keep Thy law continually for ever and ever.

I will walk at liberty: for I seek Thy precepts.

I will speak of Thy testimonies also before kings, and will not be ashamed.

I will delight myself in Thy commandments, which I have loved.

FOURTEENTH SUNDAY

FIRST READING

SPIRITUAL PERFECTION

Ye have heard that it hath been said, An eye for an eye, and a tooth for a tooth:

But I say unto you, That ye resist not evil: but whosoever shall smite thee on thy right cheek, turn to him the other also.

If any man will sue thee at the law, and take away thy coat, let him have thy cloak also.

Whosoever shall compel thee to go a mile, go with him twain.

Give to him that asketh thee, and from him that would borrow of thee turn not thou away.

Ye have heard that it hath been said, Thou shalt love thy neighbor and hate thine enemy.

But I say unto you, Love your enemies, bless them that curse you, do good to them that hate you, and pray for them which despitefully use you, and persecute you;

That ye may be the children of your Father who is in heaven:

For He maketh His sun to rise on the evil and on the good, and sendeth rain on the just and on the unjust.

For if ye love them which love you, what reward have ye? do not even the publicans the same?

If ye salute your brethren only, what do ye more than others? do not even the publicans so?

Be ye therefore perfect, even as your Father who is in heaven is perfect.

SECOND READING

YEARNING FOR GOD

Hear my prayer, O Lord, give ear to my supplications: in Thy faithfulness answer me, and in Thy righteousness.

Enter not into judgment with Thy servant: for in Thy sight shall no man living be justified.

Therefore is my spirit overwhelmed within me; my heart within me is desolate.

I remember the days of old; I meditate on all Thy works; I muse on the work of Thy hands.

I stretch forth my hands unto Thee: my soul thirsteth after Thee, as a thirsty land.

Hear me speedily, O, Lord; my spirit faileth: hide not Thy face from me, lest I be like unto them that go down into the pit.

Cause me to hear Thy loving kindness in the morning; for in Thee do I trust: cause me to know the way wherein I should walk; for I lift up my soul unto Thee.

Deliver me, O Lord, from mine enemies: I flee unto Thee to hide me.

Teach me to do Thy will; for Thou art my God: Thy Spirit is good; lead me into the land of uprightness.

Quicken me, O Lord, for Thy Name's sake: for Thy righteousness' sake bring my soul out of trouble.

FIFTEENTH SUNDAY

FIRST READING

THE COMMANDMENT OF LOVE

These things write I unto you, that ye sin not. And if any man sin, we have an advocate with the Father, Jesus Christ the righteous.

And He is the propitiation for our sins: and not for ours only, but also for the sins of the whole world.

Hereby we do know that we know Him, if we keep His commandments.

He that saith, I know Him, and

keepeth not His commandments, is a liar, and the truth is not in him.

Whoso keepeth His word, in him verily is the love of God perfected: hereby know we that we are in Him.

He that saith he abideth in Him ought himself also so to walk, even as He walked.

Brethren, I write no new commandment unto you, but an old commandment which ye had from the beginning:

The old commandment is the word which ye have heard from the beginning.

Again a new commandment I write unto you, which thing is true in Him and in you: because the darkness is past, and the true light now shineth.

He that saith he is in the light, and hateth his brother, is in darkness even until now.

He that loveth his brother abideth in the light, and there is none occasion of stumbling in him.

But he that hateth his brother is in darkness, and walketh in darkness, and knoweth not whither he goeth, because that darkness hath blinded his eyes.

Behold, what manner of love the Father hath bestowed upon us, that we should be called the sons of God;

Therefore the world knoweth us not, because it knew Him not.

Beloved, now are we the sons of God, and it doth not yet appear what we shall be: but we know that, when He shall appear, we shall be like Him; for we shall see Him as He is.

And every man that hath this

hope in him purifieth himself, even as He is pure.

SECOND READING

What Is Good?

Hear, O heavens, and give ear, O earth, for the Lord hath spoken. Hear the word of the Lord; and give ear unto the law of our God.

To what purpose is the multitude of your sacrifices unto Me? saith the Lord: I am full of the burnt offerings of rams, and the fat of fed beasts; and I delight not in the blood of bullocks or of lambs, or of he goats.

When ye come to appear before Me, who hath required this at your hand, to tread My courts?

Bring no more vain oblations; incense is an abomination unto Me; the new moons and sabbaths, the calling of assemblies, I cannot away with. It is iniquity, even the solemn meeting.

Your new moons and your appointed feasts My soul hateth; they are a trouble unto Me; I am weary to bear them.

And when ye spread forth your hands, I will hide Mine eyes from you; yea, when ye make many prayers, I will not hear: your hands are full of blood.

Wash you, make you clean; put away the evil of your doings from before Mine eyes; cease to do evil; learn to do well. Seek judgment, relieve the oppressed, judge the fatherless, plead for the widow.

Come now, and let us reason together, saith the Lord. Though your sins be as scarlet, they shall be white as snow; though they be red like crimson, they shall be as wool.

Wherewith shall I come before the Lord, and bow myself before the high God? Shall I come before Him with burnt offerings?

He hath showed thee, O man, what is good; and what doth the Lord require of thee, but to do justly, and to love mercy, and to walk humbly with thy God?

SIXTEENTH SUNDAY

FIRST READING

THE LAW OF THE SPIRIT

There is now no condemnation to them which are in Christ Jesus, who walk not after the flesh, but after the Spirit.

For the law of the Spirit of life in Christ Jesus hath made me free from the law of sin and death.

For what the law could not do, in that it was weak through the flesh, God sending His own Son in the likeness of sinful flesh, and for sin, condemned sin in the flesh:

That the righteousness of the law might be fulfilled in us, who walk not after the flesh, but after the Spirit.

For they that are after the flesh do mind the things of the flesh; but they that are after the Spirit, the things of the Spirit.

For to be carnally minded is death; but to be spiritually minded is life and peace.

Because the carnal mind is enmity against God: for it is not subject to the law of God, neither indeed can be.

So then they that are in the flesh cannot please God.

Ye are not in the flesh, but in the Spirit, if so be that the Spirit of God dwell in you. Now if any man have not the Spirit of Christ, he is none of His.

If Christ be in you, the body is dead because of sin; but the Spirit is life because of righteousness.

If the Spirit of Him that raised up Jesus from the dead dwell in you, He that raised up Christ from the dead shall also quicken your mortal bodies by His Spirit that dwelleth in you.

Therefore, brethren, we are debtors, not to the flesh, to live after the flesh.

For if ye live after the flesh, ye shall die: but if ye through the Spirit do mortify the deeds of the body, ye shall live.

For as many as are led by the Spirit of God, they are the sons of God.

For I am persuaded, that neither death, nor life, nor angels, nor principalities, nor powers, nor things present, nor things to come,

Nor height, nor depth, nor any other creature, shall be able to separate us from the love of God, which is in Christ Jesus our Lord.

SECOND READING

THE HOUSE OF GOD

How amiable are Thy tabernacles, O Lord of hosts!

My soul longeth, yea, even fainteth for the courts of the Lord: my heart and my flesh crieth out for the living God.

Yea, the sparrow hath found an house, and the swallow a nest for herself, where she may lay her young, even Thine altars, O Lord of hosts, my King, and my God.

Blessed are they that dwell in

Thy house: they will be still praising Thee.

Blessed is the man whose strength is in Thee; in whose heart are the ways of them,

Who passing through the valley of weeping make it a well; the rain also filleth the pools.

They go from strength to strength, every one of them in Zion appeareth before God.

O Lord God of hosts, hear my prayer: give ear, O God of Jacob.

Behold, O God our shield, and look upon the face of Thine anointed.

For a day in Thy courts is better than a thousand. I had rather be a doorkeeper in the house of my God, than to dwell in the tents of wickedness.

For the Lord God is a sun and shield: the Lord will give grace and glory: no good thing will He withhold from them that walk uprightly.

O Lord of hosts, blessed is the man that trusteth in Thee.

SEVENTEENTH SUNDAY

FIRST READING

CHRIST THE LIGHT

That which was from the beginning, which we have heard, which we have seen with our eyes, which we have looked upon, and our hands have handled, of the Word of life;

For the life was manifested, and we have seen it, and bear witness, and show unto you that eternal life, which was with the Father, and was manifested unto us;

That which we have seen and heard declare we unto you, that ye also may have fellowship with us.

And truly our fellowship is with the Father, and with His Son Jesus Christ.

These things write we unto you, that your joy may be full.

This then is the message which we have heard of Him, and declare unto you, that God is light, and in Him is no darkness at all.

If we say that we have fellowship with Him, and walk in darkness, we lie, and do not the truth:

But if we walk in the light, as He is in the light, we have fellowship one with another, and the blood of Jesus Christ His Son cleanseth us from all sin.

If we say that we have no sin, we deceive ourselves, and the truth is not in us.

If we confess our sins, He is faithful and just to forgive us our sins, and to cleanse us from all unrighteousness.

SECOND READING

THE STRENGTH OF LIFE

The Lord is my light and my salvation; whom shall I fear? the Lord is the strength of my life; of whom shall I be afraid?

When the wicked, even mine enemies and my foes, came upon me to eat up my flesh, they stumbled and fell.

Though a host should encamp against me, my heart shall not fear: though war should rise against me, in this will I be confident.

One thing have I desired of the Lord, that will I seek after; that I may dwell in the house of the Lord all the days of my life, to behold the beauty of the Lord, and to inquire in His temple.

For in the time of trouble He shall

hide me in His pavilion: in the secret of His tabernacle shall He hide me; He shall set me up upon a rock.

Now shall mine head be lifted up above mine enemies round about me: therefore will I offer in His tabernacle sacrifices of joy; I will sing, yea, I will sing praises unto the Lord.

Hear, O Lord, when I cry with my voice: have mercy also upon me, and answer me.

When Thou saidst, Seek ye My face; my heart said unto Thee, Thy face, Lord, will I seek.

Hide not Thy face far from me; put not Thy servant away in anger: Thou hast been my help; leave me not, neither forsake me, O God of my salvation.

When my father and my mother forsake me, then the Lord will take me up.

Teach me Thy way, O Lord, and lead me in a plain path, because of mine enemies.

Deliver me not over unto the will of mine enemies: for false witnesses are risen up against me, and such as breathe out cruelty.

I had fainted, unless I had believed to see the goodness of the Lord in the land of the living.

Wait on the Lord: be of good courage, and He shall strengthen thine heart: wait, I say, on the Lord.

EIGHTEENTH SUNDAY

FIRST READING

CHRISTIAN UNITY

As we have many members in one body, and all members have not the same office:

So we, being many, are one body in Christ, and every one members one of another.

Now there are diversities of gifts, but the same Spirit; and there are differences of administrations, but the same Lord.

And there are diversities of operations, but it is the same God who worketh all in all.

But the manifestation of the Spirit is given to every man to profit withal.

For to one is given by the Spirit the word of wisdom; to another the word of knowledge by the same Spirit;

To another faith by the same Spirit; to another the gifts of healing by the same Spirit.

All these worketh that one and the selfsame Spirit, dividing to every man severally as he will.

As the body is one, and hath many members, and all the members of that one body, being many, are one body, so also is Christ.

For by one Spirit are we all baptized into one body, and have been all made to drink into one Spirit; for the body is not one member, but many.

God hath set the members every one of them in the body, as it hath pleased Him. And now are they many members, but one body.

The eye cannot say unto the hand, I have no need of thee: nor again the head to the feet, I have no need of you.

Whether one member suffer, all the members suffer with it; or one

583

member be honored, all the members rejoice with it.

Now ye are the body of Christ, and members one of another.

SECOND READING

THE JUDGMENT

When the Son of man shall come in His glory, and all the holy angels with Him, then shall He sit upon the throne of His glory:

Before Him shall be gathered all nations: and He shall separate them one from another, as a shepherd divideth his sheep from the goats:

He shall set the sheep on His right hand, but the goats on the left.

Then shall the King say unto them on His right hand, Come, ye blessed of My Father, inherit the kingdom prepared for you from the foundation of the world:

For I was an hungered, and ye gave Me meat: I was thirsty, and ye gave Me drink: I was a stranger, and ye took Me in:

Naked, and ye clothed Me: I was sick, and ye visited Me: I was in prison, and ye came unto Me.

Then shall the righteous answer Him, saying, Lord, when saw we Thee an hungered, and fed Thee? or thirsty, and gave Thee drink?

When saw we Thee a stranger, and took Thee in? or naked, and clothed Thee?

Or when saw we Thee sick, or in prison, and came unto Thee?

The King shall answer and say unto them, Verily I say unto you, Inasmuch as ye have done it unto one of the least of these My brethren, ye have done it unto Me.

NINETEENTH SUNDAY

FIRST READING

LOVE NEVER FAILETH

Though I speak with the tongues of men and of angels and have not love, I am become as sounding brass, or a tinkling cymbal.

Though I have the gift of prophecy, and understand all mysteries, and all knowledge; and though I have all faith, so that I could remove mountains, and have not love, I am nothing.

Though I bestow all my goods to feed the poor, and though I give my body to be burned, and have not love, it profiteth me nothing.

Love suffereth long, and is kind; love envieth not; love vaunteth not itself, is not puffed up.

Doth not behave itself unseemly, seeketh not her own, is not easily provoked, thinketh no evil;

Rejoiceth not in iniquity, but rejoiceth in the truth;

Beareth all things, believeth all things, hopeth all things, endureth all things.

Love never faileth: but whether there be prophecies, they shall fail; whether there be tongues, they shall cease; whether there be knowledge, it shall vanish away.

For we know in part, and we prophesy in part.

But when that which is perfect is come, then that which is in part shall be done away.

When I was a child, I spake as a child, I understood as a child, I thought as a child:

But when I became a man, I put away childish things.

For now we see through a glass, darkly; but then face to face: now I know in part; but then shall I know even as also I am known.

Now abideth faith, hope, love, these three; but the greatest of these is love.

SECOND READING

The Favor of God

Praise waiteth for Thee, O God, in Zion: and unto Thee shall the vow be performed.

O Thou that hearest prayer, unto Thee shall all flesh come.

Iniquities prevail against me: as for our transgressions, Thou shalt purge them away.

Blessed is the man whom Thou choosest, and causest to approach unto Thee, that he may dwell in Thy courts:

We shall be satisfied with the goodness of Thy house, even of Thy holy temple.

By terrible things in righteousness wilt Thou answer us, O God of our salvation; who art the confidence of all the ends of the earth, and of them that are afar off upon the sea:

Who by His strength setteth fast the mountains; being girded with power:

Who stilleth the noise of the seas, the noise of their waves, and the tumult of the people.

They also that dwell in the uttermost parts are afraid at Thy tokens: Thou makest the outgoings of the morning and evening to rejoice.

Thou visitest the earth, and waterest it: Thou greatly enrichest it with the river of God, which is full of water; Thou preparest

them corn, when Thou hast so provided for it.

Thou waterest the ridges thereof abundantly: Thou settlest the furrows thereof: Thou makest it soft with showers: Thou blessest the springing thereof.

Thou crownest the year with Thy goodness; and Thy paths drop fatness.

They drop upon the pastures of the wilderness: and the little hills rejoice on every side.

The pastures are clothed with flocks; the valleys also are covered over with corn; they shout for joy, they also sing.

TWENTIETH SUNDAY

FIRST READING

Life and Godliness

Grace and peace be multiplied unto you through the knowledge of God, and of Jesus our Lord,

According as His divine power hath given unto us all things that pertain unto life and godliness, through the knowledge of Him that hath called us to glory and virtue:

Whereby are given unto us exceeding great and precious promises; that by these ye might be partakers of the divine nature, having escaped the corruption that is in the world through lust.

Besides this, giving all diligence, add to your faith, virtue; and to virtue, knowledge;

To knowledge, temperance; and to temperance, patience; and to patience, godliness;

To godliness, brotherly kindness; and to brotherly kindness, charity.

For if these things be in you, and abound, they make you that ye shall neither be barren nor unfruitful in the knowledge of our Lord Jesus Christ.

Brethren, give diligence to make your calling and election sure: for if ye do these things, ye shall never fall.

Rejoice in the Lord alway: and again I say, Rejoice.

Be careful for nothing; but in every thing by prayer and supplication with thanksgiving let your requests be made known unto God.

The peace of God, which passeth all understanding, shall keep your hearts and minds through Christ Jesus.

Finally, brethren, whatsoever things are true, whatsoever things are honest, whatsoever things are just, whatsoever things are pure, whatsoever things are lovely, whatsoever things are of good report; if there be any virtue, and if there be any praise, think on these things.

SECOND READING

HOPE IN GOD

As the hart panteth after the water brooks, so panteth my soul after Thee, O God.

My soul thirsteth for God, for the living God: when shall I come and appear before God?

My tears have been my meat day and night, while they continually say unto me, Where is thy God?

When I remember these things, I pour out my soul in me: for I had gone with the multitude, I went with them to the house of God, with the voice of joy and

praise, with a multitude that kept holyday.

Why art thou cast down, O my soul? and why art thou disquieted in me? hope thou in God: for I shall yet praise Him for the help of His countenance.

Deep calleth unto deep at the noise of Thy waterspouts: all Thy waves and Thy billows are gone over me.

Yet the Lord will command His loving kindness in the daytime, and in the night His song shall be with me, and my prayer unto the God of my life.

I will say unto God my rock, Why hast Thou forgotten me? why go I mourning because of the oppression of the enemy?

As with a sword in my bones, mine enemies reproach me; while they say daily unto me, Where is thy God?

Why art thou cast down, O my soul? and why art thou disquieted within me? hope thou in God: for I shall yet praise Him, who is the health of my countenance, and my God.

TWENTY-FIRST SUNDAY

FIRST READING

GOD'S EXCEEDING POWER

After I heard of your faith in the Lord Jesus, and love unto all the saints, I cease not to give thanks for you, making mention of you in my prayers;

That the God of our Lord Jesus Christ, the Father of glory, may give unto you the spirit of wisdom and revelation in the knowledge of Him;

586

The eyes of your understanding being enlightened; that ye may know what is the hope of His calling, and what the riches of the glory of His inheritance in the saints,

And what is the exceeding greatness of His power to us-ward who believe, according to the working of His mighty power,

Which He wrought in Christ, when He raised Him from the dead, and set Him at His own right hand in the heavenly places,

Far above all principality, and power, and might, and dominion, and every name that is named, not only in this world, but also in that which is to come:

And hath put all things under His feet, and gave Him to be the head over all things to the church, which is His body, the fullness of Him that filleth all in all.

For this cause I bow my knees unto the Father of our Lord Jesus Christ,

Of whom the whole family in heaven and earth is named,

That He would grant you, according to the riches of His glory, to be strengthened with might by His Spirit in the inner man;

That Christ may dwell in your hearts by faith; that ye, being rooted and grounded in love, may be able to comprehend with all saints what is the breadth, and length, and depth, and height;

And to know the love of Christ, which passeth knowledge, that ye might be filled with all the fullness of God.

Now unto Him that is able to do exceeding abundantly above all that we ask or think, according to the power that worketh in us,

Unto Him be glory in the church by Christ Jesus throughout all ages, world without end. Amen.

SECOND READING

THE LORD OUR ROCK

I will love Thee, O Lord, my strength.

The Lord is my rock, and my fortress, and my deliverer; my God, my strength, in whom I will trust; my buckler, and the horn of my salvation, and my high tower.

I will call upon the Lord, who is worthy to be praised: so shall I be saved from mine enemies.

The sorrows of death compassed me, and the floods of ungodly men made me afraid.

The sorrows of hell compassed me about: the snares of death came upon me.

In my distress I called upon the Lord, and cried unto my God:

He heard my voice out of His temple, and my cry came before Him, even into His ears.

He sent from above, He took me, He drew me out of many waters.

He delivered me from my strong enemy, and from them which hated me: for they were too strong for me.

They came upon me in the day of my calamity: but the Lord was my stay.

He brought me forth also into a large place; He delivered me, because He delighted in me.

As for God, His way is perfect: the word of the Lord is tried: He is a buckler to all those that trust in Him.

For who is God save the Lord? or who is a rock save our God?

It is God that girdeth me with strength, and maketh my way perfect.

TWENTY-SECOND SUNDAY

FIRST READING

THE SPIRIT OF FAITH

We preach not ourselves, but Christ Jesus the Lord; and ourselves your servants for Jesus' sake.

For God, who commanded the light to shine out of darkness, hath shined in our hearts, to give the light of the knowledge of the glory of God in the face of Jesus Christ.

We having the same spirit of faith, according as it is written, I believed, and therefore have I spoken; we also believe, and therefore speak;

Knowing that He who raised up the Lord Jesus shall raise up us also by Jesus, and shall present us with you.

For all things are for your sakes, that the abundant grace might through the thanksgiving of many redound to the glory of God.

For which cause we faint not; but though our outward man perish, yet the inward man is renewed day by day.

For our light affliction, which is but for a moment, worketh for us a far more exceeding and eternal weight of glory;

While we look not at the things which are seen, but at the things which are not seen: for the things which are seen are temporal; but the things which are not seen are eternal.

Now unto Him that is able to keep you from falling, and to present you faultless before the presence of His glory with exceeding joy,

To the only wise God our Saviour, be glory and majesty, dominion and power, both now and ever. Amen.

SECOND READING

TRUSTING IN GOD

Truly my soul waiteth upon God: from Him cometh my salvation.

He only is my rock and my salvation; He is my defense; I shall not be greatly moved.

My soul, wait thou only upon God; for my expectation is from Him.

He only is my rock and my salvation: He is my defense; I shall not be moved.

In God is my salvation and my glory: the rock of my strength, and my refuge, is in God.

Trust in Him at all times; ye people, pour out your heart before Him: God is a refuge for us.

God hath spoken once; twice have I heard this; that power belongeth unto God.

Also unto Thee, O Lord, belongeth mercy: for Thou renderest to every man according to his work.

Trust in the Lord, and do good; so shalt thou dwell in the land, and verily thou shalt be fed.

Delight thyself also in the Lord; and He shall give thee the desires of thine heart.

Commit thy way unto the Lord; trust also in Him; and He shall bring it to pass.

He shall bring forth thy righteousness as the light, and thy judgment as the noonday.

Rest in the Lord, and wait patiently for Him.

They that trust in the Lord shall be as Mount Zion, which cannot be removed, but abideth for ever.

As the mountains are round about Jerusalem, so the Lord is round about His people from henceforth even for ever.

Do good, O Lord, unto those that be good, and to them that are upright in their hearts.

TWENTY-THIRD SUNDAY

FIRST READING

THE NEW COVENANT

Behold, I have set before thee this day life and good, and death and evil;

In that I command thee this day to love the Lord thy God, to walk in His ways.

I call heaven and earth to witness this day that I have set before you life and death, blessing and cursing: therefore choose life,

That thou mayest love the Lord thy God, and that thou mayest obey His voice: for He is thy life and the length of thy days.

This commandment which I command thee this day, it is not hidden from thee, neither is it far off.

It is not in heaven that thou shouldest say, Who shall go up for us to heaven, and bring it unto us, that we may hear it and do it?

Neither is it beyond the sea, that thou shouldest say, Who shall go over the sea for us, and bring it unto us, that we may hear it and do it?

But the word is very nigh unto thee, in thy mouth, and in thy heart, that thou mayest do it.

Behold, the days come, saith the Lord, that I will make a new covenant with the house of Israel, and with the house of Judah:

Not according to the covenant that I made with their fathers, in the day that I took them by the hand to bring them out of the land of Egypt;

But this shall be the covenant that I will make with the house of Israel;

After those days, saith the Lord, I will put My law in their inward parts, and write it in their hearts; and I will be their God, and they shall be My people.

And they shall teach no more every man his neighbor, and every man his brother saying, Know the Lord:

For they shall all know Me, from the least of them unto the greatest of them, saith the Lord, for I will forgive their iniquity and I will remember their sin no more.

SECOND READING

THE WAY OF GOOD MEN

My son, if thou wilt receive My words, and hide My commandments with thee;

So that thou incline thine ear unto wisdom, and apply thine heart to understanding;

Yea, if thou criest after knowledge, and liftest up thy voice for understanding;

If thou seekest her as silver, and searchest for her as for hid treasures;

Then shalt thou understand the fear of the Lord, and find the knowledge of God.

For the Lord giveth wisdom: out of His mouth cometh knowledge and understanding.

He layeth up sound wisdom for the righteous: He is a buckler to them that walk uprightly.

He keepeth the paths of judgment, and preserveth the way of his saints.

Then shalt thou understand righteousness, and judgment, and equity; yea, every good path.

When wisdom entereth into thine heart, and knowledge is pleasant unto thy soul;

Discretion shall preserve thee, understanding shall keep thee:

To deliver thee from the way of the evil man, from the man that speaketh false things;

That thou mayest walk in the way of good men, and keep the paths of the righteous.

For the upright shall dwell in the land, and the perfect shall remain in it.

TWENTY-FOURTH SUNDAY

FIRST READING

The House of Prayer

Will God in very deed dwell with men on the earth?

Behold, heaven and the heaven of heavens cannot contain Thee; how much less this house which we have built!

Have respect therefore to the prayer of Thy servant, and to his supplication, O Lord my God, to hearken unto the cry and the prayer which Thy servant prayeth before Thee:

That Thine eyes may be open upon this house day and night, upon the place whereof Thou hast said that Thou wouldest put Thy Name there; to hearken unto the prayer which Thy servant prayeth toward this place.

Hearken therefore unto the supplications of Thy servant, and of Thy people Israel, which they shall make toward this place:

Hear Thou from Thy dwelling place, even from heaven; and when Thou hearest, forgive.

Blessed be Thou, Lord God of Israel our father, for ever and ever.

Thine, O Lord, is the greatness, and the power, and the glory, and the victory, and the majesty:

For all that is in the heaven and in the earth is Thine;

Thine is the kingdom, O Lord, and Thou art exalted as head above all.

Both riches and honor come of Thee, and Thou reignest over all; and in Thine hand is power and might; and in Thine hand it is to make great, and to give strength unto all.

Now therefore, our God, we thank Thee, and praise Thy glorious Name.

SECOND READING

The Goal of Faith

We are made partakers of Christ, if we hold the beginning of our confidence steadfast unto the end.

Seeing then that we have a great high priest, that is passed into the heavens, Jesus the Son of God, let us hold fast our profession.

For we have not a high priest who cannot be touched with the feeling of our infirmities; but was, in all points, tempted like as we are, yet without sin.

Let us therefore come boldly unto the throne of grace, that we may obtain mercy, and find grace to help in time of need.

The just shall live by faith. We are of them that believe, to the saving of the soul.

Now faith is the substance of things hoped for, the evidence of things not seen.

By it the elders obtained a good report. They all died in faith, not having received the promises, but, having seen them afar off, and confessed that they were strangers and pilgrims on the earth.

But now they desire a better country, that is, a heavenly: wherefore God is not ashamed to be called their God: for He hath prepared for them a city.

These all, having obtained a good report through faith, received not the promise;

God having provided some better thing for us, that they without us should not be made perfect.

Wherefore, seeing we also are compassed about with so great a cloud of witnesses,

Let us lay aside every weight, and the sin which doth so easily beset us, and let us run with patience the race that is set before us;

Looking unto Jesus, the author and finisher of our faith; who, for the joy that was set before Him, endured the cross;

Despising the shame, and is set down at the right hand of the throne of God.

For consider Him that endured such contradiction of sinners against Himself, lest ye be wearied and faint in your minds.

Despise not thou the chastening of the Lord, nor faint when thou art rebuked of Him; for whom the Lord loveth He chasteneth.

Now the God of peace, who brought again from the dead our Lord Jesus, that great Shepherd of the sheep, through the blood of the everlasting covenant;

Make you perfect in every good work to do His will, working in you that which is well pleasing in His sight, through Jesus Christ; to whom be glory for ever and ever. Amen.

TWENTY-FIFTH SUNDAY

FIRST READING

THE LAW OF CHRIST

Brethren, if a man be overtaken in a fault, ye who are spiritual, restore such an one in the spirit of meekness; considering thyself, lest thou also be tempted.

Bear ye one another's burdens, and so fulfill the law of Christ.

For if a man think himself to be something, when he is nothing, he deceiveth himself.

Let every man prove his own work, and then shall he have rejoicing in himself alone, and not in another: for every man shall bear his own burden.

Let him that is taught in the word communicate unto him that teacheth in all good things.

Be not deceived; God is not mocked: for whatsoever a man soweth, that shall he also reap.

For he that soweth to his flesh shall of the flesh reap corruption;
But he that soweth to the Spirit shall of the Spirit reap life everlasting.

Let us not be weary in well doing: for in due season we shall reap if we faint not.
As we have therefore opportunity, let us do good unto all men, especially unto them who are of the household of faith.

As many as walk according to this rule, peace be on them, and mercy, and upon the Israel of God.
The grace of our Lord Jesus Christ be with your spirit. Amen.

SECOND READING

The Everlasting Light

Arise, shine; for thy light is come, and the glory of the Lord is risen upon thee.
For, behold, the darkness shall cover the earth, and gross darkness the people: but the Lord shall arise upon thee, and His glory shall be seen upon thee.

The Gentiles shall come to Thy light, and kings to the brightness of Thy rising.
Lift up thine eyes round about, and see: all they gather themselves together, they come to thee: thy sons shall come from far, and thy daughters shall be nursed at thy side.

Then thou shalt see, and flow together, and thine heart shall fear, and be enlarged; because the abundance of the sea shall be converted unto thee, the forces of the Gentiles shall come unto thee.
For brass I will bring gold, and for iron I will bring silver, and for wood brass, and for stones iron:

I will also make thy officers peace, and thine exactors righteousness.
Violence shall no more be heard in thy land, wasting nor destruction within thy borders; but thou shalt call thy walls Salvation, and thy gates Praise.

The sun shall be no more thy light by day; neither for brightness shall the moon give light unto thee: but the Lord shall be unto thee an everlasting light, and thy God thy glory.
Thy sun shall no more go down; neither shall thy moon withdraw itself: for the Lord shall be thine everlasting light, and the days of thy mourning shall be ended.

Thy people also shall be all righteous: they shall inherit the land for ever, the branch of My planting, the work of My hands, that I may be glorified.
A little one shall become a thousand, and a small one a strong nation: I the Lord will hasten it in his time.

TWENTY-SIXTH SUNDAY

FIRST READING

The Mind of Christ

If there be any consolation in Christ, if any comfort of love, if any fellowship of the Spirit, if any tender mercies and compassions, fulfill ye my joy.
That ye be likeminded, having the same love, being of one accord, of one mind.

Let nothing be done through strife or vainglory; but in lowliness of mind let each esteem other better than themselves.

Look not every man on his own things, but every man also on the things of others.

Let this mind be in you, which was also in Christ Jesus:

Who, being in the form of God, thought it not a thing to be grasped to be equal with God:

But made Himself of no reputation, and took upon Him the form of a servant, and was made in the likeness of men:

And being found in fashion as a man, He humbled Himself, and became obedient unto death, even the death of the cross.

Wherefore God also hath highly exalted Him, and given Him a Name which is above every name:

That at the Name of Jesus every knee should bow, of things in heaven, and things in earth, and things under the earth; and that every tongue should confess that Jesus Christ is Lord, to the glory of God the Father.

SECOND READING

THE LORD THY KEEPER

I will lift up mine eyes unto the hills. From whence cometh my help?

My help cometh from the Lord, who made heaven and earth.

He will not suffer thy foot to be moved: He that keepeth thee will not slumber.

Behold, He that keepeth Israel shall neither slumber nor sleep.

The Lord is thy keeper: the Lord is thy shade upon thy right hand.

The sun shall not smite thee by day, nor the moon by night.

The Lord shall preserve thee from all evil: He shall preserve thy soul.

The Lord shall preserve thy going out and thy coming in from this time forth, and even for evermore.

TWENTY-SEVENTH SUNDAY

FIRST READING

GOD'S LOVING KINDNESS

Oh that men would praise the Lord for His goodness, and for His wonderful works to the children of men!

And let them sacrifice the sacrifices of thanksgiving, and declare His works with rejoicing.

They that go down to the sea in ships, that do business in great waters;

These see the works of the Lord, and His wonders in the deep.

For He commandeth, and raiseth the stormy wind, which lifteth up the waves thereof.

They mount up to the heaven, they go down again to the depths: their soul is melted because of trouble.

They reel to and fro, and stagger like a drunken man, and are at their wit's end.

Then they cry unto the Lord in their trouble, and He bringeth them out of their distresses.

He maketh the storm a calm, so that the waves thereof are still.

Then are they glad because they be quiet; so He bringeth them unto their desired haven.

Oh that men would praise the Lord for His goodness, and for His wonderful works to the children of men!

Let them exalt Him also in the congregation of the people, and praise Him in the assembly of the elders.

He turneth the wilderness into a standing water, and dry ground into watersprings.

And there He maketh the hungry to dwell, that they may prepare a city for habitation;

And sow the fields and plant vineyards, which may yield fruits of increase.

The righteous shall see it and rejoice: and all iniquity shall stop her mouth.

Whoso is wise, and will observe these things, even they shall understand the loving kindness of the Lord.

Oh that men would praise the Lord for His goodness, and for His wonderful works to the children of men!

SECOND READING

The Exalted Lord

The Lord is my strength and song, and is become my salvation.

The voice of rejoicing and salvation is in the tabernacles of the righteous: the right hand of the Lord doeth valiantly.

The right hand of the Lord is exalted: the right hand of the Lord doeth valiantly.

I shall not die, but live, and declare the works of the Lord.

The Lord hath chastened me sore; but He hath not given me over unto death.

Open to me the gates of righteousness: I will go into them, and I will praise the Lord:

This gate of the Lord, into which the righteous shall enter.

I will praise Thee: for Thou hast heard me, and art become my salvation.

The stone which the builders refused is become the head stone of the corner.

This is the Lord's doing; it is marvelous in our eyes.

This is the day which the Lord hath made; we will rejoice and be glad in it.

Save now, I beseech Thee, O Lord: O Lord, I beseech Thee, send now prosperity.

Blessed be he that cometh in the Name of the Lord: we have blessed you out of the house of the Lord.

Thou art my God, and I will praise Thee: Thou art my God, I will exalt Thee.

TWENTY-EIGHTH SUNDAY

FIRST READING

Spiritual Discernment

Eye hath not seen, nor ear heard, neither have entered into the heart of man, the things which God hath prepared for them that love Him.

But God hath revealed them unto us by His Spirit; for the Spirit searcheth all things, yea, the deep things of God.

For what man knoweth the things of a man, save the spirit of man which is in him?

Even so the things of God knoweth no man, but the Spirit of God.

Now we have received, not the spirit of the world, but the spirit which is of God.

That we might know the things that are freely given to us of God.

Which things also we speak, not in the words which man's wisdom teacheth, but which the Holy Spirit teacheth; comparing spiritual things with spiritual.

The natural man receiveth not the things of the Spirit of God: for they are foolishness unto him: neither can he know them, because they are spiritually discerned.

He that is spiritual judgeth all things, yet he himself is judged of no man.

For who hath known the mind of the Lord, that he may instruct him? But we have the mind of Christ.

SECOND READING

GOD'S ETERNAL RIGHTEOUSNESS

It is a good thing to give thanks unto the Lord, and to sing praises unto Thy Name, O Most High:

To show forth Thy loving kindness in the morning, and Thy faithfulness every night.

Thou, Lord, hast made me glad through Thy work; I will triumph in the works of Thy hands. O Lord, how great are Thy works! and Thy thoughts are very deep.

Thou, Lord, art most high for evermore. The righteous shall flourish like the palm tree: he shall grow like a cedar in Lebanon.

Those that be planted in the house of the Lord shall flourish in the courts of our God.

The Lord is upright. He is my rock, and there is no unrighteousness in Him.

Praise ye the Lord. Praise, O ye servants of the Lord, praise the Name of the Lord.

Blessed be the Name of the Lord from this time forth and for evermore.

From the rising of the sun unto the going down of the same the Lord's Name is to be praised.

The Lord is high above all nations, and His glory above the heavens.

Who is like unto the Lord our God, who dwelleth on high, who humbleth Himself to behold the things that are in heaven, and in the earth!

He raiseth up the poor out of the dust, that He may set him with princes, even with the princes of His people. Praise ye the Lord.

TWENTY-NINTH SUNDAY

FIRST READING

THE WORTH OF MAN

O Lord our Lord, how excellent is Thy Name in all the earth! who hast set Thy glory above the heavens.

Out of the mouth of babes and sucklings hast Thou ordained strength because of Thine enemies, that Thou mightest still the enemy and the avenger.

When I consider Thy heavens, the work of Thy fingers, the moon and the stars, which Thou hast ordained;

What is man, that Thou art mindful of him? and the son of man, that Thou visitest him?

For Thou hast made him a little

lower than the angels, and hast crowned him with glory and honor.

Thou madest him to have dominion over the works of Thy hands;

Thou hast put all things under his feet:

All sheep and oxen, yea, and the beasts of the field;

The birds of the air, and the fish of the sea, and whatsoever passeth through the paths of the seas.

O Lord our Lord, how excellent is Thy Name in all the earth!

SECOND READING

WALKING UPRIGHTLY

Lord, who shall abide in Thy tabernacle? who shall dwell in Thy holy hill?

He that walketh uprightly, and worketh righteousness, and speaketh the truth in his heart.

He that backbiteth not with his tongue, nor doeth evil to his neighbor, nor taketh up a reproach against his neighbor.

In whose eyes a vile person is contemned; but he honoreth them that fear the Lord. He that sweareth to his own hurt, and changeth not.

He that putteth not out his money to usury, nor taketh reward against the innocent. He that doeth these things shall never be moved.

Blessed is he that considereth the poor: the Lord will deliver him in time of trouble.

The Lord will preserve him, and keep him alive; and he shall be blessed upon the earth: and Thou wilt not deliver him unto the will of his enemies.

The Lord will strengthen him upon the bed of languishing: Thou wilt make all his bed in his sickness.

As for me, Thou upholdest me in mine integrity, and settest me before Thy face for ever.

Blessed be the Lord God of Israel from everlasting, and to everlasting. Amen, and Amen.

THIRTIETH SUNDAY

FIRST READING

THE VOICE OF WISDOM

Doth not wisdom cry? and understanding put forth her voice?

She crieth at the gates, at the entry of the city, at the coming in at the doors.

Unto you, O men, I call; and my voice is to the sons of man.

Hear; for I will speak of excellent things; and the opening of my lips shall be right things.

The Lord possessed me in the beginning of His way, before His works of old.

I was set up from everlasting, from the beginning, or ever the earth was.

When there were no depths, I was brought forth, when there were no fountains abounding with water.

Before the mountains were settled, before the hills was I brought forth:

When He prepared the heavens, I was there: when He set a compass upon the face of the depth:

When He established the clouds above: when He strengthened the fountains of the deep:

When He gave to the sea His decree, that the waters should not pass His commandment: when He appointed the foundations of the earth:

Then I was by Him, as one brought up with Him: and I was daily His delight, rejoicing always before Him;

Rejoicing in the habitable part of His earth; and my delights were with the sons of men.

Now therefore hearken unto me, O ye children: for blessed are they that keep my ways.

Hear instruction, and be wise, and refuse it not.

Blessed is the man that heareth me, watching daily at my gates, waiting at the posts of my doors.

For whoso findeth me findeth life, and shall obtain favor of the Lord.

But he that sinneth against me wrongeth his own soul: all they that hate me love death.

SECOND READING

UNIVERSAL PRAISE

God be merciful unto us, and bless us; and cause His face to shine upon us;

That Thy way may be known upon earth, Thy saving health among all nations.

Let the people praise Thee, O God; let all the people praise Thee.

O let the nations be glad and sing for joy: for Thou shalt judge the people righteously, and govern the nations upon earth.

Let the people praise Thee, O God; let all the people praise Thee.

Then shall the earth yield her increase; and God, even our own God, shall bless us.

God shall bless us; and all the ends of the earth shall fear Him.

Make a joyful noise unto the Lord, all ye lands.

Serve the Lord with gladness: come before His presence with singing.

Know ye that the Lord He is God: it is He that hath made us, and not we ourselves; we are His people, and the sheep of His pasture.

Enter into His gates with thanksgiving, and into His courts with praise: be thankful unto Him, and bless His Name.

For the Lord is good; His mercy is everlasting; and His truth endureth to all generations.

THIRTY-FIRST SUNDAY

FIRST READING

GOD'S MEASURELESS MERCY

Cast thy burden upon the Lord, and He shall sustain thee: He shall never suffer the righteous to be moved.

Be merciful unto me, O God: for they be many that fight against me, O Thou Most High.

What time I am afraid, I will trust in Thee. In God I will praise His word; in God I have put my trust; I will not fear what flesh can do unto me.

In God will I praise His word: in the Lord will I praise His word.

In God have I put my trust: I will not be afraid what man can do unto me. Thy vows are upon me, O God: I will render praises unto Thee.

For Thou hast delivered my soul

from death; wilt not Thou deliver my feet from falling, that I may walk before God in the light of the living?

Be merciful unto me, O God, be merciful unto me: for my soul trusteth in Thee;

Yea, in the shadow of Thy wings will I make my refuge, until these calamities be overpast.

I will cry unto God most high; unto God that performeth all things for me.

He shall send from heaven and save me. God shall send forth His mercy and His truth.

Be Thou exalted, O God, above the heavens; let Thy glory be above all the earth.

My heart is fixed, O God, my heart is fixed. I will sing and give praise.

I will praise Thee, O Lord, among the people; for Thy mercy is great unto the heavens, and Thy truth unto the clouds.

Be Thou exalted, O God, above the heavens: let Thy glory be above all the earth.

SECOND READING

THE SOURCE OF WISDOM

Surely there is a vein for the silver, and a place for gold where they refine it.

Iron is taken out of the earth, and brass is molten out of the stone.

As for the earth, out of it cometh bread: and under it is turned up as it were by fire.

The stones of it are the place of sapphires: and it hath dust of gold.

But where shall wisdom be found? and where is the place of understanding?

Man knoweth not the price thereof; neither is it found in the land of the living.

The deep saith, It is not in me: and the sea saith, It is not with me.

It cannot be gotten for gold, neither shall silver be weighed for the price thereof.

It cannot be valued with the gold of Ophir, with the precious onyx, or the sapphire.

The gold and the crystal cannot equal it: and the exchange of it shall not be for jewels of fine gold.

No mention shall be made of coral, or of pearls: for the price of wisdom is above rubies.

The topaz of Ethiopia shall not equal it, neither shall it be valued with pure gold.

Whence then cometh wisdom? and where is the place of understanding? seeing it is hid from the eyes of all living, and kept close from the birds of the air?

Destruction and death say, We have heard the fame thereof with our ears.

God understandeth the way of wisdom, and He knoweth the place thereof; for He looketh to the ends of the earth, and seeth under the whole heaven.

He maketh the weight for the winds; and He weigheth the waters by measure, when He maketh a decree for the rain, and a way for the lightning of the thunder.

Then did He see wisdom, and declare it; He prepared it, yea, and searched it out.

And unto man He said, Behold, the fear of the Lord, that is wisdom; and to depart from evil is understanding.

THIRTY-SECOND SUNDAY

FIRST READING

The Path of Wisdom

My son, attend to my words; incline thine ear unto my sayings.

Let them not depart from thine eyes; keep them in the midst of thine heart.

For they are life unto those that find them, and health to all their flesh.

Keep thy heart with all diligence; for out of it are the issues of life.

Put away from thee a deceitful mouth, and perverse lips put far from thee.

Let thine eyes look right on, and let thine eyelids look straight before thee.

Ponder the path of thy feet, and let all thy ways be established.

Turn not to the right hand nor to the left: remove thy foot from evil.

My son, forget not my law; but let thine heart keep my commandments:

For length of days, and long life, and peace, shall they add to thee.

Let not mercy and truth forsake thee: bind them about thy neck; write them upon the table of thine heart:

So shalt thou find favor and good understanding in the sight of God and man.

Trust in the Lord with all thine heart; and lean not unto thine own understanding.

In all thy ways acknowledge Him, and He shall direct thy paths.

SECOND READING

The Cleansed Way

Blessed are the undefiled in the way, who walk in the law of the Lord.

Blessed are they that keep His testimonies, and that seek Him with the whole heart.

They also do no iniquity: they walk in His ways.

Thou hast commanded us to keep Thy precepts diligently.

O that my ways were directed to keep Thy statutes!

Then shall I not be ashamed, when I have respect unto all Thy commandments.

I will praise Thee with uprightness of heart, when I shall have learned Thy righteous judgments.

I will keep Thy statutes: O forsake me not utterly.

Wherewithal shall a young man cleanse his way? by taking heed thereto according to Thy word.

With my whole heart have I sought Thee: O let me not wander from Thy commandments.

Thy word have I hid in mine heart, that I might not sin against Thee.

Blessed art Thou, O Lord: teach me Thy statutes.

With my lips have I declared all the judgments of Thy mouth.

I have rejoiced in the way of Thy testimonies, as much as in all riches.

I will meditate in Thy precepts, and have respect unto Thy ways.

I will delight myself in Thy statutes: I will not forget Thy word.

THIRTY-THIRD SUNDAY

FIRST READING

The Joy of Deliverance

If it had not been the Lord who was on our side, when men rose up against us:

Then the waters had overwhelmed us, the stream had gone over our soul. Then the proud waters had gone over our soul.

Blessed be the Lord, who hath not given us as a prey to their teeth.

Our soul is escaped as a bird out of the snare of the fowlers: the snare is broken, and we are escaped.

Our help is in the Name of the Lord, who made heaven and earth.

When the Lord turned again the captivity of Zion, we were like them that dream.

Then was our mouth filled with laughter, and our tongue with singing:

Then said they among the nations, The Lord hath done great things for them.

The Lord hath done great things for us; whereof we are glad.

Turn again our captivity, O Lord, as the streams in the south.

They that sow in tears shall reap in joy.

He that goeth forth and weepeth, bearing precious seed, shall doubtless come again with rejoicing, bringing his sheaves with him.

SECOND READING

God Our Refuge

God is our refuge and strength, a very present help in trouble.

Therefore will we not fear, though the earth be removed, and though the mountains be carried into the midst of the sea;

Though the waters thereof roar and be troubled, though the mountains shake with the swelling thereof.

There is a river, the streams whereof shall make glad the city of God, the holy place of the tabernacles of the Most High.

God is in the midst of her; she shall not be moved: God shall help her, and that right early.

The heathen raged, the kingdoms were moved:

He uttered His voice, the earth melted.

The Lord of hosts is with us; the God of Jacob is our refuge.

Come, behold the works of the Lord, what desolations He hath made in the earth.

He maketh wars to cease unto the end of the earth; He breaketh the bow, and cutteth the spear in sunder; He burneth the chariot in the fire.

Be still, and know that I am God: I will be exalted among the heathen, I will be exalted in the earth.

The Lord of hosts is with us; the God of Jacob is our refuge.

THIRTY-FOURTH SUNDAY

FIRST READING

The Lord's Benefits

I love the Lord, because He hath

heard my voice and my supplications.

Because He hath inclined His ear unto me, therefore will I call upon Him as long as I live.

The sorrows of death compassed me, and the pains of hell gat hold upon me: I found trouble and sorrow.

Then called I upon the Name of the Lord; O Lord, I beseech Thee, deliver my soul.

Gracious is the Lord, and righteous; yea, our God is merciful.

The Lord preserveth the simple: I was brought low, and He helped me.

Return unto thy rest, O my soul; for the Lord hath dealt bountifully with thee.

For Thou hast delivered my soul from death, mine eyes from tears, and my feet from falling.

What shall I render unto the Lord for all His benefits toward me?

I will take the cup of salvation, and call upon the Name of the Lord.

I will pay my vows unto the Lord now in the presence of all His people.

Precious in the sight of the Lord is the death of His saints.

O Lord, truly I am Thy servant; I am Thy servant, and the son of Thine handmaid: Thou hast loosed my bonds.

I will offer to Thee the sacrifice of thanksgiving, and will call upon the Name of the Lord.

I will pay my vows unto the Lord now in the presence of all His people,

In the courts of the Lord's house,

in the midst of thee, O Jerusalem. Praise ye the Lord.

SECOND READING

THE INCORRUPTIBLE INHERITANCE

Blessed be the God and Father of our Lord Jesus Christ, who according to His abundant mercy hath begotten us again unto a lively hope by the resurrection of Jesus Christ from the dead,

To an inheritance incorruptible, and undefiled, and that fadeth not away, reserved in heaven for you,

Who are kept by the power of God through faith unto salvation ready to be revealed in the last time,

Wherein ye greatly rejoice, though now for a season, if need be, ye are in heaviness through manifold temptations:

That the trial of your faith, being much more precious than of gold that perisheth, though it be tried with fire, might be found unto praise and honor and glory at the appearing of Jesus Christ:

Whom having not seen, ye love; in whom, though now ye see Him not, yet believing, ye rejoice with joy unspeakable and full of glory:

Receiving the end of your faith, even the salvation of your souls.

Now unto the King eternal, immortal, invisible, the only wise God, be honor and glory for ever and ever. Amen.

THIRTY-FIFTH SUNDAY

FIRST READING

FAMILY RELIGION

Hear, O Israel: The Lord our God is one Lord:

Thou shalt love the Lord thy God

with all thine heart, and with all thy soul, and with all thy might.

And these words, which I command thee this day, shall be in thine heart:

Thou shalt teach them diligently unto thy children, and shalt talk of them when thou sittest in thine house, and when thou walkest by the way, and when thou liest down, and when thou risest up.

Thou shalt bind them for a sign upon thine hand, and they shall be as frontlets between thine eyes.

Thou shalt write them upon the posts of thy house, and on thy gates.

It shall be, when the Lord thy God shall have brought thee into the land which He sware unto thy fathers, to Abraham, to Isaac, and to Jacob, to give thee great and goodly cities, which thou buildedst not,

Houses full of all good things, which thou filledst not, and wells digged, which thou diggedst not, vineyards and olive trees, which thou plantedst not; when thou shalt have eaten and be full;

Then beware lest thou forget the Lord, which brought thee forth out of the land of Egypt, from the house of bondage.

Thou shalt fear the Lord thy God, and serve Him, and shalt swear by His Name.

Thou shalt diligently keep the commandments of the Lord thy God, and His testimonies, and His statutes, which He hath commanded thee.

Thou shalt do that which is right and good in the sight of the Lord: that it may be well with thee.

The Lord commanded us to do all these statutes, to fear the Lord our God, for our good always.

It shall be our righteousness, if we observe to do all these commandments before the Lord our God, as He hath commanded us.

SECOND READING

THE INNER LAW

I waited patiently for the Lord; and He inclined unto me, and heard my cry.

He brought me up also out of an horrible pit, out of the miry clay, and set my feet upon a rock, and established my goings.

He hath put a new song in my mouth, even praise unto our God: many shall see it, and fear, and shall trust in the Lord.

Blessed is that man that maketh the Lord his trust, and respecteth not the proud, nor such as turn aside to lies.

Many, O Lord my God, are Thy wonderful works which Thou hast done, and Thy thoughts which are to usward: they cannot be reckoned up in order unto Thee: they are more than can be numbered.

Sacrifice and offering Thou didst not desire; mine ears hast Thou opened: burnt offering and sin offering hast Thou not required.

Then said I, Lo, I come: in the volume of the book it is written of me,

I delight to do Thy will, O my God: yea, Thy law is within my heart.

I have preached righteousness in the great congregation: lo, I have not refrained my lips, O Lord, Thou knowest.

I have not hid Thy righteousness within my heart; I have declared

602

Thy faithfulness and Thy salvation:

I have not concealed Thy loving kindness and Thy truth from the great congregation.

Withhold not Thou Thy tender mercies from me, O Lord: let Thy loving kindness and Thy truth continually preserve me.

THIRTY-SIXTH SUNDAY

FIRST READING

God Our Help

Bow down Thine ear, O Lord, hear me: for I am poor and needy.

Preserve my soul; O Thou my God, save Thy servant that trusteth in Thee.

Be merciful unto me, O Lord: for I cry unto Thee daily.

Rejoice the soul of Thy servant: for unto Thee, O Lord, do I lift up my soul.

For Thou, Lord, art good, and ready to forgive; and plenteous in mercy unto all them that call upon Thee.

Give ear, O Lord, unto my prayer; and attend to the voice of my supplications.

In the day of my trouble I will call upon Thee: for Thou wilt answer me.

There is none like unto Thee, O Lord; neither are there any works like unto Thy works.

All nations whom Thou hast made shall come and worship before Thee, O Lord; and shall glorify Thy Name.

For Thou art great, and doest wondrous things: Thou art God alone.

Teach me Thy way, O Lord; I will walk in Thy truth: unite my heart to fear Thy Name.

I will praise Thee, O Lord my God, with all my heart: and I will glorify Thy Name for evermore.

For great is Thy mercy toward me: and Thou hast delivered my soul from the lowest hell.

Thou, O Lord, art a God full of compassion, and gracious, longsuffering, and plenteous in mercy and truth.

O turn unto me, and have mercy upon me; give Thy strength unto Thy servant, and save the son of Thine handmaid.

Show me a token for good; that they which hate me may see it, and be ashamed: because Thou, Lord, hast helped me, and comforted me.

SECOND READING

The Fountain of Life

The Lord hear thee in the day of trouble; the Name of the God of Jacob defend thee, send thee help from the sanctuary, and strengthen thee out of Zion;

May He remember all thy offerings, and accept thy sacrifices, and grant thee according to thine own heart, and fulfill all thy counsel.

We will rejoice in thy salvation, and in the Name of our God we will set up our banners: the Lord fulfill all thy petitions.

Now know I that the Lord saveth His anointed; He will hear him from His holy heaven with the saving strength of His right hand.

Some trust in chariots, and some in horses; but we will remember the Name of the Lord our God.

Blessed be the Lord, because He hath heard the voice of my supplications.

The Lord is my strength and my shield; my heart trusted in Him, and I am helped:

Therefore my heart greatly rejoiceth; and with my song will I praise Him.

The Lord is their strength, and He is the saving strength of His anointed.

Save Thy people, and bless Thine inheritance: feed them also, and lift them up for ever.

Thy mercy, O Lord, is in the heavens; and Thy faithfulness reacheth unto the clouds.

Thy righteousness is like the great mountains; Thy judgments are a great deep. O Lord, Thou preservest man and beast.

How excellent is Thy loving kindness, O God! therefore the children of men put their trust under the shadow of Thy wings.

They shall be abundantly satisfied with the goodness of Thy house; and Thou shalt make them drink of the river of Thy pleasures.

For with Thee is the fountain of life; in Thy light shall we see light.

O continue Thy loving kindness unto them that know Thee; and Thy righteousness to the upright in heart.

THIRTY-SEVENTH SUNDAY

FIRST READING

Enduring Praise

Praise ye the Lord. I will praise the Lord with my whole heart, in the assembly of the upright, and in the congregation.

The works of the Lord are great, sought out of all them that have pleasure therein.

His work is honorable and glorious: and His righteousness endureth for ever.

He hath made His wonderful works to be remembered: the Lord is gracious and full of compassion.

He hath given meat unto them that fear Him: He will ever be mindful of His covenant.

He hath showed His people the power of His works, that He may give them the heritage of the nations.

The works of His hands are verity and judgment; all His commandments are sure.

They stand fast for ever and ever, and are done in truth and uprightness.

He sent redemption unto His people: He hath commanded His covenant for ever: holy and reverend is His Name.

The fear of the Lord is the beginning of wisdom: a good understanding have all they that do His commandments: His praise endureth for ever.

SECOND READING

God's Unsearchable Greatness

I will extol Thee, my God, O King; and I will bless Thy Name for ever and ever.

Every day will I bless Thee; and I will praise Thy Name for ever and ever.

Great is the Lord, and greatly to be

praised; and His greatness is unsearchable.

One generation shall praise Thy works to another, and shall declare Thy mighty acts.

I will speak of the glorious honor of Thy majesty, and of Thy wondrous works.

And men shall speak of the might of Thy terrible acts: and I will declare Thy greatness.

They shall abundantly utter the memory of Thy great goodness, and shall sing of Thy righteousness.

The Lord is gracious, and full of compassion; slow to anger, and of great mercy.

The Lord is good to all: and His tender mercies are over all His works.

All Thy works shall praise Thee, O Lord; and Thy saints shall bless Thee.

They shall speak of the glory of Thy kingdom, and talk of Thy power;

To make known to the sons of men His mighty acts, and the glorious majesty of His kingdom.

Thy kingdom is an everlasting kingdom, and Thy dominion endureth throughout all generations.

The Lord upholdeth all that fall, and raiseth up all those that be bowed down.

The eyes of all wait upon Thee; and Thou givest them their meat in due season.

Thou openest Thine hand, and satisfiest the desire of every living thing.

The Lord is righteous in all His ways, and holy in all His works.

The Lord is nigh unto all them that call upon Him, to all that call upon Him in truth.

THIRTY-EIGHTH SUNDAY

FIRST READING

GOD STRENGTHENS THE HEART

Truly God is good to Israel, even to such as are of a clean heart.

As for me, my feet were almost gone; my steps had well nigh slipped.

For I was envious at the foolish, when I saw the prosperity of the wicked.

For there are no pangs in their death: but their strength is firm.

They are not in trouble as other men; neither are they plagued like other men.

Therefore pride compasseth them about as a chain; violence covereth them as a garment.

Their eyes stand out with fatness: they have more than heart could wish.

They set their mouth against the heavens, and their tongue walketh through the earth.

Therefore His people return hither: and waters of a full cup are wrung out to them.

They say, How doth God know? and is there knowledge in the Most High?

Behold, these are the ungodly, who prosper in the world; they increase in riches.

Verily I have cleansed my heart in vain, and washed my hands in innocency.

For all the day long have I been

plagued, and chastened every morning.

If I say, I will speak thus; behold, I should offend against the generation of Thy children.

When I thought to know this, it was too painful for me;

Until I went into the sanctuary of God; then understood I their end.

Surely Thou didst set them in slippery places; Thou castedst them down into destruction. How are they brought into desolation, as in a moment!

Nevertheless I am continually with Thee: Thou hast holden me by my right hand.

Thou shalt guide me with Thy counsel, and afterward receive me to glory. Whom have I in heaven but Thee? and there is none upon earth that I desire besides Thee.

My flesh and my heart faileth: but God is the strength of my heart, and my portion for ever.

SECOND READING

The Secret of the Lord

Unto Thee, O Lord, do I lift up my soul.

O my God, I trust in Thee: let me not be ashamed, let not mine enemies triumph over me.

Yea, let none that wait on Thee be ashamed: let them be ashamed which transgress without cause.

Show me Thy ways, O Lord; teach me Thy paths.

Lead me in Thy truth, and teach me: for Thou art the God of my salvation; on Thee do I wait all the day.

Remember, O Lord, Thy tender mercies and Thy loving kindnesses; for they have been ever of old.

Remember not the sins of my youth, nor my transgressions: according to Thy mercy remember Thou me for Thy goodness' sake, O Lord.

Good and upright is the Lord: therefore will He teach sinners in the way.

The meek will He guide in judgment: and the meek will He teach His way.

All the paths of the Lord are mercy and truth unto such as keep His covenant and His testimonies.

For Thy Name's sake, O Lord, pardon my iniquity; for it is great.

What man is he that feareth the Lord? him shall He teach in the way that He shall choose.

His soul shall dwell at ease; and his seed shall inherit the earth.

The secret of the Lord is with them that fear Him; and He will show them His covenant.

THIRTY-NINTH SUNDAY

FIRST READING

The Path of the Just

Hear, ye children, the instruction of a father, and attend to know understanding.

For I give you good doctrine, forsake ye not my law.

Get wisdom, get understanding: forget it not; neither decline from the words of my mouth.

Forsake her not, and she shall preserve thee: love her, and she shall keep thee.

606

Wisdom is the principal thing; therefore get wisdom: and with all thy getting get understanding.

Exalt her, and she shall promote thee: she shall bring thee to honor, when thou dost embrace her.

She shall give to thine head an ornament of grace: a crown of glory shall she deliver to thee.

Hear, O my son, and receive my sayings; and the years of thy life shall be many.

I have taught thee in the way of wisdom; I have led thee in right paths.

When thou goest, thy steps shall not be straitened; and when thou runnest, thou shalt not stumble.

Take fast hold of instruction; let her not go: keep her; for she is thy life.

The path of the just is as the shining light, that shineth more and more unto the perfect day.

SECOND READING

FORGIVENESS AND JOY

Blessed is he whose transgression is forgiven, whose sin is covered.

Blessed is the man unto whom the Lord imputeth not iniquity, and in whose spirit there is no guile.

I acknowledged my sin unto Thee, and mine iniquity have I not hid. I said, I will confess my transgressions unto the Lord; and Thou forgavest the iniquity of my sin.

For this shall every one that is godly pray unto Thee in a time when .Thou mayest be found: surely in the floods of great waters they shall not come nigh unto him.

Thou art my hiding place; Thou shalt preserve me from trouble; Thou shalt compass me about with songs of deliverance.

I will instruct thee and teach thee in the way which thou shalt go: I will guide thee with Mine eye.

Many sorrows shall be to the wicked: but he that trusteth in the Lord, mercy shall compass him about.

Be glad in the Lord, and rejoice, ye righteous: and shout for joy, all ye that are upright in heart.

FORTIETH SUNDAY

FIRST READING

THE DIVINE UPHOLDING

The steps of a good man are ordered by the Lord: and He delighteth in his way.

Though he fall, he shall not be utterly cast down: for the Lord upholdeth him with His hand.

I have been young, and now am old; yet have I not seen the righteous forsaken, nor his seed begging bread.

He is ever merciful, and lendeth; and his seed is blessed.

Depart from evil, and do good; and dwell for evermore.

For the Lord loveth judgment, and forsaketh not His saints; they are preserved for ever: but the seed of the wicked shall be cut off.

The righteous shall inherit the land, and dwell therein for ever.

The mouth of the righteous speaketh wisdom, and his tongue talketh of judgment.

The law of his God is in his heart; none of his steps shall slide.

Wait on the Lord, and keep His way, and He shall exalt thee to inherit the land: when the wicked are cut off, thou shalt see it.

I have seen the wicked in great power, and spreading himself like a green bay tree.

Yet he passed away, and, lo, he was not: yea, I sought him, but he could not be found.

Mark the perfect man, and behold the upright: for the end of that man is peace.

The transgressors shall be destroyed together: the end of the wicked shall be cut off.

But the salvation of the righteous is of the Lord: He is their strength in the time of trouble.

And the Lord shall help them, and deliver them: He shall deliver them from the wicked, and save them, because they trust in Him.

SECOND READING

THE HALLOWED HOUSE

I was glad when they said unto me, Let us go into the house of the Lord.

Our feet shall stand within thy gates, O Jerusalem.

Jerusalem is builded as a city that is compact together:

Whither the tribes go up, the tribes of the Lord, unto the testimony of Israel, to give thanks unto the Name of the Lord.

For there are set thrones of judgment, the thrones of the house of David.

Pray for the peace of Jerusalem: they shall prosper that love thee. Peace be within thy walls, and prosperity within thy palaces.

For my brethren and companions' sakes, I will now say, Peace be within thee.

Because of the house of the Lord our God I will seek thy good.

FORTY-FIRST SUNDAY

FIRST READING

THE HELPER OF THE AFFLICTED

Make a joyful noise unto God, all ye lands:

Sing forth the honor of His Name: make His praise glorious.

All the earth shall worship Thee, and shall sing unto Thee; they shall sing to Thy Name.

He ruleth by His power for ever; His eyes behold the nations: let not the rebellious exalt themselves.

O bless our God, ye people, and make the voice of His praise to be heard:

Who holdeth our soul in life, and suffereth not our feet to be moved.

For Thou, O God, hast proved us: Thou hast tried us, as silver is tried.

Thou broughtest us into the net; Thou laidst affliction upon our loins.

We went through fire and through water: but Thou broughtest us out into a wealthy place.

I will go into Thy house with burnt offerings: I will pay Thee my vows,

Which my lips have uttered, and my mouth hath spoken, when I was in trouble.

Come and hear, all ye that fear God, and I will declare what He hath done for my soul.

I cried unto Him with my mouth, and He was extolled with my tongue.

If I regard iniquity in my heart, the Lord will not hear me:

But verily God hath heard me; He hath attended to the voice of my prayer.

Blessed be God, who hath not turned away my prayer, nor His mercy from me.

SECOND READING

The Faithful High Priest

Thou, Lord, in the beginning hast laid the foundation of the earth; and the heavens are the works of Thine hands.

They shall perish, but Thou remainest: and they all shall wax old as doth a garment;

And as a vesture shalt Thou fold them up, and they shall be changed:

But Thou art the same, and Thy years shall not fail.

One in a certain place testified, saying, What is man, that Thou art mindful of him? or the son of man, that Thou visitest him?

Thou madest him a little lower than the angels; Thou crownedst him with glory and honor, and didst set him over the works of Thy hands:

Thou hast put all things in subjection under His feet. For in that He put all in subjection under Him, He left nothing that is not put under Him. But now we see not yet all things put under Him.

But we see Jesus, who was made a little lower than the angels for the suffering of death, crowned with glory and honor; that He by the grace of God should taste death for every man,

And deliver them, who through fear of death were all their lifetime subject to bondage.

For verily He took not on Him the nature of angels; but He took on Him the seed of Abraham.

Wherefore in all things it behooved Him to be made like unto His brethren, that He might be a merciful and faithful high priest in things pertaining to God, to make reconciliation for the sins of the people.

For in that He Himself hath suffered being tempted, He is able to succor them that are tempted.

FORTY-SECOND SUNDAY

FIRST READING

An Unfaltering Trust

Preserve me, O God, for in Thee do I put my trust. O my soul, thou hast said unto the Lord, thou art my Lord: my goodness extendeth not to Thee;

But to the saints that are in the earth, and to the excellent, in whom is all my delight.

The Lord is the portion of mine inheritance and of my cup: Thou maintainest my lot.

The lines are fallen unto me in pleasant places; yea, I have a goodly heritage. I will bless the Lord, who hath given me counsel.

I have set the Lord always before me: because He is at my right hand, I shall not be moved.

Therefore my heart is glad, and my glory rejoiceth: my flesh also shall rest in hope.

For Thou wilt not leave my soul in

the grave; neither wilt Thou suffer Thine Holy One to see corruption.

Thou wilt show me the path of life: in Thy presence is fullness of joy; at Thy right hand there are pleasures for evermore.

SECOND READING

THE ARMOR OF GOD

Finally, my brethren, be strong in the Lord, and in the power of His might.

Put on the whole armor of God, that ye may be able to stand against the wiles of the devil.

For we wrestle not against flesh and blood, but against principalities, against powers, against the rulers of the darkness of this world, against spiritual wickedness in high places.

Wherefore take unto you the whole armor of God, that ye may be able to withstand in the evil day, and having done all, to stand.

Stand therefore, having your loins girt about with truth, and having on the breastplate of righteousness,

And your feet shod with the preparation of the gospel of peace;

Above all, taking the shield of faith, wherewith ye shall be able to quench all the fiery darts of the wicked.

Take the helmet of salvation, and the sword of the Spirit, which is the word of God:

Praying always with all prayer and supplication in the Spirit, and watching thereunto with all perseverance and supplication for all saints.

Grace be with all them that love our Lord Jesus Christ in sincerity. Amen.

FORTY-THIRD SUNDAY

FIRST READING

GOD OUR DEFENDER

Rejoice in the Lord, O ye righteous: for praise is comely for the upright.

Sing unto Him a new song; for the word of the Lord is right; and all His works are done in truth.

He loveth righteousness and judgment: the earth is full of the goodness of the Lord.

By the word of the Lord were the heavens made; and all the host of them by the breath of His mouth.

He gathereth the waters of the sea together as a heap: He layeth up the deep in storehouses.

Let all the earth fear the Lord: let all the inhabitants of the world stand in awe of Him.

For He spake, and it was done; He commanded, and it stood fast. The Lord bringeth the counsel of the nations to nought:

He maketh the devices of the people of none effect. But the counsel of the Lord standeth for ever, the thoughts of His heart to all generations.

Blessed is the nation whose God is the Lord; and the people whom He hath chosen for His own inheritance.

The Lord looketh from heaven; He beholdeth all the sons of men.

From the place of His habitation He looketh upon all the inhabitants of the earth.

He fashioneth their hearts alike; He considereth all their works.

Behold, the eye of the Lord is upon

them that fear Him, upon them that hope in His mercy; to deliver their soul from death, and to keep them alive in famine.

Our soul waiteth for the Lord: He is our help and our shield.

For our heart shall rejoice in Him, because we have trusted in His holy Name.

Let Thy mercy, O Lord, be upon us, according as we hope in Thee.

SECOND READING

Worship and Strength

I will praise Thee with my whole heart: I will sing praise unto Thee.

I will worship toward Thy holy temple, and praise Thy Name for Thy loving kindness and for Thy truth: for Thou hast magnified Thy word above all Thy Name.

In the day when I cried Thou answeredst me, and strengthenedst me with strength in my soul.

All the kings of the earth shall praise Thee, O Lord, when they hear the words of Thy mouth.

Yea, they shall sing in the ways of the Lord: for great is the glory of the Lord.

Though the Lord be high, yet hath He respect unto the lowly: but the proud He knoweth afar off.

Though I walk in the midst of trouble, Thou wilt revive me: Thou shalt stretch forth Thine hand against the wrath of mine enemies, and Thy right hand shall save me.

The Lord will perfect that which concerneth me: Thy mercy, O Lord, endureth for ever: forsake not the works of Thine own hands.

FORTY-FOURTH SUNDAY

FIRST READING

The Experience of Redemption

I will bless the Lord at all times: His praise shall continually be in my mouth.

My soul shall make her boast in the Lord: the humble shall hear thereof, and be glad.

O magnify the Lord with me, and let us exalt His Name together.

I sought the Lord, and He heard me, and delivered me from all my fears.

They looked unto Him, and were lightened: and their faces were not ashamed.

This poor man cried, and the Lord heard him, and saved him out of all his troubles.

The angel of the Lord encampeth round about them that fear Him, and delivereth them.

O taste and see that the Lord is good; blessed is the man that trusteth in Him.

O fear the Lord, ye His saints: for there is no want to them that fear Him.

The young lions do lack, and suffer hunger: but they that seek the Lord shall not want any good thing.

The righteous cry, and the Lord heareth, and delivereth them out of all their troubles.

The Lord is nigh unto them that are of a broken heart; and saveth such as be of a contrite spirit.

Many are the afflictions of the righteous: but the Lord delivereth him out of them all.

The Lord redeemeth the soul of His servants: and none of them that trust in Him shall be desolate.

SECOND READING

LIGHT AND TRUTH

The Lord is good unto them that wait for Him, to the soul that seeketh Him.

It is good that a man should both hope and quietly wait for the salvation of the Lord.

For the Lord will not cast off for ever:

But though He cause grief, yet will He have compassion according to the multitude of His mercies.

For He doth not afflict willingly nor grieve the children of men.

Judge me, O God, and plead my cause against an ungodly nation: O deliver me from the deceitful and unjust man.

For Thou art the God of my strength: why dost Thou cast me off? why go I mourning because of the oppression of the enemy?

O send out Thy light and Thy truth: let them lead me; let them bring me unto Thy holy hill, and to Thy tabernacles.

Then will I go unto the altar of God, unto God my exceeding joy: yea, upon the harp will I praise Thee, O God my God.

Why art thou cast down, O my soul? and why art thou disquieted within me? hope in God: for I shall yet praise Him, who is the health of my countenance, and my God.

FORTY-FIFTH SUNDAY

FIRST READING

SPIRITUAL SERVICE

I beseech you, brethren, by the mercies of God, that ye present your bodies a living sacrifice, holy, acceptable unto God, which is your reasonable service.

Be not conformed to this world: but be ye transformed by the renewing of your mind, that ye may prove what is that good, and acceptable, and perfect will of God.

For I say, through the grace given unto me, to every man that is among you, not to think of himself more highly than he ought to think;

But to think soberly, according as God hath dealt to every man the measure of faith.

For as we have many members in one body, and all members have not the same office:

So we, being many, are one body in Christ, and every one members one of another.

Having then gifts differing according to the grace that is given to us, whether prophecy, let us prophesy according to the proportion of faith;

Or ministry, let us wait on our ministering; or he that teacheth, on teaching;

Or he that exhorteth, on exhortation: he that giveth, let him do it with simplicity; he that ruleth, with diligence;

He that showeth mercy, with cheerfulness.

Let love be without dissimulation. Abhor that which is evil; cleave to that which is good.

Be kindly affectioned one to another with brotherly love; in honor preferring one another;

Not slothful in business; fervent in spirit; serving the Lord;

Rejoicing in hope; patient in tribulation; continuing instant in prayer;

Distributing to the necessity of saints; given to hospitality.

Bless them which persecute you: bless, and curse not.

Rejoice with them that do rejoice, and weep with them that weep.

Be of the same mind one toward another.

Mind not high things, but condescend to men of low estate. Be not wise in your own conceits.

Be not overcome of evil, but overcome evil with good.

SECOND READING

God's Messenger

The Spirit of the Lord God is upon me; because the Lord hath anointed me to preach good tidings unto the meek;

He hath sent me to bind up the brokenhearted, to proclaim liberty to the captives, and the opening of the prison to them that are bound;

To proclaim the acceptable year of the Lord and the day of justice of our God;

To comfort all that mourn; to give unto them beauty for ashes, the oil of joy for mourning, the garment of praise for the spirit of heaviness;

That they might be called trees of righteousness, the planting of the Lord, that He might be glorified.

They shall build the old wastes, they shall raise up the former desolations, and they shall repair the waste cities, the desolations of many generations.

Ye shall be named the Priests of the Lord: men shall call you the Ministers of our God.

They shall rejoice in their portion; in their land they shall possess double; everlasting joy shall be unto them; and I will make an everlasting covenant with them.

I will greatly rejoice in the Lord, my soul shall be joyful in my God; for He hath clothed me with the garments of salvation.

He hath covered me with the robe of righteousness, as a bridegroom decketh himself with ornaments, and as a bride adorneth herself with her jewels.

For as the earth bringeth forth her bud, and as the garden causeth the things that are sown in it to spring forth;

So the Lord God will cause righteousness and praise to spring forth before all the nations.

O Lord, Thou art my God; I will exalt Thee, I will praise Thy Name; for Thou hast done wonderful things; Thy counsels of old are faithfulness and truth.

Thou hast been a strength to the poor, a strength to the needy in his distress, a refuge from the storm, a shadow from the heat.

The Lord God will swallow up death in victory and will wipe away tears from off all faces; and the rebuke of His people shall He take away from off all the earth, for the Lord hath spoken it.

It shall be said in that day, Lo,

this is our God; we have waited for Him and He will save us: this is the Lord; we have waited for Him, we will be glad and rejoice in His salvation.

FORTY-SIXTH SUNDAY

FIRST READING

RECONCILED TO GOD

Being justified by faith, we have peace with God through our Lord Jesus Christ:

By whom also we have access by faith into this grace wherein we stand, and rejoice in hope of the glory of God.

And not only so, but we glory in tribulations also; knowing that tribulation worketh patience;

And patience, experience; and experience, hope:

And hope maketh not ashamed; because the love of God is shed abroad in our hearts by the Holy Spirit which is given unto us.

For when we were yet without strength, in due time Christ died for the ungodly.

For scarcely for a righteous man will one die:

Yet peradventure for a good man some would even dare to die.

But God commendeth His love toward us, in that, while we were yet sinners, Christ died for us.

Much more then, being now justified by His blood, we shall be saved from wrath through Him.

For if, when we were enemies, we were reconciled to God by the death of His Son; much more, being reconciled, we shall be saved by His life.

And not only so but we also joy in God, through our Lord Jesus Christ, by whom we have now received the reconciliation.

SECOND READING

CONFIDENCE IN GOD

In Thee, O Lord, do I put my trust; let me never be ashamed: deliver me in Thy righteousness.

Bow down Thine ear to me: deliver me speedily: be Thou my strong rock, for an house of defense to save me.

For Thou art my rock and my fortress; therefore for Thy Name's sake lead me, and guide me.

Pull me out of the net that they have laid secretly for me: for Thou art my strength.

Into Thine hand I commit my spirit: Thou hast redeemed me, O Lord God of truth.

I will be glad and rejoice in Thy mercy: for Thou hast considered my trouble; Thou hast known my soul in adversities;

Thou hast not shut me up into the hand of the enemy: Thou hast set my foot in a large room.

My times are in Thy hand: deliver me from the hand of mine enemies, and from them that persecute me.

Make Thy face to shine upon Thy servant; save me for Thy mercies' sake.

Oh how great is Thy goodness, which Thou hast laid up for them that fear Thee; which Thou hast wrought for them that trust in Thee before the sons of men!

Thou shalt hide them in the secret of Thy presence from the pride of man: Thou shalt keep them secretly in a pavilion from the strife of tongues.

Be of good courage, and He shall strengthen your heart, all ye that hope in the Lord.

FORTY-SEVENTH SUNDAY

FIRST READING

PRAISE AND THANKSGIVING

Praise ye the Lord: for it is good to sing praises unto our God; for it is pleasant; and praise is comely.

He healeth the broken in heart, and bindeth up their wounds. He telleth the number of the stars; He calleth them all by their names.

Great is our Lord, and of great power: His understanding is infinite.

The Lord lifteth up the meek: He casteth the wicked down to the ground.

Sing unto the Lord with thanksgiving; sing praise upon the harp unto our God:

Who covereth the heaven with clouds, who prepareth rain for the earth, who maketh grass to grow upon the mountains.

He giveth to the beast his food, and to the young ravens which cry.

The Lord taketh pleasure in them that fear Him, in those that hope in His mercy.

Praise the Lord, O Jerusalem; praise thy God, O Zion.

For He hath strengthened the bars of thy gates; He hath blessed thy children within thee.

He maketh peace in thy borders, and filleth thee with the finest of the wheat.

He sendeth forth His commandment upon earth: His word runneth very swiftly.

He giveth snow like wool: He scattereth the hoar frost like ashes.

He casteth forth His ice like morsels: who can stand before His cold?

He sendeth out His word, and melteth them: He causeth His wind to blow, and the waters flow.

He showeth His word unto Jacob, His statutes and His judgments unto Israel. Praise ye the Lord.

SECOND READING

THE SHADOW OF THE ALMIGHTY

He that dwelleth in the secret place of the Most High shall abide under the shadow of the Almighty.

I will say of the Lord, He is my refuge and my fortress: my God; in Him will I trust.

Surely He shall deliver thee from the snare of the fowler, and from the noisome pestilence.

He shall cover thee with His feathers, and under His wings shalt thou trust: His truth shall be thy shield and buckler.

Thou shalt not be afraid for the terror by night; nor for the arrow that flieth by day;

Nor for the pestilence that walketh in darkness; nor for the destruction that wasteth at noonday.

A thousand shall fall at thy side, and ten thousand at thy right hand; but it shall not come nigh thee.

Only with thine eyes shalt thou behold and see the reward of the wicked.

Because thou hast made the Lord,

which is my refuge, even the Most High, thy habitation;

> There shall no evil befall thee; neither shall any plague come nigh thy dwelling.

For He shall give His angels charge over thee, to keep thee in all thy ways.

> They shall bear thee up in their hands, lest thou dash thy foot against a stone.

Thou shalt tread upon the lion and adder: the young lion and the dragon shalt thou trample under feet.

> Because he hath set his love upon Me, therefore will I deliver him: I will set him on high, because he hath known My Name.

He shall call upon Me, and I will answer him: I will be with him in trouble; I will deliver him, and honor him.

> With long life will I satisfy him, and show him My salvation.

FORTY-EIGHTH SUNDAY

FIRST READING

THE WAY OF HOLINESS

The wilderness and the solitary place shall be glad; and the desert shall rejoice, and blossom as the rose.

> It shall blossom abundantly, and rejoice even with joy and singing.

The glory of Lebanon shall be given unto it, the excellency of Carmel and Sharon, they shall see the glory of the Lord, and the excellency of our God.

> Strengthen ye the weak hands, and confirm the feeble knees.

Say to them that are of a fearful heart, Be strong, fear not: behold your God will come and save you.

> Then the eyes of the blind shall be opened, and the ears of the deaf shall be unstopped.

Then shall the lame man leap as an hart, and the tongue of the dumb sing: for in the wilderness shall waters break out, and streams in the desert.

> The parched ground shall become a pool, and the thirsty land springs of water:

An highway shall be there, and a way, and it shall be called, The way of holiness;

> No lion shall be there, nor any ravenous beast shall go up thereon, it shall not be found there; but the redeemed shall walk there:

The ransomed of the Lord shall return, and come to Zion with songs and everlasting joy upon their heads.

> They shall obtain joy and gladness, and sorrow and sighing shall flee away.

SECOND READING

THE REIGN OF GOD

Praise ye the Lord. Praise the Lord, O my soul.

> While I live will I praise the Lord: I will sing praises unto my God while I have any being.

Put not your trust in princes, nor in the son of man, in whom there is no help.

> His breath goeth forth, he returneth to his earth; in that very day his thoughts perish.

Happy is he that hath the God of

Jacob for his help, whose hope is in the Lord his God:

Who made heaven, and earth, the sea, and all that therein is: who keepeth truth for ever:

Who executeth judgment for the oppressed: who giveth food to the hungry. The Lord looseth the prisoners:

The Lord openeth the eyes of the blind: the Lord raiseth them that are bowed down: the Lord loveth the righteous:

The Lord preserveth the strangers; He relieveth the fatherless and widow.: but the way of the wicked He turneth upside down.

The Lord shall reign for ever, even thy God, O Zion, unto all generations. Praise ye the Lord.

FORTY-NINTH SUNDAY

FIRST READING

THE PRINCE OF PEACE

The people that walketh in darkness have seen a great light: they that dwell in the land of the shadow of death, upon them hath the light shined.

For unto us a child is born, unto us a son is given: and the government shall be upon His shoulder.

And His Name shall be called Wonderful, Counselor, The Mighty God, The Everlasting Father, The Prince of Peace. Of the increase of His government and peace there shall be no end;

Upon the throne of David, and upon his kingdom, to order it, and to establish it with judgment and with justice from henceforth even for ever.

Behold, God is my salvation; I will

trust, and not be afraid: for the Lord Jehovah is my strength and my song:

He also is become my salvation; therefore with joy shall ye draw water out of the wells of salvation.

In that day shall ye say, Praise the Lord, call upon His Name;

Declare His doings among the people, make mention that His Name is exalted.

Sing unto the Lord; for He hath done excellent things: this is known in all the earth.

Cry out and shout, thou inhabitant of Zion: for great is the Holy One of Israel in the midst of thee.

I will also give thee for a light to the Gentiles, that thou mayest be my salvation unto the end of the earth.

For He that hath mercy on them shall lead them, even by springs of water shall He guide them.

Sing, O heavens; and be joyful, O earth; and break forth into singing, O mountains;

For the Lord hath comforted His people, and will have mercy upon His afflicted.

How beautiful upon the mountains are the feet of Him that bringeth good tidings, that publisheth peace;

That bringeth good tidings of good, that publisheth salvation; that saith unto Zion, Thy God reigneth!

Thy watchmen shall lift up the voice; with the voice together shall they sing;

Break forth into joy, sing together, ye waste places of Jerusalem: for the Lord hath comforted His people, He hath redeemed Jerusalem.

The Lord hath made bare His holy arm in the eyes of all the nations;

And all the ends of the earth shall see the salvation of our God.

SECOND READING

Salvation Made Known

O sing unto the Lord a new song; for He hath done marvelous things: His right hand, and His holy arm, hath gotten Him the victory.

The Lord hath made known His salvation: His righteousness hath He openly showed in the sight of the heathen.

He hath remembered His mercy and His truth toward the house of Israel.

All the ends of the earth have seen the salvation of our God.

Make a joyful noise unto the Lord, all the earth: make a loud noise, and rejoice, and sing praise.

Sing unto the Lord with the harp; with the harp, and the voice of a psalm.

With trumpets and sound of cornet make a joyful noise before the Lord, the King.

Let the sea roar, and the fullness thereof; the world, and they that dwell therein.

Let the floods clap their hands: let the hills be joyful together before the Lord.

For He cometh to judge the earth: with righteousness shall He judge the world, and the people with equity.

FIFTIETH SUNDAY

FIRST READING

The Messiah

Behold My servant, whom I uphold,

Mine elect, in whom My soul delighteth: I have put My spirit upon Him; He shall bring forth judgment to the Gentiles.

He shall not cry, nor lift up, nor cause His voice to be heard in the street.

A bruised reed shall He not break, and the smoking flax shall He not quench: He shall bring forth judgment unto truth.

He shall not fail nor be discouraged, till He have set judgment in the earth: and the isles shall wait for His law.

Thus saith God the Lord, He that created the heavens, and stretched them out; He that spread forth the earth, and that which cometh out of it; He that giveth breath unto the people upon it, and spirit to them that walk therein:

I the Lord have called Thee in righteousness, and will hold Thine hand, and will keep Thee, and give Thee for a covenant of the people, for a light of the Gentiles;

To open the blind eyes, to bring out the prisoners from the prison, and them that sit in darkness out of the prison house.

I will bring the blind by a way that they knew not; I will lead them in paths that they have not known:

I will make darkness light before them, and crooked things straight. These things will I do unto them, and not forsake them.

I am the Lord: that is my Name: and My glory will I not give to another, neither My praise to graven images.

Behold, the former things are come to pass, and new things do I declare: before they spring forth I tell you of them.

Sing unto the Lord a new song, and His praise from the end of the earth, ye that go down to the sea, and all that is therein; the isles, and the inhabitants thereof.

Let the wilderness and the cities thereof lift up their voice, the villages that Kedar doth inhabit: let the inhabitants of the rock sing, let them shout from the top of the mountains.

Let them give glory unto the Lord, and declare His praise in the islands.

SECOND READING

HIS GLORIOUS NAME

Give the king Thy judgments, O God, and Thy righteousness unto the king's son.

He shall judge Thy people with righteousness, and Thy poor with judgment.

The mountains shall bring peace to the people, and the little hills, by righteousness.

He shall judge the poor of the people, He shall save the children of the needy, and shall break in pieces the oppressor.

They shall fear Thee as long as the sun and moon endure, throughout all generations.

He shall come down like rain upon the mown grass: as showers that water the earth.

In His days shall the righteous flourish; and abundance of peace so long as the moon endureth.

He shall have dominion also from sea to sea, and from the river unto the ends of the earth.

Yea, all kings shall fall down before Him: all nations shall serve Him.

For He shall deliver the needy when he crieth; the poor also, and him that hath no helper.

He shall spare the poor and needy, and shall save the souls of the needy.

He shall redeem their soul from deceit and violence: and precious shall their blood be in His sight.

He shall live, and to Him shall be given of the gold of Sheba: prayer also shall be made for Him continually; and daily shall He be praised.

There shall be a handful of corn in the earth upon the top of the mountains;

The fruit thereof shall shake like Lebanon: and they of the city shall flourish like grass of the earth.

His Name shall endure for ever: His Name shall be continued as long as the sun: and men shall be blessed in Him: all nations shall call Him blessed.

Blessed be the Lord God, the God of Israel, who only doeth wondrous things.

And blessed be His glorious Name for ever: and let the whole earth be filled with His glory. Amen, and Amen.

FIFTY-FIRST SUNDAY OR CHRISTMAS DAY

FIRST READING

MESSIAH'S REIGN

There shall come forth a rod out of the stem of Jesse, and a Branch shall grow out of his roots:

And the Spirit of the Lord shall rest upon Him, the spirit of wisdom and understanding, the spirit of counsel and might, the spirit of knowledge and of the fear of the Lord;

And shall make Him of quick understanding in the fear of the Lord: and He shall not judge after the sight of His eyes, neither reprove after the hearing of His ears;

But with righteousness shall He judge the poor, and reprove with equity for the meek of the earth. Righteousness shall be the girdle of His loins, and faithfulness the girdle of His reins.

The wolf also shall dwell with the lamb, and the leopard shall lie down with the kid;

And the calf and the young lion and the fatling together, and a little child shall lead them.

The cow and the bear shall feed; their young ones shall lie down together; and the lion shall eat straw like the ox.

They shall not hurt nor destroy in all My holy mountain: for the earth shall be full of the knowledge of the Lord, as the waters cover the sea.

In that day there shall be a root of Jesse, which shall stand for an ensign of the people.

To it shall the Gentiles seek: and His rest shall be glorious.. And He shall set up an ensign for the nations.

It shall come to pass in the last days, that the mountain of the Lord's house shall be established in the top of the mountains;

It shall be exalted above the hills; and all nations shall flow into it.

And many people shall go and say, Come ye, and let us go up to the mountain of the Lord, to the house of the God of Jacob;

And He will teach us of His ways, and we will walk in His paths: for out of Zion shall go forth the law, and the word of the Lord from Jerusalem.

He shall judge among the nations, and shall rebuke many people: and they shall beat their swords into plowshares, and their spears into pruninghooks;

Nation shall not lift up sword against nation, neither shall they learn war any more. O come ye, and let us walk in the light of the Lord.

SECOND READING

The Magnificat

My soul doth magnify the Lord,

And my spirit hath rejoiced in God my Saviour.

For He hath regarded the low estate of His handmaiden: for, behold, from henceforth all generations shall call me blessed.

For He that is mighty hath done to me great things; and holy is His Name.

His mercy is on them that fear him from generation to generation.

He hath showed strength with His arm; He hath scattered the proud in the imagination of their hearts.

He hath put down the mighty from their seats, and exalted them of low degree.

He hath filled the hungry with good things; and the rich He hath sent empty away.

He hath given help to His servant Israel, in remembrance of His mercy;

As He spake to our fathers, to Abraham, and to His seed for ever.

THIRD READING

THE BENEDICTUS

Blessed be the Lord God of Israel; for He hath visited and redeemed His people.

And hath raised up a horn of salvation for us in the house of His servant David;

As He spake by the mouth of His holy prophets, which have been since the world began:

That we should be saved from our enemies, and from the hand of all that hate us;

To perform the mercy promised to our fathers, and to remember His holy covenant;

The oath which He sware to our father Abraham,

That He would grant unto us, that we, being delivered out of the hand of our enemies, might serve Him without fear,

In holiness and righteousness before Him, all the days of our life.

Thou, child, shalt be called the prophet of the Highest.

For thou shalt go before the face of the Lord to prepare His ways; to give knowledge of salvation unto His people by the remission of their sins,

Through the tender mercy of our God; whereby the dayspring from on high hath visited us,

To give light to them that sit in darkness and in the shadow of death, to guide our feet into the way of peace.

FIFTY-SECOND SUNDAY

FIRST READING

THE KING OF GLORY

The earth is the Lord's, and the fullness thereof; the world, and they that dwell therein.

For He hath founded it upon the seas, and established it upon the floods.

Who shall ascend into the hill of the Lord? or who shall stand in His holy place?

He that hath clean hands, and a pure heart; who hath not lifted up his soul unto vanity, nor sworn deceitfully.

He shall receive the blessing from the Lord, and righteousness from the God of his salvation.

This is the generation of them that seek Him, of them that seek Thy face.

Lift up your heads, O ye gates; and be ye lifted up, ye everlasting doors;

And the King of Glory shall come in.

Who is this King of Glory?

The Lord strong and mighty, the Lord mighty in battle.

Lift up your heads, O ye gates; even lift them up, ye everlasting doors;

And the King of Glory shall come in.

Who is this King of Glory?

The Lord of hosts, He is the King of Glory.

SECOND READING

THE GLAD HEART

Hear me when I call, O God of my righteousness: Thou hast enlarged me when I was in distress; have mercy upon me, and hear my prayer.

O ye sons of men, how long will ye turn My glory into shame? how long will ye love vanity, and seek after falsehood?

But know that the Lord hath set apart him that is godly for Himself: the Lord will hear when I call unto Him.

Stand in awe, and sin not: commune with your own heart upon your bed, and be still.

Offer the sacrifices of righteousness, and put your trust in the Lord.

There be many that say, Who will show us any good? Lord, lift Thou up the light of Thy countenance upon us.

Thou hast put gladness in my heart, more than in the time that their corn and their wine increased.

I will both lay me down in peace, and sleep: for Thou, Lord, only makest me dwell in safety.

FIFTY-THIRD SUNDAY OR WATCHNIGHT

FIRST READING

THE EVERLASTING GOD

Thou, O Lord, shalt endure for ever; and Thy remembrance unto all generations.

O God, take me not away in the midst of my days: Thy years are throughout all generations.

Of old hast Thou laid the foundation of the earth: and the heavens are the work of Thy hands.

They shall perish, but Thou shalt endure: yea, all of them shall wax old like a garment;

As a vesture shalt Thou change them, and they shall be changed; but Thou art the same, and Thy years shall have no end.

The children of Thy servants shall continue, and their generations shall be established before Thee.

Lord, Thou hast been our dwelling-place in all generations.

Before the mountains were brought forth, or ever Thou hadst formed the earth and the world, even from everlasting to everlasting, Thou art God.

Thou turnest man to destruction; and sayest, Return, ye children of men.

For a thousand years in Thy sight are, but as yesterday when it is past, and as a watch in the night.

Thou carriest them away as with a flood; they are as a sleep: in the morning they are like grass which groweth up.

In the morning it flourisheth, and groweth up; in the evening it is cut down, and withereth.

For we are consumed by Thine anger, and by Thy wrath are we troubled.

Thou hast set our iniquities before Thee, our secret sins in the light of Thy countenance.

For all our days are passed away in Thy wrath: we spend our years as a tale that is told. The days of our years are threescore years and ten;

And if by reason of strength they be fourscore years, yet is their strength labor and sorrow; for it is soon cut off and we fly away.

Who knoweth the power of Thine anger? even according to Thy fear, so is Thy wrath.

So teach us to number our days, that we may apply our hearts unto wisdom.

Return, O Lord, how long? and let it repent Thee concerning Thy servants.

O satisfy us early with Thy mercy; that we may rejoice and be glad all our days.

Make us glad according to the days wherein Thou hast afflicted us, and the years wherein we have seen evil.

Let Thy work appear unto Thy servants, and Thy glory unto their children.

And let the beauty of the Lord our God be upon us:

And establish Thou the work of our hands upon us; yea, the work of our hands establish Thou it.

SECOND READING

The Triumph of the Gospel

I saw a new heaven and a new earth: for the first heaven and the first earth were passed away; and there was no more sea.

And I saw the holy city, new Jerusalem, coming down from God out of heaven, prepared as a bride adorned for her husband.

I heard a great voice out of heaven saying, Behold, the tabernacle of God is with men, and He will dwell with them, and they shall be His people.

And God Himself shall be with them, and be their God; and God shall wipe away all tears from their eyes.

There shall be no more death, neither sorrow, nor crying, neither shall there be any more pain;

For the former things are passed away. And He that sat upon the throne said, Behold, I make all things new.

He said unto me, Write: for these words are true and faithful. I will give unto him that is athirst of the fountain of the water of life freely.

He that overcometh shall inherit all things; and I will be his God, and he shall be My son.

He showed me a pure river of water of life, clear as crystal, proceeding out of the throne of God and of the Lamb.

In the midst of the street of it, and on either side of the river, was there the tree of life; and the leaves of the tree were for the healing of the nations.

There shall be no more curse: but the throne of God and of the Lamb shall be in it;

And His servants shall serve Him: and they shall see His face; and His Name shall be in their foreheads.

There shall be no night there; and they need no candle, neither light of the sun;

For the Lord God giveth them light: and they shall reign for ever and ever.

My reward is with Me, to give every man according as his work shall be. I am the beginning and the end, the first and the last.

Blessed are they that do His commandments, that they may have right to the tree of life, and may enter in through the gates into the city.

SPECIAL READINGS

Special Readings

PALM SUNDAY

FIRST READING

Thus saith the Lord, Keep ye judgment, and do justice: for My salvation is near to come, and My righteousness to be revealed.

Every one that keepeth My covenant, even them will I bring to My holy mountain, and make them joyful in My house of prayer: for My house shall be called a house of prayer for all people.

Thus saith the high and lofty One that inhabiteth eternity, whose Name is Holy;

I dwell in the high and holy place, and with him also that is of a contrite and humble spirit, to revive the spirit of the humble and to revive the heart of the contrite ones.

For I will not contend for ever, neither will I be always wroth: for the spirit should fail before Me, and the souls which I have made.

Peace, peace to him that is far off, and to him that is near, saith the Lord; and I will heal him. Have we not all one Father? Hath not one God created us?

Behold, I will send My messenger, and he shall prepare the way before Me:

And the Lord, whom ye seek, shall suddenly come to His temple, even the messenger of the covenant, whom ye delight in: behold, He shall come, saith the Lord of hosts.

But who may abide the day of His coming? and who shall stand when He appeareth? for He is like refiner's fire; and He shall sit as a refiner and purifier of silver.

Unto you that fear My Name shall the Sun of righteousness arise with healing in His wings. And all nations shall call you blessed: for ye shall be a delightsome land, saith the Lord of hosts.

SECOND READING

Rejoice greatly, O daughter of Zion; shout, O daughter of Jerusalem: behold, thy King cometh unto thee:

He is just, and having salvation; lowly, and riding upon an ass, and upon a colt the foal of an ass.

And I will cut off the chariot from Ephraim, and the horse from Jerusalem, and the battle bow shall be cut off:

And He shall speak peace unto the nations: and His dominion shall be from sea even to sea, and from the river even to the ends of the earth.

Thou art fairer than the children of men: grace is poured into Thy lips: therefore God hath blessed Thee for ever.

Gird Thy sword upon Thy thigh, O Most Mighty, with Thy glory and Thy majesty.

In Thy majesty ride prosperously, because of truth and meekness and righteousness.

Thy throne, O God, is for ever

and ever: the scepter of Thy kingdom is a scepter of righteousness.

O Zion, that bringest good tidings, get thee up into the high mountain.

O Jerusalem, that bringest good tidings, lift up thy voice with strength;

Lift it up, be not afraid; say unto the cities of Judah, Behold your God!

How beautiful upon the mountains are the feet of Him that bringeth good tidings, that publisheth peace; that bringeth good tidings of good, that publisheth salvation; that saith unto Zion, thy God reigneth!

GOOD FRIDAY

FIRST READING

Who hath believed our report? and to whom is the arm of the Lord revealed?

For He shall grow up before Him as a tender plant, and as a root out of a dry ground: He hath no form nor comeliness; and when we shall see Him, there is no beauty that we should desire Him.

He is despised and rejected of men; a man of sorrows, and acquainted with grief: and we hid as it were our faces from Him; He was despised, and we esteemed Him not.

Surely He hath borne our griefs, and carried our sorrows: yet we did esteem Him stricken, smitten of God, and afflicted.

He was wounded for our transgressions, He was bruised for our iniquities: the chastisement of our peace was upon Him; and with His stripes we are healed.

All we like sheep have gone astray; we have turned every one to his own way; and the Lord hath laid on Him the iniquity of us all.

He was oppressed, and He was afflicted, yet He opened not His mouth: He is brought as a lamb to the slaughter, and as a sheep before her shearers is dumb, so He openeth not His mouth.

He was taken from prison and from judgment: and who shall declare His generation? for He was cut off out of the land of the living: for the transgression of my people was He stricken.

He made His grave with the wicked, and with the rich in His death; because He had done no violence, neither was any deceit in His mouth.

Yet it pleased the Lord to bruise Him; He hath put Him to grief: when thou shalt make His soul an offering for sin, He shall see His seed, He shall prolong His days, and the pleasure of the Lord shall prosper in His hand.

He shall see of the travail of His soul, and shall be satisfied: by His knowledge shall My righteous servant justify many; for He shall bear their iniquities.

Therefore will I divide Him a portion with the great, and He shall divide the spoil with the strong; because He hath poured out His soul unto death: and He was numbered with the transgressors; and He bare the sin of many, and made intercession for the transgressors.

SECOND READING

My God, my God, why hast Thou forsaken me? why art Thou so far from helping me, and from the words of my groaning?

O my God, I cry in the daytime, but Thou hearest not; and in the night season, and am not silent.

Thou art holy, O Thou that inhabitest the praises of Israel.

Our fathers trusted in Thee: they trusted, and Thou didst deliver them.

They cried unto Thee, and were delivered: they trusted in Thee, and were not confounded.

All they that see me laugh me to scorn: they shoot out the lip, they shake the head, saying,

He trusted on the Lord that He would deliver him: let Him deliver him, seeing he delighted in Him.

The assembly of the wicked have inclosed me: they pierced my hands and my feet.

I may tell all my bones: they look and stare upon me.

They part my garments among them, and cast lots upon my vesture.

Be not Thou far from me, O Lord: O my strength, haste Thee to help me.

My praise shall be of Thee in the great congregation:

I will pay my vows before them that fear Him.

The meek shall eat and be satisfied: they shall praise the Lord that seek Him: your heart shall live for ever.

All the ends of the world shall remember and turn unto the Lord: and all the kindreds of the nations shall worship before Thee.

For the kingdom is the Lord's:

and He is the governor among the nations.

EASTER DAY

FIRST READING

Now is Christ risen from the dead, and become the firstfruits of them that slept.

For since by man came death, by man came also the resurrection of the dead. For as in Adam all die, even so in Christ shall all be made alive.

But some man will say, How are the dead raised up? and with what body do they come?

All flesh is not the same flesh: but there is one kind of flesh of men, another flesh of beasts, another of fishes, and another of birds.

There are also celestial bodies, and bodies terrestrial: but the glory of the celestial is one, and the glory of the terrestrial is another.

There is one glory of the sun, and another glory of the moon, and another glory of the stars; for one star differeth from another star in glory.

So also is the resurrection of the dead. It is sown in corruption, it is raised in incorruption:

It is sown in dishonor, it is raised in glory: it is sown in weakness, it is raised in power:

It is sown a natural body, it is raised a spiritual body. There is a natural body, and there is a spiritual body.

So it is written, The first man Adam was made a living soul; the last Adam was made a quickening spirit.

Behold, I show you a mystery; We

shall not all sleep, but we shall all be changed,

> For this corruptible must put on incorruption, and this mortal must put on immortality.

Thanks be to God, who giveth us the victory through our Lord Jesus Christ.

> Therefore, my beloved brethren, be ye steadfast, unmovable, always abounding in the work of the Lord, forasmuch as ye know that your labor is not in vain in the Lord.

SECOND READING

If ye then be risen with Christ, seek those things which are above, where Christ sitteth on the right hand of God.

> Set your affection on things above, not on things on the earth; for your life is hid with Christ in God.

When Christ, who is our life, shall appear, then shall ye also appear with Him in glory.

> Mortify therefore your members which are upon the earth, for the sake of which things the wrath of God cometh on the children of disobedience; in the which ye walked sometime, when ye lived in them.

Ye have put off the old man with his deeds; and ye have put on the new man, which is renewed in knowledge after the image of Him that created him: for Christ is all, and in all.

> Put on therefore, as the elect of God, holy and beloved, hearts of compassion, kindness, humbleness of mind, meekness, longsuffering;

Forbearing one another, and forgiving one another, if any man have a quarrel against any: even as Christ forgave you, so also do ye.

> Above all these things put on love, which is the bond of perfectness.

Let the peace of God rule in your hearts, to the which also ye are called in one body; and be ye thankful.

> Let the word of Christ dwell in you richly in all wisdom;

Teaching and admonishing one another in psalms and hymns and spiritual songs, singing with grace in your hearts to the Lord.

> Whatsoever ye do, in word or deed, do all in the Name of the Lord Jesus, giving thanks to God and the Father by Him.

ASCENSION DAY

FIRST READING

The king shall joy in Thy strength, O Lord; and in Thy salvation how greatly shall he rejoice!

> Thou hast given him his heart's desire, and hast not withholden the request of his lips.

For Thou preventest him with the blessings of goodness: Thou settest a crown of pure gold on his head.

> He asked life of Thee, and Thou gavest it him, even length of days for ever and ever.

His glory is great in Thy salvation: honor and majesty hast Thou laid upon him.

> For Thou hast made him most blessed for ever: Thou hast made him exceeding glad with Thy countenance.

For the king trusteth in the Lord, and through the mercy of the Most High he shall not be moved.

Be Thou exalted, Lord, in Thine own strength: so will we sing and praise Thy power.

SECOND READING

I beseech you that ye walk worthy of the calling wherewith ye are called,

With all lowliness and meekness, with longsuffering, forbearing one another in love;

Endeavoring to keep the unity of the Spirit in the bond of peace.

There is one body, and one Spirit, even as ye are called in one hope of your calling; one Lord, one faith, one baptism;

One God and Father of all, who is above all, and through all, and in you all.

But unto every one of us is given grace according to the measure of the gift of Christ.

Wherefore He saith, When He ascended up, on high, He led captivity captive, and gave gifts unto men.

And He gave some, apostles; and some, prophets; and some, evangelists; and some, pastors and teachers;

For the perfecting of the saints, for the work of the ministry, for the edifying of the body of Christ:

Till we all come in the unity of the faith, and of the knowledge of the Son of God, unto a perfect man, unto the measure of the stature of the fullness of Christ:

That we henceforth be no more children, tossed to and fro, and carried about with every wind of doctrine, by the sleight of men, and cunning craftiness, whereby they lie in wait to deceive;

But speaking the truth in love, may grow up into Him in all things, which is the Head, even Christ.

WHITSUNDAY (PENTE-COST)

FIRST READING

Turn ye even to Me with all your heart, and with fasting, and with weeping, and with mourning, saith the Lord.

And rend your heart, and not your garments, and turn unto the Lord your God: for He is gracious and merciful, slow to anger, and of great kindness, and repenteth Him of the evil.

Blow the trumpet in Zion, sanctify a fast, call a solemn assembly.

Gather the people, sanctify the congregation, assemble the elders, gather the children.

Let the priests, the ministers of the Lord, weep between the porch and the altar; and let them say, Spare Thy people, O Lord.

Then will the Lord be jealous for His land and pity His people.

Fear not, O land; be glad and rejoice: for the Lord will do great things.

And ye shall know that I am in the midst of Israel, and that I am the Lord your God, and none else: and My people shall never be ashamed.

And it shall come to pass afterward, that I will pour out My spirit upon all flesh;

And your sons and your daughters shall prophesy, your old men shall dream dreams, your young men shall see visions:

And also upon the servants and upon the handmaids in those days will I pour out My spirit.

And it shall come to pass that whosoever shall call on the Name of the Lord shall be delivered.

SECOND READING

Brethren, ye have been called unto liberty; only use not liberty for an occasion to the flesh, but by love serve one another.

For all the law is fulfilled in one word, even in this: Thou shalt love thy neighbor as thyself.

This I say, then, Walk in the Spirit, and ye shall not fulfill the lust of the flesh.

For the flesh lusteth against the Spirit, and the Spirit against the flesh: and these are contrary the one to the other; so that ye cannot do the things that ye would.

But if ye be led to the Spirit, ye are not under the law. For the fruit of the Spirit is love, joy, peace, longsuffering, gentleness, goodness, faith, meekness, temperance: and against such there is no law.

And they that are Christ's have crucified the flesh with the affections and lusts. If we live in the Spirit, let us also walk in the Spirit.

If the Spirit of Him that raised up Jesus from the dead dwell in you, He that raised up Christ from the dead shall also quicken your mortal bodies by His Spirit that dwelleth in you.

Therefore, brethren, we are debtors, not to the flesh, to live after the flesh, for if ye live after the flesh ye shall die:

But if ye through the Spirit do mortify the deeds of the body, ye shall live; for as many as are led by the Spirit of God, they are the sons of God.

For ye have not received the spirit of bondage again to fear; but ye have received the Spirit of adoption, whereby we cry, Abba, Father.

The Spirit itself beareth witness with our spirit, that we are the children of God:

And if children, then heirs; heirs of God, and joint heirs with Christ; if so be that we suffer with Him, that we may be also glorified together.

COMMEMORATION SERVICES AND MEMORIAL DAYS

FIRST READING

I beheld, and lo, a great multitude, which no man could number, of all nations, and kindreds, and people, and tongues, stood before the throne, and before the Lamb, clothed with white robes, and palms in their hands;

And they cried with a loud voice, saying, Salvation to our God who sitteth upon the throne, and unto the Lamb.

And all the angels stood round about the throne, and about the elders and the four beasts, and fell before the throne on their faces, and worshiped God,

Saying, Amen: Blessing, and glory, and wisdom, and thanksgiving, and honor, and power, and might, be unto our God for ever and ever. Amen.

And one of the elders said unto me,

Who are these who are arrayed in white robes? and whence came they? **These are they which came out of great tribulation, and have washed their robes, and made them white in the blood of the Lamb.**

Therefore are they before the throne of God, and serve Him day and night in His temple: **And He that sitteth on the throne shall dwell among them.**

They shall hunger no more, neither thirst any more; neither shall the sun light on them, nor any heat. **For the Lamb which is in the midst of the throne shall feed them, and shall lead them unto living fountains of waters: and God shall wipe away all tears from their eyes.**

SECOND READING

The souls of the righteous are in the hand of God, and there shall no torment touch them. **In the sight of the unwise they seemed to die; and their departure is taken for misery,**

And their going from us to be utter destruction; but they are in peace. **God proved them and found them worthy for Himself.**

As gold in the furnace hath He tried them, and received them as a burnt offering. **And in the time of their visitation they shall shine, and run to and fro like sparks among the stubble.**

They shall judge the nations, and have dominion over the people, and their Lord shall reign for ever. **They that put their trust in Him shall understand the truth; and**

such as be faithful in love shall abide with Him, because grace and mercy are to His chosen.

THIRD READING

Let us now praise famous men, and our fathers that begat us. **The Lord manifested in them great glory; even His mighty power from the beginning.**

Such as did bear rule in their kingdoms, men renowned for their power, giving counsel by their understanding, and declaring prophecies: **Leaders of the people by their counsels, and by their understanding men of learning for the people, wise and eloquent in their instructions:**

Such as found out musical tunes, and set forth verses in writing: **Rich men furnished with ability, living peaceably in their habitations:**

All these were honored in their generations, and were the glory of their times. **There be of them, that have left a name behind them, to declare their praises.**

And some there be, who have no memorial; who are perished, as though they had never been. **But these were men of mercy, whose righteous deeds hath not been forgotten.**

With their seed shall remain continually a good inheritance, and their children are within the covenant. **Their seed standeth fast, and their children for their sakes.**

Their seed shall remain for ever,

and their glory shall not be blotted out.

Their bodies are buried in peace; and their name liveth for evermore. The people will tell of their wisdom, and the congregation will show forth their praise.

MISSIONS

FIRST READING

From the rising of the sun even unto the going down of the same My Name shall be great among the Gentiles;

For My Name shall be great among the nations, saith the Lord of hosts.

The Lord hath made known His salvation: His righteousness hath He openly showed in the sight of the nations.

I shall see Him, but not now: I shall behold Him, but not nigh; there shall come a Star out of Jacob, and a Scepter shall rise out of Israel.

The Gentiles shall come to Thy light, and kings to the brightness of Thy rising.

We have also a more sure word of prophecy; whereunto ye do well that ye take heed, as unto a light that shineth in a dark place, until the day dawn, and the daystar arise in your hearts:

For God, who commanded the light to shine out of darkness, hath shined in our hearts, to give the light of the knowledge of the glory of God in the face of Jesus Christ.

Jesus saith unto His disciples, The harvest truly is plenteous, but the laborers are few;

Pray ye therefore the Lord of the harvest, that He will send forth laborers into His harvest.

Other sheep I have, which are not of this fold: them also I must bring, and they shall hear My voice; and there shall be one fold, and one shepherd.

And I saw another angel fly in the midst of heaven, having the everlasting gospel to preach unto them that dwell on the earth, and to every nation, and kindred, and tongue, and people.

They shall come from the east, and from the west, and from the north, and from the south, and shall sit down in the kingdom of God.

SECOND READING

Sing unto the Lord, all the earth; show forth from day to day His salvation.

Declare His glory among the peoples; His marvelous works among all nations.

Fear not: for I am with thee: I will bring thy seed from the east, and gather thee from the west;

I will say to the north, Give up; and to the south, Keep not back: bring My sons from far, and My daughters from the ends of the earth;

Even every one that is called by My Name: for I have created him for My glory, I have formed him; yea, I have made him.

Bring forth the blind people that have eyes, and the deaf that have ears.

Let all the nations be gathered together, and let the people be assembled; who among them can declare this, and show us former things?

Let them bring forth their witnesses, that they may be justified; or let them hear, and say, It is truth.

Ye are My witnesses, saith the Lord, and My servant whom I have chosen.

That ye may know and believe Me, and understand that I am He:

Before Me there was no God formed, neither shall there be after Me.

I, even I, am the Lord; and beside Me there is no Saviour.

.   .   .   .   .   .

And Jesus came and spake unto them, saying, All power is given unto Me in heaven and in earth.

Go ye therefore, and teach all nations, baptizing them in the name of the Father, and of the Son, and of the Holy Spirit:

Teaching them to observe all things whatsoever I have commanded you:

And, lo, I am with you alway, even unto the end of the world.

PEACE

In the last days it shall come to pass, that the mountain of the house of the Lord shall be established in the top of the mountains.

It shall be exalted above the hills; and the people shall flow unto it.

Many nations shall come, and say, Come, and let us go up to the mountain of the Lord, and to the house of the God of Jacob.

He will teach us of His ways, and we will walk in His paths: for the law shall go forth of Zion, and the word of the Lord from Jerusalem.

He shall judge among many people, and rebuke strong nations afar off.

They shall beat their swords into plowshares, and their spears into pruninghooks:

Nation shall not lift up a sword against nation, neither shall they learn war any more.

They shall sit every man under his vine and under his fig tree.

None shall make them afraid: for the mouth of the Lord of hosts hath spoken it.

For all people will walk every one in the name of his god, and we will walk in the Name of the Lord our God for ever and ever.

Behold, I create new heavens and a new earth: and the former shall not be remembered, nor come into mind.

But be ye glad and rejoice for ever in that which I create: for behold I create Jerusalem a rejoicing, and her people a joy.

And I will rejoice in Jerusalem, and joy in My people: and the voice of weeping shall be no more heard in her, nor the voice of crying.

And they shall build houses, and inhabit them; and they shall plant vineyards, and eat the fruit of them.

They shall not build, and another inhabit; and they shall not plant, and another eat: for as the days of a tree are the days of My people, and Mine elect shall long enjoy the work of their hands.

They shall not labor in vain, nor bring forth for trouble; for they are the seed of the blessed of the Lord, and their offspring with them.

And it shall come to pass that, before they call, I will answer; and while they are yet speaking, I will hear.

The wolf and the lamb shall feed together, and the lion shall eat straw like the bullock: and dust shall be the serpent's meat. They shall not hurt nor destroy in all My holy mountain, saith the Lord.

THE LORD'S DAY

Remember the Sabbath day, to keep it holy. Six days shalt thou labor, and do all thy work; but the seventh is a Sabbath unto the Lord thy God;

In it thou shalt not do any work, thou, nor thy son, nor thy daughter, thy manservant nor thy maidservant, nor thy cattle, nor the stranger that is within thy gates;

For in six days the Lord made heaven and earth, the sea, and all that in them is, and rested the seventh day;

Wherefore the Lord blessed the Sabbath day, and hallowed it.

Moreover also I gave them My Sabbaths, to be a sign between Me and them, that they might know that I am the Lord that sanctifieth them.

Ye shall keep My Sabbaths and reverence My sanctuary. I am the Lord.

If thou turn away thy foot from the Sabbath, from doing thy pleasure on My holy day; and call the Sabbath a delight, and the holy of the Lord honorable; and shalt honor Him:

Then shalt thou delight thyself in the Lord; and I will cause thee to ride upon the high places of the earth.

. . . . . .

Jesus said, The Sabbath was made for man and not man for the Sabbath;

Therefore the Son of man is Lord even of the Sabbath.

. . . . .

Early in the morning, the first day of the week, they came unto the sepulcher at the rising of the sun;

And when they looked they saw that the stone was rolled away, for it was great.

And entering into the sepulcher they saw a young man sitting on the right side, clothed in a long white garment, and they were affrighted.

And he sayeth unto them, Be not affrighted. Ye seek Jesus of Nazareth, who was crucified. He is risen. He is not here. Behold where they laid Him.

Then the same day at evening, being the first day of the week, when the doors were shut, where the disciples were assembled for fear of the Jews, came Jesus and stood in the midst of them, saying unto them, Peace be unto you.

And when He had so said, He showed unto them His hands and His side; then were the disciples glad when they saw the Lord.

Then said Jesus unto them again, Peace be unto you; as My Father hath sent Me even so send I you.

And when He had said this, He breathed on them and saith unto them, Receive ye the Holy Spirit.

TEMPERANCE

Who hath woe? who hath sorrow? who hath contentions? who hath babbling? who hath wounds without cause? who hath redness of eyes?

They that tarry long at the wine; they that go to seek mixed wine.

Look not thou upon the wine when it is red, when it giveth his color in the cup, when it moveth itself aright.

At the last it biteth like a serpent, and stingeth like an adder.

Wine is a mocker, strong drink is raging: and whosoever is deceived thereby is not wise.

Be not among winebibbers; among riotous eaters of flesh:

It is not for kings to drink wine; nor for princes strong drink:

Lest they drink, and forget the law, and pervert the judgment of any of the afflicted.

Woe unto them that rise up early in the morning, that they may follow strong drink; that continue until night, till wine inflame them!

Woe unto them that are mighty to drink wine, and men of strength to mingle strong drink:

Which justify the wicked for reward, and take away the righteousness of the righteous from him!

Woe unto him that giveth his neighbor drink, that puttest thy bottle to him, and makest him drunken also, that thou mayest look on their nakedness!

Woe to him that buildeth a town with blood, and establisheth a city by iniquity!

Woe unto them that decree unrighteous decrees, and that write grievousness which they have prescribed;

To turn aside the needy from judgment, and to take away the right from the poor of my people, that widows may be their prey, and that they may rob the fatherless!

The wicked walk on every side, when the vilest men are exalted.

Know ye not that ye are the temple of God, and that the Spirit of God dwelleth in you?

If any man defile the temple of God, him shall God destroy;

For the temple of God is holy, which temple ye are.

This I say then, Walk in the Spirit, and ye shall not fulfill the lust of the flesh.

SOCIAL JUSTICE

FIRST READING

I will praise Thee, O Lord, with my whole heart; I will show forth all Thy marvelous works.

I will be glad and rejoice in Thee: I will sing praise to Thy Name, O Thou Most High.

When Thine enemies are turned back, they shall fall and perish at Thy presence.

For Thou hast maintained my right and my cause; Thou satest in the throne judging right.

The Lord also will be a refuge for the oppressed, a refuge in times of trouble.

And they that know Thy Name will put their trust in Thee: for Thou, Lord, hast not forsaken them that seek Thee.

Sing praises to the Lord, who dwelleth in Zion;

Declare among the people His doings; He forgetteth not the cry of the humble.

Arise, O Lord; let not man prevail: let the nations be judged in Thy sight.

Put them in fear, O Lord: that the nations may know themselves to be but men.

Why standest Thou afar off, O

Lord? why hidest Thou Thyself in times of trouble?

The wicked in his pride doth persecute the poor:

Let them be taken in the devices that they have imagined.

For the wicked boasteth of his heart's desire, and blesseth the c o v e t o u s, whom the Lord abhorreth.

He sitteth in the lurking places of the villages: in the secret places doth he murder the innocent:

His eyes are secretly set against the poor.

He lieth in wait secretly as a lion in his den: he lieth in wait to catch the poor:

He doth catch the poor, when he draweth him into his net.

He hath said in his heart, God hath forgotten: He hideth His face; He will never see it.

Arise, O Lord; O God, lift up Thine hand: forget not the humble.

SECOND READING

Hear the word of the Lord, ye children of Israel: for the Lord hath a controversy with the inhabitants of the land.

Because there is no truth, nor mercy nor knowledge of God in the land.

Your treading is upon the poor, and ye take from him burdens of wheat.

Ye have built houses of hewn stone, but ye shall not dwell in them.

Ye have planted pleasant vineyards, but ye shall not drink wine of them.

For I know your manifold transgressions and your mighty sins: ye that afflict the just and take a

bribe; and ye that turn aside from the poor.

Seek good, and not evil, that ye may live: and so the Lord, the God of hosts, shall be with you.

Hate the evil, and love the good, and establish justice in the gate.

O Lord, we have sinned, and have committed iniquity, and have done wickedly.

O Lord, according to all Thy righteousness, let Thine anger be turned away from Thy city.

Cause Thy face to shine upon the sanctuary that is desolate, for the Lord's sake.

We do not present our supplications before Thee for our righteousness, but for Thy great mercies.

O Lord, hear; O Lord, forgive; O Lord, hearken and do; defer not;

For Thine own sake, O my God: for Thy city and Thy people that are called by Thy Name.

CITIZENSHIP

FIRST READING

Cry aloud, spare not, lift up thy voice like a trumpet, and show My people their transgression, and the house of Jacob their sins.

Yet they seek Me daily, and delight to know My ways, as a nation that did righteousness, and forsook not the ordinance of their God: they ask of Me the ordinances of justice; they take delight in approaching to God.

Wherefore have we fasted, say they, and Thou seest not? wherefore have we afflicted our soul, and Thou takest no knowledge? Behold, in the day of your fast ye find pleasure, and exact all your labors.

Behold, ye fast for strife and debate, and to smite with the fist of wickedness: ye shall not fast as ye do this day, to make your voice to be heard on high.

Is it such a fast that I have chosen? a day for a man to afflict his soul? is it to bow down his head as a bulrush, and to spread sackcloth and ashes under him? wilt thou call this a fast, and an acceptable day to the Lord?

Is not this the fast that I have chosen? to loose the bands of wickedness, to undo the heavy burdens, and to let the oppressed go free, and that ye break every yoke?

Is it not to deal thy bread to the hungry, and that thou bring the poor that are cast out to thy house? when thou seest the naked, that thou cover him; and that thou hide not thyself from thine own flesh?

Then shall thy light break forth as the morning, and thine health shall spring forth speedily: and thy righteousness shall go before thee; the glory of the Lord shall be thy rearguard.

Then shalt thou call, and the Lord shall answer; thou shalt cry, and He shall say, Here I am. If thou take away from the midst of thee the yoke, the putting forth of the finger, and speaking vanity;

If thou draw out thy soul to the hungry, and satisfy the afflicted soul; then shall thy light rise in obscurity, and thy darkness be as the noonday:

The Lord shall guide thee continually, and satisfy thy soul in drought, and thou shalt be like a watered garden, and like a spring of water, whose waters fail not.

They that shall be of thee shall build the old waste places: thou shalt raise up the foundations of many generations; and thou shalt be called, The repairer of the breach, The restorer of paths to dwell in.

SECOND READING

We have heard with our ears, O God, our fathers have told us, what work Thou didst in their days, in the times of old.

For they got not the land in possession by their own sword, neither did their own arm save them: but Thy right hand, and Thine arm, and the light of Thy countenance, because Thou wast favorable unto them.

Turn us again, O God of hosts, and cause Thy face to shine; and we shall be saved.

Thou hast brought a vine out of Egypt: Thou hast cast out the nations, and planted it.

Thou preparedst room before it, and didst cause it to take deep root, and it filled the land.

The hills were covered with the shadow of it, and the boughs thereof were like the goodly cedars. She sent out her boughs unto the sea, and her branches unto the river.

Return, we beseech Thee, O God of hosts: look down from heaven, and behold, and visit this vine;

And the vineyard which Thy strong hand hath planted, and the branch that Thou madest strong for Thyself.

So will not we go back from Thee: quicken us, and we will call upon Thy Name.

Turn us again, O Lord of hosts; cause Thy face to shine, and we shall be saved.

Help us, O God of our salvation, for the glory of Thy Name: and deliver us, and purge away our sins, for Thy Name's sake.

So we Thy people and the sheep of Thy pasture will give Thee thanks for ever: we will show forth Thy praise to all generations.

Give ear, O my people, to my law; incline your ears to the words of my mouth.

I will open my mouth in a parable; I will utter dark sayings of old; which we have heard and known, and our fathers have told us.

We will not hide them from their children, showing to the generation to come the praises of the Lord, and His strength, and His wonderful works that He hath done.

For He established a testimony and appointed a law which He commanded our fathers, that they should make them known to their children;

That the generation to come might know them, even the children which should be born; who should arise and declare them to their children:

That they might set their hope in God, and not forget the works of God, but keep His commandments.

CHILDREN'S DAY

FIRST READING

The child grew, and waxed strong in spirit, filled with wisdom; and the grace of God was upon Him.

Now His parents went to Jerusalem every year at the feast of the passover.

And when He was twelve years old, they went up to Jerusalem after the custom of the feast.

And when they had fulfilled the days, as they returned, the child Jesus tarried behind in Jerusalem; and Joseph and His mother knew not of it.

But they, supposing Him to have been in the company, went a day's journey; and they sought Him among their kinsfolk and acquaintance.

And when they found Him not, they turned back again to Jerusalem, seeking Him.

And it came to pass, that after three days they found Him in the temple, sitting in the midst of the doctors, both hearing them, and asking them questions.

And all that heard Him were astonished at His understanding and answers.

And when they saw Him, they were amazed: and His mother said unto Him, Son, why hast Thou thus dealt with us? behold, Thy father and I have sought Thee sorrowing.

And He said unto them, How is it that ye sought Me? wist ye not that I must be about My Father's business?

And they understood not the saying which He spake unto them.

And He went down with them, and came to Nazareth, and was subject unto them.

But His mother kept all these sayings in her heart.

And Jesus increased in wisdom and stature, and in favor with God and man.

SECOND READING

Praise ye the Lord. Praise ye the Lord from the heavens: praise Him in the heights.

Praise ye Him, all His angels: praise ye Him, all His hosts.

Praise ye Him, sun and moon: praise Him, all ye stars of light.

Praise Him, ye heavens of heavens, and ye waters that be above the heavens.

Let them praise the Name of the Lord: for He commanded, and they were created.

He hath also stablished them for ever and ever: He hath made a decree which shall not pass.

Praise the Lord from the earth, ye dragons and all deeps:

Fire, and hail; snow, and vapor; stormy wind fulfilling His word:

Mountains, and all hills; fruitful trees, and all cedars:

Beasts, and all cattle; creeping things, and flying fowl:

Kings of the earth, and all people; princes, and all judges of the earth:

Both young men, and maidens; old men and children:

Let them praise the Name of the Lord: for His Name alone is excellent; His glory is above the earth and heaven.

He also exalteth the name of His people, the praise of all His saints; even of the children of Israel, a people near unto Him. Praise ye the Lord.

HARVEST FESTIVAL OR THANKSGIVING

All the commandments which I command thee this day shall ye observe to do, that ye may live, and multiply, and go in and possess the land which the Lord sware unto your fathers.

Thou shalt remember all the way which the Lord thy God led thee these forty years in the wilderness, to humble thee, and to prove thee, to know what was in thine heart, whether thou wouldest keep His commandments, or no.

He humbled thee, and suffered thee to hunger, and fed thee with manna, which thou knewest not, neither did thy fathers know; that He might make thee know that man doth not live by bread only, but by every word that proceedeth out of the mouth of the Lord doth man live.

Thy raiment waxed not old upon thee, neither did thy foot swell, these forty years.

Thou shalt also consider in thine heart, that, as a man chasteneth his son, so the Lord thy God chasteneth thee.

Therefore thou shalt keep the commandments of the Lord thy God, to walk in His ways, and to fear Him.

For the Lord thy God bringeth thee into a good land, a land of brooks of water, of fountains and depths that spring out of valleys and hills;

A land of wheat, and barley, and vines, and fig trees, and pomegranates; a land of oil olive, and honey;

A land wherein thou shalt eat bread without scarceness, thou shalt not lack any thing in it; a land whose stones are iron, and out of whose hills thou mayest dig brass.

When thou hast eaten and art full, then thou shalt bless the Lord thy God for the good land which He hath given thee.

Beware that thou forget not the Lord thy God, in not keeping His commandments, and His judgments, and His statutes, which I command thee this day:

Lest when thou hast eaten and art full, and hast built goodly houses, and dwelt therein;

And when thy herds and thy flocks multiply, and thy silver and thy gold is multiplied, and all that thou hast is multiplied:

Then thine heart be lifted up, and thou forget the Lord thy God, which brought thee forth out of the land of Egypt, from the house of bondage;

Who led thee through that great and terrible wilderness, wherein were fiery serpents, and scorpions, and drought, where there was no water; who brought thee forth water out of the rock of flint;

Who fed thee in the wilderness with manna, which thy fathers knew not, that He might humble thee, and that He might prove thee, to do thee good at thy latter end;

And thou say in thine heart, my power and the might of mine hand hath gotten me this wealth.

But thou shalt remember the Lord thy God: for it is He that giveth thee power to get wealth, that He may establish His covenant which He sware unto thy fathers, as it is this day.

CHURCH ANNIVERSARY

FIRST READING

Great is the Lord, and greatly to be praised in the city of our God, in the mountain of His holiness.

Beautiful for situation, the joy of the whole earth, is Mount Zion, the city of the great King. God is known in her palaces for a refuge.

We have thought of Thy lovingkindness, O God, in the midst of Thy temple.

According to Thy Name, O God, so is Thy praise unto the ends of the earth: Thy right hand is full of righteousness.

Let Mount Zion rejoice, let the daughters of Judah be glad, because of Thy judgments.

Walk about Zion, and go round about her: tell the towers thereof.

Mark ye well her bulwarks, consider her palaces; that ye may tell it to the generation following.

For this God is our God for ever and ever: He will be our guide even unto death.

The mighty God, even the Lord, hath spoken, and called the earth from the rising of the sun unto the going down thereof.

Out of Zion, the perfection of beauty, God hath shined. He shall call to the heavens from above, and to the earth, that He may judge His people.

Gather My saints together unto Me; those that have made a covenant with Me by sacrifice.

And the heavens shall declare His

righteousness: for God is judge Himself.

Hear, O My people, and I will speak: O Israel, and I will testify against thee: I am God, even thy God.

I will not reprove thee for thy sacrifices or thy burnt offerings which have been continually before Me.

I will take no bullock out of thy house, nor he goats out of thy folds; for every beast of the forest is Mine, and the cattle upon a thousand hills.

I know all the birds of the mountains; and the wild beasts of the field are Mine. If I were hungry I would not tell thee; for the world is Mine, and the fullness thereof.

Offer unto God thanksgiving; and pay thy vows unto the Most High; and call upon Me in the day of trouble; I will deliver thee and thou shalt glorify Me.

Whoso offereth praise glorifieth Me; and to him that ordereth his conversation aright will I show the salvation of God.

SECOND READING

Out of the depths have I cried unto Thee, O Lord.

Lord, hear my voice: let Thine ears be attentive to the voice of my supplications.

If Thou, Lord, shouldest mark iniquities, O Lord, who shall stand?

But there is forgiveness with Thee, that Thou mayest be feared.

I wait for the Lord, my soul doth wait, and in His word do I hope.

My soul waiteth for the Lord more than they that watch for the morning: I say, more than they that watch for the morning.

Let Israel hope in the Lord: for with the Lord there is mercy, and with Him is plenteous redemption.

And He shall redeem Israel from all his iniquities.*

---

* On the afternoon of May 24, 1738, John Wesley listened earnestly to the singing of this Psalm by the choir of St. Paul's Cathedral, London. That evening, at Aldersgate, "his heart was strangely warmed," and Methodism was born.

Biblical Contents of the Responsive Readings

Scripture Passages in the Responsive Readings, Arranged in their Biblical Order

647

Occasion or Sunday	Number
Twenty-third Sunday	II
PROV. 2. 1–12, 20, 21	
Thirty-second Sunday	I
PROV. 3. 1–6	
PROV. 4. 20–27	
Thirty-ninth Sunday	I
PROV. 4. 1, 2, 5–13, 18	
Thirtieth Sunday	I
PROV. 8. 1, 3, 4, 6, 22–25, 27–36	
Temperance	
PROV. 20. 1	
PROV. 23. 20, 29–32	
PROV. 31. 4, 5	
Fifteenth Sunday	II
ISA. 1. 2, 10–18	
Fifty-first Sunday	I
ISA. 2. 2–5	
Temperance	
ISA. 5. 11, 22, 23	
Forty-ninth Sunday	I
ISA. 9. 2, 6, 7	
Temperance	
ISA. 10. 1, 2	
Fifty-first Sunday	I
ISA. 11. 1–7, 9, 10, 12	
Forty-ninth Sunday	I
ISA. 12. 2–6	
Forty-fifth Sunday	II
ISA. 25. 1, 4, 8, 9	
Seventh Sunday	I
ISA. 26. 3, 4	
ISA. 30. 15, 18	
Forty-eighth Sunday	I
ISA. 35	
First Sunday	I
ISA. 40. 1–11, 29–31	
Palm Sunday	II
ISA. 40. 9	
Fiftieth Sunday	I
ISA. 42. 1–12, 16	
Seventh Sunday	I
ISA. 43. 1–3, 5, 10	
Missions	II
ISA. 43. 5–11	
Forty-ninth Sunday	I
ISA. 49. 6, 10, 13	
Palm Sunday	II
ISA. 52. 7	
Forty-ninth Sunday	I
ISA. 52. 7–10	
Good Friday	I
ISA. 53	
Tenth Sunday	II
ISA. 55. 1–4, 6–13	
Palm Sunday	I
ISA. 56. 1, 6, 7	
ISA. 57. 15, 16, 19	
Citizenship	I
ISA. 58. 1–12	
Lord's Day	
ISA. 58. 13, 14	
Twenty-fifth Sunday	II
ISA. 60. 1–5, 17–22	

Occasion or Sunday	Number
Missions	I
ISA. 60. 3	
Forty-fifth Sunday	II
ISA. 61. 1–4, 6, 7, 10 11	
Peace	
ISA. 65. 17–19, 21–25	
Twenty-third Sunday	I
JER. 31. 31–34	
Forty-fourth Sunday	II
LAM. 3. 25, 26, 31–33	
Sixth Sunday	II
EZEK. 34. 11–13, 15, 16, 25–27, 30	
Social Justice	II
DAN. 9. 4, 5, 16–19	
Social Justice	II
HOSEA 4. 1	
Whitsunday (Pentecost)	I
JOEL 2. 12, 13, 15–18, 21, 27–29, 32	
Social Justice	II
AMOS 5. 11, 12, 14, 15	
Peace	
MICAH 4. 1–5	
Fifteenth Sunday	II
MICAH 6. 6, 8	
Temperance	
HAB. 2. 12, 15	
Palm Sunday	II
ZECH. 9. 9, 10	
Missions	I
MAL. 1. 11	
Palm Sunday	I
MAL. 2. 10	
MAL. 3. 1–3, 12	
MAL. 4. 2	
Commemoration	II
WISDOM OF SOLOMON 3. 1–3, 5–9	
Commemoration	III
ECCLESIASTICUS 44. 1–15	
Eleventh Sunday	I
MATT. 5. 3–16	
Fourteenth Sunday	I
MATT. 5. 38–48	
Eighth Sunday	II
MATT. 6. 1–8	
Twelfth Sunday	I
MATT. 6. 19–33	
Thirteenth Sunday	I
MATT. 7. 1–12	
Missions	I
MATT. 9. 37, 38	
Fourth Sunday	I
MATT. 13. 44–46	
Eighteenth Sunday	II
MATT. 25. 31–40	
Missions	II
MATT. 28. 18–20	

Occasion or Sunday	Number
Lord's Day	
MARK 2. 27, 28	
MARK 16. 2, 4–6,	
Fifty-first Sunday	II
LUKE 1. 46–55	
Fifty-first Sunday	III
LUKE 1. 68–79	
Children's Day	I
LUKE 2. 40–52	
Fourth Sunday	I
LUKE 12. 29, 31, 32	
LUKE 13. 18–21	
Missions	I
LUKE 13. 29	
Second Sunday	I
JOHN 1. 1–14	
Third Sunday	I
JOHN 3. 6–8	
Fifth Sunday	I
JOHN 4. 13, 14	
Third Sunday	I
JOHN 4. 24	
Fifth Sunday	I
John 6. 30–35, 38	
Third Sunday	I
JOHN 6. 63	
Fifth Sunday	I
JOHN 7. 37	
Sixth Sunday	I
JOHN 10. 7–11, 14–16, 27–30	
Missions	I
JOHN 10. 16	
Tenth Sunday	I
JOHN 14. 1–16	
Ninth Sunday	I
JOHN 15. 1–14	
Lord's Day	
JOHN 20. 19–22	
Forty-sixth Sunday	I
ROM. 5. 1–11	
Sixteenth Sunday	I
ROM. 8. 1–14, 38, 39	
Whitsunday (Pentecost)	II
ROM. 8. 11–17	
Forty-fifth Sunday	I
ROM. 12. 1–16, 21	
Eighteenth Sunday	I
ROM. 12. 4, 5	
Fourth Sunday	I
ROM. 14. 17, 19	
Twenty-eighth Sunday	II
I COR. 2. 9–16	
Temperance	
I COR. 3. 16, 17	
Eighteenth Sunday	
I COR. 12. 4–9, 11–14, 18–21, 26, 27	
Nineteenth Sunday	I
I COR. 13	
Easter	I
I COR. 15. 20–22, 35, 39–45, 51, 53, 57, 58	

Occasion or Sunday	Number
Twenty-second Sunday	I
II COR. 4. 5, 6, 13–18	
Missions	I
II COR. 4. 6	
Whitsunday (Pentecost)	II
GAL. 5. 13, 14, 16–18, 22–25	
Temperance	
GAL. 5. 16	
Twenty-fifth Sunday	I
GAL. 6. 1–10, 16, 18	
Twenty-first Sunday	I
EPH. 1. 15–23	
EPH. 3. 14–21	
Ascension Day	II
EPH. 4. 1–8, 11–15	
Forty-second Sunday	II
EPH. 6. 10–18, 24	
Twenty-sixth Sunday	I
PHIL. 2. 1–11	
Twentieth Sunday	I
PHIL. 4. 4, 6–8	
Easter	II
COL. 3. 1–7, 9–17	
Thirty-fourth Sunday	II
I TIM. 1. 17	
Fourth Sunday	I
HEB. 1. 1, 2, 8, 9	
Forty-first Sunday	II
HEB. 1. 10–12	
HEB. 2. 6–9, 15–18	
Twenty-fourth Sunday	II
HEB. 3. 14	
HEB. 4. 14–16	
HEB. 10. 38, 39	
HEB. 11. 1, 2, 13–16, 39, 40	
HEB. 12. 1–3, 5, 6	
HEB. 13. 20, 21	
Thirty-fourth Sunday	II
I PET. 1. 3–9	
Twentieth Sunday	I
II PET. 1. 2–8, 10	
Missions	I
II PET. 1. 19	
Seventeenth Sunday	I
I JOHN 1. 1–9	
Fifteenth Sunday	I
I JOHN 2. 1–11	
I JOHN 3. 1–3	
Third Sunday	I
I JOHN 3. 1–3, 14, 16, 18, 24	
Twenty-second Sunday	I
JUDE 1. 24, 25	
Commemoration	I
REV. 7. 9–17	
Missions	I
REV. 14. 6	
Fifty-third Sunday	II
REV. 21. 1–7	
Fifth Sunday	I
REV. 21. 6	
Fifty-third Sunday	II
REV. 22. 1–5, 12–14	

Old Testament Lectionary

Suggested Lessons for Church Calendar Days and Occasional Services

The numbers refer to lessons on pages 649 and 650.

78	First Sunday in Advent.	80	Trinity Sunday.
80	Second Sunday in Advent.	43	Memorial Day (All Saints).
82	Third Sunday in Advent.	105	Armistice Day.
84	Fourth Sunday in Advent.	86	Missionary Meetings.
85	Christmas Day.	35	Installation.
83	First Sunday After Christmas.	103	Social Service.
86	Epiphany.	45	The Nation and Citizenship.
89	Ash Wednesday.	41	Thanksgiving Day.
92	First Sunday in Lent.	35	Children's Day and Religious Educa-tion.
97	Second Sunday in Lent.		
100	Third Sunday in Lent.	77	Children's Day and Religious Educa-tion.
101	Fourth Sunday in Lent.		
102	Fifth Sunday in Lent.	83	Temperance Reform.
85	Palm Sunday.	37	Last Sunday of the Year.
28	Thursday Before Easter.	76	Last Sunday of the Year.
11	Good Friday.	44	New Year's Day or Sunday.
26	Easter Sunday.	31	Dedication of a Church.
100	Ascension Day.	59	Dedication of a Church.
65	Sunday After Ascension.	108	Preparation for Church Building.
87	Pentecost or Whitsunday.	97	Day of Fasting and Prayer.

651

INDEXES

Index of Special Responsive Readings

Index of Responsive Readings for Occasional Services

(The number in Arabic type indicates the Sunday;
the number in Roman type indicates the reading.)

Index of Titles of Responsive Readings, Sundays 1-53

(The number in Arabic type indicates the Sunday;
the number in Roman type indicates the reading.)

Index of Topics, Key-Words and Phrases in the Responsive Readings, Sundays 1-53

657

INDEX OF TOPICS OF RESPONSIVE READINGS

Index of First Lines of Stanzas of Hymns

FIRST LINES OF STANZAS OF HYMNS

FIRST LINES OF STANZAS OF HYMNS

Topical Index

668

TOPICAL INDEX

669

TOPICAL INDEX

670

TOPICAL INDEX

GRACE
19 Let all on earth their voices raise
188 Of Him who did salvation bring
194 "Come unto me, ye weary"
195 Return, O wanderer, return
209 Amazing grace! how sweet the sound
217 Lord, in the strength of grace
349 How tedious and tasteless the hours

GRATITUDE
(See Special Days, Thanksgiving)
80 O my soul, bless God, the Father

GRIEF
(See Consolation)

GUIDANCE
20 We gather together to ask the Lord's blessing
90 As with gladness men of old
193 Art thou weary, art thou troubled
242 He leadeth me
243 Holy Spirit, faithful Guide
269 Jesus, Saviour, pilot me
271 Lead us, O Father, in the paths of peace
272 If thou but suffer God to guide thee
301 Guide me, O Thou great Jehovah
336 Jesus, still lead on
337 Saviour, like a shepherd lead us
352 In heavenly love abiding
353 The King of love my Shepherd is
360 O Thou, to whose all-searching sight
368 Sunset and evening star
376 Dear Master, in whose life I see
514 Lead, kindly Light
520 Abide with me

HEALING
(See Ministry of)

HEAVEN
Glories of
525 I will sing you a song
529 Jerusalem the golden
531 Ten thousand times ten thousand
Longing for
532 Hark, hark, my soul

HOLINESS
251 Take time to be holy

HOLY SCRIPTURES
175 Come, Holy Ghost, our hearts inspire
315 How firm a foundation
386 to 392, inclusive

HOLY SPIRIT
172 to 183, inclusive
Comforter
2 Come, Thou almighty King
177 Our blest Redeemer, ere He breathed
243 Holy Spirit, faithful Guide
Indwelling
172 Come, Holy Spirit, heavenly Dove
173 Holy Spirit, Truth divine
178 Spirit of Life, in this new dawn
179 Spirit of God, descend upon my heart
182 O Spirit of the Living God
183 Spirit of faith, come down
Invoked
175 Come, Holy Ghost, our hearts Inspire
180 Breathe on me, Breath of God
181 Send down Thy truth, O God
394 Welcome, delightful morn
438 Holy Spirit, hear us
Source of Gladness
174 I worship Thee, O Holy Ghost
176 Come, Holy Ghost, in love

HOME
(See Christian Home)

HOME, HEAVENLY
530 The Homeland, O the Homeland

HOPE
203 Father of Jesus Christ, my Lord
365 We hope in Thee, O God
522 How happy every child of grace

HOPE AND ASPIRATION
359 to 369, inclusive

IMMORTALITY
(See Eternal Life)
112 I know not how that Bethlehem's Babe
329 I know that my Redeemer lives

INFANT BAPTISM
(See Baptism)

INNER LIFE
338 Jesus, Lover of my soul
339 Thou hidden Source of calm repose
341 'Mid all the traffic of the ways
345 Jesus, Thou Joy of loving hearts
346 O Thou, in whose presence my soul takes delight
348 Jesus, the very thought of Thee
349 How tedious and tasteless the hours
363 O for a heart of calm repose
367 Make me a captive, Lord
369 Blest are the pure in heart

INSPIRATION
10 To Thee, Eternal Soul, be praise

INTEGRITY
294 to 300, inclusive

INTERCESSION
(See Prayer)
56 Sun of my soul, Thou Saviour dear
166 Hail, Thou once despisèd Jesus!
237 I have a Saviour

INTERNATIONAL GOOD WILL
(See Peace, National)

INTROITS
6 Ye watchers and ye holy ones
8 Let all the world in every corner sing
13 All people that on earth do dwell
313 Dear Shepherd of Thy people, hear

INVITATION
184 to 197, inclusive
210 I heard the voice of Jesus say
211 Arise, my soul, arise
219 Saviour, Thy dying love
227 Come, we that love the Lord
231 Pass me not, O gentle Saviour
233 Jesus calls us, o'er the tumult
234 Lord Jesus, I love Thee
237 I have a Saviour
239 Softly and tenderly
350 Come unto Me, when shadows darkly gather

JESUS
(See Jesus Christ)

JESUS, NAME OF
24 Jesus, where'er Thy people meet
25 Jesus, we look to Thee
164 All hail the power of Jesus' Name
253 Take the Name of Jesus with you
339 Thou hidden Source of calm repose
347 How sweet the Name of Jesus sounds
400 Jesus! the Name high over all

JESUS CHRIST
83 to 171, inclusive
Birth and Infancy
86 to 110, inclusive
113 We would see Jesus
434 Away in a manger
442 Once in royal David's city
Coming of Christ
83 to 85, inclusive
113 We would see Jesus
167 Hark! ten thousand harps and voices
463 "Thy kingdom come," on bended knee
Decision for
(See Decision for Christ)
The Everliving Christ
32 Christ, whose glory fills the skies
126 Lift up your heads, ye mighty gates
162 to 171, inclusive
329 I know that my Redeemer lives
Life and Ministry
48 At even, ere the sun was set
111 Fairest Lord Jesus
112 to 124, inclusive
266 O young and fearless Prophet
440 I think when I read that sweet story of old
441 Tell me the stories of Jesus
443 It fell upon a summer day
Our Light
32 Christ, whose glory fills the skies
114 Light of the world, we hail Thee
345 Jesus, Thou Joy of loving hearts!
378 Walk in the light
Our Saviour
56 Sun of my soul, Thou Saviour dear
220 Majestic sweetness sits enthroned
Passion
125 to 149, inclusive

TOPICAL INDEX

672

674

TOPICAL INDEX

675

Index of Authors, Translators, and Sources of Hymns

676

Index of Composers, Arrangers, and Sources of Tunes

INDEX OF COMPOSERS, ARRANGERS, AND SOURCES OF TUNES

Metrical Index of Tunes

Alphabetical Index of Tunes

ALPHABETICAL INDEX OF TUNES

ALPHABETICAL INDEX OF TUNES

Index of Responses

Index of Ancient Hymns and Canticles

Index of First Lines of Hymns

FIRST LINES OF HYMNS

FIRST LINES OF HYMNS